ANCIENT
IRISH TALES

ANCIENT IRISH TALES

EDITED BY
TOM PEETE CROSS
AND
CLARK HARRIS SLOVER

BARNES
&NOBLE
BOOKS
NEW YORK

This edition published by Barnes & Noble, Inc.,
by arrangement with Henry Holt and Company, Inc.

1996 Barnes & Noble Books

ISBN 1-56619-889-5

Printed and bound in the United States of America

M 9 8 7 6 5 4 3

FG

CONTENTS

INTRODUCTION

When, more than a quarter of a century ago, Standish Hayes O'Grady presented to the public his well-known collection of early Irish tales, he expressed the fear that "a promulgator of such wares" might be called upon to justify his action; today the publication of a volume of translations from Irish needs no apology. All who have even the slightest acquaintance with the early literature of western Europe now recognize the peculiar importance which attaches to the traditions of ancient Ireland.

The oldest literature of Ireland has been well called "the earliest voice from the dawn of western European civilization." The significance of this fact has been too often neglected. The all-conquering Romans looked upon the native speech of the peoples whom they subdued as vulgar tongues unworthy of notice. If any written literature ever existed in the native language of Gaul, none has come down to us, and French, though based on Latin, did not reach the dignity of a literary language until the Roman conquest had been over for at least a thousand years. In Spain the earliest national literature was composed, not in the language of the most ancient inhabitants, but in a form of neo-Latin and is no older than the earliest literary compositions in French. In Germanic territory the beginnings of literature in the German language did not appear until late in the eleventh century.

So powerful was the influence of the Latin tongue that, in the West, only nations outside the Roman Empire succeeded in preserving any early records in their native speech. Of the western peoples beyond the immediate sway of Rome, few learned the art of writing early enough to record for posterity any native pagan traditions in the vernacular. Chief among these were the Irish, the Anglo-Saxons, and the Icelanders. Of the three, the Irish were the first to receive letters and to develop a national literature, and it is perhaps ultimately to Irish influence that we owe the oldest written records in Anglo-Saxon and in Icelandic.

It is the proud boast of the Irish people that no Roman legion ever landed on their shores. Ireland never became a Roman province, and thus she preserved her native speech largely unaffected by foreign influences. Ancient Gaelic did not suffer from the contempt with which the older languages were regarded in the Roman provinces. To the early Irish their tongue was a "choice language"; and not long after they had learned the art of writing from the Christian missionaries of the fifth century, they developed a script of their own and began recording their ancient traditions in their own vernacular. Our early Irish manuscripts, though in no case written as far back as the introduction of Christianity, are, in many instances, copied from texts recorded at least as early as the eighth century and embodying pre-Christian traditions.

Both in age and in variety the literature of ancient Ireland surpasses that of any other western European vernacular during the early Middle Ages. It includes not only numerous religious and legal writings but also a large body of lyric poetry and a long list of epic and other tales written in prose alternating with passages in verse. Early Irish epic and romantic literature comprises, in addition to many outlying stories, three groups, or cycles, known respectively as (1) the Mythological cycle, (2) the Ulster, or Red Branch cycle, and (3) the Finn, or Ossianic cycle. Typical examples from all three cycles, as well as a group of outlying romances and sagas, are presented in this volume.

TALES OF THE TUATHA DE DANANN

The dominating peoples of Ireland's remotest past are traditionally represented as the Partholonians, the Nemedians, the Fir Bolg, the Tuatha De Danann, and the Milesians. The accounts of their doings, although ostensibly depicting the very earliest periods of Irish history, were composed, for the most part, later than the oldest sagas of the Ulster group (p. 127). The Tuatha De Danann (Peoples of the Goddess Danu, or Anu) are said to have come to Ireland from the north of Europe, where they had spent many years in learning arts and magic. They are represented as large, strong, and beautiful beings who mingled with mortals and yet remained superior to them. Their principal residences were Brug na Boinne, a district along the river Boyne near Stackallen Bridge in Leinster, and the fairy-mound (*síd,* " shee ") of Femin in Tipperary. Certain personages in this group, without being definitely labelled as gods, have characteristics that elevate them above the rank of ordinary mortals For example, Manannan mac Lir, whose name is associated with the Isle of Man, may have been some sort of sea divinity. Angus, often called Mac Oc, son of Boann (Boyne) and the Dagda, is regarded by some students of mythology as a sort of Irish Adonis. Nuada Silver-Arm, Lug Long-Arm, and the Dagda are also, according to the mythologically minded, partially humanized ancient Celtic divinities.

The selections included below under the "Tales of the Tuatha De Danann" belong, with one or two exceptions, to the so-called Mythological Cycle.

THE BOOK OF INVASIONS

The narratives assembled under the title "Book of Invasions (or Occupations)" are the literary embodiment of Ireland's own impressions regarding the history of her population. For the early Irish they served somewhat the same functions as the accounts of the wanderings of Aeneas did for the Romans. To say, as some have done, that the "The Book of Invasions" is a collection of Irish mythology is to give an entirely wrong impression of its contents. Some of the characters, it is true, may be rationalized gods, but the stories as they now stand belong rather to pseudo-history than to mythology. For example, Emer, Eber, and Eremon, though represented in the narrative as ancient kings, are in fact merely fictitious personages with names made up from the ancient name for Ireland, spelled in the earliest manuscripts as *Ériu*. Modern students of early Irish history are inclined to see underlying these obviously fictitious narratives a substratum of fact, and to regard the account as reflecting in a general way an historical record of early population groups.

The present version is preserved only in rather late manuscripts, but the ancient origin of at least some parts of it is convincingly supported by comparison with the early forms of the British-Latin "History of the Britons" (*Historia Britonum*).

The selections presented below are not continuous, but they form tolerably unified sections, describing the arrival of three different groups of immigrants. The first of the divisions here given is preceded in the complete text by the account of the arrival of Partholon and his people.

The account of the Tuatha De Danann serves as a background for "The Second Battle of Moytura" (p. 28) and "The Fate of the Children of Tuirenn" (p. 49).

THE CONQUEST OF NEMED

Now Ireland was waste thirty years after the plague-burial of Partholon's people, till Nemed son of Agnoman son of Pamp son of Tai son of Ser son of Sru son of Esru son of Brament son of Aitecht son of Magog, etc., of the Greeks of Scythia, reached it.

Now this is the account of Nemed. He came from Scythia westward, a-rowing the Caspian Sea, till he reached in his wandering the great Northern Ocean. Thirty-four ships were his number, and thirty in each ship. While they were thus wandering, there appeared to them a golden tower on the sea close by them. Thus it was: when the sea was in ebb the tower appeared above it, and when it flowed it rose above the tower. Nemed went with his people towards it for greed of the gold. From the greatness of their covetousness for it they did not perceive the sea filling around them, so that the eddy took their ships from them all but a few, and their crews were drowned, except those of them whom Nemed and his children rescued by dint of rowing. A year and half were they after that wandering on the sea, till they reached Ireland. They remain in it.

Now as for Nemed, he had four chiefs with him,—Starn, Iarbanel the Prophet, Fergus Redside, and Ainninn. They were the four sons of Nemed. Macha was the name of his wife. Medb, Machu, Yba, and Cera were the names of the wives of the chieftains he had.

The twelfth day after they reached Ireland, the wife of Nemed died; she was the first dead in Ireland from among them.

Four lake-bursts over Ireland in the time of Nemed; Loch Calin Ui Niallan, Loch Muuremur of Sliab Guaire, Loch Dairbrech, and Loch Ainninn in Meath. At the end of nine years after their coming to Ireland, these last two lakes burst forth.

Two royal forts were dug by Nemed in Ireland; Rath Cinn Eich in Ui Niallan, and Rath Cimbaith in Seimne. The four sons of Madan Fat-Neck of the Fomorians dug Rath Cinn Eich in one day—Boc, Roboc, Ruibne, and Rodan were their names. For they were kept in servitude by Nemed, with their father Madan, before they completed the excavation.

Twelve plains were cleared by Nemed in Ireland in servitude likewise; namely, Mag Cera and Mag Eba in Connacht, Mag Tochair in Tir Eoghain, Leccmag in Munster, Mag mBernsa in Leinster, Mag Cuile Tolad in Connacht, Mag Lugad in Ui Tuirte, Mag Sered in Tethba, Mag Seimni in Dal Araide, Mag Luirg in Connacht, Mag Muirthemne in Conaille, and Mag Macha in Argialla.

Nemed won three battles over the Fomorians; namely, the battle of Murbolg in Dal Riada, where fell Starn son of Nemed at the hands of Conann son of Faebar, in Lethet of Lachtmag in Murbolg; the battle of Ros Fraechain in Connacht, which is called the battle of Badgna; there fell two kings of the Fomorians, namely, Gann and Sengann; and the battle of Cnamros in Leinster, where fell a slaughter of the men of Ireland, with Beoan son of Starn son of Nemed, by the same Conann. Moreover, by Nemed were these three battles won, although his people suffered great hurt in them.

Nemed died afterwards of plague in the island of Ard Nemed in Ui Liathan, in Munster; and three thousand with him.

Now there was a great oppression on the Children of Nemed after that, since their champions and their chieftains were destroyed in the aforesaid battles, and since Nemed died with the number we have mentioned. Those at whose hands they suffered that oppression were Conann son of Faebar of the Fomorians, and Morc son of Dele the other chief. The fortress of Conann at that time was at Tor Conainn, which is called Torinis Cetne, to the northwest of Ireland. A sheep-land was made of Ireland by them, so that not a venture was made to let smoke be seen by day from a house that was in it, except with the consent of the Fomorians. Two-thirds of their corn, their milk, and their children, with other intolerable burdens, the Fomorians used to demand, this is what was given to them; and the men of Ireland had to deliver every item to them always on Samain eve (Hallowe'en) at Mag Cetne. For this reason it is called Mag Cetne, for the frequency they had to pay the heavy tax there to the Fomorians; and the men of Ireland had a byword at that time, asking one another, "Is it to the same plain (*mag cetne*) the tax will be brought on this occasion?" So that thence was the plain named.

Now wrath and rage seized the Children of Nemed for the heaviness of their distress and the injuriousness of their tax; so that their three chieftains plotted to cause their people throughout Ireland to collect and assemble, so that they should arrive at one place. They acted accordingly; and having reached one spot, they resolved on one counsel, to proceed to Conann's Tower to demand alleviation of their oppression from the Fomorians, or to fight with them.

These were their chieftains: Fergus Redside son of Nemed, Semeon son of Iarbanel son of Nemed, and Erglan son of Beoan son of Starn son of Nemed. There were other princes and nobles in that assembly besides, with Artur the Great son of Nemed, and Alma One-tooth son of Nemed, etc. Thirty thousand on sea, and the same number on land, was the number of the Children of Nemed who went to that destruction, besides foreigners, wastrels, and a rabble, which they brought to increase their muster against the oppression of the Fomorians.

After they had reached the shore of Torinis they made booths and huts about the borders of the bay. Then they resolved on the counsel to send Alma One-Tooth to Conann, to ask a respite in the matter of the tax to the end of three years. Alma went and reached the fortress of Conann. When he heard his speech, Conann was enraged with the martial prince, so that he got no good of his journey. Alma returned to his people and told them the words of the chief. Downcast were they at hearing them, and they induced Alma to go back again, to ask a respite of one year of Conann, to show him their poverty and need, to bear witness to their inability to produce there the heavy tax of that year, and to promise that it should come to him in its fulness at the end of that time. They said to him further, unless he should obtain the remission he was asking, to proclaim battle against Conann; for they well-nigh preferred to fall together in one place, men, women, and boys and girls, than to be under the great distress in which they were any longer.

Alma went forward to Conann and told him the words of the Children of Nemed in his presence. "They will get the grace," said Conann, "on condition that they neither separate nor scatter from one another till the end of that year, so that I and the Fomorians get them in one place, for their destruction, unless they pay the tax in full at the end of the grace."

Alma returned to his brothers and told them the news. They then accepted it, in the hope that they should send messengers to their brothers and their original stock in Greece, to ask the help of an army from them against the Fomorians. For Relbeo, daughter of the king of Greece, was mother of two of those children of Nemed, Fergus Redside and Alma One-Tooth. Smol son of Esmol was king of Greece at that time.

When the messengers from Ireland reached Greece, Smol caused the nobles of Greece to come and assemble together in common, so that he brought together an immense host of the choice of warriors, of druids and druidesses, of wolves and venomous animals throughout the coasts. He sends them before to the Children of Nemed, and himself joins them afterwards with the full muster of the Greeks, and they all set out for Ireland. The progress of that voyage is not related up to the time they took harbor at Conann's Tower

Welcoming were the Children of Nemed to them; and this was

agreed upon by them after their arrival, to declare war on Conann unless he yielded them their freedom. They send messengers to him about this. Conann was enraged with them after hearing their speech, so that he agreed to give battle. The messengers went back to their people. Conann sent for Morc son of Dele, the other prince of the Fomorians. Notwithstanding, he thought it inglorious to delay answering the battle at once, for he felt sure that the Children of Nemed were not ready to undertake battle with him, on account of the valor and multitude of his host.

Then the men of Ireland sent a spy to the tower of Conann, namely, Relbeo, daughter of the king of Greece, who came in the host of her children. A druidess was she, and she went in the form of the concubine of Conann to the tower, so that she was with him in lover's wise for a while, through the confusion of his mind. A battle was begun first between their druids, and another between their druidesses, so that it went against the Fomorians. In short, every battle which was fought for a while after that went against the Fomorians, so that their people were destroyed to a great extent.

A wall strong and hard to pull down was made by the Children of Nemed near the tower after that, at the advice of their spy; and they sent the hurtful animals the Greeks had brought to their assistance to the tower, so that they breached every quarter and every side of it before them; and the attacking party went on their trail through the ways they made, forward to the tower. The mighty men of the tower were not able to remain within it, because of the strength and venom of the hurtful strange animals mingled with them.

Conann with his war squadrons fled at once, and he thought it ignoble not to attack the hosts face to face. For he considered it easier to give them battle, than to wait in the tower for the wild venomous beasts who came through the walls after they had destroyed them. The attacking host after that secured both hounds and venomous swine, after the warriors had left the tower. They then left a guard over it, and proceeded to the combat. Each of them took his battle-duties upon him on this side and that. After they had been thus fighting together for a while, this was what happened: Conann fell by the hand of Fergus Redside son of Nemed in fair fight. The Fomorians had two valiant knightly warriors beside that, Gilcas son of Faebar, and Orcifanat; and the

Fomorians closed round them after losing their leader. They took to raising high their warlike efforts and their deeds of valor, till the Children of Nemed remembered their hostility and their cruelty to them up till then. So Semeon son of Starn and Gilcas son of Faebar were matched as well as Iarbanel and Orcifanat. This was the end of it, that the Fomorians were beheaded by the hands of those warriors who happened to be matched against them.

The battle at last went against the tribe of the Fomorians, and the men of Ireland took to encircling and surrounding them, so that not a fugitive escaped from them. The host proceeded to the tower, and took its treasures, its gold, its silver, and all its valuables in general. They put fires at every quarter of it after that, so that not higher was its smoke than its flame. Its women and women servants, its boys and girls were burnt, and not a fugitive escaped from it.

The Children of Nemed shared the booty of the tower among the nobles and the great men of the Greeks before parting from them, and they were grateful, one towards the other. Now the Children of Nemed stayed in the place of conflict after the departure of the Greeks from them, burying those of their nobles who were slain.

Not long were they thus when they saw a full-great fleet approaching them; three-score ships was its number, teeming with a choice of warriors, led by Morc son of Dele, the other chief of the Fomorians, coming to help Conann. They landed in their presence. The Children of Nemed went to hold the harbor against them, though they were worn out; for this was their resolve, not to suffer the Fomorians any longer to frequent Ireland.

Howbeit, although great was the despite and hatred of Morc son of Dele against the Children of Nemed before that, it was far the greatest on that occasion. A hot desperate battle was fought between them on every side. Such was the intensity of the fighting, and the greatness of the mutual hostility, that they did not perceive the gigantic wave of the tide filling up on every side about them, for there was not any heed in their minds but for their battle-feats alone; so that the majority were drowned and annihilated, except the people of one ship of the Fomorians and one group of thirty men of the Children of Nemed. The crew of that ship arrived back and they told their news to the people, and they were downcast at hearing it.

As for the thirty warriors of the Children of Nemed who escaped from that destruction, the three chieftains that were over them divided Ireland into three parts between them after that. These are the chieftains: Beothach son of Iarbanel son of Nemed, Semeon son of Erglan son of Beoan son of Starn son of Nemed, and Britain son of Fergus Redside son of Nemed. The third of Beothach first, from Torinis to the Boyne to Belach Conglais; the third of Semeon from the Boyne to Belach Conglais; the third of Britain from Belach Conglais to Torinis Cetne.

However, they did not abide long by that division without separating and scattering into other countries over sea; for they stood in fear of the Fomorians lest what remained of them should wreak their resentment upon them after the battles that had been fought between them. Another cause: they themselves were not friendly or heartloving one to the other; and then, in addition, they were terrified of the plagues by which the troops of their chieftains and of their men had died before the storming of the tower. So for these causes they separated one from the other. These are the lands whither they went. Semeon with his nine to the lands of Greece—he had gone after the death of his father to Ireland; Britain and his father Fergus Redside to Mon Conainn in Britain.

(The foregoing prose account is followed by a versified treatment ascribed to the poet Eochaid Ua Flainn, who died A.D. 1003.)

THE CONQUEST OF THE FIR BOLG

Now Ireland was desert for the space of two hundred years after the separation of the three groups we have mentioned, till the coming of the race of the chief group into it, that is the Fir Bolg.

Of the Children of Nemed by descent were they, for Semeon son of Erglan son of Beoan son of Starn son of Nemed was chief of one of the three nonads of the Children of Nemed who went from Ireland after the destruction of Conann's Tower, and who landed in Greece. They were there till many and divers were their children and their families. After they increased thus, the Greeks did not allow them to be with their own young men; but they imposed servitude on them. This was its amount, to make clovery plains of the stony rough-headed hills with the clay from elsewhere, after bringing it to the places in which they were ordered and commanded to put it.

Tired, weary, and despondent were they from this; so this is the counsel they discussed among themselves, to escape from the intolerable bondage in which they were. They agreed thereto at length. Then they made canoes and fair vessels of the skins and rope bags for carrying the earth till they were sound and seaworthy. They went in them thereafter, in quest of the fatherland from which their ancestors had gone. Their adventures on the sea are not related, save only that they reached Ireland in one week.

Different were their tribe-names at that time as they came, namely, Galeoin, Fir Bolg, and Fir Domnann; nevertheless, though various and dissimilar were their names, their mutual friendship was very close; for they were of one race and one origin. Five chiefs were over them—Slainge, Rudraige, Gann, Genann, and Sengann, the five sons of Dela son of Loch son of Ortecht son of Tribuad son of Oturp son of Goisten son of Uirthecht son of Semeon son of Erglan son of Nemed son of Agnoman. Now Galeoin was the name of Galeon with his people; Galeoin truly is *gal-fhian,* that is, the third who used to surpass the other two-thirds in valor and in equipment; so that from the valor *(gal)* they took the name. Fir Bolg, again, is the name of Gann and Sengann with their people; to them the name Fir Bolg properly belongs, for it is they who were carrying the earth in the bags *(bolg).* Fir Domnann, from "digging the earth" was it said: that is Fir Domanfuinn, that is the men who used to deepen *(doim-nigim)* the earth. To Rudraige and to Genann with their people was the name applied. And it was in Inber Domnann that they took harbor. However, it is correct to call them all Fir Bolg in general, for it is in the bags for carrying the earth they came over sea to Ireland, and they are one immigration and one race and one principality, though they came on different days, and landed in different creeks.

These are the creeks. Slainge, their chief prince and elder, reached the land in Inber Slainge on Saturday on the Calends of August, so far as regards the day of the week; so that from him the creek took its name; a thousand men his number. Sengann and Gann in Inber Dubglaise; a Tuesday they landed, two thousand their number. Rudraige and Genann landed in Inber Domnann as we have said, the following Friday; two thousand, moreover, was their number.

They came together afterwards in Usnech of Meath, and they divided Ireland there in five parts. The share of Slainge first, from

Inber Colptha to Commair of the Three Waters; of Gann, next, from Commair to Belach Conglais; Sengann from Belach Conglais to Limerick; Genann from Limerick to Drobais; Rudraige from Drobais to the Boyne.

THE CONQUEST OF THE TUATHA DE DANANN

As for Iobath son of Beothach son of Iarbanel son of Nemed, after his leaving Ireland with his people after the conquest before described, they settled in the northern islands of Greece. They were there till numerous were their children and their kindred. They learned druidry and many various arts in the islands where they were, what with *fithnaisecht, amaitecht, conbliocht*, and every sort of gentilism in general, until they were knowing, learned, and very accomplished in the branches thereof. They were called Tuatha De; that is, they considered their men of learning to be gods, and their husbandmen non-gods, so much was their power in every art and every druidic occultism besides. Thence came the name, which is Tuatha De, to them.

These were the cities where they were being instructed; Falias, Gorias, Findias, and Murias. They had an instructor of learning in each one of these cities. These are their names; Morfesa in Falias, Esras in Gorias, Uscias in Findias, and Semias who was in Murias. From Falias was brought the Stone of Fal (*Lia Fail*) which Lug had in Tara; that is what used to scream under every king who took the sovereignty of Ireland from the time of Lug Lamfada to the time of the birth of Christ, and it has never screamed thereafter under any king from that out; for it was a demon that had entrance into it, and the powers of every idol ceased in the time of the birth of the Lord, who was born of the Virgin Mary. From that Lia Fail is called Inis Fail (Ireland), as Cinaeth O'Hartagain [1] proves, having said:

> The stone on which my heels stand,
> From it is named Inis Fail;
> Between two strands of a mighty flood,
> Ireland altogether is called Mag Fail.

From Gorias was brought the spear that Lug had; no battle was maintained against him who had it in his hand. From Findias was brought the sword of Nuada; none used to escape who was wounded

[1] A poet who died A.D. 975.

by it. From Murias was brought the cauldron of the Dagda; no one came from it unsatisfied.

After they completed their learning, they went between the Athenians and the Philistines, so that they dwelt between them. Now there arose battles and conflicts between those races, and they were evil and maliciously disposed one to the other. Many battles were fought between them, and it was against the Athenians the battles used to be won, until all save a little remnant were exhausted. Then the Tuatha De joined in friendship with the Athenians, and they formed through druidry demon-spirits in the bodies of the soldiers of the Athenians who were slain, so that they were fit for battle; thus they used to encounter the Philistines again. The Philistines thought it immensely astonishing to see the men they had slain fighting with them the day after. They told that to their druid. Their elder gave them advice, saying, "Take," said he, "pegs of hazel and of quicken-tree to the battle on the morrow; and if yours be the victory, thrust the pins in the backs of the necks of the men who shall be slain; and if they be demons, heaps of worms will be made of them."

They did so. The Philistines were victorious, and they thrust the pegs in the backs of the necks of the warriors they slew, and they were worms on the morrow. Thence the strength of the Athenians was humbled, and the Philistines were powerful. Then they remembered their hostility and unfriendliness against the Tuatha De in the matter of the confederacy they had made with the Athenians against them; so that this is what they resolved, to assemble to attack them to revenge their spite against them.

When the Tuatha De knew that, they went in flight before the Philistines until they received patrimony and land in Dobar and Iardobar in the north of Alba. Seven years were they in that place, Nuada being prince over them. This was the plan decided upon by them by the end of that time, to attack Ireland against the Fir Bolg, as they were populous; for to go there was theirs by right of heredity.

When they arrived at this resolution, they set out on the sea; and their adventures thereon are not related until they took harbor on the coast of Ireland; a Monday on the first of May. They burned their boats and ships, in order that the Fomorians should not be able to use them against them; and further, in order that they themselves should not have them to flee therein from Ireland, if it was against them the Fir Bolg should be victorious. Then they made a great darkness around them until they reached the mountain of Conmaicne Rein in Connacht without the Fir Bolg perceiving it. Then they demanded battle or the kingship of their kinsmen the Fir Bolg.

In consequence was fought the battle of Mag Tured of Cong [1] in Conmaicne Cuile Tolad of Connacht. He who was king of the Fir Bolg then was Eochaid son of Erc. Tailltiu daughter of Magmor king of Spain was wife of that Eochaid; and Nuada son of Eochaid son of Etarlam was king over the Tuatha De. They were a long time fighting that battle. It was won at last against the Fir Bolg, and the rout was pressed northward, and eleven hundred were slaughtered from Mag Tured to the Strand of Ethaile. Edleo son of Alldae is the first man who fell in Ireland of the Tuatha De, by the hand of Nercon grandson of Siomon.

The Tuatha De were pressing upon the Fir Bolg until they came upon king Eochaid son of Erc in the place we have mentioned, so that he fell at the hands of the three sons of Nemed son of Badrae; namely, Ceasarb, Luam, and Luachra. Even the Tuatha De were slain and cut off to a great extent, and in the joining of the battle their king, Nuada, had his arm hewn off from his shoulder. Afterwards Diancecht the leech and Credne the brazier made for him a silver arm, with vitality in every finger and every joint of it. But Miach son of Diancecht lopped off the silver arm after a while, and put joint to joint and sinew to sinew, and healed it in thrice nine days; and Diancecht his father was envious of him. For this cause the king used to be called Nuada Silver-Arm.

As for Tailltiu, daughter of Magmor king of Spain, wife of Eochaid son of Erc, queen of the Fir Bolg, she wedded Eochaid the Rough son of Dul the Blind of the Tuatha De; and Tailltiu came after the fighting of the battle of Mag Tured to Coill Chuan (Cuan's Wood); and the wood was cleared at her command, so that it was a clovery plain at the end of a year, and she inhabited it afterwards. And Cian son of Diancecht (Scal the Dumb is another name of that Cian) gave his son, named Lug son of Ethne daughter

---

[1] Known as "The First Battle of Mag Tured"; the second battle (p. 28) was fought against the Fomorians.

of Balor, to Tailltiu for fosterage. And she desired of her foster-mother and of her friends that from her should be named that place that was cleared by her, and that she should be buried there after death. Then Tailltiu died in Tailltiu, and was buried; so that it is her grave that is north-westward from the assembly-place of Taillte. Her mourning games used to be performed each year by Lug and by the kings after him; a fortnight before Lugnasad (Mid-summer) and a fortnight after, they used to be held continually. Lugnasad is the *nasad* of *Lug: nasad* is an assembly or festival in commemoration or memorial of a death.

Now the Fir Bolg were all slaughtered in that battle, as we have said, save a few; and those of them who survived fled before the Tuatha De into the outermost isles and islets of the sea, so that they dwelt in them after that.

(Here follow two sections dealing with the genealogies of the Tuatha De, the succession of their kings, and the various ways in which they met death.)

The Conquest of the Sons of Mil

(The introductory sections of this part deal with the adventures of the ancestors of Mil in Scythia, Egypt, and Spain. The following selection begins with the decision to invade Ireland.)

After the death of Mil, as we have said, Emer Donn and Eremon, his two sons, took the rule and chief government of Spain between themselves.

There was a father's brother of Mil, Ith son of Bregan, with them; he was expert and accomplished in knowledge and in learning. Once when Ith, of a clear winter's evening, was on top of Bregan's Tower, contemplating and looking over the four quarters of the world, it seemed to him that he saw a shadow and a likeness of a land and lofty island far away from him. He went back to his brethren, and told them what he had seen; and said that he was mindful and desirous of going to see the land that had appeared to him. Breg son of Bregan said that it was no land he had seen but clouds of heaven, and he was hindering Ith from going on that expedition. Ith did not consent to stay, however.

Then Ith brought his ship on the sea, and came himself with his son Lugaid son of Ith, and others of his people in it. They sailed toward Ireland, and their adventures on sea are not related, save only that they took harbor in Bentracht of Mag Itha. The neighbors went to the shore to interview them, and each of them told news to the other in the Irish language. Ith asked them the name of the land to which he had come, and who was in authority over it. "Inis Elga," they said; "Mac Cuill, Mac Cecht, and Mac Greine are the names of its kings."

It happened in that day that there were many chieftains and nobles of Ireland in Ailech Neid, making peace between Mac Cuill and his brethren; for they said that he had an excess of the goods of Fiachna son of Delbaeth, who had died previously. When Ith heard that, he went with his son and with two-thirds of his people to Ailech. The kings welcomed him when he reached the assembly, and after he was a while among them, they told him the matter about which they were in opposition and contention between them. And he said to them:

"Do just righteousness. It is fitting for you to maintain a good brotherhood. It is right for you to have a good disposition. Good is the land and the patrimony you inhabit; plenteous her harvest, her honey, her fish, her wheat, and her other grain. Moderate her heat and her cold. All that is sufficient for you is in her." Then he took farewell of them and went to his ship.

The nobles plotted to kill him, in jealousy for Ireland, and for the testimony of praise he gave to their island; and they sent a great number to follow him, so that he was wounded to death in Mag Itha, and from him the plain took its name. He reached his ship wounded and bleeding, by the valor and bravery of his people; and he died with them in his ship on the sea.

Then they reached Spain and showed the body of Ith to his brethren, and they were anguished and sorrowful at his dying thus. Then the sons of Mil and the posterity of Gaedel in general thought it was fitting and proper for them to go and avenge their brother on the Tuatha De Danann. They decided on this at last: they collected their warriors and their men of valor from every place where they were, through the lands and the districts, until they were in one place in Brigantia, numerous and fully assembled. Then the sons of Mil, with their brethren and kinsmen, and their people in general, brought their ships on the sea to go to Ireland to avenge their bad welcome on the Tuatha De Danann. Three score and five ships was the number of the expedition; forty chiefs the number of their leaders, with Donn son of Mil at their head. These are the names of their chiefs.

Emer Donn	Muimne	Eber son of Ir	Lugaid	Caicer
Eremon	Luigne	Brega	Lui	Suirge
Eber Finn	Laigne	Cuala	Bile	En
Ir	Palap	Cooley	Buas	Un
Amergin	Er	Blad	Bres	Etan
Colptha	Orba	Fuad	Buaigne	Sobairce
Airech Febra	Feron	Muirthemne	Fulman	Sedga
Erannan	Fergin	Eblinne	Mantan	Goisten
		Nar		

To commemorate the names of those chiefs and leaders, this was said; Flann [1] composed it:

> The chiefs of the voyage over the sea
> By which the sons of Mil came,
> I have in recollection during my life,
> Their names without lie.
>
> Donn, Eremon, noble Emer,
> Ir, Amergin, without partiality,
> Colptha, Airech Febra the keen,
> Erannan, Muimne fine and smooth.
>
> Luigne, Laigne, Palap the lucky,
> Er, Orba, Feron, Fergin,
> Eber son of Ir, Brega, I shall say,
> Cuala, Cualgne, Blad rough and strong.
>
> Fuad, and Muirthemne with fame,
> Eblinne, Nar, Buas with battle,
> Bres, Buaigne, and Fulman.
>
> Mantan, Caicer, slender Suirge,
> En, Un, and rigid Etan,
> Sobairce, Sedga of spears,
> And Goisten the champion.
>
> They conquered noble Ireland
> Against the Tuatha De of great magic,
> In vengeance for Ith of the steeds—
> Thirty, ten, and one chieftain.

[1] Flann Mainistrech, a poet who died A.D. 1056.

As for the sons of Mil, they sailed in a great expedition on the sea to Ireland, and did not pause in the course until they saw at a distance the island from the sea. And when they saw Ireland, their warriors made a contention of rowing and sailing to their utmost in their eagerness and anxiety to reach it; so that Ir son of Mil advanced a wave before every other ship by reason of his strength and valor. So Eber Donn son of Mil, the eldest of them, was jealous and said:

> It is no good deed
> Ir before Ith to proceed—

that is before Lugaid son of Ith, for Lugaid had the name Ith. Then the oar that was in the hand of Ir split, so that Ir fell backwards across the thwart and broke his back tl ere. He died on the following night, and they preserved his body so long as they were on the sea, and buried it afterwards in Scellic of Irras Desceirt of Corco Duibne. Sorrowful were Eremon, Eber Finn, and Amergin at the death of their brother; and they said, as it were out of one mouth, it was right that Eber Donn should not enjoy the land about which he was envious of his brother, that is of Ir.

The sons of Mil advanced to a landing in Inber Stainge. The Tuatha De Danann did not allow them to come to land there, for they had not held parley with them. By their druidry they caused it to appear to the sons of Mil that the region was no country or island, territory or land at all, in front of them. They encircled Ireland three times, till at last they took the harbor at Inber Scene; a Thursday, as regards the day of the week, on the day before the first of May, the seventeenth day of the moon; the Year of the World 3500.

Then they came at the end of three days thereafter to Sliab Mis. Banba met them in Sliab Mis, with the hosts of druidry and cunning. Amergin asked her name. "Banba," [1] said she, "and it is from my name that Banba is given as a name for this country." And she asked a petition from them, that her name should remain always on the island. That was granted to her.

Then they had converse with Fodla in Eblinne, and the poet Amergin asked her name of her in like manner. "Fodla," said she, "and from me is the land named." And she prayed that her name might remain on it, and it was granted to her as she requested.

[1] Banba, Fodla, and Eriu are imaginary personages created by Irish historiographers out of ancient names for Ireland.

They held converse with Eriu in Usnech of Mide. She said to them, "Warriors," said she, "welcome to you. It is long since your coming is prophesied. Yours will be the island forever. There is not better island in the world. No race will be more perfect than your race."

"Good is that," said Amergin.

"Not to her do we give thanks for it," said Donn, "but to our gods and to our power."

"It is naught to thee," said Eriu; "thou shalt have no gain of this island nor will thy children. A gift to me, O sons of Mil and the children of Bregan, that my name may be upon this island!"

"It will be its chief name for ever," said Amergin, "namely Eriu (Erin)."

The Gaedels went to Tara. Now Drum Cain was its name at that time among the Tuatha De Danann, Liathdruim was its name among the Fir Bolg. There were three kings before them in Liathdruim; namely, Mac Cuill, Mac Cecht, and Mac Greine. The sons of Mil demanded a battle or kingship or judgment from them.

They adjudged to the sons of Mil that they should have possession of the island to the end of nine days, to depart, or to submit, or to prepare for battle. "If my advice were carried out," said Donn son of Mil, "it is a battle it would be." The sons of Mil did not grant the respite they sought to the Tuatha De Danann.

"We give," said the kings, "the judgment of your own poets to you, for if they give a false judgment against us they will die on the spot."

"Give the judgment, Amergin," said Donn.

"I speak it," said Amergin. "Let the land be left to them till we come again to take it by force."

"Whither shall we go?" said Eber Donn.

"Over nine waves," said Amergin; and he said this:

> The men you have found are in possession:
> Over the nine green-necked waves
> Of the sea advance ye:
> Unless by you power then be planted,
> Quickly let the battle be prepared.
> I assign the possession
> Of the land ye have found:
> If ye love concede this award,
> If ye love not concede it not—
> It is I that say this to you.

"If it were my counsel that were followed," said Donn son of
Mil, "battle it would be." Nevertheless the sons of Mil went by the
advice and judgment of Amergin from Liathdruim to Inber Scene,
the place where they had left their ships, and passed over nine
waves. "Let us trust to the powers," said the druids, "that they
may never reach Ireland." With that the druids cast druidic winds
after them, so that the bottom gravel was raised to the top of
the sea, so great was the storm; so that the storm took them westward in the ocean until they were weary. "A druid's wind is that,"
said Donn son of Mil. "It is indeed," said Amergin, "unless it be
higher than the mast; find out for us if it be so." Erannan the
youngest son of Mil went up the mast, and said that it was not
over them. With that he fell on the planks of the ship from the
mast, so that they shattered his limbs.

"A shame to our men of learning is it," said Donn, "not to
suppress the druidic wind."

"No shame it shall be," said Amergin, rising up; and he said:

> I invoke the land of Ireland.
> Much-coursed be the fertile sea,
> Fertile be the fruit-strewn mountain,
> Fruit-strewn be the showery wood,
> Showery be the river of water-falls,
> Of water-falls be the lake of deep pools,
> Deep-pooled be the hill-top well,
> A well of tribes be the assembly,
> An assembly of the kings be Tara,
> Tara be the hill of the tribes,
> The tribes of the sons of Mil,
> Of Mil of the ships, the barks,
> Let the lofty bark be Ireland,
> Lofty Ireland, darkly sung,
> An incantation of great cunning;
> The great cunning of the wives of Bres,
> The wives of Bres of Buaigne;
> The great lady Ireland,
> Eremon hath conquered her,
> Ir, Eber have invoked for her.
> I invoke the land of Ireland.

Immediately a tranquil calm came to them on the sea. Said Donn,
"I will put under the edge of spears and swords the warriors that
are in the land now, only let me land." The wind increased on them

thereupon, so that it separated from them the ship in which was Donn; and he was drowned at the Dumacha. Twenty-four warriors of valor, twelve women, and four mercenaries, with their folk are the number that were drowned with Donn in that ship. After that Donn was buried in the Dumacha; so that from him "Tech Duin" is called, and there is his own gravemound and the gravemound of everyone who was drowned of the chieftains of his people with him, in that place. Now Dil daughter of Mil, Eremon buried her for the love he had for her, so that he said in putting a sod on her, "This is a sod on a 'dear one' (*dil*)," said he. These are the chieftains who were drowned with Donn at that time: Bile son of Brige, Airech Febra, Buss, Bres, and Buagne. Ir was buried in Scellic of Irras, as we have said above, Erannan died in the creek after going to contemplate the wind, and after breaking his bones on the deck. Eight chieftains were their losses among their nobles up to then.

In the night in which the sons of Mil came to Ireland was the burst of Loch Luigdech over land in West Munster. When Lugaid son of Ith was bathing in the lake, and Fial daughter of Mil his wife was bathing in the river that flows out of the lake, Lugaid went to the place where was the woman, he being naked; and when she looked on him thus she died of shame at once, and from her is named the river with its creek. Downcast was Lugaid after the woman's death, so that he said:

> Sit we here over the strand,
> Stormy the cold;
> Chattering in my teeth,—a great tragedy
> Is the tragedy that has reached me.

> I tell you a woman has died,
> Whom fame magnifies;
> Fial her name, from a warrior's nakedness
> Upon the clean gravel.

> A great death is the death that has reached me,
> Harshly prostrated me;
> The nakedness of her husband, she looked upon him
> Who rested here.

Six women of their nobles were their losses on sea and land from their setting out from Spain till then. These are their names: Buan wife of Bile; Dil wife of Donn; Scene, the woman-satirist, wife of

Amergin White-Knee (she died with them on the sea while they were coming to Ireland; so that Amergin said, "The harbor where we land, the name of Scene will be on it." That was true, for from her is named Inber Scene); Fial wife of Lugaid son of Ith; the wife of Ir and the wife of Muirthemne son of Bregan, were the other two.

When the sons of Mil reached land in the creek we have mentioned, and when they had buried the troop of their nobles who had died of them, Eremon and Eber Finn divided the fleet with their chieftains and servants in two between them. After that Eremon sailed with thirty ships, keeping Ireland on his left hand, and he landed in Inber Colptha. These are the chieftains that were with him: Eber son of Ir, Amergin the poet, Palap, Muimne, Luigne, Laigne, Brega, Muirthemne, Fuad, Cualgne, Colptha, Goisten, Sedga, Suirge, and Sobairce. The three last were champions. These are the slaves that were with Eremon: Aidne, Ai, Asal, Mide, Cuib, Cera, Ser, Slan, Ligen, Dul, Trega, Line.

On putting his right foot on shore at Inber Colptha, it was then Amergin spoke this rhapsody:

> I am a wind on the sea,
> I am a wave of the ocean,
> I am the roar of the sea,
> I am a powerful ox,
> I am a hawk on a cliff,
> I am a dewdrop in the sunshine,
> I am a boar for valor,
> I am a salmon in pools,
> I am a lake in a plain,
> I am the strength of art,
> I am a spear with spoils that wages battle,
> I am a man that shapes fire for a head.
>
> Who clears the stone-place of the mountain?
> What the place in which the setting of the sun lies?
> Who has sought peace without fear seven times?
> Who names the waterfalls?
> Who brings his cattle from the house of Tethra?
> What person, what god,
> Forms weapons in a fort?
> In a fort that nourishes satirists,
> Chants a petition, divides the Ogam letters,
> Separates a fleet, has sung praises?
> A wise satirist.

He sang afterwards to increase fish in the creeks:

> Fishful sea—
> Fertile land—
> Burst of fish—
> Fish under wave—
> With courses of birds—
> Rough sea—
> A white wall—
> With hundreds of salmon—
> Broad whale—
> A port song—
> A burst of fish.

As for Eber Finn son of Mil, he stayed in the south with thirty ships with him, until they came in the hosts of the battles that were fought between them and the Tuatha De Danann. These are the chieftains that were with Eber: Lugaid son of Ith, Er, Orba, Feron, Fergna, the four sons of Eber, Cuala, Blad, Ebleo, Nar, En, Un, Etan, Caicher, Mantan, Fulman. The six last,—En, Un, etc., were champions. These are the slaves that were with him: Adar, Aigne, Deisi, Deala, Cliu, Morba, Fea, Liffe, Femen, Feara, Meda, and Olba.

When the sons of Mil reached their landing-place they made no delay until they reached Sliab Mis; and the battle of Sliab Mis was fought between them and the Tuatha De Danann, and the victory was with the sons of Mil. Many of the Tuatha De Danann were killed in that battle. It is there that Fas wife of Un son of Uicce fell, from whom is named Glen Faise. Scota wife of Mil fell in the same valley; from her is named "Scota's grave," between Sliab Mis and the sea. The sons of Mil went afterwards to Tailltiu, and another battle was fought between them and the Tuatha De Danann there. Vehemently and whole-heartedly was it fought, for they were from morning to evening contending, bone-hewing, and mutilating one another; till the three kings and the three queens of Ireland fell there—Mac Cecht by Eremon, Mac Cuill by Eber Finn, Mac Greine by Amergin, Eriu by Suirge, Banba by Caicer, and Fodla by Etan. Those were the deaths of their chiefs and princes. After that the Tuatha De Danann were routed to the sea, and the sons of Mil and their host were a long time following the rout. There fell, however, two noble chiefs of the people of the sons of Mil in inflicting the rout, namely, Fuad

in Sliab Fuait, and Cualgne in Sliab Cualgne, together with other
warriors besides, who fell together on both sides. When the Tuatha
De Danann were crushed and expelled in the battles that were
fought between them, the sons of Mil took the lordship of Ireland.

After that there arose a contention between the sons of Mil about
the kingship, that is between Eremon and Eber, so that Amergin
was brought to make peace between them. He said that the inheritance of the eldest, of Donn, should go to the youngest, to
Eremon, and his inheritance to Eber after him; Eber did not
accept that, but insisted on dividing Ireland. Eremon agreed to
do so. Accordingly Ireland was divided in two between them,
the northern half to Eremon, from Srub Brain to the Boyne, the
southern half to Eber, from the Boyne to Tonn Clidna. There
were five chieftains in the division of each of them. With Eremon
first, Amergin, Sedga, Goisten, Suirge, and Sobairce. Now in that
year these forts were dug by Eremon and his people: Rath Beothaig, above the Nore in Argat Ros; Rath Oinn, in the territory of
Cuala, by Eremon; the Causeway of Inber Mor, in the territory of
Ui Enechglais, by Amergin; the building of Dun Nair, in Sliab
Modoirn, by Goisten; the building of Dun Delginnse, in the territory of Cuala, by Sedga; the building of his fort by Sobairce in
Morbolg of Dal Riada; the building of Dun Edar by Suirge. These
are the forts built by Eber and these the chieftains that were with
him: Etan, Un, Mantan, Fulman, and Caicer were his five chief-
tains. Rath Uaman, in Leinster, was dug by Eber; Rath Arda
Suird by Etan son of Uicce; the building of Carrig Blaraige by
Mantan; the building of Carrig Fethnaide by Un son of Uicce;
the building of Dun Ardinne by Caicer; the building of Rath
Riogbard, in Muiresc, by Fulman.

So that for the commemoration of certain of the aforesaid matters this was said:

> The expeditions of the sons of Mil over sea
> From Spain of clear ships,
> They took, it is no deed of falsehood,
> The battle-plain of Ireland in one day.
>
> This is the tale that they went on sea,
> With multitude of wealth and people,
> To a brave show God brought them,
> With sixty-five choice vessels.

They landed at the noble creek
Which is called the White Rampart;
It was a cause of sickness, and attempt without failure,
From the sight of the warrior Lugaid.

From thence it is from that out
The creek of Fial of generous bands;
From the day she died in white Banba—
Fial daughter of Mil of Spain.

At the end of three days, brilliant preparation,
The Tuatha De fought
The battle of Sliab Mis,—glory that was not failure,
Against the great sons of Mil.

They won, a saying without reproach,
The battle against fair-headed Banba,
Where died Fas, woven in verse,
With the very fair daughter of Pharaoh.

Before the end of a year, it was lasting fame,
Among the chieftains of the heavy hosts,
Into twice six divisions, a pleasant course,
They afterwards divided Ireland.

Over the north side, a progress without sorrow,
Eremon was taken as high prince;
From Srub Brain, which verses adorn,
Over every tribe to the Boyne.

These are the five guardians of control
Whom he accepted to accompany him;
Amergin, Sedga also,
Goisten, Sobairce, Suirge.

Eber, son of Mil grace-abounding,
Takes the southern half,
From the eternal Boyne, choice the share,
To the wave of the daughter of Genann.

These are the five, with hundreds of exploits,
The chiefs who were subordinate to him;
Etan, and Un of joyous rule,
Mantan, Fulman, and Caicer.

In this same year
The royal forts were dug,
By the sons of Mil,—honor of pledges,
After the full division of Ireland's island.

Rath Oinn, Rath Beothaig here,
By Eremon in Argat Ros;
In Sliab Mis, after a series of omens,
The building of Dun Nair by Goisten.

Suirge wide-extended, who displayed valor,
Built the high Dun Edar;
And the sounding, glorious achievement,
Of his fort by Sobairce.

By Eber of bright valor, was dug
Rath Uaman in the plain of Leinster;
Rath Arda Suird, it enriched him,
Was dug by Etan son of Uicce.

Rath Carraig Fetha thus,
Was made by Un son of Uicce;
And by Mantan,—glorious deed,
The founding of Carrig Blaraige.

Rath Rigbard in good Muiresc,
Very keen Fulman built it;
Caicer of battles, a pleasant fulfilment,
Took Dun Inne in the west of Ireland.

These are their deeds of valor,
Of the clear, glorious, great royal host;
It was a great achievement, after battle, without stain;
Theirs was every profit, every expedition.

Of the adventures of the Gaedels from the time when they went
from Scythia till they took Ireland, and the division of Ireland
between them, with their chieftains, the poet Roigne Roscadach
son of Ugaine Mor said to Mal son of Ugaine his brother, when Mal
questioned him: "Sing thy description in the great knowledge of
Ireland, O Roigne," Roigne answered him and said:

O noble son of Ugaine,
How does one arrive at knowledge of Ireland,
The conquest of its company?
Before they overflowed Scythia,
They reached the host-king of Shinar;
They approached Egypt,
Where Cingcris was extinguished,
So that a great troop was destroyed,
Who died in the Red Sea.
They flowed through a space very faithful,
With Pharaoh fought;

Niul contracts with Scota,
The conception of our fathers.
They took the name "Gaedels,"
The name "Scots" spreads,
The fair daughter of Pharaoh.
They overspread lands,
Burst into Scythia,
Determined long combat—
The children of Nel and Noenbal.
Golam was a young lord,
Who slew the son of Neman,
Escaped to Egypt,
Where was Nectanebus.
Pharaoh was welcoming
To Golam; gave
A marriage Nectanebus,
Scota was at Scots' head;
A name was changed from them.
They advance past Africa,
Good was the man under whom they trembled;
Fenius Farsad, the keen,
Well he spread for us a lasting name.
They approached Spain,
Where was born a numerous progeny,
Donn, Airech, Amergin,
Eber, Ir, Colptha himself,
Eremon, Erannan,
The eight sons of Golam.
Mil's renown came upon them,
The sons of Mil wealthy;
Their scholars resolved,
Divided ships,
The men returned from the burial of Fial.
They divided Ireland,
In twice six, an inheritance of chieftains.
Seek the truth of every law,
Relate sharply the inquiry,
        O Son!

After Eremon and Eber had divided the chieftains, they had two distinguished artists, who had come in their company from the east, namely, a poet and a harper. Cir son of Cis was the poet, Cennfinn the harper. They cast a lot on them to know which of them should be with each of them; so that, through the decision of the lot, the harper went southward to Eber and thence melody of music and harmony followed in the Southern Half of Ireland. The poet went to Eremon, and knowledge of poetry and song followed him in the North ever after. To commemorate this it was said:

> The two sons of Mil, famous in dignity,
> Took Ireland and Britain;
> With them there followed hither
> A gentle poet and a harper.

> Cir son of Cis, the bright poet,
> The name of the harper Cennfinn;
> With the sons of Mil, of bright fame,
> The harper sounded his harp.

> The princes, with many battles,
> Took the kingdom of Ireland;
> They did it with brightness, merry the sound,
> Eber and Eremon.

> They cast a lot swiftly
> About the great men of art;
> So that there fell to the lot of the southerner
> The harper, just and fair.

> Melody of music more beautiful than any company
> Is from the southward in the south of Ireland;
> It is thus it will be to the fortunate Judgment
> With the famous seed of Eber.

> There fell to the lot of the northerner
> The man of learning with great excellence;
> Hence the tribes who brought him boast
> Knowledge of poetry and learning.

THE SECOND BATTLE OF MAG TURED (MOYTURA)

The central heroic tale of the group dealing with the Tuatha De Danann and the so-called Mythological Cycle is "The Second Battle of Mag Tured." The text, though not so early in date as most of the stories of the Ulster cycle (p. 127), still preserves much of the rugged strength and directness for which the older tales are admired. It also exhibits something of the rough exaggerated humor of the earlier texts. The diversity of material, the repetitions, and the contradictions all go to show that the story as we now have it is a compilation made up of a number of independent narratives.

The Tuatha De Danann lived in the northern isles of the world, learning lore and magic and druidism and wizardry and cunning, until they surpassed the sages of the arts of heathendom. There were four cities in which they learned lore and science and diabolic arts, to wit Falias and Gorias, Murias and Findias. Out of Falias was brought the Stone of Fal, which was in Tara. It used to roar under every king that would take the realm of Ireland. Out of Gorias was brought the Spear that Lug had. No battle was ever won against it or him who held it in his hand. Out of Findias was brought the Sword of Nuada. When it was drawn from its deadly sheath, no one ever escaped from it, and it was irresistible. Out of Murias was brought the Dagda's Cauldron. No company ever went from it unthankful. Four wizards (there were) in those four cities. Morfesa was in Falias: Esras was in Gorias: Uscias was in Findias: Semias was in Murias. Those are the four poets of whom the Tuatha De learnt lore and science.

Now the Tuatha De Danann made an alliance with the Fomorians, and Balor grandson of Net gave his daughter Ethne to Cian son of Diancecht, and she brought forth the gifted child, Lug.

The Tuatha De came with a great fleet to Ireland to take it from the Fir Bolg. They burnt their ships at once on reaching the district of Corcu Belgatan (that is, Connemara today), so that they should not think of retreating to them; and the smoke and the mist that came from the vessels filled the neighboring land and air. Therefore it was conceived that they had arrived in clouds of mist.

The first battle of Moytura was fought between them and the

Fir Bolg; and the Fir Bolg were routed, and a hundred thousand of them were slain, including their king Eochaid son of Erc.

In that battle, moreover, Nuada's hand was stricken off—it was Sreng son of Sengann that struck it off him—, so Diancecht the leech put on him a hand of silver with the motion of every hand; and Credne the brazier helped the leech.

Now the Tuatha De Danann lost many men in the battle, including Edleo son of Alla, and Ernmas and Fiachra and Turill Bicreo.

But such of the Fir Bolg as escaped from the battle went in flight to the Fomorians, and settled in Arran and in Islay and in Mann and Rathlin.

A contention as to the sovereignty of the men of Ireland arose between the Tuatha De and their women; because Nuada, after his hand had been stricken off, was disqualified to be king. They said that it would be fitter for them to bestow the kingdom on Bres son of Elotha, on their own adopted son; and that giving the kingdom to him would bind the alliance of the Fomorians to them. For his father, Elotha son of Delbaeth, was king of the Fomorians.

Now the conception of Bres came to pass in this way:

Eri, Delbaeth's daughter, a woman of the Tuatha De, was one day looking at the sea and the land from the house of Maeth Sceni, and she beheld the sea in perfect calm as if it were a level board. And as she was there she saw a vessel of silver on the sea. Its size she deemed great, but its shape was not clear to her. And the stream of the wave bore it to land. Then she saw that in it was a man of fairest form. Golden-yellow hair was on him as far as his two shoulders. A mantle with bands of golden thread was around him. His shirt had trimmings of golden thread. On his breast was a brooch of gold, with the sheen of a precious stone therein. He carried two white silver spears, and in them two smooth riveted shafts of bronze. Five circlets of gold adorned his neck, and he was girded with a golden-hilted sword with inlayings of silver and studs of gold.

The man said to her: "Is this the time that our lying with thee will be easy?"

"I have not made a tryst with thee, verily," said the woman. But they stretched themselves down together. The woman wept when the man would rise.

"Why weepest thou?" said he.

"I have two things for which I should lament," said the woman. "Parting from thee now that we have met. And the fair youths of the Tuatha De Danann have been entreating me in vain, and my desire is for thee since thou hast possessed me."

"Thy anxiety from these two things shall be taken away," said he. He drew his golden ring from his middle-finger, and put it into her hand, and told her that she should not part with it, by sale or by gift, save to one whose finger it should fit.

"I have another sorrow," said the woman. "I know not who hath come to me."

"Thou shalt not be ignorant of that," said he. "Elotha son of Delbaeth, king of the Fomorians, hath come to thee. And of our meeting thou shalt bear a son, and no name shall be given him save Eochaid Bres, that is Eochaid the beautiful; for every beautiful thing that is seen in Ireland, whether plain or fortress or ale or torch or woman or man or steed, will be judged in comparison with that boy, so that men say of it then 'it is a *bres*.' "

After that the man went back again by the way he had come, and the woman went to her house, and to her was given the famous conception.

She brought forth the boy, and he was named, as Elotha had said, Eochaid Bres. When a week after the woman's lying-in was complete the boy had a fortnight's growth; and he maintained that increase till the end of his first seven years, when he reached a growth of fourteen years. Because of the contest which took place among the Tuatha De the sovereignty of Ireland was given to the boy; and he gave seven hostages to Ireland's champions, that is, to her chiefs, to guarantee the restoring of the sovereignty if his own misdeeds should give cause. His mother afterwards bestowed land upon him, and on the land he had a stronghold built, called Dun Brese; and it was the Dagda that built that fortress.

Now when Bres had assumed the kingship, the Fomorians, —Indech son of Dea Domnann, and Elotha son of Delbaeth, and Tethra, three Fomorian kings, laid tribute upon Ireland, so that there was not a smoke from a roof in Ireland that was not under tribute to them. The champions were also reduced to their service; to wit, Ogma had to carry a bundle of firewood, and the Dagda became a rath-builder, and had to dig the trenches about Rath Brese.

The Dagda became weary of the work, and he used to meet in the house an idle blind man named Cridenbel, whose mouth was out of his breast. Cridenbel thought his own ration small and the Dagda's large. Whereupon he said: "O Dagda! of thy honor let the three best bits of thy ration be given to me!" So the Dagda used to give them to him every night. Large, however, were the lampooner's bits, the size of a good pig. But those three bits were a third of the Dagda's ration. The Dagda's health was the worse for that.

One day, then, as the Dagda was in the trench digging a rath, he saw the Mac Oc [1] coming to him. "That is good, O Dagda," says the Mac Oc.

"Even so," said the Dagda.

"What makes thee look so ill?" said the Mac Oc.

"I have cause for it," said the Dagda; "every evening Cridenbel the lampooner demands the three best bits of my portion."

"I have a counsel for thee," said the Mac Oc. He put his hand into his purse, took out three crowns of gold, and gave them to him.

"Put these three gold pieces into the three bits which thou givest at close of day to Cridenbel," said the Mac Oc. "These bits will then be the goodliest on thy dish; and the gold will turn in his belly so that he will die thereof, and the judgment of Bres thereon will be wrong. Men will say to the king: 'The Dagda has killed Cridenbel by means of a deadly herb which he gave him.' Then the king will order thee to be slain. But thou shalt say to him: 'What thou utterest, O king of the warriors of the Fene, is not a prince's truth. For I was watched by Cridenbel when I was at my work, and he used to say to me "Give me, O Dagda, the three best bits of thy portion. Bad is my housekeeping tonight." So I should have perished thereby had not the three gold coins which I found today helped me. I put them in my ration. I then gave it to Cridenbel, for the gold was the best thing that was before me. Hence, then, the gold is inside Cridenbel, and he died of it.'" The Dagda followed this advice, and was called before the king.

"It is clear," said the king. "Let the lampooner's belly be cut open to know if the gold be found therein. If it be not found, thou shalt die. If, however, it be found, thou shalt have life."

[1] Angus. See p. 1.

After that they cut open the lampooner's belly, and the three coins of gold were found in his stomach, so the Dagda was saved. Then the Dagda went to his work on the following morning, and to him came the Mac Oc and said: "Thou wilt soon finish thy work, but thou shalt not seek reward till the cattle of Ireland are brought to thee, and of them choose a heifer black-maned."

Thereafter the Dagda brought his work to an end, and Bres asked him what he would take as a reward for his labor. The Dagda answered: "I charge thee," said he, "to gather the cattle of Ireland into one place." The king did this as the Dagda asked, and the Dagda chose of them the heifer which the Mac Oc had told him to choose. That seemed weakness to Bres: he thought that the Dagda would have chosen somewhat more.

Now Nuada was in his sickness, and Diancecht put on him a hand of silver with the motion of every hand therein. That seemed evil to his son Miach. Miach went to the hand which had been replaced by Diancecht, and he said "joint to joint of it and sinew to sinew," and he healed Nuada in thrice three days and nights. The first seventy-two hours he put it against his side, and it became covered with skin. The second seventy-two hours he put it on his breast. . . . That cure seemed evil to Diancecht. He flung a sword on the crown of his son's head and cut the skin down to the flesh. The lad healed the wound by means of his skill. Diancecht smote him again and cut the flesh till he reached the bone. The lad healed this by the same means. He struck him a third blow and came to the membrane of his brain. The lad healed this also by the same means. Then he struck the fourth blow and cut out the brain, so that Miach died, and Diancecht said that the leech himself could not heal him of that blow.

Thereafter Miach was buried by Diancecht, and herbs three hundred and sixty-five, according to the number of his joints and sinews, grew through the grave. Then Airmed opened her mantle and separated those herbs according to their properties. But Diancecht came to her, and he confused the herbs, so that no one knows their proper cures unless the Holy Spirit should teach them afterwards. And Diancecht said "If Miach be not, Airmed shall remain."

So Bres held the sovereignty as it had been conferred upon him. But the chiefs of the Tuatha De murmured greatly against him, for their knives were not greased by him, and however often they visited him their breaths did not smell of ale. Moreover, they saw not their poets nor their bards nor their lampooners nor their harpers nor their pipers nor their jugglers nor their fools amusing them in the household. They did not go to the contests of their athletes. They saw not their champions proving their prowess at the king's court, save only one man, Ogma son of Ethliu. This was the duty which he had, to bring fuel to the fortress. He used to carry a bundle every day from the Clew Bay islands. And because he was weak from want of food, the sea would sweep away from him two thirds of his bundle. So he could only carry one third, and yet he had to supply the host from day to day. Neither service nor taxes were paid by the tribes, and the treasures of the tribe were not delivered by the act of the whole tribe.

Once upon a time there came a-guesting to Bres's house, Cairbre son of Etain, poet of the Tuatha De. He entered a cabin narrow, black, dark, wherein there was neither fire nor furniture nor bed. Three small cakes, and they dry, were brought to him on a little dish. On the morrow he arose and he was not thankful. As he went across the enclosure, he said:

> Without food quickly on a dish:
> Without a cow's milk whereon a calf grows:
> Without a man's abode in the gloom of night:
> Without paying a company of story-tellers, let that be Bres's condition.
> Let there be no increase in Bres.

Now that was true. Nought save decay was on Bres from that hour. That is the first satire that was ever made in Ireland.

Now after that the Tuatha De went together to have speech with their fosterson, Bres son of Elotha, and demanded of him their sureties. He gave them the restitution of the realm, and he was not well-pleased with them for that. He begged to be allowed to remain till the end of seven years. "That shall be granted," said the same assembly; "but thou shalt remain on the same security. Every fruit that comes to thy hand, both house and land and gold and silver, cows and food, and freedom from rent and taxes until then."

"Ye shall have as ye say," said Bres.

This is why they were asked for the delay: that he might gather the champions of the fairy-mound, the Fomorians, to seize the tribes by force. Grievous to him seemed his expulsion from his kingdom.

Then he went to his mother and asked her whence was his race. "I am certain of that," said she; and she went on to the hill whence she had seen the vessel of silver in the sea. She then went down to the strand, and gave him the ring which had been left with her for him, and he put it round his middle-finger, and it fitted him. For the sake of no one had she formerly given it up, either by sale or gift. Until that day there was none whom it suited.

Then they went forward till they reached the land of the Fomorians. They came to a great plain with many assemblies therein. They advanced to the fairest of these assemblies. Tidings were demanded of them there. They replied that they were of the men of Ireland. They were then asked whether they had hounds; for at that time it was the custom, when a body of men went to an assembly, to challenge them to a friendly contest. "We have hounds," said Bres. Then the hounds had a coursing-match, and the hounds of the Tuatha De were swifter than the hounds of the Fomorians. Then they were asked whether they had steeds for a horse-race. They answered, "We have"; and their steeds were swifter than the steeds of the Fomorians. They were then asked whether they had any one who was good at sword-play. None was found save Bres alone. So when he set his hand to the sword, his father recognized the ring on his finger and inquired who was the hero. His mother answered on his behalf and told the king that Bres was a son of his. Then she related to him the whole story even as we have recounted it.

His father was sorrowful over him. Said the father: "What need has brought thee out of the land wherein thou didst rule?"

Bres replied: "Nothing has brought me save my own injustice and arrogance. I stript them of their jewels and treasures and their own food. Neither tribute nor taxes had been taken from them up to that time."

"That is bad," said the father. "Better were their prosperity than their kingship. Better their prayers than their curses. Why hast thou come hither?"

"I have come to ask you for champions," said he. "I would take that land by force."

"Thou shouldst not gain it by injustice if thou didst not gain it by justice," said the father.

"Then what counsel hast thou for me?" said Bres.

Thereafter he sent Bres to the champion, to Balor grandson of Net, the king of the Isles, and to Indech son of Dea Domnann the king of the Fomorians; and these assembled all the troops from Lochlann westwards unto Ireland, to impose their tribute and their rule by force on the Tuatha De, so that they made one bridge of vessels from the Foreigners' Isles to Erin. Never came to Ireland an army more horrible or fearful than that host of the Fomorians. Men from Scythia of Lochlann and men out of the Western Isles were rivals in that expedition.

Now as to the Tuatha De, this is what they were doing. After Bres, Nuada was again in sovereignty over the Tuatha De. At that time he held a mighty feast at Tara for them. Now there was a certain warrior on his way to Tara, whose name was Lug Samildanach. And there were then two doorkeepers at Tara, namely Gamal son of Figal and Camall son of Riagall. When one of these was on duty he saw a strange company coming towards him. A young warrior fair and shapely, with a king's trappings, was in the forefront of that band. They told the doorkeeper to announce their arrival at Tara. The doorkeeper asked: "Who is there?"

"Here there is Lug Lamfada (i.e., Lug Long-Arm) son of Cian son of Diancecht and of Ethne daughter of Balor. Fosterson, he, of Tailltiu daughter of Magmor king of Spain and of Eochaid the Rough son of Duach."

The doorkeeper asked of Lug Samildanach: "What art dost thou practise?" said he; "for no one without an art enters Tara."

"Question me," said he: "I am a wright."

The doorkeeper answered: "We need thee not. We have a wright already, even Luchta son of Luachaid."

He said: "Question me, O doorkeeper! I am a smith."

The doorkeeper answered him: "We have a smith already, Colum Cualleinech of the three new processes."

He said: "Question me: I am a champion."

The doorkeeper answered: "We need thee not. We have a champion already, Ogma son of Ethliu."

He said again: "Question me: I am a harper."

"We need thee not. We have a harper already, Abcan son

of Bicelmos whom the Tuatha De Danann chose in the fairy-mounds."

Said he: "Question me: I am a hero."

The doorkeeper answered: "We need thee not. We have a hero already, even Bresal Etarlam son of Eochaid Baethlam."

Then he said: "Question me, O doorkeeper! I am a poet and I am a historian."

"We need thee not. We have already a poet and historian, even En son of Ethaman."

He said, "Question me: I am a sorcerer."

"We need thee not. We have sorcerers already. Many are our wizards and our folk of might."

He said: "Question me: I am a leech."

"We need thee not. We have for a leech Diancecht."

"Question me," said he; "I am a cupbearer."

"We need thee not. We have cupbearers already, even Delt and Drucht and Daithe, Tae and Talom and Trog, Glei and Glan and Glesi."

He said: "Question me: I am a good brazier."

"We need thee not. We have a brazier already, Credne Cerd."

He said again, "Ask the king," said he, "whether he has a single man who possesses all these arts, and if he has I will not enter Tara."

Then the doorkeeper went into the palace and declared all to the king. "A warrior has come before the enclosure," said he. "His name is Samildanach (many-gifted), and all the arts which thy household practise he himself possesses, so that he is the man of each and every art."

The king said then that the chess-boards of Tara should be taken to Samildanach, and he won all the stakes, so that then he made the *Cro* of Lug. (But if chess was invented at the epoch of the Trojan war, it had not reached Ireland then, for the battle of Moytura and the destruction of Troy occurred at the same time.) [1]

Then that was related to Nuada. "Let him into the enclosure," says he; "for never before has man like him entered this fortress."

Then the doorkeeper let Lug pass him, and he entered the fortress and sat down in the sage's seat, for he was a sage in every art.

[1] This is the author's own comment.

Then the great flag-stone, to move which required the effort of four-score yoke of oxen, Ogma hurled through the house, so that it lay on the outside of Tara. This was a challenge to Lug. But Lug cast it back, so that it lay in the center of the palace; and he put the piece which it had carried away into the side of the palace and made it whole.

"Let a harp be played for us," said the company. So the warrior played a sleep-strain for the hosts and for the king the first night. He cast them into sleep from that hour to the same time on the following day. He played a wail-strain, so that they were crying and lamenting. He played a laugh-strain, so that they were in merriment and joyance.

Now Nuada, when he beheld the warrior's many powers, considered whether Samildanach could put away from them the bondage which they suffered from the Fomorians. So they held a council concerning the warrior. The decision to which Nuada came was to change seats with the warrior. So Samildanach went to the king's seat, and the king rose up before him till thirteen days had ended. Then on the morrow he met with the two brothers, Dagda and Ogma, on Grellach Dollaid. And his brothers Goibniu and Diancecht were summoned to them. A full year were they in that secret converse, wherefore Grellach Dollaid is called Amrun of the Tuatha De Danann.

Thereafter the wizards of Ireland were summoned to them, and their medical men and charioteers and smiths and farmers and lawyers. They held speech with them in secret. Then Nuada inquired of the sorcerer whose name was Mathgen, what power he could wield? He answered that through his contrivance he would cast the mountains of Ireland on the Fomorians, and roll their summits against the ground. And he declared to them that the twelve chief mountains of the land of Erin would support the Tuatha De Danann, in battling for them, to wit, Sliab League, and Denna Ulad and the Mourne Mountains, and Bri Ruri and Sliab Bladma and Sliab Snechtai, Sliab Mis and Blai-sliab and Nevin and Sliab Maccu Belgadan and Segais and Cruachan Aigle.

Then he asked the cupbearer what power he could wield. He answered that he would bring the twelve chief lochs of Ireland before the Fomorians, and that they would not find water therein, whatever thirst might seize them. These are those lochs: Derg-loch, Loch Luimnigh, Loch Corrib, Loch Ree, Loch Mask, Strangford Loch, Belfast Loch, Loch Neagh, Loch Foyle, Loch Gara, Loch Reag, Marloch. They would betake themselves to the twelve chief rivers of Ireland,—Bush, Boyne, Baa, Nem, Lee, Shannon, Moy, Sligo, Erne, Finn, Liffey, Suir; and they will all be hidden from the Fomorians, so that they will not find a drop therein. Drink shall be provided for the men of Ireland, though they bide in the battle to the end of seven years.

Then said Figol son of Mamos, their druid: "I will cause three showers of fire to pour on the faces of the Fomorian host, and I will take out of them two thirds of their valor and their bravery and their strength, and I will bind their urine in their own bodies and in the bodies of their horses. Every breath that the men of Ireland shall exhale will be an increase of valor and bravery and strength to them. Though they bide in the battle till the end of seven years, they will not be weary in any wise."

Said the Dagda: "The power which ye boast I shall wield it all by myself." "It is thou art the Dagda (good hand), with everyone": wherefore thenceforward the name "Dagda" adhered to him. Then they separated from the council, agreeing to meet again that day three years.

Now when the provision of the battle had then been settled, Lug and Dagda and Ogma went to the three Gods of Danu, and these gave Lug the plan of the battle; and for seven years they were preparing for it and making their weapons.

The Dagda had a house in Glenn Etin in the north, and he had to meet a woman in Glenn Etin a year from that day, about Samain (Hallowe'en) before the battle. The river Unius of Connacht roars to the south of it. He beheld the woman in Unius in Corann, washing herself, with one of her two feet at Allod Echae (*i.e.*, Echumech), to the south of the water, and the other at Loscuinn, to the north of the water. Nine loosened tresses were on her head. The Dagda conversed with her, and they made a union. "The Bed of the Couple" is the name of the place thenceforward. The woman that is here mentioned is the Morrigu. Then she told the Dagda that the Fomorians would land at Mag Scetne, and that he should summon Erin's men of art to meet her at the Ford of Unius, and that she would go into Scetne to destroy Indech son of Dea Domnann, the king of the Fomorians, and would deprive him of the blood of his heart and the kidneys of his valor. Afterwards she gave two handfuls of that blood to the hosts that were waiting at the Ford of Unius. "Ford of Destruction" became its name, because of that destruction of the king. Then that was done by the wizards, and they chanted spells on the hosts of the Fomorians.

This was a week before Samain, and each of them separated from the other until all the men of Ireland came together on Samain. Six times thirty hundred was their number, that is, twice thirty hundred in every third.

Then Lug sent the Dagda to spy out the Fomorians and to delay them until the men of Ireland should come to the battle. So the Dagda went to the camp of the Fomorians and asked them for a truce of battle. This was granted to him as he asked. Porridge was then made for him by the Fomorians, and this was done to mock him, for great was his love for porridge. They filled for him the king's cauldron, five fists deep, into which went four-score gallons of new milk and the like quantity of meal and fat. Goats and sheep and swine were put into it, and they were all boiled together with the porridge. They were spilt for him into a hole in the ground, and Indech told him that he would be put to death unless he consumed it all; he should eat his fill so that he might not reproach the Fomorians with inhospitality.

Then the Dagda took his ladle, and it was big enough for a man and woman to lie on the middle of it. These then were the bits that were in it, halves of salted swine and a quarter of lard. "Good food this," said the Dagda. . . .

At the end of the meal he put his curved finger over the bottom of the hole on mold and gravel. Sleep came upon him then after eating his porridge. Bigger than a house-cauldron was his belly, and the Fomorians laughed at it. Then he went away from them to the strand of Eba. Not easy was it for the hero to move along owing to the bigness of his belly. Unseemly was his apparel. A cape to the hollow of his two elbows. A dun tunic around him, as far as the swelling of his rump. It was, moreover, long-breasted, with a hole in the peak. Two brogues on him of horse-hide, with the hair outside. Behind him a wheeled fork to carry which required the effort of eight men, so that its track after him was enough for the boundary-ditch of a province. Wherefore it is called "The Track of the Dagda's Club."

Then the Fomorians marched till they reached Scetne. The men of Ireland were in Mag Aurfolaig. These two hosts were threatening battle. "The men of Ireland venture to offer battle to us," said Bres son of Elotha to Indech son of Dea Domnann. "I will fight anon," said Indech, "so that their bones will be small unless they pay their tributes."

Because of Lug's knowledge the men of Ireland had made a resolution not to let him go into the battle. So his nine fosterers were left to protect him, Tollus-dam and Ech-dam and Eru, Rechtaid the white and Fosad and Fedlimid, Ibor and Scibar and Minn. They feared an early death for the hero owing to the multitude of his arts. Therefore they did not let him forth to the fight.

The chiefs of the Tuatha De Danann were gathered round Lug. And he asked his smith, Goibniu, what power he wielded for them? "Not hard to tell," said he. "Though the men of Erin bide in the battle to the end of seven years, for every spear that parts from its shaft, or sword that shall break therein, I will provide a new weapon in its place. No spear-point which my hand shall forge," said he, "shall make a missing cast. No skin which it pierces shall taste life afterwards. That has not been done by Dolb the smith of the Fomorians."

"And thou, O Diancecht," said Lug, "what power canst thou wield?"

"Not hard to tell," said he. "Every man who shall be wounded there, unless his head be cut off, or the membrane of his brain or his spinal marrow be severed, I will make quite whole in the battle on the morrow."

"And thou, O Credne," said Lug to his brazier, "what is thy power in the battle?"

"Not hard to tell," said Credne. "Rivets for their spears, and hilts for their swords, and bosses and rims for their shields, I will supply them all."

"And thou, O Luchta," said Lug to his wright, "what service wilt thou render in the battle?"

"Not hard to tell," said Luchta. "All the shields and javelin-shafts they require, I will supply them all."

"And thou, O Ogma," said Lug to his champion, "what is thy power in the battle?"

"Not hard to tell," said he. "I will repel the king and three enneads of his friends, and capture up to a third of his men." . . .

"And ye, O sorcerers," said Lug, "what power will you wield?"

"Not hard to tell," said the sorcerers. "We shall fill them with fear when they have been overthrown by our craft, till their heroes are slain, and deprive them of two thirds of their might, with constraint on their urine."

"And ye, O cupbearers," said Lug, "what power?"

"Not hard to tell," said the cupbearers. "We will bring a strong thirst upon them, and they shall not find drink to quench it."

"And ye, O druids," said Lug, "what power?"

"Not hard to tell," said the druids. "We will bring showers of fire on the faces of the Fomorians, so that they cannot look upwards, and so that the warriors who are contending with them may slay them by their might."

"And thou, O Cairbre son of Etain," said Lug to his poet, "what power canst thou wield in the battle?"

"Not hard to tell," said Cairbre. "I will make a satire on them. And I will satirize them and shame them, so that through the spell of my art they will not resist warriors."

"And ye, O Be-culle and O Dianann," said Lug to his two witches, "what power can ye wield in the battle?"

"Not hard to tell," said they. "We will enchant the trees and the stones and the sods of the earth, so that they shall become a host under arms against them, and shall rout them in flight with horror and trembling."

"And thou, O Dagda," said Lug, "what power canst thou wield on the Fomorian host in the battle?"

"Not hard to tell," said the Dagda. "I will take the side of the men of Erin both in mutual smiting and destruction and wizardry. Under my club the bones of the Fomorians will be as many as hailstones under the feet of herds of horses where you meet on the battlefield of Moytura."

So thus Lug spoke with every one of them in turn; and he strengthened and addressed his army, so that each man of them had the spirit of a king or a mighty lord. Now every day a battle was fought between the tribe of the Fomorians and the Tuatha De, save only that kings or princes were not delivering it, but only keen and haughty folk.

Now the Fomorians marvelled at a certain thing which was revealed to them in the battle. Their spears and their swords were blunted and broken and such of their men as were slain did not return on the morrow. But it was not so with the Tuatha De. For though their weapons were blunted and broken to-day, they were renewed on the morrow, because Goibniu the smith was in the forge making swords and spears and javelins. For he would make those weapons by three turns. Then Luchta the wright would make the spearshafts by three chippings, and the third chipping was a finish and would set them in the ring of the spear. When the spearheads were stuck in the side of the forge he would throw the rings with the shafts, and it was needless to set them again. Then Credne the brazier would make the rivets by three turns, and would cast the rings of the spears to them; and thus they used to cleave together.

This then is what used to put fire into the warriors who were slain, so that they were swifter on the morrow. Because Diancecht and his two sons, Octriuil and Miach, and his daughter Airmed sang spells over the well named Slane. Now their mortally wounded men were cast into it as soon as they were slain. They were alive when they came out. Their mortally wounded became whole through the might of the incantation of the four leeches who were about the well. Now that was harmful to the Fomorians, so they sent a man of them to spy out the battle and the actions of the Tuatha De, namely Ruadan son of Bres and of Brig the Dagda's daughter. For he was a son and a grandson of the Tuatha De. Then he related to the Fomorians the work of the smith and the wright and the brazier and the four leeches who were around the well. He was sent again to kill one of the artisans, that is Goibniu. From him he begged a spear, its rivets from the brazier and its shaft from the wright. So all was given to him as he asked. There was a woman there grinding the weapons, Cron mother of Fianlug; she it is that ground Ruadan's spear. Now the spear was given to Ruadan by a chief, wherefore the name "a chief's spear" is still given to weavers' beams in Erin.

Now after the spear had been given to him, Ruadan turned and wounded Goibniu. But Goibniu plucked out the spear and cast it at Ruadan, so that it went through him, and he died in the presence of his father in the assembly of the Fomorians. Then Brig came and bewailed her son. She shrieked at first, she cried at last.

So that then for the first time crying and shrieking were heard in Erin. Now it was that Brig who invented a whistle for signalling at night.

Then Goibniu went into the well, and he became whole. There was a warrior with the Fomorians, Octriallach son of Indech son of Dea Domnann, son of the Fomorian king. He told the Fomorians that each man of them should bring a stone of the stones of Drowes to cast into the well of Slane in Achad Abla to the west of Moytura, to the east of Loch Arboch. So they went, and a stone for each man was cast into the well. Wherefore the cairn thus made is called Octriallach's Cairn. But another name for that well is Loch Luibe, for Diancecht put into it one of every herb (*lub*) that grew in Erin.

Now when the great battle came, the Fomorians marched out of their camp, and formed themselves into strong battalions. Not a chief nor man of prowess of them was without a hauberk against his skin, a helmet on his head, a broad spear in his right hand, a heavy sharp sword on his belt, a firm shield on his shoulder. To attack the Fomorian host on that day was "striking a head against a cliff," was "a hand in a serpent's nest," was "a face up to fire." These were the kings and chiefs that were heartening the host of the Fomorians, namely, Balor son of Dot son of Net, Bres son of Elotha, Tuiri Tortbuillech son of Lobos, Goll and Irgoll Loscenn-lomm son of Lommglunech, Indech son of Dea Domnann the king of the Fomorians, Octriallach son of Indech, Omna and Bagna, Elotha son of Delbaeth.

On the other side the Tuatha De Danann arose and left their nine comrades keeping Lug, and they marched to the battle. When the battle began, Lug escaped from his guardians with his charioteer, so that it was he who was in front of the hosts of the Tuatha De. Then a keen and cruel battle was fought between the tribe of the Fomorians and the men of Ireland. Lug was heartening the men of Ireland that they should fight the battle fervently, so that they should not be any longer in bondage. For it was better for them to find death in protecting their fatherland than to bide under bondage and tribute as they had been. . . .

The hosts uttered a great shout as they entered the battle. Then they came together and each of them began to smite the other. Many fine men fell there. Great the slaughter and the grave-lying that was there. Pride and shame were there side by side. There was anger and indignation. Abundant was the stream of blood there over the white skin of young warriors mangled by hands of eager men. Harsh was the noise of the heroes and the champions mutually fending their spears and their shields and their bodies when the others were smiting them with spears and with swords. Harsh, moreover, was the thunder that was there throughout the battle, the shouting of the warriors and the clashing of the shields, the flashing and whistling of the glaives and the ivory-hilted swords, the rattling and jingling of the quivers, the sound and winging of the darts and the javelins, and the crashing of the weapons. The ends of their fingers and of their feet almost met in the mutual blows, and owing to the slipperiness of the blood under the feet of the soldiers, they would fall from their upright posture and beat their heads together as they sat. The battle was a gory, ghastly melee, and the river Unsenn rushed with corpses.

Then Nuada Silver-Hand and Macha, daughter of Ernmass, fell by Balor grandson of Net. And Cassmael fell by Octriallach son of Indech. Lug and Balor of the Piercing Eye met in the battle. An evil eye had Balor the Fomorian. That eye was never opened save only on a battle-field. Four men used to lift up the lid of the eye with a polished handle which passed through its lid. If an army looked at that eye, though they were many thousands in number, they could not resist a few warriors. It had a poisonous power. Once when his father's druids were concocting charms, he came and looked out of the window, and the fume of the concoction came under it, so that the poison of the concoction afterwards penetrated the eye that looked. He and Lug met. "Lift up mine eyelid, my lad," said Balor, "that I may see the babbler who is conversing with me."

The lid was raised from Balor's eye. Then Lug cast a sling-stone at him, which carried the eye through his head while his own army looked on. And the sling-stone fell on the host of the Fomorians, and thrice nine of them died beside it, so that the crowns of their heads came against the breast of Indech son of Dea Domnann, and a gush of blood sprang over his lips. Said Indech: "Let Loch Half-green my poet be summoned to me!" Half-green was he from the ground to the crown of his head.

Loch went to the king. "Make known to me," said Indech, "who has flung this cast on me."

Then the Morrigu, daughter of Ernmass, came, and heartened the Tuatha De to fight the battle fiercely and fervently. Thereafter the battle became a rout, and the Fomorians were beaten back to the sea. The champion Ogma son of Ethliu, and Indech son of Dea Domnann the king of the Fomorians, fell in single combat. Loch Half-green besought Lug for quarter. "Give me my three wishes," said Lug.

"Thou shalt have them," said Loch. "Till Doom I will ward off from Ireland all plundering by the Fomorians, and, at the end of the world, every ailment." So Loch was spared. Then he sang to the Gael the "decree of fastening."

Loch said that he would bestow names on Lug's nine chariots because of the quarter that had been given him. So Lug told him to name them.[1]

.   .   .   .

"What is the number of the slain?" said Lug to Loch.

"I know not the number of peasants and rabble. As to the number of Fomorian lords and nobles and champions and kings' sons and overkings, I know, even five thousand three score and three men: two thousand and three fifties: four score thousand and nine times five: eight score and eight: four score and seven: four score and six: eight score and five: two and forty including Net's grandson. That is the number of the slain of the Fomorian overkings and high nobles who fell in the battle. Howbeit, as to the number of peasants and common people and rabble, and folk of every art besides who came in company with the great army—for every champion and every high chieftain and every overking of the Fomorians came with his host to the battle, so that all fell there, both his freemen and his slaves—we reckon only a few of the servants of the overkings. This then is the number that I have reckoned of these as I beheld: seven hundred, seven score and seven men . . . together with Sab Uanchennach son of Cairbre Colc, son was he of a servant of Indech son of Dea Domnann, that is, a son of a servant of the Fomorian king. As to what fell besides of 'half-men' and of those who reached not the heart of the battle,

[1] At this point the original gives a list of the names of the chariots, charioteers, and their equipment.

these are in no wise numbered till we number stars of heaven, sand of sea, flakes of snow, dew on lawn, hailstones, grass under feet of herds, and Manannan mac Lir's horses (waves) in a sea-storm."

Thereafter Lug and his comrades found Bres son of Elotha unguarded. He said: "It is better to give me quarter than to slay me."

"What then will follow from that?" said Lug.

"If I be spared," says Bres, "the cows of Erin will always be in milk."

"I will set this forth to our wise men," said Lug.

So Lug went to Maeltne Mor-brethach, and said to him: "Shall Bres have quarter for giving constant milk to the cows of Erin?"

"He shall not have quarter," said Maeltne; "he has no power over their age or their offspring, though he can milk them so long as they are alive."

Lug said to Bres: "That does not save thee: thou hast no power over their age and their offspring, though thou canst milk them. Is there aught else that will save thee, O Bres?" said Lug.

"There is in truth. Tell thy lawyer that for sparing me the men of Ireland shall reap a harvest in every quarter of the year."

Said Lug to Maeltne: "Shall Bres be spared for giving the men of Ireland a harvest of corn every quarter?"

"This has suited us," saith Maeltne: "the spring for ploughing and sowing, and the beginning of summer for the end of the strength of corn, and the beginning of autumn for the end of the ripeness of corn and for reaping it. Winter for consuming it."

"That does not rescue thee," said Lug to Bres; "but less than that rescues thee."

"What?" said Bres.

"How shall the men of Ireland plough? How shall they sow? How shall they reap? After making known these three things thou wilt be spared."

"Tell them," said Bres, "that their ploughing be on a Tuesday, their casting seed into the field be on a Tuesday, their reaping on a Tuesday." So through that stratagem Bres was let go free.

In that fight, then, Ogma the champion found Orna the sword of Tethra, a king of the Fomorians. Ogma unsheathed the sword and cleansed it. Then the sword related whatsoever had been done by it; for it was the custom of swords at that time, when unsheathed, to set forth the deeds that had been done by them. And therefore swords are entitled to the tribute of cleansing them after they have been unsheathed. Hence, also, charms are preserved in swords thenceforward. Now the reason why demons used to speak from weapons at that time was because weapons were worshipped by human beings at that epoch, and the weapons were among the safeguards of that time. . . .

Now Lug and the Dagda and Ogma pursued the Fomorians, for they had carried off the Dagda's harper, whose name was Uaitne. Then they reached the banqueting-house in which were Bres son of Elotha and Elotha son of Delbaeth. There hung the harp on the wall. That is the harp in which the Dagda had bound the melodies so that they sounded not until by his call he summoned them forth; when he said this below:

> Come Daurdabla!
> Come Coir-cethar-chuir!
> Come summer, Come winter!
> Mouths of harps and bags and pipes!

Now that harp had two names, Daur-da-bla "Oak of two greens" and Coir-cethar-chuir "Four-angled music."

Then the harp went forth from the wall, and killed nine men, and came to the Dagda. And he played for them the three things whereby harpers are distinguished, to wit, sleep-strain and smile-strain and wail-strain. He played wail-strain to them, so that their tearful women wept. He played smile-strain to them, so their women and children laughed. He played sleep-strain to them, and the company fell asleep. Through that sleep the three of them escaped unhurt from the Fomorians though these desired to slay them.

Then the Dagda brought with him the heifer which had been given to him for his labor. For when she called her calf all the cattle of Ireland which the Fomorians had taken as their tribute, grazed.

Now after the battle was won and the corpses cleared away, the Morrigu, daughter of Ernmas, proceeded to proclaim that battle and the mighty victory which had taken place, to the royal heights of Ireland and to its fairy hosts and its chief waters and its river-mouths. And hence it is that Badb (*i.e.*, the Morrigu) also describes high deeds. "Hast thou any tale?" said every one to her then. And she replied:

> Peace up to heaven,
> Heaven down to earth,
> Earth under heaven,
> Strength in every one, etc.

Then, moreover, she was prophesying the end of the world, and foretelling every evil that would be therein, and every disease and every vengeance. Wherefore then she sang this lay below:

> I shall not see a world that will be dear to me.
> Summer without flowers,
> Kine will be without milk,
> Women without modesty,
> Men without valor,
> Captures without a king. . . .
> Woods without mast,
> Sea without produce. . . .
> Wrong judgments of old men,
> False precedents of lawyers,
> Every man a betrayer,
> Every boy a reaver.
> Son will enter his father's bed,
> Father will enter his son's bed,
> Every one will be his brother's brother-in-law. . . .
> An evil time!
> Son will deceive his father,
> Daughter will deceive her mother.

THE FATE OF THE CHILDREN OF TUIRENN

"The Fate of the Children of Tuirenn" is one of a group of narratives known in Irish tradition as "The Three Sorrows of Story-Telling," the others being "The Exile of the Sons of Usnech" (see p. 239), and "The Fate of the Children of Lir." The first part of the story, telling how Nuada got his silver arm and how the Fomorians came to invade Ireland, merely serves as an introduction and has only a superficial connection with the main plot, which is concerned with the tragically desperate attempts of the sons of Tuirenn to carry out the impossible tasks imposed upon them by Lug as the blood-price for his father, who, like the other major personages, is of the Tuatha De Danann. The narrative contains numerous references to the "Book of Invasions" (p. 3), and "The Second Battle of Mag Tured" (p. 28). The tale, although it deals with events of the remote past, is comparatively late in date. Contrasted with the earlier and sterner pieces that compose the Ulster cycle, it may appear somewhat overwrought and unduly burdened with romantic incident; yet it builds up to a conclusion full of tragic pathos.

A comely, freeborn king took sovereignty and rule over the beautifully complexioned Tuatha De Danann; his name was Nuada Argatlam (that is, Nuada Silver-Arm), the son of Echtach the son of Etarlam the son of Ordan the son of Ionnaoi. And that king was remarkable for two things: he had an arm of silver; and he had for doorkeeper a young man with but one eye.

Now it happened that one day this young man went out beyond the walls of Tara; he saw two beautiful noble-faced youths coming over the green towards him; and they saluted him, and he saluted them in return. And the doorkeeper asked news of them: "What place have ye come from, ye two noble-faced youths?"

"We are good doctors," said they.

"If ye are good doctors," said he, "ye will put an eye in the place of my lost eye."

"I could put the eye of that cat in your lap into the place of your eye," said one of them.

"I should like that well," said the doorkeeper.

And so they put the cat's eye into the place of the young man's lost eye.

This turned out to be a convenience and an inconvenience for

49

him: for when he wished to sleep or take rest, then the eye would start at the squeaking of the mice and the flying of the birds, and the motion of the rushes; and when he wished to watch a host or an assembly, it was then it was surely in deep repose and sleep with him.

However, he went in and told the king that excellent doctors had come to Tara. "For they have put a cat's eye in the place of my eye," said he.

"Bring them in," said the king.

And as they came in they heard a deep piteous groan. Then Miach, one of the doctors, said, "I hear the groan of a champion."

Ormiach, the other, said, "See if it is not the groan of a champion over a chafer which is blackening him on one side."

Then the king was brought forward from where he was, and they examined him; and one of them drew his arm out from his side, and a chafer darted out of it and ran through the court; and the household arose and killed the chafer.

And Miach made another arm of the same length and thickness for him; and all the Tuatha De Danann were sought, and no arm was found that would serve him but the arm of Modan the swineherd. "Would the bones of his own arm (*i.e.*, of the arm of this very man) serve you?" said the people.

"It is what we should prefer," said they. And a person was sent to fetch it, and brought it with him to Tara; and it was given to Miach.

Miach said to Ormiach, "Do you wish to set the arm, or to go to bring herbs for the purpose of putting flesh upon it?"

"I prefer to set the arm," said he. Miach then went to seek herbs, and returned without them; but the arm was set without defect.

The state of things in the time of this king was this: the Fomorians enforced a great tribute and rule over the Tuatha De Danann in his time; such as a tribute upon the kneading trough, and a tribute upon the quern, and a tribute upon the baking flags, and a polltax calculated at an ounce of gold for every nose of the Tuatha De Danann, on the Hill of Usnech, on the west side of Tara. And they extorted this tribute every year; and if any man neglected to pay it, his nose was taken off from his face.

At this time a fair assembly was held by the king of Erin on

Balor's Hill, which is now called Usnech. And the people had not long been assembled there before they saw the array of a goodly army coming over the plain from the east towards them; and one young man came in front of that army, high in command over the rest; and like to the setting sun was the splendor of his countenance and his forehead; and they were not able to look in his face from the greatness of its splendor.

And he was Lug Lamfada (*i.e.*, Lug of the Long Arm) and his army was from the fairy-mounds, from the Land of Promise (fairyland), and his own foster-brothers, the sons of Manannan, namely Sgoith Glegeal son of Manannan, and Rabach Slaitin, and Gleigal Garb, and Goithne Gormsuileach, and Sine Sinderg, and Domnall Donnruad, and Aed the son of Eathall. And thus was the personal array of Lug Lamfada, namely: the steed Aenbarr of Manannan was under him, and she was as fleet as the naked cold wind of spring, and sea and land were the same to her, and the charm was such that her rider was never killed off her back; and he wore Manannan's corselet upon him, and its charm was such that no one could be wounded below it or above it; and he wore Manannan's breast-piece upon the ridge of his breast and front, so that no weapon could pierce him; and he had a helmet on his head to protect it, with a beautiful precious stone set behind in it, and two of them in its front; and as bright as the sun on a dry summer's day was the complexion of his face and forehead when he took this helmet off; and he had the Fregartach (Retaliator), Manannan's sword, at his side; and its charm was such that it never wounded anyone who could come away alive from it; and that sword was never bare on the scene of a battle or combat, in which so much strength as that of a woman in childbirth would remain to any person who saw the sword who was opposed to it.

Then came that array to where the king of Erin was, and the Tuatha De Danann. And they exchanged welcomes. And they were not long before they saw a gloomy grim-looking body of men coming towards them, namely, nine times nine of the collectors of the Fomorians who were coming to demand taxes and tributes of the men of Erin. The following are the names of the fiercest and most cruel four of them; viz., Eine, and Ethfaith, Coron, and Compar; and so great was the fear of the Tuatha De Danann of these collectors, that not one of them dared inflict punishment even on his own son or his foster-son.

And they came into the presence of the king of Erin, and the fairy cavalcade; and the king of Erin and all the Tuatha De Danann stood up before them. And Lug Lamfada asked of the Tuatha De Danann, "Why did ye stand up before that gloomy grim-looking body of men, and have not stood up before us?"

"We were obliged to do this," said the king of Erin, "for if there were but a month-old child of us sitting before them, they would not deem it a cause too little to kill us."

"By my word," said Lug, "I feel a great desire to kill them." And then Lug said again that the desire to kill them came strongly upon him.

"That would be a deed to bring evil to us," said the king of Erin, "for we should meet our own death and destruction through it."

"It is a long time that ye have been under this oppression," said Lug. And he started up and attacked the Fomorians, slaughtering and disfiguring them, until he had killed eight times nine of them; but the remaining nine he allowed to receive sanctuary under the dignity and protection of the king of Erin. "I should kill you also," said Lug, "but that I prefer that you should go with the news to the foreigners rather than my own messengers, lest they should receive dishonor."

And then these nine went forth until they reached the country of Lochlann, where the Fomorian people were; and they related to them their story from beginning to end; and how the young noble-faced boy had come into Erin, and all the collectors had been killed by him but themselves; "and," said they, "the reason that he allowed us to escape was in order that we might relate the story to you."

Thereupon Balor, king of the Fomorians, said, "Do you know who he is?"

"I know," said Cathleann, Balor's wife, "he is a daughter's son of yours and mine; and it is presaged and prophecied for us that from the time that he should come into Erin we would never again have power there."

Then the chief men of the Fomorians went into a council, namely, Eab the grandson of Net, and Senchab the grandson of Net, and

Sotal Salmor, and Luath Leborcham, and Tinne Mor of Triscadal, and Loisginn Lomgluineach, and Luath Lineach, and Lobais the druid, and Liathlabar the son of Lobais; and the nine deeply learned poets and prophetic philosophers of the Fomorians, and Balor of the Stout Blows himself, and the twelve white-mouthed sons of Balor, and Cathleann the crooked-toothed, Balor's queen. And it was then Bres the son of Balor said, "I shall go with seven valiant and great battalions of the horsemen of the Fomorians into Erin; and I shall give battle to Lug Ildanach; and I shall cut off his head, and I shall bring it to you upon the green of the ·Lochlan-nachs of Berbe."

"It would well become you to do so," said they.

And then Bres said, "Let my ships and my swift barks be made ready for me; and let food and stores be put into them." And then they quickly and actively handled his ships and his quick barks; and they put an abundance of food and drink into them; and Luath Lineach and Luath Leborcham were sent to assemble his army to him. And when they had all been assembled together, they prepared their habiliments, and their armor, and their weapons of valor; and they set out forward towards Erin.

And Balor followed them to the port, and he said, "Give battle to Lug Ildanach, and cut off his head; and tie that island which is called Erin at the sterns of your ships and your good barks, and let the dense verging waters take its place, and place it upon the north side of Lochlann, and not one of the Tuatha De Danann will ever follow it there."

And then they pushed out their ships and their swift barks from the port; and they filled them with pitch and with frankincense and with myrrh; and they hoisted their sliding variegated sailing-cloths; and they made a sudden start from the harbor and the shore-port, along the land that is not cultivated, and out upon the wide-lying sea, and upon the wonderful abyss, and upon the ridge-backs of the flood, and upon the wet-high, cold-venomed mountains of the truly-deep ocean; and they never slackened from that sailing-course until they reached harbor and shore-port at Es Dara.

He who was king of Connacht at that time was Bodb Derg son of the Dagda.

And Lug Lamfada was at that time in Tara, along with the king of Erin. And it was revealed to him that the Fomorians had landed

at Es Dara. And upon Lug's receiving this information he prepared Manannan's steed Aenbarr at the junction of the day and
night; and then he went into where the king of Erin was, and told
him that the foreigners had landed at Es Dara and that they had
plundered Bodb Derg; "and," said he, "I am desirous to gain
assistance from you to give them battle."

"I shall not give it," said the king of Erin, "for a deed that has
not been done against me I shall not go to avenge."

Now when Lug Lamfada heard this evil answer, he went on
horseback and rode from Tara westwards. And soon he perceived
three warriors, armed and accoutred, approach him and these were
the three sons of Cainte; [1] and they saluted him.

"Why this thy early rising?" said they.

"Great is my cause," said Lug; "namely, that foreigners have
come into Erin and have plundered Bodb Derg the son of the
Dagda; and what assistance will ye give me?"

"We will," said they, "ward off a hundred warriors, each man
of us, from thee in the battle."

"That is a good help," said he; "but there is a help which I
should prefer to receive from you, even rather than that; namely to
assemble the men of the fairy-mounds to me from all the places in
which they are."

And then Cu and Cethen went to the south and Cian set out
northwards, and he rested not until he reached Mag Muirthemne.
And as he was traversing the plain it was not long before he saw
three warriors, armed and mailed, before him, walking on the plain;
and these were the three sons of Tuirenn, whose names were
Brian, Iucharba, and Iuchar. And the state of things between the
three sons of Cainte and the three sons of Tuirenn was, that they
were in hatred and enmity towards each other; so that wherever
they met each other it was impossible to avoid a deadly contest,
such that only the strongest should survive it.

Then Cian said, "If my two brothers had been here, what a
brave fight we should make; but since they are not, it is good
counsel for me to retreat." And he perceived a large herd of swine
near him; and he struck himself with a druidic wand into the form
of a pig of the herd; and he began to root up the ground like every
one of the other pigs.

[1] One of these was Cian, the father of Lug.

And then Brian, the son of Tuirenn, said, "My brethren, have you seen the warrior who was walking the plain a while ago?"

"We have seen him," said they.

"What has taken him away?" said he.

"We know not," said they.

"It is cowardice in you," said he, "not to exercise proper vigilance in time of war over the plains and open country; and I know what has carried him away; for he has stricken himself with a golden wand into a form of one of these pigs; and he is rooting up the ground like any pig; and he is no friend of ours."

"This is bad for us," said the other two; "for the pigs belong to someone of the Tuatha De Danann, and even if we kill them all it may happen that the druidic pig might escape after all."

"Badly have ye acquired your learning in the city of learning," said Brian, "when you cannot distinguish a druidical beast from a natural beast." And as he was saying this he struck his two brothers with a metamorphosing druidical wand, and he turned them into two excellent fleet hounds; upon which they howled impatiently upon the trail of the druidical pig.

And it was not long until the druidical pig fell out from the other pigs; and no other fled but she alone; and she saw a wooded grove and made for it; and at her entering the wood Brian gave a cast of his spear at her, and drove it through the trunk of her chest. And the pig screamed and said, "Ill is the deed you have done, to have cast at me, since ye have known me."

"Methinks that is human language you have," said Brian.

"I am originally a human being," said he, "and I am Cian the son of Cainte; give me quarter."

"We shall indeed," said Iucharba and Iuchar, "and we regret what has happened to thee."

"I swear by my aërial gods," said Brian, "that if the life returned seven times to thee, I should deprive thee of it."

"Well, then," said Cian, "grant me a request." . . .

"We shall grant it," said Brian.

"Allow me to pass into my own shape," said Cian.

"We shall allow it," said Brian, "for I often feel less reluctant to kill a man than a pig."

And Cian then assumed his own shape, and said, "Give me manly quarter now."

"We shall not give it," said Brian.

"Well then I have deceived you," said Cian, "for, if it had been in the shape of a pig you had killed me, there could be but the fine of a pig paid for me; but as it is in my own shape I shall be killed, a noble person, there never was killed and never will be killed a person for whom a greater fine shall be paid than me; and the weapons with which I shall be slain shall recount the deed to my son."

"It is not with arms you shall be slain, but with the surface stones of the earth," said Brian. And after that they pelted him in many ways with stones, fiercely and roughly until they reduced the champion to an insignificant, crushed mass; and they buried him a man's height in the earth; and the earth did not receive that fratricide from them, but cast him above the surface of the earth again.

Brian said that it should go again into the earth; and Cian was buried again a second time; and the earth again did not receive him. In short the Children of Tuirenn buried the body six different times, and the earth rejected it; and the seventh time they put him under the ground the mould received him. And the Children of Tuirenn went forward after Lug Long-Arm towards the battle.

To return to Lug. Upon parting with his father (Cian), he went forward from Tara westwards to Garech and Ilgarech, and to Athlone Mic Luigdech, and to Bearna na Hedargana, which is now called Roscommon, and over Mag Luirg, and to Corr Sliab na Seagsa and to the head of Sean Sliab, which is now called Ces Corann; and through the territory of the bright-faced Corann, and from that to Mag Mor of the Assembly, where the foreigners were, and the spoils of Connacht in their hands.

Then arose Bres son of Balor, and he said, "It is a wonder to me that the sun should rise in the west today, and in the east every other day."

"It were better that it were so," said the druids.

"What else is it?" said he.

"The radiance of the face of Lug Long-Arm," said they.

And then Lug Ildanach came to them and saluted them. "What is the cause of thy salutation?" said they.

"Great is the cause of my saluting you," said he, "for there is but one half of me belongs to the Tuatha De Danann and one half of me to you; therefore restore to me the milch cows of the men of Erin."

"May early good luck not come to you," said a man of them, angrily and valiantly answering him, "until you obtain a dry or a milch cow here." And then Lug cast a druidical spell upon the cattle-spoils, and sent its milch cows home to the door of every house in Erin; and he left them the dry ones, so that they should not leave that territory until the men of the fairy-mounds should overtake them.

And Lug remained three days and three nights about them, until the men of the fairy-mounds came and sat around Lug.

And Bodb Derg son of the Dagda came with twenty-nine hundred men to them and said, "What is the cause of your delay from giving battle?"

"Waiting for you," said Lug.

Lug then put on Manannan's corselet; and its charm was such that the man upon whom it should be could not be wounded through it, nor below it, nor above it. He put on Manannan's breast-piece at the small of his neck; and he put on his helmet, which was called the Cennbarr; and his countenance had the radiance of the sun, from the reflection of the helmet; and he took up his black-blue, splendid-colored, broad-sheltering, chafer-marked shield upon the arch-slope of his back; and he took his shadowy, truly-handsome, close-edged sword upon his left side; and he took his two wide-socketed, thick-handled, hard-venomed spears, which had been annealed in the blood of poisonous adders. And the kings and chiefs of the men of Erin took their array of combat and battle upon them; and they raised pointed forests of spears over their heads; they made perfectly firm fences of their shields around them.

And then they attacked Mag Mor of the Assembly, and the foreigners responded to them; and they threw their wounding, whizzing spears at each other; and after having shivered their spears, they drew their broad-edge, gold-cross swords from their blue-bordered scabbards, and they commenced to strike each other bravely; and forests of broad flames arose above them, from the poison of these arms and the many-edged weapons of these brave men.

And then Lug saw the battle-pen in which was Bres the son of

Balor, and he attacked him fiercely and wrathfully; and he fell to striking these brave men, until two hundred champions of these bodyguards of the son of Balor fell by him in his presence.

And then Bres bound Lug to give him quarter. "Grant my life," said he, "this time; and I will bring over the Fomorian race to you to the battle of Mag Tured; and I will give you the sun and moon, the sea and land, as guarantee upon myself, not to come and fight against you again, unless I lose all the Fomorian race now." And upon these guarantees Lug gave him safety of his life.

And then the druids said that Lug ought to grant them safety of their lives. "I give my word," said Lug, "that if the entire Fomorian race had gone under your protection, they should not be destroyed by me." And then Bres the son of Balor, and the druids went away to seek their own country.

As regards Lug. After the trophies and the victories of that battle, he perceived two of his friends, and he asked them if they had seen his father in the battle. "We have not," said they.

"Could it be the Fomorians that killed him?" said Lug.

"It was not," said they.

"He lives not," said Lug, "and I give my word for it, that neither food nor drink shall enter my mouth until I have received knowledge of what kind of death my father has met."

And so Lug, accompanied by the men of the fairy-mounds, went forward until they reached the place at which he and his father had parted from each other; and from that to the place where the father had gone into the shape of a pig upon his recognizing the Children of Tuirenn. And here the ground spoke to Lug and said, "Great was the danger in which thy father was here, O Lug, upon his seeing the Children of Tuirenn, for he was forced to go into the shape of a pig; however, they killed him in his own shape."

And Lug told this to his companions and he discovered the spot in which his father was, and he went to it and ordered it to be dug up, in order that he should know in what way the Children of Tuirenn had slain him.

The body was raised out of the grave, and they fell to examining his wounds, and he was found to be a litter of wounds, upon which Lug said, "This is a murderous death which the Children of Tuirenn have inflicted upon my beloved father." And he kissed him thrice and said, "Ill am I for this death, for I cannot hear anything through my ears, and I cannot see anything through my eyes, and there is not one pulse living in my heart, for grief of my father, and ye gods whom I adore," said he, "I grieve that I was not present when this deed was perpetrated. And it is a great deed that has been done here, namely, that the Tuatha De Danann have committed a fratricide upon one another; and long shall be its loss to them"; and he spoke this following:

> A dreadful fate did Cian meet at evening.
> It has dismembered my body,—the mangling of the hero.
> The road sometime eastwards; the sod for a time westwards.
> Erin shall never be but in evil.

> Through the killing of Cian, the champion of accomplished feats,
> My vigor is overpowered,
> My face has become black,
> My senses have declined.

> His grave is laid low;
> The Children of Tuirenn have killed him;
> Disabled shall be the Tuatha De Danann for this deed,
> In anguish of strength and debility.

Then Cian was placed under the mound again; and after that his tombstone was raised over his tomb, and his funeral games were held: and his name was written in ogam.

"It is from Cian this mound shall be named," said Lug, and he spoke the following poem:

> From Cian shall this mound be named,
> Though he himself is now in a dismantled place.
> Great is the deed that has been here perpetrated,
> A fratricide upon the Tuatha De Danann.

> The sons of Tuirenn it was that committed this deed,—
> I tell you the truth;—
> I say unto you it is not false news;—
> It shall fall upon their grand- and great-grandsons!

> The three sons of Cainte—brave the company!—
> And the Children of Tuirenn Begrenn,—
> From this has come the death of Cian,
> That they were equally high in degree.

> Broken is my heart in my breast,
> Since the champion Cian lives not;
> For the sons of Delbaeth it is no false tale
> That they shall be cast into anguish.

After this poem Lug said, "Ill shall the Tuatha De Danann fare from this deed; and long shall fratricide continue to be perpetrated in Erin after it. And pitiful is my condition from this deed which the Children of Tuirenn have perpetrated." And he ordered his people, "Go ye to Tara, where the king of Erin and the Tuatha De Danann are," said he, "and do not divulge these things there until I have divulged them myself."

When Lug reached Tara, he sat nobly and honorably at the shoulder of the king of Erin. And Lug looked around him, and he saw the three sons of Tuirenn; and these were of all men the three of the best activity and hand-feats, the most beautiful and most honored that were in Tara at that time; and the best of hand in the battle against the Fomorians.

And then Lug ordered the Chain of Attention of the Court to be shaken, and so it was done; and so they all listened. Lug said, "What is your attention now, O Tuatha De Danann?"

"It is upon thee, indeed," said they.

"A question I ask of you nobly," said he; "what would be the vengeance each of you would take upon him that should kill the father of each of you?"

A great astonishment seized upon every one upon their hearing this; and the king of Erin answered him first, and thus spoke he, "We know it is not your father that has been killed?"

"It is indeed," said Lug, "and I see in the house now the party that killed him; and they know themselves the way in which they killed him better than I."

Then the king of Erin said, "It is not the killing of one day I myself would visit upon the person who should kill my father, but to cut one of his members off every day one after the other, until he had fallen by me, should he be in my power." All the nobles said the same, and the Children of Tuirenn like the rest.

"There are making this declaration," said Lug, "the three persons who have killed my father, and let them pay me a compensation for him, since the Tuatha De Danann are all in one house; and if they do not, I shall not violate the law of the king of Erin, nor his sanctuary; however, they shall not attempt to leave the Tech Midcuarta (House of the Meadcircling) until they have settled with me."

"If I myself had killed your father," said the king of Erin, "I should deem it well that you accepted a compensation from me for him."

"It is toward us that Lug says this," said the Children of Tuirenn among themselves; "and let us acknowledge the killing of his father to him," said Iuchar and Iucharba, "for it is to seek the account of his father he has remained until now, until he has obtained a knowledge of his death."

"We may fear," said Brian, "that it is seeking an admission from us he is in the presence of all the rest, and that he would not accept a compensation from us afterwards."

"We shall," said the other sons, "admit it to him, and do you give it openly, since you are the eldest."

"I will give it," said Brian. And with that Brian, the son of Tuirenn, said, "It is toward us you say this, O Lug, these three of us, for we are they whom you supposed before now to have risen in combat against the sons of Cainte; and yet we have not killed your father, although we shall give a compensation for him the same as if we had performed the deed."

"I shall receive a compensation from you, though ye do not think it," said Lug; "and I shall name it here; and if ye think it is too great, ye shall have remission of part of it."

"Let us hear it from thee," said they.

"Here it is," said Lug; "namely, three apples, and the skin of a pig, and a spear, and two steeds, and a chariot, and seven pigs, and a puppy dog, and a cooking spit, and three shouts upon a hill; —that is the compensation which I demand," said Lug; "and if ye think it too great, part of it shall be remitted you presently here; and if ye do not think it too great, pay it from you."

"We do not think it too great," said Brian son of Tuirenn, "nor its hundredfold as a compensation; and we the more suspect your having a treacherous and murderous design in reserve for us, from its smallness as a fine."

"I do not deem what I have named as a compensation too little," said Lug; "and I shall give you the guarantee of the Tuatha De Danann, to ask no more, and to be faithful to you forever; and give you the same guarantee to me."

"This is a pity," said the Children of Tuirenn, "though for the guarantees of the world we are not insufficient ourselves."

"I do think it too little," said Lug, "for it is often your sort have promised to pay a fine in this way, in the presence of all the people, and would yet endeavor to go back on it."

The Children of Tuirenn then gave pledges to the king of Erin and Bodb Derg son of the Dagda, and the nobles of the Tuatha De Danann besides, as guarantees for payment of that fine to Lug.

"It is better that I should now," said Lug, "give you a knowledge of the compensation."

"It is better, indeed," said they.

"Well, then," said Lug, "the three apples which I have demanded from you are the three Apples of the Garden of the Hesperides, in the east of the world; and no other apples but these will do for me; for these are the most gifted and beautiful apples in the world; and the description of them is this: they are of the color of burnished gold; and the head of a month-old child is not larger than each apple of them; and they have the taste of honey when eaten; and they heal the effects of bloody wounds or malignant disease in any person who eats part of them; and they are not diminished by being constantly eaten forever; and every one who casts an apple of them performs by it whatever feat he desires, and it comes back to him again; and though brave ye be, ye three champions, ye have not, what I do not regret for your sakes, the power to carry away these apples from the people who have them; because it has been foretold to them that three young warriors from the west of Europe would go to deprive them of them by force.

"The pig's skin, now, which I have demanded of you, is the skin of the pig of Tuis the king of Greece; and it cures and perfectly heals all the wounded and diseased persons of the world, be they in ever so great danger, if it only overtakes the life in them; and such was the nature of that pig that every stream of water through which it might pass would be converted into wine for nine days; and every wound which it touched was healed; and the druids of Greece told them (the Greeks) that it was not the pig herself that had this virtue, but the skin; and they had it skinned and they have had the skin ever since; and I think it will not be easy to obtain it either with or without consent.

"And do ye know what spear it is I have demanded of you?"

"We do not," said they.

"An excellent poisoned spear, of which Pisear king of Persia is possessed: Aredbair it is called; and every choicest deed is performed with it; and its blade is always in a cauldron of water, lest it melt down by its fiery heat the city in which it is kept; and it is difficult to obtain it.

"And do ye wish to know what two steeds and chariot I would wish to receive from you?"

"We do not know," said they.

"They are the two noble wonderful steeds of Dobar the king of Sicily; and such is their nature that sea and land are equally convenient to them; and there are not swifter or stronger steeds than they; and there is no chariot of equal goodness in form and firmness.

"And do ye know which are the seven pigs that I have demanded from you? They are the pigs of Asal king of the Golden Pillars," said Lug, "and though they are killed every night they are found alive the next day; and every person that eats part of them shall not have disease or ill-health.

"And the hound-whelp which I demanded of you is, namely, a whelp of the king of Iruad, and Failinis is her name; and all the wild beasts of the world that she should see, they would fall down out of their standing; she is more splendid than the sun in his fiery wheels; and it is difficult to obtain her.

"The cooking spit which I have demanded of you is, namely, a spit of the spits of the women of Inis Findcuire.

"And the three shouts which I have demanded of you to give on a hill are, namely, to give three shouts on Cnoc Midcain in the north of Lochlann; and it is prohibited to Midcain and his sons to suffer shouts to be given upon that hill; and it was with these that my father received his military education; and though I should forgive his death to you, they would not; and though you should succeed in all your adventures until you reach them, I am of opinion that they would avenge his death upon you.

"And that is the compensation that I demand of you," said Lug.

Silence and astonishment fell upon the Children of Tuirenn at the naming of this compensation. And they went to where their father was and told him of this oppression. "These are bad tidings," said Tuirenn, "and ye shall have death and permanent destruction inflicted upon you in seeking for that fine; and it is just that it should so happen to you. And yet, notwithstanding that, if Lug

himself wished it, ye could work out the compensation; and all the
men in the world could not procure it without the powers of Manannan or Lug. Therefore go ye and ask of Lug the loan of Manannan's steed Aenbarr, and if he expects to obtain the fine he will
give you the steed; and if he does not expect it, he will not give her
to you, but what he will say is, that she does not belong to him,
and that he cannot give the loan of a loan away; and then ask him
for the loan of Manannan's curach (boat), that is, the Scuabtinne,
and he will give you that, for it is taboo to him not to give the
second request from him; and the curach is better for you than the
steed."

And then the Children of Tuirenn went to where Lug was; and
they saluted him; and they said that they could not procure the
compensation without his own assistance; and that they should like
for that reason to get from him a loan of Manannan's horse Aenbarr.

"I have not that steed myself," said Lug, "but upon a loan, and
I shall not give a loan of the loan away."

"If so, give us a loan of Manannan's curach," said Brian, son of
Tuirenn.

"I shall give it," said Lug.

"What place is it in?" said they.

"At Brug na Boinne," said Lug.

And they came again to where Tuirenn was, and Ethne, daughter
of Tuirenn, their sister; and they told them that they had obtained
the curach. "It is not you will be the better of obtaining it," said
Tuirenn; "however, Lug is desirous to have every part of this
compensation that could be available for him against the battle of
Mag Tured to be brought to him; and that which would not be
available for him, that is yourselves, he would be very glad that
you should fall at last in seeking it."

Then they set forward, and left Tuirenn in sorrow and lamentation. And Ethne accompanied them to the port in which the curach
was. And Brian went into the curach, and he said, "There is room
for but one other person along with me here"; and he began to
grumble at its narrowness.

"It is prohibited to the curach to be grumbled at in that way,"
said Ethne; "and, my beloved brothers, that was a lamentable
deed you committed, to kill the father of Lug Lamfada; and every

evil whatever that shall come upon you in consequence of it is but just"; and she made this lay:

> Lamentable the deed you have committed,
> You generous fair-haired youths;
> The Father of Lug of the Long Arm
> To kill, is in my mind indeed an evil.
>
> O Ethne! do not say so, they responded;
> Active is our cheerfulness, brave our deeds;
> We prefer an hundred times to be killed
> Than to die like unheroic cowards.
>
> Search ye the lands and islands, said she,
> Till you reach the borders of the Red Sea.
> To drive you out of Erin,—alas!
> There is not a deed more lamentable.

After these words this warrior band pushed their curach out from the beautiful clear-bayed borders of Erin. "What course shall we now first take?" said they.

"We shall go to seek the apples," said Brian, "as they were the first that were demanded of us. Accordingly we ask of thee, thou curach of Manannan, which art under us, to sail with us to the garden of the Hesperides."

And this command was not neglected by the curach, as was its custom, for it sailed forward in its career upon the tops of the green-sided waves, straight across all abysses, until it reached harbor and shore-port in the lands of the Hesperides.

And upon their arriving there Brian asked of his brothers, "In what way do you desire to approach the garden of the Hesperides now? for I think," said he, "the royal champions and warriors of the country are always guarding it, and with the king himself as chief over them."

"What should we do," said the other brothers, "but make directly to attack them, and carry the apples away from them, or fall ourselves in the attempt; since it is not fated to us to escape these dangers which impend over us, without dying in some place?"

"Instead of that," said Brian, "we should prefer that our fame and our renown should be proclaimed aloud upon us, and that our cunning and our valor should be recounted after us, rather than that folly and cowardice should be charged aloud upon us. And, accordingly, the best counsel for us to take on this occasion is, to go in the shape of strong swift hawks towards this garden; and its guardians have nothing but their light missive weapons to cast at us; and take care that these pass you by, with agility and full activity; and when they have thrown what they have ready and fit to be thrown, descend ye upon the apples, and carry off each man an apple of them; and if I can I shall take two apples with me, that is, an apple in my talons, and an apple in my mouth."

They applauded this counsel; and Brian struck them with a transforming druidical wand, each of the three, and transformed them into beautiful, wonderful hawks. And they went forth towards the apples; and the guarding party perceived them; and they shouted upon all sides of them; and they threw angry, poisonous showers of weapons at them; and these were upon their guard, as Brian had charged them, until the guarding party had cast all their missive weapons; and then they swept down upon the apples courageously; and Brian carried off two apples of them, and each man of the other two an apple, and they returned safely without bleeding or red wounding.

And this news spread throughout the city and through the land in general. And the king had three cunning, wise daughters; and they put themselves into the shapes of three taloned ospreys; and they pursued the hawks into the sea; and they let fly shafts of lightning after them and before them; and these lightnings were scorching them greatly.

"Pity the condition that we are in now," said the Children of Tuirenn, "for we are being scorched by these lightnings, if we do not obtain some relief."

"If I could," said Brian, "I would give you some relief." And he struck himself with the transforming druidical wand, and also his two brothers; and he turned them into two swans, and himself into another swan; and they darted down into the sea; and the ospreys went away from them then, and the Children of Tuirenn went to their curach.

After that they resolved in council to go to Greece to seek the skin of the pig, by consent or by force; and they went forward until they came near the court of the king of Greece.

"In what shape should we go to this place?" said Brian.

"In what shapes should we go there," said the other sons, "but in our own shapes?"

"It is not so it appears best to me," said Brian, "but to go in the shape of poets and professional men of Erin: for it is thus our honor and our respect will be the greater among the nobles of Greece."

"That is hard for us to do," said they, "when we have no poem; and as little do we know how to compose one."

However, they put the tie of poets upon their hair, and they struck the door of the court. The doorkeeper asked who was there. "We are professional poets of Erin," said Brian, "who have come with a poem to Tuis the king."

The doorkeeper therefore went to inform the king that there were poets of Erin before the door. "Let them be admitted," said the king; "for it is in search of a good patron they have come so far from their own country to this." And the king commanded that the court should be put in proper order to receive them, that they might be able to say that they had seen no place as grand as it in their travels.

The Children of Tuirenn were admitted then in the shape of men of poetry; and they fell to drinking and making merry at once; and they thought there was not in the world, and that they had never seen, a court so good as that, nor a household so numerous, nor had they met with so much warm attention to themselves.

Then arose the king's men of poetry to sing their lays and poetry for the people. And then Brian son of Tuirenn desired his brothers to sing a poem for the king. "We have no poem," said they, "and do not you require of us anything but the art that we have ever practiced, namely, to take by force of our arms whatever is wanting to us, if we be the stronger; and if they be the stronger, to fall by them."

"That is not a happy mode of composing a poem," said Brian, and upon that he arose to his feet, and requested attention until himself had sung a poem; and he was listened to, and said:

> O King Tuis, we conceal not thy fame,
> We praise thee as the oak above the kings;—
> The skin of a pig, bounty without hardness,
> This is the reward which I ask for it (the poem).
>
> The war of a neighbor against an Ear,—
> The fair Ear of his neighbor will be against him;
> He who gives us his property,
> His court shall not be the scarcer of it.

> A stormy host and raging sea
> Are a dangerous power, should one oppose it;—
> The skin of a pig, bounty without hardness,
> This is the reward I ask, O Tuis.

"That is a good poem," said the king, "but I do not understand a word of its sense."

"I shall tell thee its sense," said Brian.

> O Tuis, I conceal not thy fame,
> We praise thee as the oak above the kings.

"That is, in the same way that the oak excels the king trees of the wood, it is in this way that you excel the kings of the world, for bounty, and nobility, and generosity.

> The skin of a pig, bounty without hardness.

"That is, the skin of a pig, O Tuis, which thou hast, which I should wish to get from thee in reward of my poetry.

> The war of a neighbor against an Ear,
> The fair Ear of his neighbor will be against him.

"That is, *ó* is the same as 'ear,' and thou and I shall be ear to ear, that is by the ears with each other for the skin, if I do not get it from thee with thy consent; and it is to that the sense of my poem refers," said Brian son of Tuirenn.

"I should praise thy poem," said the king, "if my pig's skin had not been so much mentioned in it; and it is not wise for thee, O man of poetry," said he, "to ask that request of me, for I would not give it to all the poets and professional men, and the best and the greatest nobles of the world, since they would not be able to take it against my consent from me; and I shall give the three fulls of that skin of red gold to thee as the price of thy poem."

"May all good be thine, O king," said Brian, "and I knew it was not easy to make the request; but that I knew that I should receive a good ransom for it; however, I am so covetous that I shall not take less than to have the gold measured well and faithfully by the skin."

The servants and attendants of the king were then sent with them to the treasure-house to measure the gold. "Measure two skins of it out to my brothers first," said Brian, "and the last full faithfully to myself, since it was I who made the poem."

But upon the skin being brought out, Brian made a covetous, swift-handed snatch at it with his left hand; and at the same time he bared his sword and dealt a stroke to the man nearest to him, and made two parts of him to his middle; and then he took possession of the skin and put it round himself; and the three sons of Tuirenn rushed out of the court, hewing down the host wherever they happened to be before them, insomuch that not a noble escaped being slaughtered, not a champion escaped being mutilated, nor a warrior killed by them.

And then Brian went to where the king of Greece himself was; nor was the king more slow to attack him; and they made a valiant, champion-like, hard, brave combat with each other; and the end of that fight was that the king of Greece fell by the venom of the arm of Brian the son of Tuirenn.

As for the other two, they killed and slaughtered widely the hosts upon all sides, until they waged indescribable destruction among the hosts of the court, and until they quite subdued them; after which they remained for three days and three nights in the court to put off their fatigue, after their labor and their great slaughter; and the three champions had the choicest of the ladies of the palace as arm and bed companions as long as they remained there.

They then determined upon going to seek for more of the fine, and his brothers asked of Brian where they should go first. "We shall go to the king of Persia," said Brian, "to seek the spear."

And they went forward towards their curach; and they left the blue-streamy confines of Greece; and then they said, "We are well off when we have the apples and the skin." And then they made no delay until they reached the land of Persia.

"In what shape shall we go to the court of the king of Persia?" said Brian.

"In what shape should we go there but in our own shape?" said the other sons.

"That is not what appears best to me," said Brian, "but to go there in the shape of poets, as we went to the king of Greece."

"We approve of that," said they, "because of the success which it brought us the last time we took to poetry; not that it is easy for us to assume a profession that we have not."

And they put the tie of poets upon their hair; and they came to the door of the court and asked to have it opened. The doorkeeper asked who they were, and of what country. "We are poets from Erin," they said, "who have come with a poem to the king." They were admitted and made welcome by Pisear the king and the nobles of his household; and they were seated with honor and distinction by the king around himself.

And the king's poets arose to sing their lays, their songs, and their fine poems. And Brian the son of Tuirenn called upon his brothers to arise and sing a poem for the king. "Do not ask for the art which we have not from us," said they, "but if you wish it, we shall exercise the art with which we are acquainted, namely, mighty striking and beating."

"That would be a rare exercise of poetry," said Brian, "and as it is I myself that have the poem, I shall sing it for the king"; and he delivered this address:

> Small the esteem of any spear with King Pisear;
> The battles of foes are broken;
> No oppression to Pisear,—
> Every one whom he wounds.
>
> A yew tree, the finest of the wood,
> It is called king without opposition;
> May the splendid shaft drive on
> Yon crowd into their wounds of death.

"That is a good poem," said the king; "but I do not understand what that mention of my spear in it means, O man of poetry from Erin."

"It is this," said Brian son of Tuirenn, "that the reward I should wish to receive for my poem is that very spear which you have."

"It was unwise for you to ask that gift from me," said the king; "and, besides, the nobles and the high personages never gave a greater honor or protection for a poem than not to cause thy death upon this spot."

When Brian heard this language from the king, he bethought him of the apple which he held in his hand and he made a successful cast of it at the king, and struck him in the flesh of his forehead, so that he drove his brain back out through the pole of his head; and he bared his sword and fell to hewing down the hosts around him. And this was not neglected by the other two brothers; and they fell to helping him bravely and valiantly, until slaughter was made of all whom they encountered of the people of the court. And they had the women and the princesses of the great court at their disposal; and they found the spear, with a cauldron of water around its blade in order that its heat should not scorch the people of the court.

And after a while the Children of Tuirenn said that it was time for them to go and seek more of the compensation which was due of them. And they left the court after that, and they asked of each other what direction they should go in. "We shall go to Dobar the king of the island of Sicily," said Brian, "for it is he that has the two steeds and the chariot which Lug Ildanach has demanded of us."

They went forward, then, and carried the spear with them; and high were the souls of the three champions after that exploit they had performed. And they went on till they had arrived at the court of the island of Sicily.

"In what shape shall we go to this court?" said Brian.

"What shape should we go to it in but in our own shapes?" said they.

"That is not the proper way," said Brian; "but let us go there in the shape of mercenary soldiers of Erin, and let us make friendship with the king, for it is in that way that we shall obtain knowledge of where the steeds and chariot are kept." And when they had determined upon this counsel they went forward to the green before the king's court.

The king and the chiefs, and great nobles of his people went out to meet them through the fair-assembly which was then being held among that people. And the Children of Tuirenn made obeisance to the king; and the king asked them who they were. "We are mercenary soldiers from Erin," said they, "who are earning wages from the kings of the world."

"Do you wish to remain with me for a while?" said the king.

"We do wish it," said they; and accordingly they entered into an engagement and made their agreement with the king.

They remained in that court for a fortnight and a month, and they did not see the steeds during that time. And then Brian said, "This is a bad state of things for us, my beloved brothers, that we have no more account of the steeds now than the first day we came to this court."

"What is it you would wish to do in that case?" said they.

"Let us do this," said Brian; "let us gird on our arms and our many weapons and our array of travelling and journeying, and let us go to the presence of the king, and let us tell him that we shall leave the land and this part of the world unless he shows us the steeds."

They went forth that day to the presence of the king, and the king asked them what it was that induced them to put themselves into that travelling array. "Thou shalt be informed of that, O high-king," said Brian; "it is because soldiers from Erin, such as we, are always the guards and confidants of the kings who have jewels of virtue and victory; and we are accustomed to be the repositories of the whispers, the counsels, and the secrets of all those by whom we are retained; and thou hast not so treated us since we have come to thee: for thou hast two steeds and a chariot, the best in the world, according as we have been informed; and we have not yet seen them."

"It was ill for you to depart on that account," said the king, "when I would have shown them to you the first day, had I thought that you had sought to see them; and since it is now ye seek them, ye shall see them; for I think that there never came to this court soldiers from Erin in whom my confidence and the confidence of the people of this court was greater than in you."

He sent for the steeds then, and the chariot was yoked to them; and fleet as the cold wind of spring was their career of running; and that career was equally facile for them upon the sea and upon the land.

And Brian watched the steeds attentively; and suddenly he laid hold of the chariot, and caught the charioteer and dashed him against the rock of stone that was nearest to him, and killed him; and he himself sprang into his place in the chariot, and made a cast of the spear of Pisear against the king, which clove his heart in his chest; and then he and his brothers fell upon the hosts of the court and scattered red slaughter among as many of them as they could find.

And when they had finished this undertaking, Iuchar and Iucharba asked where they should go then. "We shall go to Asal king of the Pillars of Gold," said Brian, "to seek the seven pigs which Lug Ildanach has demanded from us."

And then they sailed onwards without accident, straightway to that noble land. And they found the people of that country on the alert guarding their harbors from fear of the sons of Tuirenn; for the fame of these skilful champions was heard throughout all the countries of the world; how they had been driven out of Erin by oppression, and how they were carrying away with them all the gifted jewels of the world.

Asal king of the Pillars of Gold came to the verge of the harbor to meet them; and he asked them reprovingly whether it was by them, as he had heard, that the kings of the world had fallen, in all the countries in which they had been. Brian answered that it was, whatever punishment he might wish to inflict on them for it. "What is it that caused you to do that?" said Asal. Brian told him that it was the oppression and tyrannical sentence of another that drove them to it; and he related to him the way in which it had happened; and how they had subdued all that had offered to stand against them until this time.

"What did you come to this country for now?" said the king.

"For the pigs that you have," said Brian, "to carry them away with us as part of that compensation."

"In what way would you wish to obtain them?" said the king.

"If we get them with good will," said Brian, "to accept them with thanks, and if we do not, to give battle to you and to your people on their account, and that you should fall by us, and that we shall carry off the pigs with us in despite of you in that way."

"If that should be the end of it," said the king, "it would be evil to us to fight the battle."

"It would be, indeed," said Brian.

And then the king went in to counsel and whisper with all his people; and the counsel which they gave was to give up the pigs of their own will to the sons of Tuirenn, since they could not see that they had been withstood in any place in which they had been up to that time.

The Children of Tuirenn therefore expressed their gratitude and thanks to Asal; and their wonder was the greater at having obtained the pigs in that way, seeing that they had not obtained any other part of the fine without battle but these; and not that alone, but that they had left much of their blood in every place through which they had passed until then.

Asal took them with him to his court and royal residence that night; and they were supplied and served with food and drink, and soft beds to their utmost desires. They arose on the following day and came to the king's presence; and the pigs were given to them. "It is well that thou hast given us these pigs," said Brian, "for we have not obtained any part of the fine without battle, but these alone"; and Brian spoke this poem:

> These pigs, O Asal,
> Thou hast let us have with grace;
> The other treasures which we have obtained
> We took in right of hard combats.
>
> We gave Pisear a battle
> In which fell many champions,
> Until we took away from him
> The Yew, the gifted weapon.
>
> Of the battle of the king of the island of Sicily
> It would be impossible to give a sufficient description;
> We should all have fallen in that affray,
> Were it not for the skin of the great pig.
>
> O Asal, who hast not whispered treachery,—
> Should the three sons of Tuirenn live,
> The greater will be thy triumph and thy renown,
> From the manner in which thou hast given up these pigs!

"What journey do you propose to take now, O Children of Tuirenn?" said Asal.

"We go," said they, "to Iruad for the puppy hound which is there."

"Grant me a request, O Children of Tuirenn," said Asal; "and the request which I ask of you is this, to take me along in your company to the king of Iruad, because a daughter of mine is his wife, and I would wish to prevail upon him to give you the hound without battle and without a war."

"We think well of that," said they.

And the king's ship was prepared for him; and their adventures on either side are not told further until they reached the delightful, wonderful shores of Iruad. The hosts and the muster of Iruad were watching their harbors and their shore-ports before them; and they shouted at them at once, because they knew them.

Then Asal went ashore peaceably; and he went to where his

son-in-law the king of Iruad was; and he told him of the adventures of the Children of Tuirenn from beginning to end.

"What has brought them to this country?" said the king of Iruad.

"For the hound which you have," said Asal.

"It was ill thought for you to come along with them to me for it," said the king of Iruad; "for the gods have not given the luck to any three champions in the world that they could by will or by force obtain my hound."

"Not so it should be," said Asal, "but since many of the kings of the world have been subdued by these, you had better give them the hound without fighting and without battle."

But all that Asal said was but thrown away on him; and Asal went to where the Children of Tuirenn were, and told them these things. Accordingly these answers were not neglected by the warriors, but they put quick hands upon their arms; and they challenged the army of Iruad to battle; and when that brave host had reached their presence, a mighty and ardent combat and battle was fought between them on both sides.

As for the Children of Tuirenn, they hewed down the champions and slew the warriors, until they themselves separated from each other in the battle, from the vehemence and fury of the contest and the hardness of the fight; so that Iuchar and Iucharba happened to be on the one side, and Brian by himself on the other side. It was a gap of danger and a breach of ranks, and a broken retreat before Brian in every path that he passed through, until he reached the king of Iruad in the battle-pen in which he was; and the two champions entered upon a single combat and fight, stoutly, bloodily, venomously; and theirs was indeed a powerful hardy striking of one another, and a fierce, valorous, unmerciful sledging.

And this combat was a brave one, until at last Brian vanquished and bound the king of Iruad; and he brought him with him through the center of the host until he reached the place in which was Asal; and this is what he said, "There is thy son-in-law for thee, and I swear by my arms of valor that I think it would be easier to kill him three times than to bring him here once to thee this way."

However, the end was that the hound was given to the Children of Tuirenn; and the king was unbound; and peace and unity was made between them. And after having finished all things in this way, they took leave of Asal and of all the rest in like manner.

And now to return to Lug Lamfada. It was revealed to him that the Children of Tuirenn had obtained all the things that were wanting to himself against the battle of Mag Tured; upon which he sent a druidical spell after them for the purpose of putting them into forgetfulness and want of recollection of what they had not obtained of the fine; and he inspired them with a mind and a great desire to return to Erin with the fine to Lug Lamfada; because of a truth they did not recollect what part of the fine was still wanting to them. And they came onward in that career into Erin.

And the place in which Lug Lamfada was at that time was in a fair and an assembly along with the king of Erin on the green of Tara. And the Children of Tuirenn came ashore at Brugh na Boinne. And this was revealed to Lug, and he left the assembly secretly; and he went to Cathair Crobaing, which is called Tara; and he closed the gates of Tara behind him; and he arrayed himself in Manannan's noble suit, namely Manannan's smooth Greek armor, and the cloak of the daughter of Flidais; and his arms of valor from that out.

And the Children of Tuirenn came to where the king was; and they were made welcome by the king and all the Tuatha De Danann. And the king inquired of them if they had obtained the compensation.

"We have obtained it," said they, "and where is Lug, that we may deliver it to him?"

"He was here a while ago," said the king. And the fair assembly was searched for him, but he was not found.

"I know where he is," said Brian, "for it has been revealed to him that we have come to Erin, having these poisoned arms with us; and he has gone to Tara to avoid us." And messengers were sent after him then; and the answer that he gave the messengers who went after him was, that he would not come, but that the fine should be given to the king of Erin. And the sons of Tuirenn did this; and the king having got the fine, they all went to the palace of Tara; and Lug came out then upon the lawn, and the fine was given to him, and this is what he said:

"There never was killed, and there never will be killed, any one whose full compensation is not here (*i.e.*, in full value); however, there is a residue, namely, the residue of the fine: where is the cooking spit, and where are the three shouts upon the hill which ye have not yet given?"

When the sons of Tuirenn heard this, they fell into a swoon and a faintness; and they left the fair assembly and went to the house of their father that night, and they told him their adventures, and how Lug behaved to them.

Gloom and grief seized upon Tuirenn; and they spent the night together. And the next day they went to their ship, and Ethne, the daughter of Tuirenn, went along with them; and the maiden fell to grief-crying and lamentation; and she spoke this lay:

> Alas for this, O Brian of my soul!
> That thy progress leads not to Tara,
> After all thy troubles in Erin;
> Though I go not to follow thee.
>
> Thou salmon of the silent Boyne;—
> Thou salmon of the stream of Liffey,—
> Since I cannot detain thee,
> I am loth to separate from thee.
>
> Thou horseman of the Wave of Tuaid,
> Thou man most lasting in combat,—
> Shouldst thou return as I hope,
> It shall not be pleasant for thy foe.
>
> Do ye pity the sons of Tuirenn?
> Upon the elbows of their green shields—
> Greatly hast thou disturbed my mind—
> Their departure is a cause of pity.
>
> That you are this night at Benn Etair,—
> You party who have increased our grief,—
> You champions to whom valor has bowed,—
> Until the early morning comes.
>
> Pity your journey from Tara,—
> And from Tailltiu of the pleasant plains,—
> And from great Usnech of Meath;—
> There is not an event more pitiful.

After this poem they went forth upon the tempestuous waves of the green sea; and they were a quarter of a year upon the sea, without having gained any intelligence of the island.

And then Brian put on his water-dress, with his transparency of glass upon his head; and he made a water leap; and it is said that he was a fortnight walking in the salt water seeking the island of Findcuire, and he found it at last; and he went to search for its court; and upon his going to the court he found in it only a troop of women engaged at embroidery and border-making; and among all the other things that they had by them they happened to have the cooking-spit.

When Brian saw it, he took it in his hand, and he was going to carry it with him towards the door. Each of the women burst into a laugh on seeing that act, and this is what they said: "Bold is the deed thou hast put thy hand to; for even if thy two brothers were along with thee, the least valorous of the thrice fifty women of us here would not let that spit go with thee or them; however, take one of the spits with thee since thou hadst the heroism to attempt to take it despite us." Brian took leave of them and went forth to seek his ship. And his brothers thought it too long that Brian had been away from them; and just as they proposed to depart, it was then they saw him coming towards them, and that greatly raised their spirits.

And he went to his ship, and they went forward to seek the Hill of Midcain. And when they arrived upon the hill, Midcain, the guardian of the hill, came towards them; and when Brian saw him he attacked him; and the fight of these two champions was like the rapidity of two bears and the laceration of two lions, until Midcain fell in the combat.

Midcain's three sons then came out to fight the sons of Tuirenn, after Midcain himself had previously fallen by Brian; and if any one should come from the land of the Hesperides in the east of the world to look at the fight of these heroes he ought to come, for the greatness of their blows, for the liveliness of their spirits, and the strength of their minds. And these are the names of these three sons of Midcain, namely, Corc, Con, and Aod. And they drove their three spears into the bodies of the sons of Tuirenn. However, this did not produce fear or weakness in the sons of Tuirenn, for they drove their own three spears through the bodies of the sons of Midcain; and they fell into the trance and unconsciousness of death.

After these mighty deeds Brian said, "What state are ye in, my beloved brothers?"

"We are dead," said they.

"Let us arise," said he, "for I perceive signs of death approaching us, and let us give the shouts upon the hill."

"We are not able to do that," said they. But Brian arose then, and raised one of them in each hand, while his blood flowed copiously, until they raised the three shouts.

After this Brian took them with him to the ship, and they continued to tread the sea for a long time; but at last Brian said, "I see Benn Etair, Dun Tuirinn, and Tara of the Kings."

"We should be full of health could we but see these," said one of them; "and for the love of thy honor, O brother, raise our heads on thy breast in order that we may see Erin, and we care not which to receive, death or life, afterwards." And they spoke a lay and Brian answered:

> Take these heads unto thy breast, O Brian,—
> Thou son of generous red-armed Tuirenn;—
> Thou torch of valor without guile,—
> That we may see the land of Erin.
>
> Hold upon thy breast and upon thy shoulder
> These heads, thou manly champion,—
> That we may from off the water see
> Usnech, Tailltiu, and Tara.
>
> Ath Cliath, and the smooth Brugh with thee,—
> Fremann, Tlachtga, along with them,—
> The Plain of Liffey, the dewy Mag Breg,—
> And the mountains about the fair green of Tailltiu.
>
> Could I but see Benn Etair from me,
> And Dun Tuirinn in the north,
> Welcome death from that out,
> Though it should be a suffering death.
>
> A pity this, brave sons of Tuirenn,—
> Birds could fly through my two sides;
> And it is not so much my two sides that sicken me
> As to think of you likewise to have fallen.
>
> We should prefer death to take us,—
> O Brian, son of Tuirenn, who fled not,—
> Than to see thee with wounds upon thy body,
> And no physicians to cure three.
>
> Since we have not to heal our wounds
> Miach, Ormiach, nor Diancecht,
> Alas, O Brian, who designedst not guile,
> To have given away from us the skin!

After this lay they reached Benn Etair, and from that they went on to Dun Tuirinn; and they said to Tuirenn, "Go, beloved father, to Tara and deliver this cooking spit to Lug, and bring us the gifted skin to relieve us"; and Brian spoke the lay and Tuirenn answered:

> O Tuirenn! depart from us,
> To speak to Lug the gifted;
> Catch him asleep in the south;
> Beg the healing skin from him through friendship.
>
> For the world's jewels, south and north,—
> And all to be given to Lug the gifted,—
> What certainly would come of it would be
> Your graves and your burial.
>
> Near are we related in blood and flesh
> To Lug the son of Cian son of just Cainte;
> Let him not deal us wrath for wrath,
> Though we have killed his father.
>
> O father, beloved, noble, swift,
> Be not long upon thy visit,
> For if thou art, thou shalt not find us
> Alive before thee.

After this Tuirenn went forward to Tara and found Lug Lamfada there before him; and he gave him the spit, and begged the skin from him to cover his sons with; and Lug said he would not give it. And Tuirenn turned back to his sons, and told them that he had not obtained the skin. And then Brian said, "Take me with you to Lug to try if I should obtain the skin."

It was done accordingly; and he went to Lug and begged the skin from him. And Lug said that he would not give it; and that though he gave him the breadth of the earth in gold, that he would not accept it from him unless he thought their death would ensue, in revenge of the deed which they had perpetrated.

When Brian heard this he went to where his two brothers were; and he lay down between them, and his life departed out of him, and out of the other two at the same time; and Tuirenn made the following lay over his sons:

> Grieved is my heart over you!
> You three fair youths who fought many fights,
> After your activity and your feats,
> It were well for me that you should live!

> The makings of two kings over Banba,
> Iuchar and Iucharba;—
> Brian, that conquered Greece,—
> It is a loss that their like are not alive!
>
> I am Tuirenn, without strength
> Over your grave, you fierce champions;
> As long as ships shall ply the sea,
> So long shall I not write lay or song more.

After this Tuirenn dropped on the bodies of his sons, and his soul departed out of him; and they were buried at once in one grave.

And such is the Tragical Fate of the Children of Tuirenn.

THE WOOING OF ETAIN

"The Wooing of Etain," composed in its oldest form as early as the eighth century, is one of the most charming pieces of romantic fiction preserved from the vernacular literature of medieval Europe. Though, unfortunately, the story exists only in a series of disconnected and mutilated fragments, enough remains to illustrate admirably the highly developed style and delicate treatment of sentiment which characterize ancient Irish literature.

In her earlier career (not recounted here), Etain is associated not only with Mider but also with Angus Oc, a well-known supernatural personage who figures in the Mythological cycle. According to the annals, her mortal husband, Eochaid Airem, became high-king of Ireland about 134 B.C. "The Wooing of Etain" is connected with "The Destruction of Da Derga's Hostel" (p. 93) by the fact that Etain's grandson, King Conaire Mor, meets his death as the result of Eochaid's having destroyed the fairy-mound of Bri Leith, whither Etain had been abducted by Mider.

There was an admirable, noble king in the high-kingship over Ireland, namely, Eochaid Airem. . . . The first year after he ascended the throne, a proclamation was made throughout Ireland that the feast of Tara was to be celebrated, and that all the men of Ireland should attend it, that their taxes and their levies might be known. And the one answer made by all the men of Ireland to Eochaid's summons was: That they would not attend the feast of Tara during such time, whether it be long or short, as the king of Ireland was without a wife that was suitable for him; for there was not a noble of the men of Ireland who was without a wife suitable for him, and there was not a king without a queen, and there would not come a man without his wife to the feast of Tara, nor would there come a woman without a husband.

Thereupon Eochaid sent out from him his horsemen, and his entertainers, and his spies, and his messengers of the border throughout Ireland, and they searched all Ireland for a woman who should be suitable for the king in respect to form, and grace, and countenance, and birth. And besides all this, there was one more condition regarding her: the king would never take a wife who had been given to any one else before him. And the king's officers sought all Ireland, both south and north, and they found at Inber Cichmany a woman suitable for him; that is, Etain the daughter of Etar, who was king of Echrad. Then his messengers returned to Eochaid and gave him a description of the maiden in regard to form and grace and countenance.

And Eochaid set forth to take the maiden, and the way that he went was across the fair-green of Bri Leith. And there he saw a maiden upon the brink of a spring. She held in her hand a comb of silver decorated with gold. Beside her, as for washing, was a basin of silver whereon were chased four golden birds, and there were little bright gems of carbuncle set in the rim of the basin. A cloak pure-purple, hanging in folds about her, and beneath it a mantle with silver borders, and a brooch of gold in the garment over her bosom. A tunic with a long hood about her, and as for it, smooth and glossy. It was made of greenish silk beneath red embroidery of gold, and marvellous bow-pins of silver and gold upon her breasts in the tunic, so that the redness of the gold against the sun in the green silk was clearly visible to the men. Two tresses of golden hair upon her head, and a plaiting of four strands in each tress, and a ball of gold upon the end of each plait.

And the maiden was there loosening her hair to wash it, and her two arms out through the armholes of her smock. As white as the snow of one night was each of her two arms, and as red as the foxglove of the mountain was each of her two cheeks. As blue as the hyacinth was each of her two eyes; delicately red her lips; very high, soft, and white her two shoulders. Tender, smooth, and white were her two wrists; her fingers long and very white; her nails pink and beautiful. As white as snow or as the foam of the wave was her side, slender, long, and as soft as silk. Soft, smooth, and white were her thighs; round and small, firm and white were her two knees; as straight as a rule were her two ankles; slim and foamwhite were her two feet. Fair and very beautiful were her two eyes; her eyebrows blackish blue like the shell of a beetle. It was she the maiden who was the fairest and the most beautiful that the eyes of men had ever seen; and it seemed probable to the king and his companions that she was out of a fairy-mound. This is the maiden concerning whom is spoken the proverb: "Every lovely form must be tested by Etain, every beauty by the standard of Etain."

A desire for her seized the king immediately, and he sent a man of his company to hold her before him. Then Eochaid approached the maiden and questioned her. "Whence art thou, O maiden?" said the king, "and whence hast thou come?"

"Not hard to answer," replied the maiden. "Etain the daughter of the king of Echrad out of the fairy-mounds I am called."

"Shall I have an hour of dalliance with thee?" said Eochaid.

"It is for that I have come hither under thy protection," said she. "I have been here for twenty years since I was born in the fairy-mound, and the men of the fairy-mound, both kings and nobles, have been wooing me, and naught was got by any of them from me, because I have loved thee and given love and affection to thee since I was a little child and since I was capable of speaking. It was for the noble tales about thee and for thy splendor that I have loved thee, and, although I have never seen thee before, I recognized thee at once by thy description. It is thou, I know, to whom I have attained," said she.

"That is by no means the invitation of a bad friend," replied Eochaid; "thou shalt be welcomed by me, and all other women shall be left for thy sake, and with thee alone will I live as long as it is pleasing to thee."

"Give me my fitting bride-price," said the maiden, "and thereafter let my desire be fulfilled."

"That shall be to thee," said the king.

The value of seven bond-slaves was given to her for a bride-price; and after that he took her with him to Tara, and a truly hearty welcome was given to her.

Now there were three brothers of one blood who were the sons of Finn: Eochaid Airem and Eochaid Fedlech and Ailill Anglonnach, or Ailill of the One Stain, because the only stain that was upon him was that he loved his brother's wife. At that time came the men of Ireland to hold the feast of Tara, and they were there fourteen days before Samain (Hallowe'en) and fourteen days after Samain. It was at the feast of Tara that Ailill Anglonnach fell in love with Etain the daughter of Etar. Ailill gazed at the woman as long as he was at the feast of Tara. Then Ailill's wife, the daughter of Luchta Red-Hand from the borders of Leinster, said to her husband: "Ailill," said she, "why doest thou keep gazing far off from thee? for such long-looking is a sign of love." Thereupon

Ailill became ashamed and blamed himself for that thing, and he did not look at Etain after that.

After the feast of Tara the men of Ireland separated from one another, and then it was that the pains of jealousy and great envy filled Ailill, and a heavy illness came upon him. As a result he was carried to Dun Fremain in Tethba, the favorite stronghold of his brother, the king. Ailill remained there to the end of a year in long-sickness and in long-pining, but he did not confess the cause of his sickness to any one. And thither came Eochaid to enquire after Ailill. He put his hand upon Ailill's breast, whereupon Ailill heaved a sigh.

"Now," said Eochaid, "the sickness in which thou art does not appear to be serious. How is everything with thee?"

"By my word," replied Ailill, "not easier is it with me, but worse in all respects every day and every night."

"What ails thee?" asked Eochaid.

"By my true word," said Ailill, "I do not know."

"Let there be brought to me some one who shall make known the cause of this illness," said Eochaid.

Then was brought to them Fachtna, the physician of Eochaid. And Fachtna put his hand upon Ailill's breast, and Ailill sighed.

"Now," said Fachtna, "the matter is not serious. There is nothing the matter with thee but one of two things; that is, either the pains of jealousy or love which thou hast given, and thou hast found no help till now." Thereupon Ailill was ashamed. He did not confess the cause of his illness to the physician, and the physician went from him.

Now, as regards Eochaid, he went out to make his royal circuit throughout Ireland, and he left Etain in the stronghold of Fremain, and he said to her: "Deal gently with Ailill as long as he is alive, and should he die," said he, "have his grave of sod dug, and let his pillar-stone be raised, and let his name be written on it in ogam." The king then departed on his royal circuit of Ireland, leaving Ailill there in Dun Fremain in expectation of death and dissolution for the space of that year.

Into the house in which Ailill was, Etain used to go each day to consult with and minister to him. One day she asked him: "What is the matter with thee? Thy sickness is indeed great, and if we knew anything that would satisfy thee, thou shouldst get it from us." It was thus that she spoke, and she sang a little lay and Ailill answered her. . . .

(As the result of their dialogue Etain finally understands that her brother-in-law is suffering from love of herself.)

Etain continued to come every day to Ailill to bathe him and to divide his food for him, and she helped him greatly, for she was sad at seeing him perish because of her. One day she said to Ailill, "Come to-morrow at daybreak to tryst with me in the house that stands outside the stronghold, and there shalt thou have granted thy request and thy desire." On that night Ailill lay without sleep until the coming of the morning; and when the time had come that was appointed for his tryst, his sleep lay heavily upon him; so that till the hour of his rising he lay deep in his sleep. And Etain went to the tryst, nor had she long to wait ere she saw a man coming towards her in the likeness of Ailill, weary and feeble; but she knew that he was not Ailill, and continued there waiting for Ailill. And the lady came back from her tryst, and Ailill awoke, and thought that he would rather die than live; and he was in great sadness and grief. And the lady came to speak with him, and when he told her what had befallen him: "Come," said she, "to the same place to meet with me to-morrow." And upon the morrow it was the same as upon the first day; each day came the same man to her tryst. And she came again upon the last day that was appointed for the tryst, and the same man met her. " 'Tis not with thee that I trysted," said she, "why dost thou come to meet me? and for him whom I would have met here, neither from desire of his love nor for fear of harm from him had I appointed to meet him, but only to heal him, and to cure him from the sickness which had come upon him for his love of me." "It were more fitting for thee to come to tryst with me," said the man, "for when thou wast Etain, daughter of the king of Echrad, and when thou wast the daughter of Ailill, I myself was thy first husband." "Why," said she, "what is thy name at all, if it were to be demanded of thee?" "It is not hard to answer thee," he said, "Mider of Bri Leith is my name." "And what made thee to part from me, if we were as thou sayest?" said Etain. "Easy again is the answer," said Mider; "it was the sorcery of Fuamnach and the spells of Bressal Etarlam that put us apart." And Mider said to Etain: "Wilt thou come with me?"

"Nay," answered Etain, "I will not exchange the king of all Ireland for thee; for a man whose kindred and whose lineage is unknown." "It was I myself indeed," said Mider, "who filled all the mind of Ailill with love for thee; it was I also who prevented his coming to the tryst with thee, and allowed him not to spoil thy honor."

After all this the lady went back to her house, and she came to speech with Ailill, and she greeted him. "It hath happened well for us both," said Ailill, "that the man met thee there: for I am cured forever from my illness, thou also art unhurt in thine honor, and may a blessing rest upon thee!" "Thanks be to our gods," said Etain, "that both of us do indeed deem that all this hath chanced so well." And after that, Eochaid came back from his royal progress, and he asked at once for his brother; and the tale was told to him from the beginning to the end, and the king was grateful to Etain, in that she had been gracious to Ailill; and "What hath been related in this tale," said Eochaid, "is well-pleasing to ourselves."

.   .   .   .

Now upon another time it chanced that Eochaid Airem, the king of Tara, arose upon a certain fair day in the time of summer and he ascended the high ground of Tara to behold the plain of Breg; beautiful was the color of that plain, and there was upon it excellent blossom, glowing with all hues that are known. And, as the aforesaid Eochaid looked about and around him, he saw a young strange warrior upon the high ground at his side. The tunic that the warrior wore was purple in color, his hair was of golden yellow, and of such length that it reached to the edge of his shoulders. The eyes of the young warrior were lustrous and grey; in the one hand he held a five-pointed spear, in the other a shield with a white central boss, and with gems of gold upon it. And Eochaid held his peace, for he knew that none such had been in Tara on the night before, and the gate that led into the enclosure had not at that hour been thrown open.

The warrior came, and placed himself under the protection of Eochaid; and "Welcome do I give," said Eochaid, "to the hero who is yet unknown."

"Thy reception is such as I expected when I came," said the warrior.

"We know thee not," answered Eochaid.

"Yet thee in truth I know well!" he replied.

"What is the name by which thou art called?" said Eochaid.

"My name is not known to renown," said the warrior; "I am Mider of Bri Leith."

"And for what purpose art thou come?" said Eochaid.

"I have come that I may play a game of chess with thee," answered Mider. "Truly," said Eochaid, "I myself am skilful at chess-play."

"Let us test that skill!" said Mider.

"Nay," said Eochaid, "the queen is even now in her sleep; and hers is the apartment in which the chessboard lies."

"I have here with me," said Mider, "a chessboard which is not inferior to thine." It was even as he said, for that chessboard was silver, and the men to play with were gold; and upon that board were costly stones, casting their light on every side, and the bag that held the men was of woven chains of brass.

Mider then set out the chessboard, and he called upon Eochaid to play. "I will not play," said Eochaid, "unless we play for a stake."

"What stake shall we have upon the game then?" said Mider.

"It is indifferent to me," said Eochaid.

"Then," said Mider, "if thou dost obtain the forfeit of my stake, I will bestow on thee fifty steeds of a dark grey, their heads of a blood-red color, but dappled; their ears pricked high, and their chests broad; their nostrils wide, and their hoofs slender; great is their strength, and they are keen like a whetted edge; eager are they, high-standing and spirited, yet easily stopped in their course."

Several games were played between Eochaid and Mider; and since Mider did not put forth his whole strength, the victory on all occasions rested with Eochaid. But instead of the gifts which Mider had offered, Eochaid demanded that Mider and his folk should perform for him services which should be of benefit to his realm; that he should clear away the rocks and stones from the plains of Meath, should remove the rushes which made the land barren around his favorite fort of Tethba, should cut down the forest of Breg, and finally should build a causeway across the moor or bog of Lamrach that men might pass freely across it.

All these things Mider agreed to do, and Eochaid sent his steward to see how that work was done. And when it came to the time after sunset, the steward looked, and he saw that Mider and his fairy host, together with fairy oxen, were laboring at the causeway over the bog; and thereupon much of earth and of gravel and of stones was poured into it. Now it had, before that time, always been the custom of the men of Ireland to harness their oxen with a strap over their foreheads, so that the pull might be against the foreheads of the oxen; and this custom lasted up to that very night, when it was seen that the fairy folk had placed the yoke upon the shoulders of the oxen, so that the pull might be there; and in this way were the yokes of the oxen afterwards placed by Eochaid, and thence comes the name by which he is known; even Eochaid Airem, or Eochaid the Ploughman, for he was the first of all the men of Ireland to put the yokes on the necks of the oxen, and thus it became the custom for all the land of Ireland. And this is the song that the host of the fairies sang, as they labored at the making of the road:

> Thrust it in hand! force it in hand!
> Noble this night, the troop of oxen:
> Hard is the task that is asked, and who
> From the bridging of Lamrach shall receive gain or harm?

Not in all the world could a road have been found that should be better than the road that they made, had it not been that the fairy folk were observed as they worked upon it; but for that cause a breach has been made in that causeway. And the steward of Eochaid thereafter came to him; and he described to him that great laboring band that had come before his eyes, and he said that there was not over the chariot-pole of life a power that could withstand its might. And, as they spoke thus with each other, they saw Mider standing before them; high was he girt, and ill-favored was the face that he showed; and Eochaid arose, and he gave welcome to him. "Thy welcome is such as I expected when I came," said Mider. "Cruel and senseless hast thou been in thy treatment of me, and much of hardship and suffering hast thou given me. All things that seemed good in thy sight have I got for thee, but now anger against thee hath filled my mind!" "I return not anger for anger," answered Eochaid; "what thou wishest shall be done." "Let it be as thou wishest," said Mider;

"shall we play at the chess?" said he. "What stake shall we set upon the game?" said Eochaid. "Even such stake as the winner of it shall demand," said Mider. And in that very place Eochaid was defeated, and he forfeited his stake.

"My stake is forfeited to thee," said Eochaid.

"Had I wished it, it had been forfeited long ago," said Mider.

"What is it that thou desirest me to grant?" said Eochaid.

"That I may hold Etain in my arms and obtain a kiss from her!" answered Mider.

Eochaid was silent for a while, and then he said: "One month from this day thou shalt come, and that very thing that thou hast asked for shall be given to thee." Now for a year before that Mider first came to Eochaid for the chess-play, had he been at the wooing of Etain, and he obtained her not; and the name which he gave to Etain was Befind, or Fair-haired Woman, so it was that he said:

> Wilt thou come with me, fair-haired woman?

as has before been recited. And it was at that time that Etain said: "If thou obtainest me from him who is the master of my house, I will go; but if thou art not able to obtain me from him, then I will not go." And thereupon Mider came to Eochaid, and allowed him at the first to win the victory over him, in order that Eochaid should stand in his debt; and therefore it was that he paid the great stakes to which he had agreed, and therefore also was it that he had demanded of him that he should play that game in ignorance of what was staked. And when Mider and his folk were paying those agreed-on stakes, which were paid upon that night; to wit, the making of the road, and the clearing of the stones from Meath, the rushes from around Tethba, and the forest that is over Breg, it is thus that he spoke, as it is written in the Book of Drum Snechta:

> Pile on the soil; thrust on the soil;
> Red are the oxen who labor;
> Heavy the troops that obey my words.
> Heavy they seem, and yet men are they.
> Strongly, as piles, are the tree-trunks placed:
> Red are the wattles bound above them:
> Tired are your hands, and your glances slant;
> One woman's winning this toil may yield!

Oxen ye are, but revenge shall see;
Men who are white shall be your servants:
Rushes from Tethba are cleared:
Grief is the price that the man shall pay:
Stones have been cleared from the rough Meath ground;
Whose shall the gain or the harm be?

Now Mider appointed a day at the end of the month when he was to meet Eochaid, and Eochaid called the armies of the heroes of Ireland together, so that they came to Tara; and all the best of the champions of Ireland, ring within ring, were about Tara, and they were in the midst of Tara itself, and they guarded it, both without and within; and the king and the queen were in the midst of the palace, and the outer court thereof was shut and locked, for they knew that the great might of men would come upon them. And upon the appointed night Etain was dispensing the banquet to the kings, for it was her duty to pour out the wine, when in the midst of their talk they saw Mider standing before them in the center of the palace. He was always fair, yet fairer than he ever was seemed Mider to be upon that night. And he brought to amazement all the hosts on which he gazed, and all thereupon were silent, and the king gave a welcome to him.

"Thy reception is such as I expected when I came," said Mider; "let that now be given to me that has been promised. 'Tis a debt that is due when a promise hath been made; and I for my part have given to thee all that was promised by me."

"I have not yet considered the matter," said Eochaid.

"Thou hast promised Etain's very self to me," said Mider; "that is what has come from thee." Etain blushed for shame when she heard that word.

"Blush not," said Mider to Etain, "for in no wise has thy wedding-feast been disgraced. I have been seeking thee for a year with the fairest jewels and treasures that can be found in Ireland, and I have not taken thee until the time came when Eochaid might permit it. 'Tis not through any will of thine that I have won thee." "I myself told thee," said Etain, "that until Eochaid should resign me to thee I would grant thee nothing. Take me then for my part, if Eochaid is willing to resign me to thee."

"But I will not resign thee!" said Eochaid; "nevertheless he shall take thee in his arms upon the floor of this house as thou art."

"It shall be done!" said Mider.

He took his weapons in his left hand and the woman beneath his right shoulder; and he carried her off through the smoke-hole of the house. And the hosts rose up around the king, for they felt that they had been disgraced, and they saw two swans circling round Tara, and the way that they took was the way to the elf-mound of Femen. And Eochaid with an army of the men of Ireland went to the elf-mound of Femen, which men call the mound of the Fair-haired Women. And he followed the counsel of the men of Ireland, and he dug up each of the elf-mounds that he might take his wife from thence. And Mider and his host opposed them and the war between them was long: again and again the trenches made by Eochaid were destroyed; for nine years, as some say, lasted the strife of the men of Ireland to enter into the fairy palace. And when at last the armies of Eochaid came by digging to the borders of the fairy-mound of Bri Leith, Mider sent to the side of the palace sixty women all in the shape of Etain, and so like to her that none could tell which was the Queen, and Eochaid himself was deceived, and he chose instead of Etain her daughter Mess Buachalla (or, as some say, Esa). But when he found that he had been deceived, he returned again to sack Bri Leith, and this time Etain made herself known to Eochaid by proofs that he could not mistake, and he bore her away in triumph to Tara, and there she abode with the king.

[Another version of the story adds: It was on this account that the fairy folk of Mag Breg and Mider of Bri Leith broke the taboos of Conaire and ended his life and brought about the laying waste of Mag Breg—because of the destruction of Bri Leith and Eochaid Airem's taking away Etain by force.]

THE DESTRUCTION OF DA DERGA'S HOSTEL

"The Destruction of Da Derga's Hostel" is one of the longest and most pathetic Irish sagas. It is among the few complete narratives of any great extent preserved from ancient Irish literature. The oldest manuscript was copied about the year 1100, but the saga existed in written form as early as the eighth or ninth century. According to the annals, Conaire was high-king of Ireland about the beginning of the Christian era. Da Derga's Hostel was situated among the hills overlooking the village of Bray near Dublin, and was built over the Dodder, a little stream that flows through Donnybrook and empties into Dublin Bay. The story, though rambling and disconnected in spots, is told with real power and contains some of the finest descriptive passages in early Irish literature.

After giving an account of Conaire's antecedents and birth, the story goes on to tell how the youthful king met his tragic and untimely death. He is represented as the grandson of the beautiful and unfortunate Etain, whose life history is recorded in "The Wooing of Etain" (p. 82). Like numerous other characters in early Irish fiction, he is subject to certain *gesa*, or taboos, which he violates only at the peril of his life. The fairy folk, in revenge for the injury which Conaire's grandfather had done them in destroying their mound, bring it about that Conaire breaks his taboos and so falls a victim to the perfidy of his own foster-brothers and of the British pirates who act as their allies. Though dealing primarily with one of the traditional kings of Ireland (p. 469), the story is given here because of its connection with "The Wooing of Etain," to which it forms a natural sequel.

The following translation is complete except for the omission of a few unimportant repetitious passages.

There was a famous and noble king over Erin, named Eochaid Fedlech.[1] Once upon a time he came over the fair-green of Bri Leith, and he saw at the edge of a well a woman with a bright comb of silver adorned with gold, washing in a silver basin wherein were four golden birds and little, bright gems of purple carbuncle in the rims of the basin. A mantle she had, curly and purple, a beautiful cloak, and in the mantle silvery fringes arranged, and a brooch of fairest gold. A kirtle she wore, long, hooded, hardsmooth, of green silk, with red embroidery of gold. Marvellous

[1] According to "The Wooing of Etain" (p. 82), the king was Eochaid Airem.

clasps of gold and silver in the kirtle on her breasts and her shoulders and spaulds on every side. The sun kept shining upon her, so that the glistening of the gold against the sun from the green silk was manifest to the men. On her head were two golden-yellow tresses, in each of which was a plait of four strands, with a bead of gold at the point of each strand. The hue of that hair seemed to the king and his companions like the flower of the iris in summer, or like red gold after the burnishing thereof.

There she was, undoing her hair to wash it, with her arms out through the sleeve-holes of her smock. White as the snow of one night were the two hands, soft and even, and red as foxglove were the two clear-beautiful cheeks. Dark as the back of a stag-beetle the two eyebrows. Like a shower of pearls were the teeth in her head. Blue as a hyacinth were the eyes. Red as rowan-berries the lips. Very high, smooth and soft-shining the shoulders. Clear-white and long the fingers. Long were the hands. White as the foam of a wave was the flank, slender, long, tender, smooth, soft as wool. Polished and warm, sleek and white were the two thighs. Round and small, hard and white the two knees. Short and white and rulestraight the two shins. Justly straight and beautiful the two heels. If a measure were put on the feet it would hardly have found them unequal. The bright radiance of the moon was in her noble face; the loftiness of pride in her smooth eyebrows; the light of wooing in each of her regal eyes. A dimple of delight in each of her cheeks, with a variegation in them at one time of purple spots with redness of a calf's blood, and at another with the bright lustre of snow. Soft womanly dignity in her voice; a step steady and slow she had; a queenly gait was hers. Verily, of the world's women 'twas she was the dearest and loveliest and justest that the eyes of men had ever beheld. It seemed to king Eochaid and his followers that she was from the fairy-mounds. Of her was said: "Shapely are all till compared with Etain; dear are all till compared with Etain."

A longing for her straightway seized the king; so he sent forward a man of his people to detain her. The king asked tidings of her and said, while announcing himself: "Shall I have an hour of dalliance with thee?"

"'Tis for that we have come hither under thy safeguard," said she.

"Whence art thou and whence hast thou come?" asked Eochaid.

"Easy to say," answered she. "Etain am I, daughter of Etar, king of Echrad. I have been here for twenty years since I was born in a fairy-mound. The men of the fairy-mound, both kings and nobles, have been wooing me; but nought was gotten from me, because ever since I was able to speak, I have loved thee and given thee a child's love for the high tales about thee and thy splendor. And though I have never seen thee, I knew thee at once from thy description: it is thou, then, I have found."

"No 'seeking of an ill friend afar' shall be thine," said Eochaid. "Thou shalt have welcome, and for thee every other woman shall be left by me, and with thee alone will I live so long as thou hast honor."

"Pay me my proper bride-price," she said, "and afterwards grant my wish."

"Thou shalt have both," said Eochaid. The value of seven bondmaids was given to her, and she became Eochaid's wife.

Then the king, Eochaid Fedlech, died leaving one daughter named, like her mother, Etain, and she was wedded to Cormac, king of Ulster. After the end of a time Cormac, king of Ulster, "the man of the three gifts," forsook Eochaid's daughter, because she was barren save for one daughter that she had borne to Cormac after the making of the pottage which her mother—the woman from the fairy-mounds—gave her. Then she said to her mother: "Bad is what thou hast given me: it will be a daughter that I shall bear."

"That will not be good," said her mother; "a king's pursuit will be on her."

Then Cormac again wedded his wife, even Etain, and this was his desire, that the daughter of the woman who had before been abandoned (i.e., his own daughter) should be killed. So Cormac would not leave the girl to her mother to be nursed. Then his two thralls took her to a pit, but she smiled a laughing smile at them as they were putting her into it. Then their kindly nature came to them. They carried her into the calfshed of the cowherds of Eterscel great-grandson of Iar king of Tara, and they fostered her till she became a good embroideress; and there was not in Ireland a king's daughter dearer than she.

A fenced house of wickerwork was made by the thralls for her, without any door, but only a window and a skylight. King Eterscel's folk espied that house and supposed that it was food that the cowherds kept there. But one of them went and looked through the skylight, and he saw in the house the dearest, most beautiful maiden! This was told to the king, and straightway he sent his people to wreck the house and carry her off without asking the cowherds. For the king was childless, and it had been prophesied to him by his wizards that a woman of unknown race would bear him a son. Then said the king: "This is the woman that has been prophesied to me!"

Now while she was there next morning she saw a bird on the skylight coming to her, and he left his birdskin on the floor of the house, and went to her and captured her, and said: "They are coming to thee from the king to wreck thy house and to bring thee to him perforce. And thou wilt be pregnant by me, and bear a son, and that son must not kill birds. And Conaire, son of Mess Buachalla shall be his name"; for hers was Mess Buachalla, "the Cowherds' Fosterchild."

And then she was brought to the king, and with her went her fosterers, and she was betrothed to the king, and he gave her the value of seven bondmaids and to her fosterers a like amount. And afterwards they were made chieftains, so that they all became lawworthy, whence are the two Fedlimids the stewards. And then she bore a son to the king, called Conaire son of Mess Buachalla, and these were her three urgent prayers to the king,—the nursing of her son among three households; that is, the fosterers who had nurtured her, and Mane Honeywords, and herself the third; and she said that such of the men of Erin as should wish to do aught for this boy should give securities to those three households for the boy's protection.

So thus he was reared, and the men of Erin straightway knew this boy on the day he was born. And other boys were fostered with him, to wit, Fer Le and Fer Gair and Fer Rogain, three sons of Donn Desa the champion.

Now Conaire possessed three gifts,—the gift of hearing and the gift of eyesight and the gift of judgment; and of those three gifts he taught one to each of his three foster-brothers. And whatever meal was prepared for him, the four of them would go to it. Even though three meals were prepared for him each of them would go to his meal. The same raiment and armor and color of horses had the four.

Then King Eterscel died. A bull-feast was prepared by the men of Erin in order to determine their future king; that is, a bull was killed by them and thereof one man ate his fill and drank its broth, and a spell of truth was chanted over him in his bed. Whomsoever he would see in his sleep would be king, and the sleeper would perish if he uttered a falsehood.

Four men in chariots were on the Plain of Liffey at their game, Conaire himself and his three fosterbrothers. Then his fosterers went to him and summoned him to the bull-feast. The bull-feaster, in his sleep, at the end of the night had beheld a man stark-naked, passing along the road of Tara, with a stone in his sling. "I will go in the morning after you," said Conaire.

He left his fosterbrothers at their game, and turned his chariot and his charioteer and fared to Dublin. There he saw great white-speckled birds, of unusual size and color and beauty. He pursued them until his horses were tired. The birds would go a spearcast before him, and would not go any farther. He alighted, took his sling out of the chariot, and went after them until he reached the sea. The birds betook themselves to the waves. He went after them and overcame them. The birds quit their birdskins, and turned upon him with spears and swords. One of them protected him, and addressed him, saying: "I am Nemglan, king of thy father's birds; and thou hast been forbidden to cast at birds, for here there is no one that should not be dear to thee because of his father or mother."

"Till today," said Conaire, "I knew not this."

"Go to Tara tonight," said Nemglan; "'tis fittest for thee. A bull-feast is there, and through it thou shalt be king. A man stark-naked, who shall go at the end of the night along one of the roads of Tara, having a stone and a sling—'tis he that shall be king."

So Conaire fared forth naked; and on each of the four roads whereby men go to Tara there were three kings awaiting him, and they had raiment for him, since it had been foretold that he would come stark-naked. Then he was seen from the road on which his fosterers were, and they put royal raiment about him, and placed him in a chariot, and he took sureties.

The folk of Tara said to him: "It seems to us that our bull-feast and our spell of truth are a failure, if it be only a young, beardless lad that we have visioned therein."

"That is of no moment," said he. "For a young, generous king like me to be in the kingship is no disgrace, since the taking of Tara's sureties is mine by right of father and grandsire."

"Excellent! excellent!" said the host. They set the kingship of Erin upon him. And he said: "I will take counsel of wise men that I myself may be wise."

He uttered all this as he had been taught by the bird-man at the sea, who had said this to him: "Thy reign will be subject to a restriction, but the bird-reign will be noble, and these shall be thy taboos:

"Thou shalt not go righthandwise round Tara and lefthandwise round Mag Breg.

"The evil-beasts of Cerna must not be hunted by thee.

"And thou shalt not go out every ninth night beyond Tara.

"Thou shalt not sleep in a house from which firelight is manifest outside after sunset, and in which light is manifest from without.

"And three Reds shall not go before thee to Red's house.

"And no rapine shall be wrought in thy reign.

"And after sunset a company of one woman or one man shall not enter the house in which thou art.

"And thou shalt not settle the quarrel of thy two thralls."

Now there were in Conaire's reign great bounties, to wit, seven ships in every June of every year arriving at Inver Colptha, and oak-mast up to the knees in every autumn, and plenty of fish in the rivers Bush and Boyne in June of each year, and such abundance of good-will that no one slew another in Erin during his reign. And to every one in Erin his fellow's voice seemed as sweet as the strings of lutes. From mid-spring to mid-autumn no wind disturbed a cow's tail. His reign was neither thunderous nor stormy.

Now his foster-brothers murmured at the taking from them of their father's and their grandsire's gifts, namely theft and robbery and slaughter of men and rapine. They thieved the three thefts from the same man,—a swine and an ox and a cow, every year, that they might see what punishment therefor the king would inflict upon them, and what damage the theft in his reign would cause to the king. Every year the farmer would come to the king to complain, and the king would say to him, "Go thou and address Donn Desa's three sons, for 'tis they that have taken the beasts." Whenever he went to speak to them, they would almost kill him and he would not return to the king lest Conaire should add to his hurt.

Since, then, pride and wilfulness possessed them, they took to marauding, surrounded by the sons of the lords of the men of Erin. Thrice fifty men had they as pupils who in the form of were-wolves were destroying in the province of Connacht, until Mane Milscothach's swineherd saw them, and he had never seen that before. He fled in fright. When they heard him they pursued him. The swineherd shouted, and the people of the two Manes came to him, and the thrice fifty men were arrested, along with their auxiliaries, and taken to Tara. They consulted the king concerning the matter, and he said: "Let each father slay his son, but let my foster-brothers be spared."

"Let be, let be!" said every one: "you shall be obeyed."

"But mind you," said he; "there is no lengthening of life in the judgment I have delivered. The men shall not be hanged; but let veterans go with them in banishment that they may wreak their rapine on the men of Scotland and Britain."

This they did. They put to sea and met the son of the king of Britain, even Ingcel the One-eyed, grandson of Conmac: thrice fifty men and their veterans they met upon the sea.

They made an alliance, and went with Ingcel and wrought rapine with him.

This was the destruction which Ingcel did of his own will. On a certain night his mother and his father and his seven brothers had been bidden to the house of the king of his district. All of them were destroyed by Ingcel in a single night. Then the Irish pirates put out to sea to the land of Erin to inflict equal destruction upon their own people as payment for that to which Ingcel had been entitled from them.

In Conaire's reign there was perfect peace in Erin, save that in Thomond there was a battle between the two Cairbres. Two fosterbrothers of his were they. And until Conaire came it was impossible to make peace between them. 'Twas a taboo of his to go to separate them before they had appealed to him. He went, however, although to do so was one of his taboos, and he made peace between them. He remained five nights with each of the two. That also was a taboo of his.

After settling the quarrel, he was travelling to Tara. The way he took to Tara was past Usnech in Meath; and he saw raiding from east and west, and from south and north, and he saw warbands and hosts, and men stark-naked; and the land of the southern O'Neills was a cloud of fire around him.

"What is this?" asked Conaire. "Easy to say," his people answered. "Easy to know that the king's law has broken down therein, since the country has begun to burn."

"Whither shall we betake ourselves?" said Conaire.

"To the northeast," said his people.

So then they went righthandwise round Tara, and lefthandwise round Mag Breg, and the evil beasts of Cerna were hunted by him. But he saw it not till the chase had ended. They that made of the world that smoky mist of magic were the fairy folk, and they did so because Conaire's taboos had been violated. Great fear then fell on Conaire because they had no way to go save upon the Road of Midluachar and the Road of Cualu. So they took their way by the coast of Ireland southward.

Then said Conaire on the Road of Cualu: "Whither shall we go tonight?"

"By my word, my fosterling Conaire," said Mac Cecht, son of Snade Teiched, the champion of Conaire son of Eterscel, "it is more usual that the men of Erin should contend for thee every night than that thou shouldst wander about for a guesthouse."

"Judgment goes with good times," said Conaire. "I had a friend in this country, if only we knew the way to his house!"

"What is his name?" asked Mac Cecht.

"Da Derga ('Two Reds') of Leinster," answered Conaire. "He came to me to seek a gift from me, and he did not meet a refusal. I gave him a hundred cows of the drove. I gave him a hundred fatted swine. I gave him a hundred mantles made of close cloth. I gave him a hundred blue-colored weapons of battle. I gave him ten red, gilded brooches. I gave him ten vats of mead good and brown. I gave him ten thralls. I gave him ten nags. I gave him thrice nine hounds all-white in their silver chains. I gave him a hundred race-horses. There would be no abatement in his case though he should come again, and he on his part make to me a return. It would be strange if he were surly to me tonight when I reach his abode."

"I am acquainted with his house," said Mac Cecht; "the road whereon thou art going is the boundary of his abode. It continues till it enters his house, for through the house passes the road. There are seven doorways into the house, and seven rooms between every two doorways; but there is only one door-way covering, and that covering is turned to every doorway to which the wind blows."

"With all that thou hast here," said Conaire, "thou shalt go with this large company until thou alightest in the midst of the house."

"If so be," answered Mac Cecht, "that thou goest thither, I go on that I may strike fire there ahead of thee."

When Conaire after this was journeying along the Road of Cualu, he marked before him three horsemen riding towards the house. Three red frocks had they, and three red mantles: three red bucklers they bore, and three red spears were in their hands: three red steeds they bestrode, and three red heads of hair were on them. Red were they all, both body and hair and raiment, both steeds and men.

"Who is it that fares before us?" asked Conaire. "It was a taboo of mine for those three to go before me—the three Reds to the house of Red. Who will follow them and tell them to come behind me?"

"I will follow them," said Le Fri Flaith, Conaire's son.

He went after them, lashing his horse, but he overtook them not. There was the length of a spearcast between them: but they did not gain upon him and he did not gain upon them. He told them not to go before the king. He overtook them not; but one of the three men sang a lay to him over his shoulder: "Lo, my son, great the news, news from a hostel. Lo, my son!" They went away from him then: he could not detain them.

The boy waited for the company of his father. He told his father what was said to him. Conaire liked it not.

"After them!" said Conaire, "and offer them three oxen and three bacon-pigs, and so long as they shall be in my household, no one shall be among them from fire to wall."

So the lad went after them, and offered them that, and overtook them not. But one of the three men sang a lay to him over his shoulder: "Lo, my son, great the news! A generous king's great ardor whets thee, burns thee. Through ancient men's enchantments a company of nine yields. Lo, my son!" The boy turned back and repeated the lay to Conaire.

"Go after them," said Conaire, "and offer them six oxen and six bacon-pigs, and my leavings, and gifts tomorrow, and so long as they shall be in my household, no one shall be among them from fire to wall."

The lad then went after them, and overtook them not; but one of the three men answered and said: "Lo, my son, great the news! Weary are the steeds we ride. We ride the steeds of Donn Tetscorach from the fairy-mounds. Though we are alive we are dead. Great are the signs: destruction of life, sating of ravens, feeding of crows, strife of slaughter, wetting of sword-edge, shields with broken bosses in hours after sundown. Lo, my son!" Then they went from him.

"I see that thou hast not detained the men," said Conaire.

"Indeed it is not because I failed to try," said Le Fri Flaith. He recited the last answer that they gave him.

Conaire and his retainers were not pleased thereat; and afterwards evil forebodings of terror were on them. "All my taboos have seized me tonight," said Conaire, "since those Three Reds were the fairy folk."

The three Reds went forward to the house and took their seats therein, and fastened their red steeds to the door of the house.

That is the Forefaring of the Three Reds in the Hostel of Da Derga.

Then, as Conaire was going to Da Derga's Hostel, a man with black, cropt hair, with one hand and one eye and one foot, overtook them. Rough cropt hair was upon him. Though a sackful of wild apples were flung on his crown, not an apple would fall to the ground, but each of them would stick on a hair. Though his snout were flung on a branch they would remain together. Long and thick as an outer yoke was each of his two shins. Each of his buttocks was the size of a cheese on a withe. A forked pole of iron, black-pointed, was in his hand. A swine, black-bristled, singed, was on his back, squealing continually, and a woman big-mouthed, huge, dark, ugly, hideous, was behind him. Though her snout were flung on a branch, the branch would support it. Her lower lip would reach her knee.

He started forward to meet Conaire, and made him welcome. "Welcome to thee, O master Conaire! Long hath thy coming hither been known."

"Who gives the welcome?" asked Conaire.

"Fer Caille here, with his black swine for thee to consume that thou be not fasting tonight, for 'tis thou art the best king that has come into the world!"

"What is thy wife's name?" said Conaire.

"Cichuil," he answered.

"Any other night," said Conaire, "that pleases you, I will come to you, but leave us alone tonight."

"Nay," said the churl, "for we will go to thee in the place wherein thou wilt be tonight, O fair little master Conaire!"

So the churl went towards the house, with his great, big-mouthed wife behind him, and his swine short-bristled, black, singed, squealing continually, on his back. That was one of Conaire's taboos, and that plunder should be taken in Ireland during his reign was another taboo of his.

Now plunder was taken by the sons of Donn Desa, and five hundred there were in the body of their marauders, besides what underlings were with them. This, too, was a taboo of Conaire's. There was a good warrior in the north country, "Wain Over Withered Sticks," this was his name. Why he was so called was because he used to go over his opponent even as a wain would go over withered sticks. Now plunder was taken by him, and there were five hundred in that body of marauders alone, besides underlings. There was besides a troop of still haughtier heroes, namely, the seven sons of Ailill and Medb of Connacht, each of whom was called "Mane." And each Mane had a nickname, to wit, Mane Fatherlike and Mane Motherlike, and Mane Gentle-pious, Mane Very-pious, Mane Unslow, and Mane Honeywords, Mane Grasp-them-all, and Mane the Talkative. Rapine was wrought by them. As to Mane Motherlike and Mane Unslow, there were fourteen score in the body of their marauders. Mane Fatherlike had three hundred and fifty. Mane Honeywords had five hundred. Mane Grasp-them-all had seven hundred. Mane the Talkative had seven hundred. Each of the others had five hundred in the body of his marauders. There was a valiant trio of the men of Cualu of Leinster, namely, the three Red Hounds of Cualu, called Cethach and Clothach and Conall. Now rapine was wrought by them, and twelve score were in the body of their marauders, and they had a troop of madmen. In Conaire's reign a third of the men of Ireland were marauders. He was of sufficient strength and power to drive them out of the land of Erin so as to transfer their marauding to Britain, but after this transfer they returned to their country.

When they had reached the shoulder of the sea, they met Ingcel the One-eyed and Eiccel and Tulchinne, three great-grandsons of Conmac of Britain, on the raging of the sea. A man ungentle, huge, fearful, uncouth was Ingcel. A single eye in his head, as broad as an oxhide, as black as a chafer, with three pupils therein. Thirteen hundred were in the body of his marauders. The marauders of the men of Erin were more numerous than they. The marauders of Erin were about to attack them on the sea. "Ye should not do this," said Ingcel; "do not violate fair play with us, for ye are more in number than we."

"Nought but a combat on equal terms shall befall thee," said the reavers of Erin.

"There is somewhat better for you," said Ingcel; "let us make peace since ye have been cast out of the land of Erin, and we have been cast out of the land of Scotland and Britain. Let us make an agreement between us. Come ye and wreak your rapine in my country, and I will go with you and wreak my rapine in your country."

They followed this counsel, and they gave pledges therefor on the one side and the other. These are the sureties that were given to Ingcel by the men of Erin, namely Fer Gair and Gabur (or Fer Le) and Fer Rogain, for the destruction that Ingcel should choose to cause in Ireland and for the destruction that the sons of Donn Desa should choose to cause in Scotland and Britain. A lot was cast upon them to see with which of them they should go first. It fell that they should go with Ingcel to his country. So they made for Britain, and there his father and mother and his seven brothers were slain, as we have said before. Thereafter they made for Scotland, and there they wrought destruction, and then they returned to Erin.

It was just at this time that Conaire son of Eterscel went towards the Hostel of Da Derga along the Road of Cualu. 'Tis then that the reavers came till they were on the sea off the coast of Breg over against Howth. Then said the reavers: "Strike the sails, and make one band of you on the sea that ye may not be sighted from land; and let some lightfoot be found from among you to go on shore to see if we could save our honor with Ingcel; that is, a destruction in exchange for the destruction he has given us."

"Who will go on shore to act as spy? Let some one go," said Ingcel, "who should have there three gifts, namely, gift of hearing, gift of far sight, and gift of judgment."

"I," said Mane Honeywords, "have the gift of hearing."

"And I," said Mane Unslow, "have the gift of far sight and of judgment."

" 'Tis well for you to go thus," said the reavers: "good is that plan."

Then nine men went till they were on the Hill of Howth, to discover what they might hear and see.

"Be still a while!" said Mane Honeywords.

"What is that?" asked Mane Unslow.

"The sound of a cavalcade under a king I hear."

"By the gift of far sight, I see," said his comrade.

"What seest thou there?"

"I see there," said he, "cavalcades splendid, lofty, beautiful, warlike, somewhat slender, wary, active, keen, whetted, vehement, a good course that shakes a great covering of land. They fare to many heights, with wondrous waters and estuaries."

"What are the waters and heights and estuaries that they traverse?"

"Easy to say: Indeoin, Cult, Cuilten, Mafat, Ammat, Iarmafat, Finne, Goiste, Guistine, gray spears over chariots, ivory-hilted swords on thighs, silvery shields above their elbows. Half-wheels and half horses. Garments of every color about them. Thereafter I see before them special horses, thrice fifty dark-gray steeds. Small-headed are they, red-nosed, pointed, broad-hoofed, big-nosed, red-chested, fat, easily-stopt, easily-yoked, battle-nimble, keen, whetted, vehement, with their thrice fifty bridles of red enamel upon them."

"I swear by what my tribe swears," said the man of the long sight, "these are the steeds of some good lord. This is my judgment thereof: it is Conaire son of Eterscel, with multitudes of the men of Erin around him, who is travelling the road."

Back then they went that they might tell the reavers. "This," they said, "is what we have heard and seen."

Of this host, then, there was a multitude, both on this side and on that, namely, thrice fifty boats, with five thousand in them, and ten hundred in every thousand. Then they hoisted the sails on the boats, and steered them thence to shore, till they landed on the Strand of Fuirbthe. Just at the time when the boats reached land, then was Mac Cecht striking fire in Da Derga's Hostel. At the sound of the spark the thrice fifty boats were hurled out, so that they were on the shoulders of the sea.

"Be silent a while!" said Ingcel. "Liken thou that, O Fer Rogain."

"I know not," answered Fer Rogain, "unless it be Luchdonn the satirist in Emain Macha, who makes this hand-smiting when his food is taken from him perforce: or the scream of Luchdonn in Tara Luachra: or Mac Cecht's striking a spark, when he kindles a fire before a king of Erin where he sleeps. Every spark and every shower which his fire would let fall on the floor would broil a hundred calves and two half-pigs."

"May God not bring Conaire there tonight!" said Donn Desa's sons, Conaire's fosterbrothers. "Sad that he is under the hurt of foes!"

"It seems to me," said Ingcel, "it should be no sadder for me than the destruction I gave you. It is a feast for me that Conaire should chance to come there."

Their fleet was steered to land. The noise that the thrice fifty vessels made in running ashore shook Da Derga's Hostel so that no spear nor shield remained on its rack therein, but the weapons uttered a cry and fell all on the floor of the house.

"Liken thou that, O Conaire," said every one; "what is this noise?"

"I know nothing like it unless it be the earth that has broken, or the Leviathan that surrounds the globe and strikes with its tail to overturn the world, or the ships of the sons of Donn Desa that have reached the shore. Alas, that it should not be they who are here! Beloved fosterbrothers of our own were they! Dear were the champions. We should not have feared them tonight." Then came Conaire out upon the green of the Hostel.

When Mac Cecht heard the tumultuous noise, it seemed to him that warriors had attacked his people. Thereat he leapt into his armor to help them. Vast as the thunder-feat of three hundred did they deem his act in leaping to his weapons. Thereof there was no profit.

Now in the bow of the ship wherein were Donn Desa's sons was the champion, greatly-accoutred, wrathful, the lion hard and awful, Ingcel the One-eyed, great-grandson of Conmac. Wide as an oxhide was the single eye protruding from his forehead, with seven pupils therein, which were black as a chafer. Each of his knees as big as a stripper's cauldron; each of his two fists was the size of a reaping-basket; his buttocks as big as a cheese on a withe; each of his shins as long as an outer yoke.

So after that, the thrice fifty boats, and those five thousands—with ten hundred in every thousand—landed on the Strand of Fuirbthe.

Then Conaire with his people entered the Hostel, and each took his seat within, both taboo and non-taboo. And the three Reds took their seats, and Fer Caille with his swine took his seat. Thereafter Da Derga came to them, with thrice fifty warriors, each of them having a long head of hair to the hollow of his poll, and a short cloak to their buttocks. Speckled-green drawers they wore, and in their hands were thrice fifty great clubs of thorn with bands of iron.

"Welcome, O master Conaire!" said he. "Though the bulk of the men of Erin were to come with thee, they themselves would have a welcome."

When they were there they saw a lone woman coming to the door of the Hostel, after sunset, and seeking to be let in. As long as a weaver's beam was each of her two shins, and they were as dark as the back of a stag-beetle. A greyish, woolly mantle she wore. Her lower hair reached as far as her knee. Her lips were on one side of her head. She came and put one of her shoulders against the doorpost of the house, casting the evil eye on the king and the youths who surrounded him in the Hostel. He himself addressed her from within.

"Well, O woman," said Conaire, "if thou art a soothsayer, what fortune seest thou for us?"

"Truly I see for thee," she answered, "that neither fell nor flesh of thine shall escape from the place into which thou hast come, save what birds will bear away in their claws."

"It was not thy omen we foreboded, O woman," said he: "it is not thou that always augurs for us. What is thy name, O woman?"

"Cailb," she answered.

"That is not much of a name," said Conaire.

"Lo, many are my names besides."

"What are they?" asked Conaire.

"Easy to say," quoth she. "Samon, Sinand, etc." On one foot, and holding up one hand, and breathing one breath she sang all that to them from the door of the house.

"I swear by the gods whom I adore," said Conaire, "that I will call thee by none of these names whether I shall be here a long or a short time. What dost thou desire?"

"That which thou, too, desirest," she answered.

"'Tis a taboo of mine," said Conaire, "to admit the company of one woman after sunset."

"Though it be a taboo," she replied, "I will not go until my guesting come at once this very night."

"Tell her," said Conaire, "that an ox and a bacon-pig shall be taken out to her, and my leavings, provided that she stays tonight in some other place."

"If in sooth," she said, "it has befallen that the king has not room in his house for the meal and bed of a lone woman, they will be got from some one else possessing generosity—if the hospitality of the prince in the Hostel has departed."

"Savage is the answer!" said Conaire. "Let her in, though it is a taboo of mine."

Great loathing they felt after that from the woman's converse and ill-foreboding; but they knew not the cause thereof.

The reavers afterwards landed, and went on till they were at Lecca Cinn Slebe, on the way to Da Derga's Hostel. Ever open was the *Bruden* (Hostel). . . .

Great was the fire which was kindled by Conaire every night; that is, a *torc caille* (Boar of the Wood). Seven outlets it had. When a log was taken out of its side every flame that used to come forth at each outlet was as big as the blaze of a burning oratory. There were seventeen of Conaire's chariots at every door of the house, and by the robbers from the vessels, who were looking on, that great light was clearly seen through the wheels of the chariots.

"Canst thou say, O Fer Rogain," said Ingcel, "what that great light yonder resembles?"

"I cannot liken it to anything," answered Fer Rogain, "unless it be the fire of a king. May God not bring that man here tonight! 'Tis a pity to destroy him!"

"What then deemest thou," said Ingcel, "of that man's reign in the land of Erin?"

"Good is his reign," replied Fer Rogain. "Since he assumed the kingship, no cloud has veiled the sun for the space of a day from the middle of spring to the middle of autumn. And not a dewdrop has fallen from grass till midday, and wind would not touch a cow's tail until noon. And in his reign, from year's end to year's end, no wolf has attacked anything save one bullcalf of each byre; and to maintain this rule there are seven wolves in hostageship at the sidewall in his house, and behind this a further security, that is, Maclocc, and 'tis he that pleads for them at Conaire's house. In Conaire's reign are the three crowns on Erin, namely, a crown of corn ears, and a crown of flowers, and a crown of oak mast. In his reign, too, each man deems the other's voice as melodious as the strings of lutes, because of the excellence of the law and the peace and the good-will prevailing throughout Erin. May God not bring that man there tonight! 'Tis sad to destroy him. 'Tis 'a branch through its blossom.' 'Tis 'a swine that falls before mast.' 'Tis 'an infant in age.' Sad is the shortness of his life!"

"It was my good luck," said Ingcel, "that he should be there, and there should be one destruction for another. His destruction is not more grievous to me than my father and my mother and my seven brothers, and the king of my country, whom I gave up to you before coming on the exchange of the rapine."

"'Tis true, 'tis true!" said the evildoers who were along with the British marauders.

The robbers made a start from the Strand of Fuirbthe, and brought a stone for each man to make a cairn; for this was the distinction which at first the Fians made between a "Destruction" and a "Rout." A pillar-stone they used to plant when there would be a Rout. A cairn, however, they used to make when there would be a Destruction. At this time, then, they made a cairn, for it was a Destruction. Far from the house was this, that they might not be heard or seen therefrom.

For two causes they built their cairn: first, since this was a custom in marauding; and, secondly, that they might find out their losses at the Hostel. Every one that would come safe from it would take his stone from the cairn: thus the stones of those that were slain would be left, and thence they would know their losses. And this is what men skilled in story recount, that for every stone in Carn Lecca there was one of the reavers killed at the Hostel. From that Carn Lecca in O'Kelly's country is named.

A "boar of a fire" was kindled by the sons of Donn Desa to give warning to Conaire. So that was the first warning-beacon that was made in Erin, and from it to this day every warning-beacon is kindled. This is what others recount: that it was on the eve of Samain (Allsaints) the destruction of the Hostel was wrought, and that from that beacon the beacon of Samain followed, and stones are placed in the Samain-fire.

Then the reavers held a council at the place where they had put the cairn.

"Well, then," said Ingcel to the guides, "what is nearest to us here?"

"Easy to say: the Hostel of Da Derga, chief-hospitaller of Erin."

"Good men indeed," said Ingcel, "were likely to seek their fellows at that Hostel tonight."

This, then, was the counsel of the reavers, to send one of them to see how things were there.

"Who will go there to espy the house?" asked every one.

"Who should go," said Ingcel, "but I, for 'tis I that am entitled to dues."

Ingcel went to reconnoiter the Hostel with one of the seven pupils of the single eye which stood out of his forehead, to fit his eye into the house in order to destroy the king and the warriors who were around him therein. And Ingcel saw them through the wheels of the chariots. Then Ingcel was perceived from the house. He hurried from it after being perceived. He went till he reached the reavers in the place wherein they were. Each circle of them was set around another to hear the tidings, the chiefs of the reavers being in the very center of the circles. There were Fer Ger and Fer Gel and Fer Rogel and Fer Rogain and Lomna the Buffoon, and Ingcel the One-eyed—six in the center of the circles. And Fer Rogain questioned Ingcel.

"How is it, O Ingcel?" asks Fer Rogain.

"However it be," answered Ingcel, "royal is the behavior, hostful is the tumult: kingly is the noise thereof. Whether a king be there or not, I will take the house for what I have a right to. Thence my return for your depredations comes."

"We have left it in thy hand, O Ingcel!" said Conaire's foster-brothers. "But we should not wreak the destruction till we know who may be present in the Hostel."

"Question: hast thou examined the house well, O Ingcel?" asked Fer Rogain.

"My eye cast a rapid glance around it, and I will accept it for my dues as it stands."

"Thou mayest well accept it, O Ingcel," said Fer Rogain: "the foster-father of us all is there, Erin's overking, Conaire son of Eterscel. Question: what sawest thou in the champion's high seat of the house, facing the king, on the opposite side?"

The Room of Cormac Conlonges [1]

"I saw there," said Ingcel, "a man of noble countenance, large, with a clear and sparkling eye, an even set of teeth, a face narrow below, broad above; fair, flaxen, golden hair upon him, and a proper fillet around it; a brooch of silver in his mantle, and in his hand a gold-hilted sword. A shield with five golden circles upon it; a five-barbed javelin in his hand. A visage just, fair, ruddy he has; he is also beardless. Modest-minded is that man!"

"And after that, whom sawest thou there?" said Fer Rogain.

The Room of Cormac's Nine Comrades

"There," said Ingcel, "I saw three men to the west of Cormac, and three to the east of him, and three in front of the same man. Thou wouldst deem that the nine of them had one mother and

---

[1] Cormac Conlonges figures prominently in the Ulster cycle (p. 127) as the son of the famous king Conchobar of Ulster. Other characters from the Ulster cycle appear or are referred to later in the story.

one father. They are of the same age, equally goodly, equally beautiful, all alike. Greenish mantles they all wore. Thin rods of gold in their mantles. Curved shields of bronze they bear. Ribbed javelins above them. An ivory-hilted sword in the hand of each. An unique feat they have, to wit, each of them takes his sword's point between his two fingers, and they twirl the swords round their fingers, and the swords afterwards extend themselves by themselves. Liken thou that, O Fer Rogain," said Ingcel.

"Easy," said Fer Rogain, "for me to liken them. It is Conchobar's son Cormac Conlonges, the best hero behind a shield in the land of Erin. Of modest mind is that boy! Evil is what he dreads tonight. He is a champion of valor for feats of arms: he is an hospitaller for householding. These are the nine who surround him, the three Dungusses, and the three Doelgusses, and the three Dangusses, the nine comrades of Cormac Conlonges son of Conchobar. They have never slain men on account of their misery, and they never spared them on account of their prosperity. Good is the hero who is among them, even Cormac Conlonges. I swear what my tribe swears, nine times ten will fall by Cormac in his first onset, and nine times ten will fall by his people, besides a man for each of their weapons, and a man for each of themselves. And Cormac will share prowess with any man before the Hostel, and he will boast of victory over a king or crown-prince or noble of the reavers; and he himself will chance to escape, though all his people be wounded.

.   .   .   .

The Room of the Picts

"And whom sawest thou next?" said Fer Rogain.

"I saw another room there, with a huge trio in it: three brown, big men: three round heads of hair on them, even, equally long at nape and forehead. Three short black cowls about them reaching to their elbows: long hoods were on the cowls. Three black, huge swords they had, and three black shields they bore, with three dark broad-green javelins above them. Thick as the spit of a cauldron was the shaft of each. Liken thou that, O Fer Rogain!"

"Hard it is for me to find their like. I know not at all that trio, unless it be the trio of Pictland, who went into exile from their country, and are now in Conaire's household. These are their names: Dublonges son of Trebuat, and Trebuat son of O'Lonsce, and Curnach son of O'Faich. The three who are best in Pictland at taking arms are that trio. Nine times ten will fall at their hands in their first encounter, and a man will fall for each of their weapons, besides one for each of themselves. And they will share prowess with every trio in the Hostel. They will boast a victory over a king or a chief of the robbers; and they will afterwards escape though wounded. Woe to him who shall wreak the destruction, though it be only on account of those three! . . . And whom sawest thou there afterwards?"

The Room of the Pipers

"There," said Ingcel, "I beheld a room with nine men in it. Hair fair and yellow was on them: they all are equally handsome. Mantles speckled with color they wore, and above them were nine bagpipes, four-tuned, ornamented.   Enough light in the palace were the ornaments on those four-tuned pipes. Liken thou them, O Fer Rogain."

"Easy for me to liken them," said Fer Rogain.   "Those are the nine pipers that came to Conaire out of the fairy-mound of Breg, because of the noble tales about him. These are their names: Bind, Robind, Riarbind, Sibe, Dibe, Deichrind, Umall, Cumal, Ciallglind. They are the best pipers in the world. Nine times nine will fall before them, and a man for each of their weapons, and a man for each of themselves. And each of them will boast a victory over a king or a chief of the robbers. And they will escape from the destruction; for a conflict with them will be a conflict with a shadow. They will slay, but they will not be slain, for they are out of a fairy-mound. Woe to him who shall wreak the destruction, though it be only because of those nine! . . . And after that, whom sawest thou there?" said Fer Rogain.

The Room of Conaire's Majordomo

"There," said Ingcel, "I saw a room with one man in it. Rough cropt hair upon him. Though a sack of crab-apples should be flung on his head, not one of them would fall on the floor, but every apple would stick on his hair. His fleecy mantle was over him in the house. Every quarrel therein about seat or bed comes to his decision. Should a needle drop in the house, its fall would be heard when he speaks. Above him is a huge black tree, like a millshaft, with its paddles and its cap and its spike. Liken thou him, O Fer Rogain!"

"Easy for me is this. Tuidle of Ulster is he, the steward of Conaire's household. 'Tis needful to hearken to the decision of that man, the man that rules seat and bed and food for each. 'Tis his household staff that is above him. That man will fight with you. I swear what my tribe swears, the dead at the destruction slain by him will be more numerous than the living. Thrice his number will fall by him, and he himself will fall there. Woe to him who shall wreak the destruction! . . . What sawest thou there after that?" said Fer Rogain.

The Room of Mac Cecht, Conaire's Champion

"There I beheld another room with a trio in it, three half-furious nobles: the biggest of them in the middle, very noisy, rock-bodied, angry, smiting, dealing strong blows, who beats nine hundred in battle-conflict. A wooden shield, dark, covered with iron, he bears, with a hard rim, a shield whereon would fit the proper litter of four troops of ten weaklings. A boss thereon, the depth of a cauldron, fit to cook four oxen, a hollow maw, a great boiling, with four swine in its mid-maw. At his two smooth sides are two five-thwarted boats fit for three parties of ten in each of his two strong fleets. A spear he has, blue-red, hand-fitting, on its strong shaft. It stretches along the wall on the roof and rests on the ground. An iron point upon it, dark-red, dripping. Four amply-measured feet between the two points of its edge. Thirty amply-measured feet in his deadly-striking sword from dark point to iron hilt. It sends forth fiery sparks which illumine the Mid-court House from roof to ground. 'Tis an overpowering sight that I saw. A swoon from horror almost befell me while staring at those three. There is nothing stranger.

"Two bald men were there by the man with hair. Two lakes by a mountain, two hides by a tree. Two boats near them full of thorns of a white thorntree on a circular board. And there seemed to me something like a slender stream of water on which the sun is shining, and its trickle down from it, and a hide arranged behind it, and a palace-housepost shaped like a great lance above it. A good weight of a plough-yoke is the shaft that is therein. Liken thou that, O Fer Rogain!"

"Easy to liken him!" answered Fer Rogain. "That is Mac Cecht son of Snaide Teichid; the battle-soldier of Conaire son of Eterscel. Good is the hero Mac Cecht! Supine he was in his room, in his sleep, when thou beheldest him. The two bald men which thou sawest by the man with hair, these are his two knees by his head. The two lakes by the mountain which thou sawest, these are his two eyes by his nose. The two hides by a tree which thou sawest, these are his two ears by his head. The two five-thwarted boats on a circular board, which thou sawest, these are his two sandals on his shield. The slender stream of water which thou sawest, whereon the sun shines, and its trickle down from it, this is the flickering of his sword. The hide which thou sawest arranged behind him, that is his sword's scabbard. The palace-housepost which thou sawest, that is his lance; and he brandishes this spear till its two ends meet, and he hurls a wilful cast of it when he pleases. Good is the hero Mac Cecht!

"Six hundred will fall by him in his first encounter, and a man for each of his weapons, besides a man for himself. And he will share prowess with every one in the Hostel, and he will boast of triumph over a king or chief of the robbers in front of the Hostel. He will chance to escape though wounded. And when he shall come upon you out of the house, as numerous as hailstones, and grass on a green, and stars of heaven will be your cloven heads and skulls, and the clots of your brains, your bones and the heaps of your bowels, crushed by him and scattered throughout the ridges."

Then with trembling and terror of Mac Cecht the robbers fled over three ridges.

. . . .

"And whom sawest thou next, O Ingcel?" said Fer Rogain.

The Room of the Fomorians

"I beheld there a room with a trio in it, to wit, a trio horrible, unheard-of, a triad of champions. . . .

"Liken thou that, O Fer Rogain." said Ingcel.

"'Tis hard for me to liken that trio. Neither of the men of Erin nor of the men of the world do I know it, unless it be the trio that Mac Cecht brought out of the land of the Fomorians by dint of combats. Not one of the Fomorians was found to fight him, so he brought away those three, and they are in Conaire's house as sureties that, while Conaire is reigning, the Fomorians destroy neither corn nor milk in Erin beyond their fair tribute. Well may their aspect be loathly! Three rows of teeth in their heads from one ear to the other. An ox with a bacon-pig, this is the ration of each of them, and that ration which they put into their mouths is visible till it comes down past their navels. Bodies of bone without a joint in them all those three have. I swear what my tribe swears, more will be killed by them at the destruction than those they leave alive. Six hundred warriors will fall by them in their first conflict, and a man for each of their weapons, and one for each of the three themselves. And they will boast a triumph over a king or chief of the robbers. It will not be more than with a bite or a blow or a kick that each of those men will kill, for no arms are allowed them in the house, since they are in 'hostageship at the wall' lest they do a misdeed therein. I swear what my tribe swears, if they had armor on them, they would slay us all but a third. Woe to him that shall wreak the destruction, because it is not a combat against sluggards." . . . And whom sawest thou there after that?" said Fer Rogain.

The Room of Munremur mac Gerrcind and Birderg son of Ruan and Mal son of Telband

"I beheld a room there, with a trio in it," said Ingcel. "Three brown, big men, with three brown heads of short hair. Thick ankles they had. As thick as a man's waist was each of their limbs. Three brown and curled masses of hair upon them, with a thick head; three cloaks, red and speckled, they wore; three black shields with clasps of gold, and three five-barbed javelins; and each had in hand an ivory-hilted sword. This is the feat they perform with their swords: they throw them high up, and they throw the scabbards after them, and the swords, before reaching the ground, place themselves in the scabbards. Then they throw the scabbards first, and the swords after them, and the scabbards meet the swords and place themselves round them before they reach the ground. Liken thou that, O Fer Rogain!"

"Easy for me to liken them! Mal son of Telband, and Munremur mac Gerrcind, and Birderg son of Ruan. Three crownprinces, three champions of valor, three heroes the best behind weapons in Erin! A hundred heroes will fall by them in their first conflict, and they will share prowess with every man in the Hostel, and they will boast of the victory over a king or chief of the robbers, and afterwards they will chance to escape. The destruction should not be wrought even because of those three."

. . . .

"And after that whom sawest thou?" said Fer Rogain.

The Room of Conaire Himself

"There I beheld a room, more beautifully decorated than the other rooms of the house. A silvery curtain around it, and there were ornaments in the room. I beheld a trio in it. The outer two of them were, both of them, fair, with their hair and eyelashes; and they are as bright as snow. A very lovely blush on the cheek of each of the twain. A tender lad in the midst between them. The ardor and energy of a king has he, and the counsel of a sage. The mantle I saw around him is even as the mist of Mayday. Diverse are the hue and semblance each moment shewn upon it. Lovelier is each hue than the other. In front of him in the mantle I beheld a wheel of gold which reached from his chin to his navel. The color of his hair was like the sheen of smelted gold. Of all the world's forms that I ever beheld, this is the most beautiful. I saw his golden-hilted sword down beside him. A forearm's length of the sword was outside the scabbard. That part was so bright that a man down in the front of the house could see a fleshworm by the shadow of the sword! Sweeter is the melodious sounding of the sword than the melodious sound of the golden pipes that accompany music in the palace.

. . . .

"Now the young warrior was asleep, with his feet in the lap of one of the two men and his head in the lap of the other."

. . . .

"Liken thou him, O Fer Rogain," said Ingcel.

"Easy for me to liken him," said Fer Rogain. "No 'conflict without a king' this. He is the most splendid and noble and beautiful and mighty king that has come into the whole world. He is the mildest and gentlest and most perfect king that has come to it, that is, Conaire son of Eterscel. 'Tis he that is high-king of all Erin. There is no defect in that man, whether in form or shape or vesture: whether in size or fitness or proportion, whether in eye or hair or brightness, whether in wisdom or skill or eloquence, whether in weapon or dress or appearance, whether in splendor or abundance or dignity, whether in knowledge or valor or kindred.

"Great is the tenderness of the sleepy, loveable man till he has chanced on a deed of valor; but if his fury and his courage be awakened when the champions of Erin and Alba are with him in the house, the destruction will not be wrought so long as he is therein. Six hundred will fall by Conaire before he shall attain his arms, and seven hundred will fall by him in his first conflict after attaining his arms. I swear what my tribe swears, unless drink be taken from him, though there be no one else in the house but he alone, he would hold the Hostel until help would reach it which men would prepare for him from the Wave of Clidna and the Wave of Assaroe while ye are at the Hostel.

"Nine doors there are to the house, and at each door a hundred warriors will fall by his hand. And when every one in the house has ceased to ply his weapon, 'tis then he will resort to a deed of arms. And if he chance to come upon you out of the house, as numerous as hailstones and grass on a green will be your halves of heads and your cloven skulls and your bones under the edge of his sword.

"'Tis my opinion that he will not chance to get out of the house. Dear to him are the two that are with him in the room, his two fosterers, Dris and Snithe. Thrice fifty warriors will fall before each of them in front of the Hostel, and not farther than a foot from him, on this side and that, will they fall," said Fer Rogain.

"Woe to him who shall wreak the destruction, were it only because of that pair and the prince that is between them, the high-king of Erin, Conaire son of Eterscel! Sad were the quenching of that reign!" said Lomna the Buffoon son of Donn Desa. . . . "And after that, whom sawest thou there?" said Fer Rogain.

The Room of Tulchinne the Juggler

"There," said Ingcel, "I beheld a great champion, in front of the same room, on the floor of the house. The shame of baldness is on him. White as mountain cotton-grass is each hair that grows through his head. Earrings of gold around his ears. A mantle speckled, colored, he wore. Nine swords in his hand, and nine silvern shields, and nine apples of gold. He throws each of them upwards, and none of them falls on the ground, and there is only one of them on his palm; each of them rising and falling past another is like the movement to and fro of bees on a day of beauty. When he was swiftest, I beheld him at the feat, and as I looked, the company uttered a cry about him and his implements were all on the house-floor. Then the prince who is in the house said to the juggler: 'We have been together since thou wast a little boy, and till tonight thy juggling never failed thee.'

"'Alas, alas, fair master Conaire, good cause have I. A keen, angry eye looked at me: a man with the third of a pupil which sees the going of the nine bands. Not much to him is that keen, wrathful sight! Battles are fought with it,' said he. 'It should be known till doomsday that there is evil in front of the Hostel.'"

.   .   .   .

"And after that whom sawest thou?" said Fer Rogain.

The Room of Sencha and Dubtach and Goïbniu Son of Lurgnech

"I beheld the room that is next," said Ingcel. "Three chief champions, in their first greyness, are therein. As thick as a man's waist is each of their limbs. They have three black swords, each as long as a weaver's beam. These swords would split a hair on water. A great lance in the hand of the midmost man, with fifty rivets through it. The shaft therein is a good load for the yoke of a plough team. The midmost man brandishes that lance so that its edge studs hardly stay therein, and he strikes the shaft thrice against his palm. There is a great boiler in front of them, as big as a calf's cauldron, wherein is a black and horrible liquid, and he plunges the lance into that black fluid. If its quenching be delayed, it flames on its shaft and then thou wouldst suppose that there is a fiery dragon in the top of the house. Liken thou that, O Fer Rogain!"

"Easy to say. Three heroes who are best at grasping weapons in Erin, namely, Sencha the beautiful son of Ailill, and Dubtach Chafertongue of Ulster, and Goibniu son of Lurgnech. And the spear Luin of Celtchar mac Uthecair, which was found in the battle of Mag Tured, this is in the hand of Dubtach Chafertongue of Ulster. That feat is usual for it when it is ripe to pour forth a foeman's blood. A cauldron full of poison is needed to quench it when a deed of manslaying is expected. Unless this come to the lance, it flames on its haft and will go through its bearer or the master of the palace wherein it is. It will kill a man at every blow, when it is at its work, from one hour to another, even though it may not reach him. It will kill nine men at every cast, and one of the nine will be a king or crown-prince or chieftain of the robbers.

"I swear what my tribe swears, there will be a multitude unto whom tonight the Luin of Celtchar will deal drinks of death in front of the Hostel. I swear what my tribe swears, that in their first encounter three hundred will fall by those three heroes, and they will share prowess with every three in the Hostel tonight. And they will boast of victory over a king or chief of the robbers, and the three will chance to escape. And after that, whom sawest thou there?" said Fer Rogain.

The Room of the Three Manx Giants

"There I beheld a room with a trio in it," said Ingcel. "Three men mighty, manly, overbearing, which see no one abiding at their three hideous, crooked aspects. A fearful view because of the terror of them. A dress of rough hair covers them; their savage eyes look out through a thatch of cows' hair, without garments, enwrapping them down to the heels. With three manes, equine, awful, majestic, down to their sides. Fierce heroes who wield against foemen hard-smiting swords. A blow they give with three iron flails having seven chains triple-twisted, three-edged, with seven iron knobs at the end of every chain: each of them as heavy as an ingot of ten smeltings. Three big brown men. Dark equine back-manes on them, which reach their two heels. Two good thirds of an oxhide in the girdle round each one's waist, and each quadrangular clasp that closes it as thick as a man's thigh. The raiment that is round them is the hairy coat that grows on them. Tresses of their back-manes were outspread, and a long staff of iron, as long and thick as an outer yoke, was in each man's hand, and an iron chain out of the end of every club, and at the end of every chain an iron pestle as long and thick as a middle yoke. They stand in their sadness in the house, and enough is the horror of their aspect. There is no one in the house that would not be avoiding them. Liken thou that, O Fer Rogain!"

Fer Rogain was silent. "Hard for me to liken them. I know none such of the world's men unless they be that trio of giants to whom Cu Chulainn gave quarter at the beleaguerment of the Men of Falga (the Isle of Man), and when they were getting quarter they killed fifty warriors. But Cu Chulainn would not let them be slain, because of their wondrousness. These are the names of the three: Srubdaire son of Dordbruige, and Conchenn of Cenn Maige, and Fiad Sceme son of Scipe. Conaire bought them from Cu Chulainn; so they are along with him. Three hundred will fall by them in their first encounter, and they will surpass in prowess every three in the Hostel; and if they come forth upon you, the fragments of you will be fit to go through the sieve of a cornkiln, from the way in which they will destroy you with the flails of iron. Woe to him that shall wreak the destruction, though it were only on account of those three! And after that, whom sawest thou there?" said Fer Rogain.

The Room of Da Derga

"There I beheld another room," said Ingcel, "with one man therein and in front of him two servants with two manes upon them, one of the two dark, the other fair. Red hair on the warrior, and red eyebrows. Two ruddy cheeks he had, and an eye very blue and beautiful. He wore a green cloak and a shirt with a white hood and a red insertion. In his hand was a sword with a hilt of ivory, and he supplied attendants of every room in the house with ale and food, and he quick-footed in serving the whole host. Liken thou that, O Fer Rogain!"

"I know those men. The chief one is Da Derga. 'Tis by him that the Hostel was built, and since it was built its doors have never been shut save on the side to which the wind comes—the opening is closed against it—and since he began house-keeping his cauldron was never taken from the fire, but it has been boiling food for the men of Erin. The pair before him, those two youths, are his fosterlings, two sons of the king of Leinster, namely Muredach and Cairbre. Three tens will fall by that trio in front of their house and they will boast of victory over a king or a chief of the robbers. After this they will chance to escape from it. . . . And after that whom sawest thou there?" said Fer Rogain.

The Room of the Three Champions from the Fairy-Mounds

"There I beheld a room with a trio in it," said Ingcel. "Three red mantles they wore, and three red shirts, and three red heads of hair were on them. Red were they all even together with their teeth. Three red shields above them. Three red spears in their hands. Three red horses in their bridles in front of the Hostel. Liken thou that, O Fer Rogain!"

"Easily done. Three champions who wrought falsehood in the fairy-mounds. This is the punishment inflicted upon them by the king of the fairy-mounds, to be destroyed thrice by the king of Tara. Conaire son of Eterscel is the last king by whom they are destroyed. Those men will escape from you. To fulfil their own destruction, they have come. But they will not be slain, nor will they slay anyone."

.   .   .   .

"Rise up, then, ye champions!" said Ingcel, "and get you on to the Hostel!"

With that the marauders marched to the Hostel, and made a murmur about it.

"Silence a while!" said Conaire, "what is that?"

"Champions at the house," said Conall Cernach of Ulster.

"There are warriors for them here," answered Conaire.

"They will be needed tonight," Conall Cernach rejoined.

Then went Lomna the Buffoon before the host of robbers into the Hostel. The doorkeepers struck off his head. Then the head was thrice flung into the Hostel, and thrice cast out of it.

Then Conaire himself sallied out of the Hostel together with some of his people, and they fought with the host of robbers, and six hundred fell by Conaire before he could get to his arms. Then the Hostel was thrice set on fire, and thrice put out by the other side: and it was found that the destruction would never have been wrought had not the use of his weapons been taken from Conaire. Thereafter Conaire went to seek his arms, and he donned his battledress, and fell to plying his weapons on the marauders, together with the band that he had. Then, after getting his arms, six hundred fell by him in his first encounter.

After this the reavers were routed. "I have told you," said Fer Rogain son of Donn Desa, "that if the champions of the men of Erin and Alba attack Conaire at the house, the destruction will not be wrought unless Conaire's fury and valor be quelled."

"Short will his time be," said the wizards along with the robbers. This was the quelling they brought: a great thirst that seized him.

Thereafter Conaire entered the house, and asked for a drink. "A drink to me, O master Mac Cecht!" says Conaire.

Says Mac Cecht: "This is not the office that I have fulfilled for thee, to give thee a drink. There are waiters and cupbearers who bring drink to thee. The command I have hitherto had from thee is to protect thee when the champions of the men of Erin and Alba may be attacking thee around the Hostel. Thou wilt go safe from them, and no spear shall enter thy body. Ask a drink of thy waiters and thy cupbearers."

Then Conaire asked a drink of his waiters and his cupbearers who were in the house.

"In the first place there is none," they said; "all the liquids that had been in the house have been spilt on the fires." The cupbearers found no drink for him in the River Dodder, and the Dodder had flowed through the house.

Then Conaire again asked for a drink. "A drink to me, O fosterer, O Mac Cecht! 'Tis equal to me what death I shall die, for anyhow I shall perish." Then Mac Cecht gave a choice to the champions of valor of the men of Erin who were in the house, whether they cared to protect the king or to seek a drink for him. Conall Cernach answered this in the house—and cruel he deemed the choice offered, and afterwards he had always a feud with Mac Cecht.—"Leave the defence of the king to us," says Conall, "and go thou to seek the drink, for of thee it is demanded."

So then Mac Cecht fared forth to seek the drink, and he took Conaire's son, Le Fri Flaith, under his armpit, and Conaire's golden cup, in which an ox with a bacon-pig would be boiled; and he bore his shield and his two spears and his sword, and he carried the cauldron-spit, a spit of iron.

He burst forth upon the marauders, and in front of the Hostel he dealt nine blows with the iron spit, and at every blow nine robbers fell. Then he made a sloping feat of the shield and an edge-feat of the sword about his head, and he delivered a hostile attack upon them. Six hundred fell in his first encounter, and after cutting down hundreds he went through the band outside.

The doings of the folk of the Hostel, this is what is here examined, presently.

.   .   .   .

Howbeit then, but it is long to relate, 'tis weariness of mind, 'tis confusion of the senses, 'tis tediousness to hearers, 'tis superfluity of narration to go over the same things twice. But the folk of the Hostel came forth in order, and fought their combats with the robbers, and fell by them, as Fer Rogain and Lomna the Buffoon had said to Ingcel, to wit, that the folk of every room would sally forth still and deliver their combat, and after that escape. So that none were left in the Hostel in Conaire's company save Conall and Sencha and Dubtach.

Now from the vehement ardor and the greatness of the contest which Conaire had fought, his great drouth of thirst attacked him, and he perished of a consuming fever, for he got not his drink. So when the king died those three sallied out of the Hostel, and delivered a cunning deed of reaving on the marauders, and fared forth from the Hostel, wounded, broken and maimed.

As for Mac Cecht, however, he went his way till he reached the Well of Casair [the source of the River Dodder], which was near him in the district of Cualu; but of water he found not therein the full of his cup, that is, Conaire's golden cup which he had brought in his hand. Before morning he had gone round the chief rivers of Erin; to wit, Bush, Boyne, Bann, Barrow, Neim, Luae, Laigdae, Shannon, Suir, Sligo, Samair, Find, Ruirthech, Slaney, and in them he found not the full of his cup of water.

Then before morning he had travelled to the chief lakes of Erin; to wit, Loch Derg, Loch Luimnig, Loch Foyle, Loch Mask, Loch Corrib, Loch Laig, Loch Cuan, Loch Neagh, Morloch, and of water he found not therein the full of his cup.

He went his way till he reached Uaran Garad on Mag Ai. It could not hide itself from him: so he brought thereout the full of his cup, and the boy fell under his covering. After this he went on and reached Da Derga's Hostel before morning.

When Mac Cecht went across the third ridge towards the house, there were two men striking off Conaire's head. Then Mac Cecht struck off the head of one of the two men who had beheaded Conaire. The other man then was fleeing with the king's head. A pillar-stone chanced to be under Mac Cecht's feet on the floor of the Hostel. He hurled it at the man who had Conaire's head and drove it through his spine, so that his back broke. After this Mac Cecht beheaded him. Mac Cecht then spilt the cup of water into Conaire's gullet and neck. Then said Conaire's head, after the water had been put into its neck and gullet:

> A good man Mac Cecht! an excellent man Mac Cecht!
> A good warrior without, good within;
> He gives a drink he saves a king, he doth a noble deed;
> Well he ended the champions I found;
> He sent a flagstone on the warriors;
> Well he hewed by the door of the Hostel. . . .
> So that it is at one hip that he is cut.
> Good should I be to far-renowned Mac Cecht
> If I were alive. A good man!

After this Mac Cecht followed the routed foe.

.   .   .   .

Now when Mac Cecht was lying wounded on the battlefield, at the end of the third day, he saw a woman passing by. "Come hither, O woman!" said Mac Cecht.

"I dare not go thus," said the woman, "for horror and fear of thee."

"There was a time, O woman, when people had horror and fear of me; but now thou shouldst fear nothing. I accept thee on the truth of my honor and my safeguard." Then the woman went to him.

"I know not," said he, "whether it is a fly, or a gnat, or an ant that nips me in the wound." It really was a hairy wolf that was there, as far as its two shoulders in the wound! The woman seized it by the tail, dragged it out of the wound, and it took the full of its jaws out of him. "Truly," said the woman, "this is 'an ant of ancient land.' "

Said Mac Cecht, "I swear what my people swears, I deemed it no bigger than a fly, or a gnat, or an ant." And Mac Cecht took the wolf by the throat, and struck it a blow on the forehead, and killed it with a single blow.

Then Le Fri Flaith son of Conaire died under Mac Cecht's armpit, for the warrior's heat and sweat had dissolved him.

Thereafter Mac Cecht, having cleansed the slaughter, at the end of the third day, set forth, and he dragged Conaire with him on his back, and buried him at Tara, as some say. Then Mac Cecht departed into Connacht, to his own country, that he might work his cure in Mag Brengair. Wherefore the name clave to the plain from Mac Cecht's misery, that is, Mag Brengair.

Now Conall Cernach escaped from the Hostel, and thrice fifty spears had gone through the arm which upheld his shield. He fared forth till he reached his father's house, with half his shield in his hand, and his sword, and the fragments of his two spears. Then he found his father before the enclosure surrounding his stronghold in Tailltiu.

"Swift are the wolves that have hunted thee, my son," said his father.

"This is what we have had of conflict against warriors, thou old hero," Conall Cernach replied.

"Hast thou then news of Da Derga's Hostel?" asked Amergin. "Is thy lord alive?"

"He is not alive," said Conall.

"I swear by the gods by whom the great tribes of Ulster swear, it is cowardly for the man who went thereout alive, having left his lord with his foes in death," said the father of Conall Cernach.

"My wounds are not white, thou old hero," said Conall. He showed him his shield-arm, whereon were thrice fifty wounds which had been inflicted upon it. The shield that guarded it is what saved it. But the right arm had been played upon, as far as two thirds thereof, since the shield had not been guarding it. That arm was mangled and maimed and wounded and pierced, save that the sinews kept it to the body without separation.

"That arm fought tonight, my son," says Amergin.

"True is that, thou old hero," says Conall Cernach. "Many there are unto whom it gave drinks of death tonight in front of the Hostel."

Now as to the marauders, every one of them that escaped from the Hostel went to the cairn which they had built on the night before last, and they brought thereout a stone for each man not mortally wounded. So this is what they lost by death at the Hostel, a man for every stone that is now in Carn Lecca.

THE ULSTER CYCLE

The Ulster, or Red Branch, cycle consists of a group of sagas and romantic tales dealing for the most part with the traditional heroes of what is now eastern Ulster, especially the district included by the present counties of Louth and Down. The chief stronghold of ancient Ulster was Emain Macha, which is said to have been destroyed A.D. 332, and which has been identified with the Navan Fort, a grassy mound not far from Armagh. Here, according to tradition, ruled the powerful king Conchobar, surrounded by a band of chosen warriors, whose exploits suggest at times those of King Arthur's knights of the Round Table. Prominent among the warriors of the Red Branch (*Craeb Ruad*) stand Fergus mac Roig, Bricriu of the Poison Tongue, Conall the Victorious, Loegaire (Leary) the Triumphant, Sencha mac Ailill the wise old counsellor, Cathbad the druid, and, most famous of all, the youthful Cu Chulainn, whose great deeds form the subject of some of our finest Irish heroic tales.

In the ancient sagas Ulster occupies the position of a proud and haughty antagonist to the rest of Ireland, though her special hereditary enemy is Connacht, ruled by the amazonian queen Medb and her husband Ailill, who, like Conchobar, are represented as surrounded by a court composed of distinguished warriors. Rath Cruachan (now Rath Croghan), the ancient capital of Connacht, is often referred to in the sagas of the Ulster cycle.

As a portrayal of Irish civilization in pagan times, the stories of the Ulster cycle are of the highest significance. Preserved in manuscripts dating from the twelfth to the fifteenth century, these sagas in most cases go back to a much earlier period, some having been transcribed from originals written as early as the eighth century. The culture portrayed is, moreover, in general that which prevailed in Ireland before the beginning of the Christian era. The population, not yet united under a central government headed by the *ardrí*, or "high-king," is divided into groups, each inhabiting its own district, or province, known as a *cóiced*, or "fifth": the Ulaid, or Ulstermen, occupying the north, with their capital at

Emain Macha; the Connachta, or Connaughtmen, the west, with their capital at Cruachan, near the Shannon; in the southeast, the North and the South Laigin (Leinstermen); and in the southwest the inhabitants of the province now known as Munster. The historical district of Meath, carved out of the center of Ireland after the establishment of the high-kingship in the second century after Christ, is unknown to the earliest sagas, as is also Tara (Temrach), which did not become the center of government for all Ireland till several centuries later. Each *cóiced* was occupied by numerous *tuatha*, or tribes, which again were subdivided into still smaller groups bound together by an elaborate system of blood kinship and ruled over by kinglets and chieftains of varying degrees of importance, all subject, at least in theory, to the *rí cóicid*, or king of the province.

The civilization reflected in the older sagas is pastoral, though generally lacking the idyllic elements often associated with pastoral life as depicted in literature outside Ireland. The chief wealth consisted in cattle and swine, which fed on the wide moors or in the great forests that anciently clothed a large part of the island. The unit of value was one cow. Even female slaves, also a medium of exchange, were valued in terms of cows. It is also significant that one of the most important groups of Irish heroic tales consists of *tana*, or "cattle-raids." The longest epic of the Ulster cycle has for its central theme an attempt made by the men of Connacht and their allies to carry off a famous bull belonging to an Ulster chieftain.

Both dwellings and household equipment were simple. The typical establishment of a chieftain consisted of a barn-like structure, or hall, the interior of which was a single large room with bunks or couches around the sides, and in the middle a fire along with a cooking kettle and a beer vat. The smoke was allowed to find its way out through a hole in the roof. During inclement weather the doorways might be closed by screens made of woven wattles. The hall and adjacent structures were surrounded by one or more moats and earth-mounds, the latter surmounted by sharpened stakes or timbers for defence.

Of the religion of the pagan Irish we learn little of a specific nature from the sagas, or, indeed, from any other source. From the meager evidence at our disposal we infer that the ancient

Celts worshipped the sun and natural objects such as trees and waters, but just what gods they adored or what religious rituals they practiced is largely a matter of speculation. For the readers of this volume the most significant point lies in the fact that they believed in another world located within natural or artificial mounds or beneath lakes and springs, and inhabited by a race of fairy folk endowed with youth, beauty, and immortality, who issued forth from time to time, married or abducted mortals, and even took part in tribal feuds. These, an ancient manuscript informs us, were the *dei terreni*, or earth gods, of the ancient Irish. They are often referred to in early Irish literature as the *Tuatha De Danann* ("Tribes of the Goddess Anu, or Danu") or the *aes sídhe*, the *sídhe* (shee) of modern Irish folk-lore. An important rôle as intermediaries between mortals and supernatural beings appears to have been played by the druids, who also acted as wise men and seers.

We should be far wrong if we concluded from these facts that the ancient Irish were merely a parcel of scrambling, lawless, superstitious savages. They possessed an elaborate system of laws which reveals a highly developed sense of personal and property rights and of legal procedure. Their skill in music made Irish minstrels and popular entertainers famous throughout medieval Europe. Their literary men were not only required to know a large number of traditional stories, but were trained in the art of composing new ones. The poets of ancient Ireland were highly skilled in metrical devices, including a large number of complicated verse forms unknown to modern English poetry. Early Irish lyric poetry also reveals a delicate feeling for nature which would be difficult to parallel in any other literature. Pagan Irish decorative art, as illustrated by many gold ornaments and other objects discovered in recent centuries, is marked by designs of extraordinary complication and beauty. Early Celtic art formed the basis of manuscript decorations which were imitated widely in medieval times and are greatly admired even today. Above all, the ancient Irish shared with the Gaulish Celts the ideals of honor, fair play, and respect for women which were later destined to become the essentials of twelfth-century chivalry at its best.

THE BIRTH OF CONCHOBAR

If we attempt to arrange the material of the Ulster cycle in its traditional order, we come first upon a group of narratives dealing with the births of several of the leading personages. There are certain facts in the life of every hero that the folk feel they are entitled to know. Among these are his birth, his marriage, and his death. Birth stories, though naturally coming first in traditional chronology, are usually later in date of composition than stories dealing with the hero's mature achievements.

"The Birth of Conchobar" exists in two versions, of which at least one was composed as early as the eighth century. According to the oldest account, Conchobar, who figures as king of Ulster in the most ancient Irish tales, was the son of Nessa, princess of Ulster, by Cathbad, the official druid of the Ulster court. Both in the sagas and in the annals Conchobar is represented as having been born on the same day as Christ and as having died upon receiving the news of his crucifixion. Through the stratagem of his mother he displaced Fergus mac Roig, the rightful king of Ulster, and reigned in his stead. Though he appears at times cruel and unscrupulous, he is generally represented as a brave warrior and a just ruler.

Conchobar mac Nessa was the son of Cathbad the druid, or, as some say, of Fachtna Fathach, king of Ulster. He was a great and admirable king, and well indeed he might be, for the hour of his birth was the hour of the birth of Christ in Palestine. For seven years before his birth had the prophets foretold that on the same night that Christ should be born, a notable chief should be born in Erin. And this is the prophecy of his father, of Cathbad, on the night on which he was born, to Nessa his wife:

> O Nessa, thou art in peril;
> Let every one rise at thy birth-giving,
> Beautiful is the color of thy hands,
> O daughter of Eochaid Yellow-heel.
> Be not sorrowful, O wife,
> A head of hundreds and of hosts
> Of the world will he be, thy son.
>
> The same propitious hour
> To him and to the King of the World.
> Every one will praise him
> For ever to the day of Doom;
> The same night he will be born.
> Heroes will not defy him,
> As hostage he will not be taken,
> He and Christ.

In the plain of Inis thou wilt bear him
Upon the flagstone in the meadow.
Glorious will be his story;
He will be the king of grace,
He will be the hound of Ulster,
Who will take pledges of Kings:
Awful will be the disgrace
When he falls.

Conchobar his name,
Whoso will call him.
His weapons will be red;
He will excel in many routs.
There he will find his death,
In avenging the suffering God.
Clear will be the track of his sword
Over the slanting plain of Laim.

Conchobar was called from the name of his mother, mac Nessa.
But her name in the beginning had been Assa, "docile" or "gentle,"
and it was on this manner that it was changed to Niassa, "ungentle."
She was daughter of Eochaid Yellow-heel, king of Ulster, and by
his desire she had been trained up by twelve tutors, to whom she
was ever docile and full of teachableness. But in one night the
entire number of her tutors fell by the hand of Cathbad the druid,
who from the southern part of Ulster went on a raid through Erin
with three times nine men. He was a man of knowledge and of
druidical skill; moreover, he was endowed with great bodily
strength. Now the girl had no knowledge who they were who had
slain her guardians, but from that moment she turned woman-
warrior, and with her company set out to seek the author of the
deed. In every district of Erin she destroyed and plundered, so
that her name was changed to Niassa (Nessa) after that, because
of the greatness of her prowess and of her valor.

Once upon a time, she had gone upon a quest into a wilderness,
and her people were preparing food. And seeing a clear beautiful
spring of water, the maiden went off alone to bathe. Now while
she was bathing Cathbad passed by and saw her. And he bared
his sword above her head, and stood between the maiden and her
dress and weapons.

"Spare me!" she cried.

"Grant then my three requests," replied the druid.

"They are granted," she said.

"I stipulate that thou be loyal to me, and that I have thy friendship, and that for so long as I live thou wilt be my one and only wife," said he.

"It is better for me to consent than to be killed by thee, and my weapon is gone," said the maiden. Then they and their people united in one place. In a favorable hour Cathbad proceeded into Ulster, and the father of the maiden made them welcome and gave them land, namely, Rath Cathbad in the country of the Picts near the river Conchobar in Crith Rois. By-and-by she bore him a son, namely Conchobar son of Cathbad. Cathbad took the boy to his bosom, and gave thanks for him and prophesied to him; and it was then that he uttered this lay:

> Welcome the stranger that has come here!
> They have told it to you,
> He will be the gracious lord,
> The son of gentle Cathbad.
>
> The son of gentle Cathbad,
> And of Nessa the young,
> Above the fortress of Brig na m-Brat,
> My son and my grandson.
>
> My son and my grandson,
> Grand ornament of the world,
> He will be King of Rath Line,
> He will be a poet, he will be generous.
>
> He will be a poet, he will be generous,
> He will be the head of warriors beyond the sea,
> My little bird from the Brug,
> My lamb,—welcome!

THE BIRTH OF CU CHULAINN

Cu Chulainn is the greatest figure in ancient Irish heroic literature. He has been appropriately compared to Achilles in Greek and to Siegfried in Germanic tradition. The story-tellers of ancient Ireland never tired of recounting his deeds and attributing to him new exploits. His original name, Setanta, appears to go back to remote times, and it is possible that he may be a personage adopted by the Gaels from a still older population. The story of his birth, composed originally in the eighth or ninth century, exists in two versions, one of which is a combination of several conflicting accounts. According to what seems the oldest tradition, Cu Chulainn was the son of the Tuatha De Danann prince Lug and Dechtire (or Dechtine), the sister of King Conchobar of Ulster. Later accounts represent him as son of Conchobar by his own sister, or of the princess and Sualtam (or Sualtach), a petty chieftain of Ulster, who is generally regarded as her mortal husband. The version here given, though probably later than that found in the oldest manuscripts, is less obviously a patchwork of several accounts and is therefore chosen for inclusion in this volume.

Throughout his short but brilliant career Cu Chulainn reveals his supernatural origin. Even as a child of five years he possesses remarkable strength and skill (p. 138); when only six he slays the terrible watchdog of Culann the Smith, thereby winning the name "Hound of Culann" (Cu Chulainn) (p. 142); at seven he becomes a full-fledged warrior (p. 143); at seventeen he holds at bay the entire army of Connacht and her allies (p. 281); and he is only twenty-seven when he meets his death, fighting against overpowering odds (p. 333).

Dechtire, the sister of King Conchobar of Ulster, went, along with fifty other maidens, upon an elopement without the knowledge of the Ulstermen and Conchobar. No track nor trace of them was found, and the Ulstermen were seeking them to the end of three years.

Dechtire and her attendant maidens came then in the form of a bird-flock to the plain about Emain Macha, and destroyed the vegetation, so that they did not leave even the roots of the grass in the ground there. That thing was a great cause of vexation to the Ulstermen. They accordingly harnessed nine chariots for the hunting of the birds, for bird hunting was a custom of theirs. Among the hunting party were Conchobar and Fergus mac Roig and Amergin and Blai the Hospitaller and Bricriu.

The birds went before them southward across Sliab Fuait, over the Ford of Lethan and the Ford of Garach, and over the Plain of Gossa between the men of Ross and the men of Arda. Night then overtook them and the bird-flock escaped; so they unharnessed their chariots. Fergus went in search of a lodging, and he came upon a small new house, wherein he found a married couple. They welcomed him and offered him food, but he would not accept their hospitality because his companions were still abroad without shelter.

"Come thou with thy companions into the house, and welcome to you all," said they. Fergus thereupon went out to his companions and brought them all in, both men and horses, so that they were all in the house (which had suddenly become large and magnificent).

Then Bricriu went out, and he heard Cnu Deroil.[1] He heard the sound of the wistful fairy music, but he did not know what it meant. He went toward the sound until he came upon a great, fair, adorned house before him. He approached the door, and, on looking in, beheld the master of the house.

"Come in, O Bricriu," said he; "why standest thou outside?"

"Welcome indeed," said a woman who stood beside the master of the house.

Bricriu regarded the handsome, noble-looking warrior, and asked, "Why does the woman also welcome us?"

"It is on her account that I welcome thee," said the man; "is anyone lacking to you in Emain?"

"There is indeed," replied Bricriu; "fifty maidens have been lost to us for the space of three years."

"Wouldst thou recognize them if thou sawest them?" asked the man.

"I might not recognize them," said Bricriu; "the lapse of three years or sickness of three years may perhaps cause ignorance or lack of recognition on my part."

"Nevertheless, try to recognize them," said the man. "The fifty maidens whom you seek are here in the house, and the chief of them is she who is here by my side. Dechtire is her name, and it is they who came in the form of the bird-flock to Emain Macha in order to induce the Ulstermen to come hither."

[1] A famous harper of the fairy folk.

The woman gave a purple, bordered mantle to Bricriu, and he went back thereafter to his companions. While returning to his company, Bricriu thought to himself as follows: "These fifty maidens who are lacking to Conchobar—to find them would be to flatter him. Therefore I will conceal from him that I have found his sister with her attendants; I will only say that I have found a house and a company of lovely women therein."

When Bricriu arrived, Conchobar asked him the news.

"What is that to thee?" asked Bricriu. "I came upon a magnificent house; therein I saw a queen radiant and noble, dear and lovable; a company of women fair and pure; a household generous and shining."

"Off with you to the house," commanded Conchobar. "The master of that house is a subject of mine, for it is in my land he dwells. Let his wife come and sleep with me to-night."

No one was found who would go upon this errand except Fergus. He went and spoke his message, and he was welcomed and the woman came with him. She complained to Fergus that the pains of childbirth were upon her. Then Fergus said to Conchobar that a respite should be granted to her. Thereupon the company lay down beside each other and slept. When they awoke in the morning, they saw a little boy in the fold of Conchobar's cloak.

"Take the child to thee," said Conchobar to his sister Finnchoem. When Finnchoem looked at the little boy beside Conchobar, she said, "My heart loves this boy so that he is the same with me as my own son Conall."

"There is indeed little difference between them," said Bricriu; "that child is the son of thine own sister Dechtire. She it is, who, with her fifty maidens, has been absent from Emain for three years and is now here."

(The mysterious stranger who was with Dechtire was Lug Long-Arm, of the Tuatha De Danann. The little child was named Setanta until he slew the hound of Culann the smith, after which he was known as Cu Chulainn [Hound of Culann].)

THE BOYHOOD DEEDS OF CU CHULAINN

Among the most striking of the many narratives dealing with Cu Chulainn is a group of episodes from his childhood. The incidents in the following selection not only serve to illustrate his precocity, a trait which is widespread among heroes of the folk, but also to exemplify the conditions of child-fosterage among the ancient Irish. This and other tales of Cu Chulainn's youth are incorporated in the great Ulster epic "The Cattle-Raid of Cooley" (p. 281), where they are represented as told to King Ailill and Queen Medb of Connacht by several of the Ulster exiles enlisted in the Connacht army (p. 239). They form a body of tradition which was probably old at the time when the epic was composed.

"This boy," said Fergus, "was reared in his father's and his mother's house, by the seaside northwards in the plain of Muirthemne, where someone gave him an account of the *macrad* or 'boy-corps' of Emain Macha; how that Conchobar divides his day into three parts: the first being devoted to watching the boy-corps at their sport, especially that of hurling; the second to the playing of chess and draughts; the third to pleasurable consuming of meat and drink until drowsiness sets in, which then is promoted by the exertions of minstrels and musicians to induce favorable placidity of mind and disposition. And, for all that we are banished from him," continued Fergus, "by my word I swear that neither in Ireland nor in Scotland is there a warrior his (*i.e.*, Conchobar's) counterpart. The little lad, then, as aforesaid, having heard of all this, one day told his mother that he was bent on a visit to Emain Macha to test the boy-corps at their own sports. She objected that he was immature, and ought to wait until some grown warrior or other, or some confidential of Conchobar's should, in order to insure his safety, bind over the boy-corps to keep the peace toward him. He told his mother that that was too long an outlook, that he could not wait, and that all she had to do was to set him a course for Emain Macha, since he did not know in which direction it lay.

" 'It is a weary way from here,' said the mother, 'for between thee and it lies Sliab Fuait.'

" 'Give me the bearings,' said he; and she did so.

137

" Away he went then, taking with him his hurly of brass, his ball of silver, his throwing javelin, and his toy spear; with which equipment he fell to shortening the way for himself. He did it thus: with his hurly he would strike the ball and drive it a great distance; then he pelted the hurly after it, and drove it just as far again; then he threw his javelin, lastly the spear. Which done, he would make a playful rush after them all, pick up the hurly, the ball and the javelin, while, before the spear's tip could touch the earth, he had caught the missile by the other end.

"In due course Cu Chulainn reached Emain Macha, where he found the boy-corps, thrice fifty in number, hurling on the green and practising martial exercises with Conchobar's son Follamain at their head. The lad dived right in among them and took a hand in the game. He got the ball between his legs and held it there, not suffering it to travel higher up than his knees or lower down than his ankle-joints, and so making it impossible for them to get in a stroke or in any other way to touch it. In this manner he brought it along and sent it home over the goal. In utter amazement the whole corps looked on; but Follamain mac Conchobar cried: 'Good now, boys, all together meet this youngster as he deserves, and kill him; because it is taboo to have such a one join himself to you and interfere in your game, without first having had the civility to procure your guarantee that his life should be respected. Together then and at once attack him and avenge violation of your taboo; for we know that he is the son of some petty Ulster warrior, such as without safe-conduct is not accustomed to intrude into your play.'

"The whole of them assailed Cu Chulainn, and simultaneously sent their hurlies at his head; he, however, parried all the hundred and fifty and was unharmed. The same with the balls, which he fended off with fists, fore-arms, and palms alone. Their thrice fifty toy spears he received in his little shield, and still was unhurt. In turn now, Cu Chulainn went among them, and laid low fifty of the best: five more of them," said Fergus, "came past the spot where myself and Conchobar sat at chess-play, with the young lad close in their wake.

" 'Hold, my little fellow,' said Conchobar, 'I see this is no gentle game thou playest with the boy-corps.'

" 'And good cause I have too,' cried Cu Chulainn: 'after coming out of a far land to them, I have not had a guest's reception.'

" 'How now, little one,' said the king, 'knowest thou not the boy-corps' conditions: that a newcomer must have them bound by their honor to respect his life?'

" 'I knew it not,' said the boy, 'otherwise I had conformed, and taken measures beforehand.'

" ' 'Tis well,' said the king: 'take it now upon yourselves to let the boy go safe.'

" 'We do,' the boy-corps answered.

"They resumed play; Cu Chulainn did as he would with them, and again laid out fifty of them on the ground. Their fathers deemed they could not but be dead. No such thing, however; it was merely that with his blows and pushes and repeated charges, he so terrified them that they took to the grass.

" 'What on earth is he at with them now?' asked Conchobar.

" 'I swear by my gods,' said Cu Chulainn, 'that until they in their turn come under my protection and guarantee, I will not lighten my hand from off them.'

"This they did at once. Now," said Fergus in conclusion, "I submit, that a youngster who did all this when he was just five years old, needs not to excite our wonder because, now being turned of seventeen years, he in this Cattle-Raid of Cooley cut a four-pronged pole and the rest, and that he should have killed a man, or two, or three men, or even, as indeed he has done, four."

Conchobar's son Cormac Conlonges spoke now, saying, "In the year after that, the same little boy did another deed."

"And what was that?" Ailill asked.

"Well," continued Cormac, "in Ulster there was a good smith and artificer, by name Culann. He prepared a banquet for Conchobar, and traveled to Emain Macha to bid him to it. He begged Conchobar to bring with him only a moderate number of warriors, because neither land nor domain had he, but merely the product of his hammer, of his anvil, and of his tongs. Conchobar promised that he would bring no more than a small company. Culann returned home to make his last preparations, Conchobar remaining in Emain Macha until the meeting broke up and the day came to a close. Then the king put on his light convenient travelling garb, and betook him to the green in order to bid the boy-corps farewell before he started. There, however, he saw a curious sight. One hundred and fifty youths at one end of the green, and at the other, a single one and he taking the goal against the crowd of them. Again, when they played the hole-game and it was their turn to aim at the hole, it being his to defend it, he stopped all thrice fifty balls just at the edge of the hole, so that not one went in; when the defence was theirs and it was his turn to shoot, he would hole the entire set without missing one. When the game was to tear one another's clothes off, he would have the mantles off them all, while the full number could not even pull out his brooch. When it was to upset each other, he would knock over the hundred and fifty and they could not stretch him on the ground. All which when Conchobar had witnessed, he said: 'I congratulate the land into which the little boy has come; were his full-grown deeds to prove consonant with his boyish exploits, he would indeed be of some solid use.'

"To this doubtful expression Fergus objected, saying to Conchobar, 'That is not justly said; for according as the little boy grows, so also will his deeds increase with him.'

" 'Have the child called to us,' said the king, 'that he may come with us to share the banquet.'

" 'I cannot go thither just now,' said the boy.

" 'How so?' asked Conchobar.

" 'The boy-corps have not yet had enough of play.'

" 'It would be too long for us to wait until they had,' said the king.

" 'Wait not at all; I will follow after you.'

" 'But, young one, knowest thou the way?'

" 'I will follow the trail of the company, of the horses, and the chariots' tracks.'

"Thereupon Conchobar started; eventually he reached Culann's house, was received in becoming fashion, fresh rushes were laid, and they fell to the banquet. Presently the smith said to Conchobar, 'Good now, O king, has any one promised that this night he would follow thee to this dwelling?'

" 'No, not one,' answered Conchobar (quite forgetting the little boy); 'but wherefore do you ask?'

" 'It is only that I have an excellent ban-dog, from which when his chain is taken off no one may dare to be near him; for saving myself he knows not any man, and in him resides the strength of an hundred.'

"Conchobar said, 'Loose him then, and let him guard this place.'

"So Culann did; the dog made the circuit of his country, then took up his usual position whence to watch the house, and there he couched with his head on his paws. Surely an extraordinary, cruel, fierce and savage dog was he.

"As for the boy-corps, until it was time to separate, they continued in Emain Macha; then they dispersed, each one to his parent's house, or to his nurse's, or to his guardian's. But the little fellow, trusting to the trail, as aforesaid, struck out for Culann's house. With his club and his ball he shortened the way for himself as he went. So soon as ever he came to the green of Culann's fort, the ban-dog became aware of him and gave tongue in such a way as to be heard throughout all the countryside; not was it to carve the boy decently as for a feast that he was minded, but at one gulp to swallow him down. The child was without all reasonable means of defence; therefore as the dog charged at him open-jawed he threw his playing ball down his throat with great force, which mortally punished the creature's inwards. Cu Chulainn seized him by the hind legs and banged him against a rock to such purpose that he strewed all the ground in broken fragments.

"The whole company within had heard the ban-dog's challenge, at the sound of which Conchobar said, ' 'Tis no good luck has brought us on our present trip.'

" 'Your meaning?' asked the others.

" 'I mean that the little boy, my sister Dechtire's son, Setanta mac Sualtach, had promised to come after me; and he even now must be killed by the ban-dog.'

"To a man the heroes rose; and though the fort's doors were thrown open, out they stormed over the ramparts to seek him. Speedy as they were, yet did Fergus outstrip them; he picked up the boy, hoisted him on his shoulder, and carried him to Conchobar. Culann himself had come out, and there he saw his ban-dog lie in scraps and pieces; which was a heart's vexation to him. He went back indoors and said, 'Thy father and thy mother are welcome both, but most unwelcome thou.'

" 'Why, what hast thou against the little fellow?' asked Conchobar.

" 'It was no good luck that inspired me to make my feast for thee, O Conchobar: my dog now being gone, my substance is but substance wasted; my livelihood, a means of living set all astray. Little boy,' he continued, 'that was a good member of my family thou tookest from me: a safeguard of raiment, of flocks, and of herds.'

" 'Be not angered thereat,' said the child; 'for in this matter myself will pronounce a just award.'

" 'And what might that be?' inquired Conchobar.

"The little boy replied, 'If in all Ireland there be a whelp of that dog's breed, by me he shall be nurtured till he be fit for action as was his sire. In the meantime I, O Culann, myself will do thee a ban-dog's service, in guarding of thy cattle and substance and stronghold.'

" 'Well hast thou made the award,' said Conchobar; and Cathbad the druid, chiming in, declared that not in his own person could he have done it better, and that henceforth the boy must bear the name *Cu Chulainn*, 'Culann's Hound.' The youngster, however, objected; 'I like my own name better: Setanta mac Sualtach.'

" 'Say not so,' Cathbad remonstrated; 'for all men in the world shall have their mouths full of that name.'

"The boy answered that on those terms the name would be well pleasing to him, and in this way it came to pass that it stuck to him. Now the little fellow," continued Cormac Conlonges the narrator of all this, "who when just touching six years of age slew the dog which even a great company did not dare to approach, it were not reasonable to be astonished though the same at seventeen should come to the border of the province, and kill a man, or two, or three, or four, on the Cattle-Raid of Cooley."

Another exiled Ulsterman, Fiacha mac Firaba, taking up the recital, said that in the very year following that adventure of the dog, the little boy had performed a third exploit.

"And what was that?" Ailill asked.

"Why, it was Cathbad the druid," continued Fiacha, "who to the north-east of Emain Macha taught his pupils, there being with him eight from among the students of his art. When one of them questioned him as to what purpose that day was more especially favorable, Cathbad told him that any stripling who on that day should for the first time assume arms and armor, the name of such an one forever would surpass those of all Ireland's youths besides.

His life, however, must be fleeting, short. The boy was some distance away on the south side of Emain Macha; nevertheless he heard Cathbad's speech. He put off his playing suit and laid aside his implements of sport; then he entered Conchobar's sleeping house and said, 'All good be thine, O king.'

"Conchobar answered, 'Little boy, what is thy request?'

" 'I desire to take arms.'

" 'And who prompted thee to that?'

" 'Cathbad the druid,' answered the boy.

" 'Thou shalt not be denied,' said the king, and forthwith gave him two spears with sword and shield. The boy suppled and brandished the weapons and in the process broke them all to shivers and splinters. In short, whereas in Emain Macha Conchobar had seventeen weapon-equipments ready for the boy-corps' service—since whenever one of them took arms, Conchobar it was who invested him with the outfit and brought him luck in the using of it—the boy made fragments of them all. Which done, he said, 'O my master, O Conchobar, these arms are not good; they suffice me not.' Thereupon the king gave him his own two spears, his own sword, and his own shield. In every possible way the boy tested them; he even bent them point to hilt and head to butt, yet never broke them: they endured him. 'These arms are good,' said he, 'and worthy of me. Fair fall the land and the region which for its king has him whose arms and armor are these.'

"Just then it was that Cathbad the druid came into the house and wondering asked, 'Is the little boy assuming arms?'

" 'Ay, indeed,' said the king.

" 'It is not his mother's son we would care to see assume them on this day,' said the druid.

" 'How now,' said the king, 'was it not thyself that prompted him?'

" 'Not I, of a surety.'

" 'Brat,' cried the king, 'what meanest thou by telling me that it was so, wherein thou hast lied to me?'

" 'O king, be not wroth,' the boy pleaded; 'for he it was that prompted me when he instructed his other pupils. For when they asked him what special virtue lay in this day, he told them that the name of whatsoever youth should therein for the first time take arms, would top the fame of all other Erin's men; nor thereby should he suffer resulting disadvantage, save that his life must be fleeting, short.'

" 'And it is true for me,' said Cathbad; 'noble and famous indeed thou shalt be, but transitory, soon gone.'

" 'Little care I,' said Cu Chulainn, 'nor though I were but one day or one night in being, so long as after me the history of myself and doings may endure.'

"Then said Cathbad again, 'Well then, get into a chariot, boy, and proceed to test in thine own person whether mine utterance be truth.'

"So Cu Chulainn mounted a chariot; in divers ways he tried its strength, and reduced it to fragments. He mounted a second, with the same result. In brief, whereas in Emain Macha for the boy-corps' service Conchobar had seventeen chariots, in like wise the little fellow smashed them all; then he said, 'These chariots of thine, O Conchobar, are no good at all, nor worthy of me.'

" 'Where is Iubar mac Riangabra?' cried Conchobar.

" 'Here I am,' he answered.

" 'Prepare my own chariot and harness my own horses for him there.'

"The driver did his will, Cu Chulainn mounted, tested the chariot, and it endured him. 'This chariot is good,' he said, 'and my worthy match.'

" 'Good now, little boy,' said Iubar, 'let the horses be turned out to grass.'

" 'Too early for that yet, Iubar; drive on and round Emain Macha.'

" 'Let the horses go out to graze.'

" 'Too early yet, Iubar; drive ahead, that the boy-corps may give me salutation on this the first day of my taking arms.'

"They came to the place where the boy-corps was, and the cry of them resounded, 'These are arms that thou hast taken.'

" 'The very thing indeed,' he said.

"They wished him success in spoil-winning and in first-slaying, but expressed regret that he was weaned away from them and their sports. Cu Chulainn assured them that it was not so, but that it was something in the nature of a charm that had caused him to take arms on this day of all others. Again Iubar pressed him to have the horses taken out, and again the boy refused. He questioned the driver, 'Whither leads this great road here running by us?' Iubar answered that it ran to Ath an Foraire (the Look-out Ford) in Sliab Fuait. In answer to further questions with which he plied the charioteer, Cu Chulainn learned that the ford had that name from the fact that daily there some prime warrior of the Ulstermen kept watch and ward to see that no foreign champion came to molest them, it being his duty to do single combat on behalf of his whole province. Should poets and musicians be coming away from Ulster dissatisfied with their treatment, it was his duty, acting for the whole province, to solace them with gold and other gifts. On the other hand, did poets and musicians enter his province, his duty was to see that they had safe-conduct up to Conchobar's bed-side. This sentinel's praise then would be the theme of the first pieces, in divers forms of verse, the poets would rehearse upon arriving in Emain Macha.

"Cu Chulainn inquired whether Iubar knew who it was that on this particular day mounted guard. 'I know it well,' the charioteer replied; 'it is Conall mac Amergin, surnamed Cernach (the Victorious), Ireland's pre-eminent warrior.'

" 'Onward to that ford, then, driver!' cried the boy.

"Sure enough at the water's edge they came upon Conall, who received them with, 'And is it arms that you have taken today, little boy?'

" 'It is indeed,' Iubar answered for him.

" 'May his arms bring him triumph and victory and drawing of first blood,' said Conall. 'The only thing is that in my judgment thou hast prematurely assumed them, seeing that as yet thou art not fit for exploits.'

"For all answer the boy said, 'And what dost thou here, Conall?'

" 'On behalf of the province I keep watch and ward.'

" 'Come,' said the youngster, 'for this day let me take the duty.'

" 'Never say it,' replied Conall, 'for as yet thou art not up to coping with a real fighting man.'

" 'Then will I go down to the shallows of Loch Echtra, to see whether I may draw blood on either friend or foe.'

" 'And I,' said Conall, 'will go to protect thee and to safeguard, so that thou wilt not run into dangers on the border.'

" 'Nay,' said Cu Chulainn, 'come not.'

" 'I will so,' Conall insisted, 'for were I to permit thee all alone to frequent the border, the Ulstermen would avenge it on me.'

"Conall had his chariot made ready and his horses harnessed; he started on his errand of protection, and soon overtook Cu Chulainn, who had cut the matter short and had gone on before. They now being abreast, the boy deemed that, in event of opportunity to do some deed of mortal daring, Conall would never allow him to execute it. From the ground therefore he picked up a stone about the size of his fist, and took very careful aim at Conall's chariot-yoke. He broke it in two, the vehicle came down, and Conall was hurled prone, so falling that his mouth was brought over one shoulder.

"'What's all this, boy?'

"'It was I: in order to see whether my marksmanship was good and whether there was in me the material of a good warrior.'

"'Poison take both thy shot and thyself as well; and though thy head should fall as a prize to some foe over yonder, yet never a foot further will I budge to save thee!'

"'The very thing I crave of thee,' said the boy; 'and I do this in this particular manner because to you Ulstermen it is taboo to persist after violence is done to you.' With that Conall went back to his post at the ford.

"As for the little boy, southwards he went his way to the shallows of Loch Echtra, and until the day's end abode there. Then spoke Iubar: 'If to thee we might venture to say so much, little one, I should be more than rejoiced that we made instant return to Emain Macha. For already for some time the carving has been going on there; and whereas there thou hast thine appointed place kept till thou come—between Conchobar's knees— I on the contrary can do nothing but join the messengers and jesters of his house, to fit in where I may; for which reason I judge it now fitting that I were back in time to scramble with them.'

"Cu Chulainn ordered him to harness the chariot; which being done, they drove off, and Cu Chulainn inquired the name of a mountain that he saw. He learned that it was Sliab Morne, and further asked the meaning of a white cairn which appeared on a summit. It was Finnchairn; the boy thought it inviting, and ordered the driver to take him thither. Iubar expressed great reluctance and Cu Chulainn said, 'Thou art a lazy loon, considering that this is my first adventure-quest, and this is thy first trip with me.'

"'And if it is,' said Iubar, 'and if I ever reach Emain Macha, for ever and for ever may it be my last!'

"'Good now, driver,' said the boy when they were on the top of the hillock; 'in all directions point out to me the topography of Ulster, a country in which I know not my way about.' The charioteer from that position pointed out the hills and the plain lands and the strongholds of the province.

"'Tis well, O driver; and what now is yon well-defined glen-seamed plain before us to the southward?'

"'That is the plain of Bray (Mag Breg).'

"'Proceed then and instruct me concerning the strongholds and forts of that plain.' Then Iubar pointed out to him Tara and Tailltiu, Cletty and Knowth and the brug of Angus mac Oc on the Boyne, and the stronghold of Nechtan Sceine's sons.

"'Are they those sons of Nechtan of whom it is said, that the number of Ulstermen now alive exceeds not the number of them fallen by their hands?'

"'The same,' said Iubar.

"'Away with us then to the stronghold of Nechtan's sons.'

"'Woe waits on such a speech; and whosoever he be that goes there, I will not be the one.'

"Cu Chulainn said, 'Alive or dead, thither shalt thou go, however.'

"'Alive I go then, and dead I shall be left there.'

"They made their way to the stronghold, and the little boy dismounted upon the green, a green with this particular feature: in its center stood a pillar stone, encircled with an iron collar, test of heroic accomplishment; for it bore graven writing to the effect that any man (if only he were one that carried arms) who should enter on this green, must hold it taboo to him to depart from it without challenging to single combat some of the dwellers in the stronghold. The little boy read the Ogam, threw his arms around the stone to start it, and eventually pitched it, collar and all, into the water close at hand.

"'In my poor opinion,' ventured Iubar, 'it is no better so than it was before; and I well know that this time at all events thou wilt find the object of thy search: a prompt and violent death.'

"'Good, good, O driver, spread me now the chariot-coverings that I may sleep a little while.'

"'Alas that one should speak so; for a land of foemen and not of friends is this.'

"Iubar obeyed, and on the green at once the little fellow fell asleep. Just then it was that Foill mac Nechtain issued forth, and, at the sight of the chariot, called out, 'Driver, do not unharness those horses!' Iubar made answer that he still held the reins in his hand—a sign that he was not about to unharness them.

"'What horses are these?'

"'Conchobar's two piebalds.'

"'Even such at sight I took them to be,' said Foill; 'and who has brought them into these borders?'

"'A young bit of a little boy; one who for luck has taken arms to-day, and for the purpose of showing off his form and fashion has come into the borders.'

"'Never let it thrive with him,' said Foill; 'were it sure that he is capable of action, it is dead in place of alive that he would go back to Emain Macha.'

"'Indeed he is not capable, nor could it be rightly imputed to him; this is but the seventh year since his birth.' Here the little one lifted his face from the ground; not only that but his whole body to his feet, blushed deep at the affront which he had overheard, and said, 'Ay, I am fit for action!'

"But Foill rejoined, 'I rather would incline to hold that thou art not.'

"'Thou shalt know what to hold in this matter, only let us repair to the ford; but first, go fetch thy weapons; in cowardly guise thou art come hither, for nor drivers nor messengers nor folk unarmed slay I.' Foill rushed headlong for his weapons, and Iubar advised the boy that he must be careful with him. Cu Chulainn asked the reason, and was told that the man was Foill mac Nechtain Sceine, invulnerable to either point or edge of any kind.

"'Not to me should such a thing be spoken,' he replied, 'for I will take in hand my special feat: the tempered and refined iron ball, which shall land in his forehead's midst and backwards through his skull shall carry out his brain, so leaving his head traversed with a fair conduit for the air.' With that, out came

Foill mac Nechtain again; the little lad grasped his ball, hurled it with the exact effect foretold, and he took Foill's head.

"Out of the stronghold now the second son emerged on the green, whose name was Tuachall mac Nechtain, and he said, 'Belike thou art inclined to boast of that much.' Cu Chulainn replied that the fall of a single warrior was for him no matter of boast, and Tuachall told him that in that case he should not boast at all, because straightway he would perish by his hand. 'Then make haste for thy weapons,' said the boy, 'for in cowardly guise thou comest hither.'

"Away went Tuachall; Iubar repeated his admonitions. 'Who is that?' asked the boy. He was told not only that he was a son of Nechtan but also that he must be slain by the first stroke or shot or other attempt of whatsoever sort, or not at all; and this because of the extraordinary activity and skill which in front of weapons' points he displayed to avoid them. Again Cu Chulainn objected that such language ought not to be addressed to him. Said he, 'I will take in my hand Conchobar's great spear, the Venomous; it shall pierce the shield over his breast and, after holing the heart within him, shall break three ribs in his side that is the farthest from me.' This also the boy performed, and took the victim's head before his body touched the ground.

"Now came out the youngest of the sons, Fainnle mac Nechtain, and said, 'But simpletons they were with whom thou hast had to do.' Cu Chulainn asked him what he meant, and Fainnle invited him to come away down and out upon the water where his foot would not touch bottom, himself on the instant darting to the ford. Still Iubar warned the boy to be on his guard. 'How is that then?' said Cu Chulainn.

"'Because that is Fainnle mac Nechtain; and the reason why he bears that name is that as it were a *fáinnle* (swallow) or a weasel, even so for swiftness he travels on the water's surface, nor can the whole world's swimmers attempt to cope with him.'

"'Not to me ought such a thing to be said,' objected the boy again; 'for thou knowest the river which we have in Emain Macha, the Callan: well, when the boy-corps break off from their sports and plunge into it to swim, on either shoulder I take a lad of them, on either palm another, nor in the transit across that water ever wet as much as my ankles.'

"Then he and Fainnle entered the ford and there wrestled. The youngster clasped his arms around him and got him just flush with the water; then he dealt him a stroke with Conchobar's sword and took his head, letting the body go with the current. To finish up, Cu Chulainn entered the stronghold and harried it; then he and Iubar fired it and left it burning brightly, then turned about to retrace their steps through Sliab Fuait, not forgetting to carry with them the heads of Nechtan Sceine's sons.

"Soon they saw in front of them a herd of deer, and the boy sought to know what were those numerous and restless cattle. Iubar explained that they were not cattle, but a herd of wild deer that kept in the dark glens of Sliab Fuait. He being urged to goad the horses in their direction, did so; but the king's fat horses could not attain to join company with the hard-conditioned deer. Cu Chulainn dismounted therefore and by sheer running and mere speed captured in the moor two stags of the greatest bulk, which he made fast to the chariot with thongs. Still they held a course for Emain Macha, and by-and-by, when nearing it, perceived a certain flock of whitest swans. The boy asked were they pet birds or wild, and learned that they were wild swans which used to congregate from rocks and islands of the sea, and for feeding's sake, infest the country. Cu Chulainn questioned further, and wished to know which was the rarer thing: to bring some of them back to Emain Macha alive, or to bring them dead. Iubar did not hesitate to say that bringing them back living would be the more creditable by far; 'for,' said he, 'you may find plenty to bring them in dead; perhaps not one to bring them in living.'

"Into his sling Cu Chulainn laid a little stone, and with it at a cast brought down eight swans of the number. Again he loaded, this time with a larger stone, and now brought down sixteen. 'Driver, bring along the birds,' he said.

"But Iubar hesitated. 'I hardly can do that.'

"'And why not?' said the boy.

"'Because if I quit my present position, the horses' speed and the action being what they are, the chariot wheels will cut me into pieces; or else the stags' antlers will pierce and otherwise wound me.'

"'No true warrior art thou, Iubar; but come, the horses I will gaze upon with such a look that they shall not break their regulation pace; as for the gaze that I will bend upon the stags, they will stoop their heads for awe.'

"At this Iubar ventured down and retrieved the swans, which with more of the thongs and ropes he secured to the chariot. In this manner they covered the rest of the way to Emain Macha.

"Leborcham, daughter of Aed and messenger to the king, perceived them now and cried, 'A solitary chariot-fighter draws near to thee now, O Conchobar, and terribly he comes! The chariot is graced with the bleeding heads of his enemies; beautiful white birds he has which in the chariot bear him company, and wild unbroken stags bound and tethered to the same. Indeed if measures be not taken to receive him prudently, the best of the Ulstermen must fall by his hand.'

"'I know that little chariot-fighter,' Conchobar said: 'the little boy, my sister's son, who this very day went to the border. Surely he will have reddened his hand; and should his fury not be timely met, all Emain Macha's young men will perish by him.'

"At last they hit upon a method to abate his manly rage (the result of having shed blood), and it was this: Emain Macha's women all (six score and ten in number) bared their bosoms, and without subterfuge of any kind trooped out to meet him (their manoeuver being based on Cu Chulainn's well-known modesty, which, like all his other qualities, was excessive). The little fellow leaned his head against the rail of the chariot and shut them from his sight. Then was the desired moment; all unawares he was seized, and soused in a vat of cold water ready for the purpose. In this first vessel the heat generated by his immersion was such that the staves and hoops flew asunder instantly. In a second vat the water escaped (by boiling over); in yet a third the water still was hotter than one could bear. By this time, however, the little boy's fury had died down in him; from crown to sole he blushed a beautiful pink red all over, and they clad him in his festive clothes. Thus his natural form and feature were restored to him.

"A beautiful boy indeed was that: seven toes to each foot he had, and to either hand as many fingers; his eyes were bright with seven pupils apiece, each one of which glittered with seven gem-like sparkles. On either cheek he had four moles: a blue, a crimson, a green, and a yellow one. Between one ear and the other he had fifty clear-yellow long tresses that were as the yellow wax of bees, or like a brooch of white gold as it glints in the sun unobscured. He wore a green mantle silver-clasped upon his breast, a gold-thread shirt. The small boy took his place between Conchobar's knees, and the king began to stroke his hair. Now the stripling who by the time seven years were completed since his birth, had done such deeds: had destroyed the champions by whom two-thirds of the Ulstermen had fallen unavenged,—I hold," said Fiacha mac Firaba, the narrator, "that there is scant room for wonder though at seventeen he comes to the border, and kills a man, ay, two or three, or four, all in the Cattle-Raid of Cooley."

THE WOOING OF EMER

According to the most ancient tradition, Cu Chulainn, it seems, was unmarried, but stories of *tochmarca*, or "wooings," were popular in early Irish literature, and we are not surprised to find that ere long the greatest of all the Ulster heroes, though still a boy, was supplied with a wife. "The Wooing of Emer" exists in several versions, the oldest of which was composed as early as the eighth century. The wandering and incoherent character of the narrative is probably due in large part to the fact that the author has added to the simple tale of Cu Chulainn's wooing numerous themes derived from older sagas, notably the account of how Cu Chulainn went to learn feats of arms from the amazonian Scathach. Cu Chulainn's dialogue with Emer is couched in a veiled and highly poetical language which was comprehensible only to the initiated and hence means little when rendered into modern English.

PART I

CU CHULAINN'S WOOING

There lived once upon a time a great and famous king in Emain Macha, whose name was Conchobar, son of Fachtna Fathach. In his reign there was much store of good things enjoyed by the men of Ulster. Peace there was, and quiet, and pleasant greeting; there were fruits and fatness and harvest of the sea; there was power and law and good lordship during his time among the men of Erin. In the king's house at Emain was great state and rank and plenty. Of this form was that house, the Red Branch of Conchobar, namely, after the likeness of the Tech Midchuarta of Tara. Nine compartments were in it from the fire to the wall. Thirty feet was the height of each bronze partition in the house. Carvings of red yew therein. A wooden floor beneath, and a roofing of tiles above. The compartment of Conchobar was in the front of the house, with a ceiling of silver with pillars of bronze. Their headpieces glittered with gold and were set with carbuncles, so that day and night were equally light therein. There was a gong of silver above the king, hung from the roof-tree of the royal house. Whenever Conchobar struck the gong with his royal rod, all the men of Ulster were silent. The twelve cubicles of the twelve chariot-chiefs were round about the king's compartment. All the valiant warriors of the men of Ulster found space in that king's house at the time of drinking, and yet no man of them would crowd the other. Splendid, lavish, and beautiful were the valiant warriors of the men of Ulster in that house. In it were held great and numerous gatherings of every kind, and wonderful pastimes. Games and music and singing there, heroes performing their feats, poets singing, harpers and players on the timpan striking up their sounds.

Now, once the men of Ulster were in Emain Macha with Concho-bar, drinking from the beer vat known as the "Iron-Chasm." A hundred fillings of beverage went into it every evening. Such was the drinking of the "Iron-Chasm," which at one sitting would satisfy all the men of Ulster. The chariot-chiefs of Ulster were performing on ropes stretched across from door to door in the house at Emain Macha. Fifteen feet and nine score was the size of that house. The chariot-chiefs were performing three feats,— the spear-feat, the apple-feat, and the sword-edge feat. The chariot-chiefs who performed those feats were these: Conall the Victorious, son of Amergin; Fergus, son of Roig, the Over-bold; Loegaire the Triumphant, son of Connad; Celtchar, son of Uithe-char; Dubtach, son of Lugaid; Cu Chulainn, son of Sualtam; Scel, son of Barnene (from whom the Pass of Barnene is named), the warder of Emain Macha. From him is the saying "a story of Scel's," for he was a mighty story-teller. Cu Chulainn surpassed them all at those feats for quickness and deftness.

The women of Ulster loved Cu Chulainn greatly for his dexterity in the feats, for the nimbleness of his leap, for the excellence of his wisdom, for the sweetness of his speech, for the beauty of his face, for the loveliness of his look. For in his kingly eyes were seven pupils, four of them in his one eye, and three of them in the other. He had seven fingers on either hand, and seven toes on either of his two feet. Many were his gifts. First, his gift of prudence until his warrior's flame appeared, the gift of feats, the gift of *buanfach* (a game like draughts), the gift of chess-playing, the gift of calculating, the gift of sooth-saying, the gift of dis-cernment, the gift of beauty. But Cu Chulainn had three defects: that he was too young, for his beard had not grown, and all the more would unknown youths deride him, that he was too daring,

and that he was too beautiful. The men of Ulster took counsel
about Cu Chulainn, for their women and maidens loved him
greatly. For Cu Chulainn had no wife at that time. This was their
counsel, that they should seek out a maiden whom Cu Chulainn
might choose to woo. For they were sure that a man who had a
wife to attend to him would be less likely to spoil their daughters
and accept the love of their women. And, besides, they were
troubled and afraid that Cu Chulainn would perish early, so that
for that reason they wished to give him a wife that he might leave
an heir; knowing that his rebirth would be of himself.

Then Conchobar sent out nine men into each province of Erin to
seek a wife for Cu Chulainn, to see if in any stronghold, or in any
chief place in Erin they could find the daughter of a king, or of a
chief, or of a hospitaller, whom it might please Cu Chulainn to woo.

All the messengers returned that day a year later, and had not
found a maiden whom Cu Chulainn chose to woo. Thereupon Cu
Chulainn himself went to woo a maiden that he knew in Luglochta
Loga ("the Gardens of Lug"), namely Emer, the daughter
of Forgall the Wily. Cu Chulainn himself, and his charioteer
Loeg son of Riangabar, went in his chariot. That was the one
chariot which the host of the horses of the chariots of Ulster could
not follow, on account of the swiftness and speed of the chariot,
and of the chariot-chief who sat in it. Then Cu Chulainn found
the maiden on her playing-field, with her foster-sisters around
her, daughters of the land-owners that lived around the stronghold of Forgall. They were learning needlework and fine handiwork from Emer. Of all the maidens of Erin, she was the one
maiden whom he deigned to address and to woo. For she had the
six gifts: the gift of beauty, the gift of voice, the gift of sweet
speech, the gift of needlework, the gifts of wisdom and chastity.
Cu Chulainn had said that no maiden should go with him but
she who was his equal in age and form and race, in skill and deftness, who was the best handiworker of the maidens of Erin, for
that none but such as she was a fitting wife for him. Now, as
Emer was the one maiden who fulfilled all these conditions,
Cu Chulainn went to woo her above all.

It was in his festal array that Cu Chulainn went forth that
day to address Emer, and to show his beauty to her. As the
maidens were sitting on the bench of gathering at the stronghold,

they heard coming towards them the clatter of horses' hoofs, with the creaking of the chariot, the cracking of straps, the grating of wheels, the rush of the hero, and the clanking of weapons.

"Let one of you see," said Emer, "what it is that is coming toward us."

"Truly, I see," said Fial, daughter of Forgall, "two steeds alike in size, beauty, fierceness, and speed, bounding side by side. Spirited they are and powerful, pricking their ears: their manes long and curling, and with curling tails. At the right side of the pole of the chariot is a grey horse, broad in the haunches, fierce, swift, wild; thundering he comes along, taking small bounds, with head erect and chest expanded. Beneath his four hard hoofs the firm and solid turf seems aflame. A flock of swift birds follows, but, as he takes his course along the road, a flash of breath darts from him, a blast of ruddy flaming sparks is poured from his curbed jaws.

"The other horse is jet-black, his head firmly knit, his feet broad-hoofed and slender. Long and curly are his mane and tail. Down his broad forehead hang heavy curls of hair. Spirited and fiery, he fiercely gallops along, stamping firmly on the ground. Beautifully he sweeps along as having outstripped the horses of the land; he bounds over the smooth dry sward, following the levels of the mid-glen, where no obstacle obstructs his pace.

"I see a chariot of fine wood with wicker work, moving on wheels of white bronze. A pole of white silver, with a mounting of white bronze. Its frame very high of creaking copper, rounded and firm. A strong curved yoke of gold; two firm-plaited yellow reins; the shafts hard and straight as sword-blades.

"Within the chariot a dark sad man, comeliest of the men of Erin. Around him a beautiful crimson five-folded tunic, fastened at its opening on his white breast with a brooch of inlaid gold, against which it heaves, beating in full strokes. A shirt with a white hood, interwoven red with flaming gold. Seven red dragon-gems on the ground of either of his eyes. Two blue-white, blood-red cheeks that breathe forth sparks and flashes of fire. A ray of love burns in his look. Methinks, a shower of pearls has fallen into his mouth. As black as the side of a charred beam each of his eye-brows. On his two thighs rests a golden-hilted sword, and fastened to the copper frame of the chariot is a blood-red spear with a sharp mettlesome blade, on a shaft of wood well-fitted to the hand. Over his shoulders a crimson shield with a rim of silver, chased with figures of golden animals. He leaps the hero's salmon-leap into the air, and does many like swift feats. This is the description of the chariot-chief of the single chariot.

"Before him in that chariot there is a charioteer, a very slender, tall, much-freckled man. On his head is very curly bright-red hair, held by a fillet of bronze upon his brow which prevents the hair from falling over his face. On both sides of his head patins of gold confine the hair. A shoulder mantle about him with sleeves opening at the two elbows, and in his hand a goad of red gold with which he guides the horses."

Meanwhile Cu Chulainn had come to the place where the maidens were. He wished a blessing to them. Emer lifted up her lovely face and recognised Cu Chulainn, and she said, "May God make smooth the path before you!"

"And you," he said, "may you be safe from every harm!"

"Whence comest thou?" she asked.

"From Intide Emna," he replied.

"Where did you sleep?" said she.

"We slept," he said, "in the house of the man who tends the cattle of the plain of Tethra."

"What was your food there?" she asked.

"The ruin of a chariot was cooked for us there," he replied.

"Which way didst thou come?"

"Between the Two Mountains of the Wood," said he.

"Which way didst thou take after that?"

"That is not hard to tell," he said. "From the Cover of the Sea, over the Great Secret of the Tuatha De Danann, and the Foam of the two steeds of Emain Macha; over the Morrigu's Garden, and the Great Sow's Back; over the Glen of the Great Dam, between the god and his prophet; over the Marrow of the Woman Fedelm, between the boar and his dam; over the Washing-place of the horses of Dea; between the King of Ana and his servant, to Monnchuile of the Four Corners of the World; over Great Crime and the Remnants of the Great Feast; between the Vat and the Little Vat, to the Gardens of Lug, to the daughters of Tethra's nephew, Forgall, the king of the Fomorians. And what, O maiden, is the account of thee?" said Cu Chulainn.

"Truly, that is not hard to tell," said the maiden. "Tara of the women, whitest of maidens, the paragon of chastity, a prohibition that is not taken, a watcher that yet sees no one. A modest woman is a dragon, which none comes near. The daughter of a king is a flame of hospitality, a road that cannot be entered. I have champions that follow me to guard me from whoever would carry me off against their will, without their and Forgall's knowledge of my act."

"Who are the champions that follow thee, O maiden?" said Cu Chulainn.

"Truly, it is not hard to tell," said Emer. "Two called Lui, two Luaths; Luath and Lath Goible, son of Tethra; Triath and Trescath, Brion and Bolor; Bas, son of Omnach; eight called Connla; and Conn, son of Forgall. Every man of them has the strength of a hundred and the feats of nine. Hard it were, too, to tell the many powers of Forgall himself. He is stronger than any laborer, more learned than any druid, more acute than any poet. It will be more than all your games to fight against Forgall himself. For many powers of his have been recounted of manly deeds."

"Why dost thou not reckon me, O maiden, with those strong men?" said Cu Chulainn.

"If thy deeds have been recounted, why should I not reckon thee among them?"

"Truly, I swear, O maiden," said Cu Chulainn, "that I shall make my deeds to be recounted among the glories of the strength of heroes."

"What then is thy strength?" said Emer.

"That is quickly told," said he; "when my strength in fight is weakest, I fight off twenty. A third part of my strength is sufficient for thirty. Alone, I make combat against forty. Under my protection a hundred are secure. From dread of me, warriors avoid fords and battlefields. Hosts and multitudes and many armed men flee before the terror of my face."

"Those are goodly fights for a tender boy," said the maiden, "but thou hast not yet reached the strength of chariot-chiefs."

"Truly, O maiden," said he, "well have I been brought up by my dear foster-father Conchobar. Not as a churl strives to bring up his children, between flag and kneading-trough, between fire and wall, nor on the floor of a single larder have I been brought up

by Conchobar; but among chariot-chiefs and champions, among
jesters and druids, among poets and learned men, among the
nobles and landlords of Ulster have I been reared, so that I have all
their manners and gifts."

"Who then were they who brought thee up in all those deeds
of which thou dost boast?" said Emer.

"That, truly, is easily told. Fair-speeched Sencha has taught
me, so that I am strong, wise, swift, deft. I am prudent in judgment, my memory is good. Before wise men, I make answer to
many; I give heed to their arguments. I direct the judgments of all
the men of Ulster, and, through the training of Sencha, my deci-
sions are unalterable.

"Blai, the lord of lands, on account of his racial kinship, took
me to himself, so that I got my due with him. I invite the men of
Conchobar's province with their king. I entertain them for the
space of a week, I settle their gifts and their spoils, I aid them in
their honor and their fines.

"Fergus has so fostered me, that I slay mighty warriors through
the strength of valor. I am fierce in might and in prowess, so that
I am able to guard the borders of the land against foreign foes. I
am a shelter for every poor man, I am a rampart of fight for every
wealthy man; I give comfort to him who is wretched, I deal out
mischief to him who is strong: all this through the fosterage of
Fergus.

"Amergin the poet, to his knee I came. Therefore I am able to
praise a king for the possession of any excellency; therefore I can
stand up to any man in valor, in prowess, in wisdom, in splendor,
in cleverness, in justice, in boldness. I am a match for any chariot-
chief. I yield thanks to none, save Conchobar the Battle-Victorious.

"Finnchoem has reared me, so that Conall the Victorious is my
fosterbrother. For the sake of Dechtire, Cathbad of the gentle
face has taught me, so that I am an adept in the arts of the gods of
druidism, and learned in the excellencies of knowledge.

"All the men of Ulster have taken part in my bringing up, alike
charioteers and chariot-chiefs, kings and chief poets, so that
I am the darling of the host and multitude, so that I fight
for the honor of them all alike. Honorably was I called into
being by Lug son of Conn mac Ethlenn, when Dechtire went to

the house of the Mighty One of the Brug. And thou, O maiden," said Cu Chulainn, "how hast thou been reared in the Gardens of Lug?"

"It is not hard to relate that to thee, truly," answered the maiden. "I was brought up," said she, "in ancient virtues, in lawful behavior, in the keeping of chastity, in rank equal to a queen, in stateliness of form, so that to me is attributed every noble grace of demeanor among the hosts of Erin's women."

"Good indeed are those virtues," said Cu Chulainn. "Why, then, should it not be fitting for us both to become one? For I have not hitherto found a maiden capable of holding converse with me at a meeting in this wise."

"One more question," said the maiden. "Hast thou a wife already?"

"Not so," said Cu Chulainn.

Said the maiden, "I may not marry before my sister is married, for she is older than I; namely, Fial, daughter of Forgall, whom thou seest with me here. She is excellent in handiwork."

"It is not she, truly, with whom I have fallen in love," said Cu Chulainn. "Nor have I ever accepted a woman who has known a man before me, and I have been told that yon girl was once Cairbre Niafer's."

While they were thus conversing, Cu Chulainn saw the breasts of the maiden over the bosom of her smock. And he said: "Fair is this plain, the plain of the noble yoke."

Then the maiden spake these words: "No one comes to this plain who does not slay as many as a hundred on every ford from the Ford of Scenn Menn at Ollbine to Banchuing Arcait, where swift Brea breaks the brow of Fedelm."

"Fair is this plain, the plain of the noble yoke," said Cu Chulainn.

"No one comes to this plain," said she, "who has not achieved the feat of leaping over three walls and slaying three times nine men at one blow, one of each of my brothers being in each group of nine, and yet preserve the brother in the midst of each nine of them alive; and then, accompanied by them and my foster-sister, bring out of Forgall's stronghold my weight in gold."

"Fair is this plain, the plain of the noble yoke," said Cu Chulainn.

"None comes to this plain," said she, "who does not go without sleep from summer's end to the beginning of spring, from the beginning of spring to May-day, and again from May-day to the beginning of winter."

"Even as thou hast commanded, so shall all by me be done," said Cu Chulainn.

"And by me thy offer is accepted, it is taken, it is granted," said Emer. "Yet one question more. What is thy account of thyself?" said she.

"I am the nephew of the man that disappears in another in the wood of Badb," [1] said he.

"And thy name?" she said.

"I am the hero of the plague that befalls dogs," [2] said he. After those notable words, Cu Chulainn went from thence, and they did not hold any further converse on that day.

While Cu Chulainn was driving across Breg, Loeg, his charioteer, asked him: "Now," said he, "the words that thou and the maiden Emer spoke, what didst thou mean by them?"

"Dost thou not know," answered Cu Chulainn, "that I am wooing Emer? And it is for this reason that we disguised our words, lest the girls should understand that I am wooing her. For, if Forgall knew it, we should not meet with his consent." Cu Chulainn then repeated the conversation from the beginning to his charioteer, explaining it to him, to beguile the length of their way. They slept that night in Emain Macha.

Then the daughters of the land-owners told their parents of the youth who had come in his splendid chariot, and of the conversation held between him and Emer; that they did not know what they had said to one another; and that he had turned from them across the plain of Breg northward. The land-owners related all this to Forgall the Wily, and told him that the girl had spoken to Cu Chulainn.

"It is true," said Forgall the Wily. "The madman from Emain Macha has been here to converse with Emer, and the girl has fallen in love with him: that is why they talked one to another. But it shall avail them nothing. I shall hinder them," he said.

---

[1] A punning use of the name Conchobar. There is in Ros a brook named Conchobar that unites with the Dofolt.

[2] A punning reference to his own name, the Hound of Culann. See the story of how he got his name in "The Boyhood Deeds of Cu Chulainn." (p. 142).

Thereupon Forgall the Wily went to Emain Macha disguised in the garb of a foreigner, as if it were an embassy from the King of the Gauls that had come to confer with Conchobar, with an offering to him of golden treasures, and wine of Gaul, and all sorts of good things besides. In number they were three. Great welcome was made to him. When on the third day he had sent away his men, Cu Chulainn and Conall and other chariot-chiefs of Ulster were praised before him. He said that it was true, that the chariot-chiefs performed marvellously, but that were Cu Chulainn to go to Donall the Soldierly in Alba (Scotland), his skill would be more wonderful still; and that if he went to Scathach to learn soldierly feats, he would excel the warriors of all Europe. But the reason for which he proposed this to Cu Chulainn was that he might never return again. For he thought that if Cu Chulainn became Scathach's friend, he would come to his death thereby, through the wildness and fierceness of that warrior. Cu Chulainn consented to go, and Forgall bound himself to give Cu Chulainn whatever he desired, if he should go within a certain time. Forgall went home, and the warriors arose in the morning and set themselves to do as they had vowed.

So they started; Cu Chulainn and Loegaire the Triumphant, and Conchobar; and Conall the Victorious, some say, went with them. But Cu Chulainn first went across Mag Breg to visit the maiden. He talked to Emer before going into the ship, and the maiden told him that it had been Forgall who in Emain Macha had desired him to go and learn soldierly feats, in order that they two might not meet. And she bade him be on his guard wherever he went, lest Forgall should destroy him. Either of them promised the other to keep their chastity until they should meet again, unless either of them died meanwhile. They bade each other farewell, and he turned towards Alba.

PART II

CU CHULAINN'S EDUCATION IN ARMS

When they reached Donall in Alba, they were taught by him to blow a leathern bellows under the flagstone of the small hole. On it they would perform till their soles were black or livid. They were taught another thing on a spear, on which they would jump and perform on its point; this was called "the champion's coiling round the points of spears," or "dropping on its head." Then the daughter of Donall, Dornolla, Big-Fist by name, fell in love with Cu Chulainn. Her form was very gruesome, her knees were large, her heels turned before her, her feet behind her; big dark-grey eyes in her head, her face as black as a bowl of jet. A very large forehead she had, her rough bright-red hair in threads wound round her head. Cu Chulainn refused her. Then she swore to be revenged on him for this.

Donall said that Cu Chulainn would not have perfect knowledge of their learning until he went to Scathach, who lived to the east of Alba. So the four went across Alba, Cu Chulainn, Conchobar King of Ulster, Conall the Victorious, and Loegaire the Triumphant. Then before their eyes appeared unto them in a vision Emain Macha, past which Conchobar and Conall and Loegaire were not able to go. The daughter of Donall had raised that vision in order to sever Cu Chulainn from his companions to his ruin. Other versions say that it was Forgall the Wily who raised this vision before them to induce them to turn back, so that by returning Cu Chulainn should fail to fulfil what he had promised him in Emain Macha, and thereby he would be shamed; or that, were he peradventure in spite of it to go eastward to learn soldierly feats, both known and unknown, of Scathach, he would be still more likely to be killed, being alone. Then, of his own free will, Cu Chulainn departed from them along an unknown road, for the powers of the girl Dornolla were great, and she wrought evil against him, and severed him from his companions.

Now, when Cu Chulainn went across Alba, he was sad and gloomy and weary for the loss of his comrades, neither knew he whither he should go to seek Scathach. For he had promised his comrades that he would not return again to Emain Macha, unless he either reached Scathach or met his death. Now, seeing that he was lost, he lingered; and while he was there, he beheld a terrible great beast like a lion coming towards him, which kept watching him, but did not do him any harm. Whichever way he went, the beast went before him, turning its side towards him. Then he took a leap and was on its back. He did not guide it, but went wherever the beast liked. In that wise they journeyed four days, until they came to the uttermost bounds of men, and to an island where

lads were rowing on a small loch. The lads laughed at the un-
wonted sight of the hurtful beast doing service to a man. Cu
Chulainn then leaped off, and the beast parted from him, and he
bade it farewell.

He passed on, and came to a large house in a deep glen, wherein
was a maiden fair of form. The maiden addressed him, and bade
him welcome. "Welcome art thou, O Cu Chulainn!" said she. He
asked her how she knew him. She answered that they both had
been dear foster-children with Wulfkin the Saxon, "when I was
there, and thou learning sweet speech from him," said she. She
then gave him meat and drink and he turned away from her.
Then he met a brave youth who gave him the same welcome. They
conversed together, and Cu Chulainn inquired of him the way to
the stronghold of Scathach. The youth taught him the way across
the Plain of Ill-luck that lay before him. On the hither half of the
plain the feet of men would stick fast; on the farther half the grass
would rise and hold them fast on the points of its blades. The youth
gave him a wheel, and told him to follow its track across one-half
of the plain. He gave him also an apple, and told him to follow
the way along which the apple ran, and that in such wise he would
reach the end of the plain. Thus Cu Chulainn went across the
plain; afterwards proceeding farther on. The youth had told him
that there was a large glen before him, and a single narrow path
through it, which was full of monsters that had been sent by Forgall
to destroy him, and that his road to the house of Scathach lay
across terrible mountain fastnesses. Then each of them wished a
blessing to the other, Cu Chulainn and the youth Eochaid Bairche.
It was he who taught him how he should win honor in the house of
Scathach. The same youth also foretold to him what he would
suffer of hardships and straits in the Cattle-Raid of Cooley, and
what evil and exploits and contests he would achieve against the
men of Erin.

Then Cu Chulainn, following the young man's instructions,
went on that road across the Plain of Ill-luck and through the
Perilous Glen. This was the road that Cu Chulainn took to the
camp where the scholars of Scathach were. He asked where she
was. "In yonder island," said they.

"Which way must I take to reach her?"

"By the Bridge of the Cliff, which no man can cross until he has achieved valor." For thus was that bridge: it had two low ends and the mid-space high, and whenever anybody leaped on one end of it, the other end would lift itself up and throw him on his back. Some versions relate that a crowd of the warriors of Erin were in that stronghold learning feats from Scathach; namely, Ferdiad son of Daman, and Naisi son of Usnech, and Loch Mor son of Egomas, and Fiamain son of Fora, and an innumerable host besides. But in this version it is not told that they were there at that time.

Cu Chulainn tried three times to cross the bridge and could not do it. The men jeered at him. Then in a frenzy he jumped upon the head of the bridge, and made "the hero's salmon-leap," so that he landed on the middle of it; and the other head of the bridge had not fully raised itself up when he reached it; he threw himself from it, and was on the ground of the island. He went up to the stronghold, and struck the door with the shaft of his spear, so that it went through it. Scathach was told. "Truly," said she, "this must be some one who has achieved valor elsewhere." And she sent her daughter Uathach to know who the youth might be. Then Uathach came and conversed with Cu Chulainn. On the third day she advised him, if it were to achieve valor that he had come, that he should go through the hero's salmon-leap to reach Scathach, in the place where she was teaching her two sons, Cuar and Cett, in the great yew-tree; that he should set his sword between her breasts until she yielded him his three wishes: namely, to teach him without neglect; that without the payment of wedding-gifts he might wed Uathach; and that she should foretell his future, for she was a prophetess.

Cu Chulainn then went to the place where Scathach was. He placed his two feet on the two edges of the basket of the feats, and bared his sword, and put its point to her heart, saying, "Death hangs over thee!"

"Name thy three demands!" said she; "thy three demands, as thou canst utter them in one breath."

"They must be fulfilled," said Cu Chulainn. And he pledged her. Uathach then was given to Cu Chulainn, and Scathach taught him skill of arms.

During the time that he was with Scathach, and was the husband of Uathach her daughter, a certain famous man who lived

in Munster, by name Lugaid son of Nos son of Alamac, the renowned king and fosterbrother of Cu Chulainn, went eastwards
with twelve chariot-chiefs of the high kings of Munster, to woo
twelve daughters of Cairbre Niafer, but they had all been betrothed before. When Emer's father, Forgall the Wily, heard
this, he went to Tara, and told Lugaid that the best maiden in
Erin, both as to form and chastity and handiwork, was in his
house unmarried. Lugaid said it pleased him well. Then Forgall
betrothed the maiden to Lugaid; and to the twelve under-kings
that were together with Lugaid, he betrothed twelve daughters of
twelve landed proprietors in Breg.

The king accompanied Forgall to his stronghold for the wedding.
When now Emer was brought to Lugaid, to sit by his side, she
took between both her hands his two cheeks, and laid it on the
truth of his honor and his life, confessing that it was Cu Chulainn
she loved, that Forgall was against it, and that any one who should
take her as his wife would suffer loss of honor. Then, for fear of
Cu Chulainn, Lugaid did not dare to take Emer, and so he returned
home again.

Scathach was at that time carrying on war against other tribes,
over whom the Princess Aife ruled. The two hosts assembled to
fight, but Cu Chulainn had been put in bonds by Scathach, and
a sleeping-potion given him beforehand to prevent him going
into the battle, lest anything should befall him there. She did
this as a precaution. But after an hour Cu Chulainn suddenly
started out of his sleep. This sleeping-potion, that would have
held anybody else for twenty-four hours in sleep, held him for
only one hour. He went forth with the two sons of Scathach against
the three sons of Ilsuanach, namely, Cuar, Cett, and Cruife, three
warriors of Aife's. Alone he encountered them all three, and they
fell by him. On the next morning again the battle was set, and
the two hosts marched forward until the two lines met, face to
face. Then the three sons of Ess Enchenn advanced, namely,
Cire, Bire, and Blaicne, three other of Aife's warriors, and began
to combat against the two sons of Scathach. They went on the
path of feats. Thereupon Scathach uttered a sigh, for she knew
not what would come of it; first, because there was no third man
with her two sons against those three, and next, because she was
afraid of Aife, who was the hardest woman-warrior in the world.

Cu Chulainn, however, went up to her two sons, and sprang upon the path, and met all three, and they fell by him.

Aife then challenged Scathach to combat, and Cu Chulainn went forth to meet Aife. Before going he asked what it was Aife loved most. Scathach said: "What most she loves are her two horses, her chariot, and her charioteer." Cu Chulainn and Aife went on the path of feats, and began combat there. Aife shattered Cu Chulainn's weapon, and his sword was broken off at the hilt. Then Cu Chulainn cried: "Ah me, the charioteer of Aife, her two horses, and her chariot have fallen down the glen, and all have perished!" At that Aife looked up.

Then Cu Chulainn sprang toward her, seized her under her two breasts, took her on his back like a shoulder-load, and bore her away to his own host. Then he threw her from him to the ground, and over her held his naked sword.

"Life for life, O Cu Chulainn!" said Aife.

"My three demands to me!" said he.

"Thou shalt have them as thou breathest them," she said.

"These are my three demands," he said, "that thou give hostages to Scathach, nor ever afterwards oppose her, that thou remain with me this night before thy stronghold, and that thou bear me a son."

"I promise all this to thee," said she. And thus it was done. Cu Chulainn went with Aife and remained with her that night. Then Aife said she was with child, and that she would bear a boy. "On this day seven years I will send him to Erin," she said, "and leave thou a name for him."

Cu Chulainn left a golden finger-ring for him, and told her that the boy was to go and seek him in Erin, so soon as the ring should fit on his finger. And he said that Connla was the name to be given him, and charged her that he should not make himself known to any one man; also, that he should not turn out of the way of any man; nor refuse combat to any. Thereupon Cu Chulainn returned again to his own people.

As he went along the same road, he met an old woman on the road, blind of her left eye. She asked him to beware, and to avoid the road before her. He said there was no other footing for him, save on the cliff of the sea that was beneath him. She besought him to leave the road to her. Then he left the road, only clinging to it with his toes. As she passed over him she hit his great toe to throw him off the path, down the cliff. He had foreseen it, and leaped the hero's salmon-leap up again, and struck off the woman's head. She was Ess Enchenn, the mother of the last three warriors that had fallen by him, and it was in order to destroy him that she had come to meet him.

After that the hosts returned with Scathach to her own land, and hostages were given to her by Aife. And Cu Chulainn stayed there for the day of his recovery.

At last, when the full lore of soldierly arts with Scathach had been mastered by Cu Chulainn—as well as the apple-feat, the thunder-feat, the blade-feat, the supine-feat, and the spear-feat, the rope-feat, the body-feat, the cat's-feat, the salmon-feat of a chariot-chief, the throw of the staff, the whirl of a brave chariot-chief, the *gae bulga* (bag spear), the wheel-feat, the breath-feat, the hero's whoop, the blow, the counter-blow, running up a lance and righting the body on its point, the scythe-chariot, and the hero's twisting round spear points—then came to him a message to return to his own land, and he took his leave.

Then Scathach told him what would befall him in the future, and sang to him in the seer's large shining ken, and spoke these words:

> Welcome, oh victorious, warlike Cu Chulainn;
> At the Raid of the Cattle of Breg,
> Thou wilt be a chariot-chief in single combat.
> Great peril awaits thee,
> Alone against a vast herd.
> The warriors of Cruachan, thou wilt scatter them.
> Thy name shall reach the men of Scotland.
> Thirty years I reckon the strength of thy valor;
> Further than this I do not add.

Then Cu Chulainn went on board his ship, to set out for Erin. These were the voyagers in the ship: Lugaid and Luan, the two sons of Loch; Ferbaeth, Larin, Ferdiad, and Durst son of Serb. They came to the house of Ruad, king of the Isles, on Samain-night. Conall the Victorious, and Loegaire the Triumphant, were there before them levying tribute; for at that time a tribute was paid to Ulster from the Isles of the Foreigners (the Western Isles).

Then Cu Chulainn heard sounds of wailing before him in the stronghold of the king. "What is that lamentation?" asked Cu Chulainn

"It is because Dervorgil, the daughter of Ruad, is given as tribute to the Fomorians," said they.

"Where is the maiden?" he said.

They answered, "She is on the shore below." Cu Chulainn went down to the strand, and drew near to the maiden. He asked her the meaning of her plight, and she told him fully. Said he, "Whence do the men come?"

"From that distant land yonder. Remain not here," she said, "in sight of the robbers." But he remained there awaiting them, and he killed the three Fomorians in single combat. The last man wounded him in the wrist, and the maiden gave him a strip from her garment to bind round his wound. Then he departed without making himself known to her. The maiden came to the stronghold, and told her father the whole story; and afterwards came Cu Chulainn to the stronghold, like every other guest. Conall and Loegaire bade him welcome, and there were many in the stronghold who boasted of having slain the Fomorians, but the maiden believed them not. Then the king had a bath prepared, and afterwards each one was brought to her separately. Cu Chulainn came, like all the rest, and the maiden recognised him.

"I will give the maiden to thee," said Ruad, "and I myself will pay her wedding-dowry."

"Not so," said Cu Chulainn. "But if it please her, let her follow me this day year to Erin; there she will find me."

Then Cu Chulainn came to Emain Macha and related all his adventures. When he had cast his fatigue from him, he set out to seek Emer at the rath of Forgall. For a whole year he remained near it, but could not approach her for the number of the watch.

At the end of the year he came and said to his charioteer, "It is to-day, O Loeg, that we have our tryst with the daughter of Ruad, but we know not the exact place, for we were not wise. Let us go to the coast."

When they came to the shore of Loch Cuan (Strangford Lough), they beheld two birds on the sea. Cu Chulainn put a stone in his sling, and aimed at the birds. The men ran up to them, after having hit one of the birds. When they came up to them, lo! they saw two women, the most beautiful in the world. They were Dervorgil, the daughter of Ruad, and her handmaid. "Evil is the deed that thou hast done, O Cu Chulainn," said she; "it was to meet thee we came, and now thou hast hurt us." Cu Chulainn sucked the stone out of her, with its clot of blood round it. "I cannot wed thee now," said Cu Chulainn, "for I have drunk thy blood. But I will give thee to my companion here, Lugaid of the Red Stripes." And so it was done.

Then Cu Chulainn desired to go to the rath of Forgall. And that day the scythe-chariot was prepared for him. It was called the scythe-chariot (*carpat serrda*) on account of the iron scythes that stood out from it, or, perhaps, because it was first invented by the Serians. When he arrived at the rath of Forgall, he jumped the hero's salmon-leap across the three ramparts, so that he was on the ground of the stronghold. And he dealt three blows in the liss, so that eight men fell from each blow, and one escaped in each group of nine, namely, Scibur, Ibur, and Cat, three brothers of Emer. Forgall made a leap on to the rampart of the rath without, fleeing from Cu Chulainn, and he fell lifeless. Then Cu Chulainn carried off Emer, and her foster-sister, with their two weights of gold and silver, leaping back again across the third rampart, and so went forth.

From every direction cries were raised around them. Scenn Menn rushed against them. Cu Chulainn killed her at the ford, hence called the Ford of Scenn Menn. Thence they escaped to Glondath, and there Cu Chulainn killed a hundred of them. "Great is the deed (*glond*) that thou hast done," said Emer; "to have killed a hundred armed able-bodied men."

"Glond-ath (Ford of Deeds) shall be its name for ever," said Cu Chulainn. He reached Crufoit (Blood-turf), which until then had been called Rae-ban (White Field). He dealt great angry blows on the hosts in that place, so that streams of blood broke over it on every side. "By thy work, the hill is covered with a blood-stained turf to-day, O Cu Chulainn," cried the maiden. Hence it is called Cru-foit (Turf of Blood).

The pursuers overtook them at Ath n-Imfuait on the Boyne. Emer left the chariot, and Cu Chulainn pursued them along the banks, the clods flying from the hoofs of the horses across the ford northward. Then he turned, and pursued them northward, so that the clods flew over the ford southward from the hoofs of the horses. Hence is it called the Ford of the Two Clods, from the flying of the sods hither and thither. Now at each ford from

Ath Scenn Menn at Ollbine to the Boyne of Breg, Cu Chulainn killed a hundred, and so he fulfilled all the deeds that he had vowed to the maiden, and he came safely out of all, and reached Emain Macha towards the fall of night.

Emer was brought into the House of the Red Branch to Conchobar and to the men of Ulster, and they bade her welcome. Cu Chulainn then took to himself his wife, and thenceforward they were not separated until they died.

THE TRAGIC DEATH OF CONNLA

Connla is the son whom, according to "The Wooing of Emer" (p. 167), the warlike Aife was destined to bear to Cu Chulainn. The story of how the boy followed Cu Chulainn to Ireland and was there slain by his own father reminds us of the famous epic tale of Sohrab and Rustem, best known to English readers through Matthew Arnold's poem of that name. The story of Connla probably existed in tradition before it was first recorded in the eighth century, and it is one of the few tales of the Ulster cycle that has maintained its popularity among the folk in more recent times. Numerous versions of a ballad on the death of Connla have been taken down from popular recitation during the last century. The title is sometimes given as "The Tragic Death of the Only Son of Aife (*Oenfer Aife*)."

What was the cause for which Cu Chulainn slew his son?

Not hard to tell. Cu Chulainn went to be taught craft of arms by Scathach, daughter of Ardgeimm, in Letha, until he attained mastership of feats with her. And Aife, a neighboring princess, went to him, and he left her pregnant. And he said to her that she would bear a son. "Keep this golden thumb-ring," said he, "until it fits the boy. When it fits him, let him come to seek me in Ireland. Let no man put him off his road, let him not make himself known to any man, nor let him refuse combat to any."

That day seven years the boy went forth to seek his father. The men of Ulster were at a gathering by Tracht Eisi (Strand of the Track), when they saw the boy coming towards them across the sea, a skiff of bronze under him, and gilt oars in his hand. In the skiff he had a heap of stones. He would put a stone in his staff-sling, and launch a stunning shot at the sea-birds, so that he brought them down, and they alive. Then would he let them up into the air again. He would perform his palate-feat, between both hands, so that it was too quick for the eye to perceive. He would tune his voice for them, and bring them down for the second time. Then he revived them once more.

"Well, now," said Conchobar, "woe to the land into which yonder lad comes! If grown-up men of the island from which he comes were to come, they would grind us to dust, when a small

172

boy makes that practice. Let some one go to meet him! Let him not allow the boy to come on land at all!"

"Who shall go to meet him?"

"Who should it be," said Conchobar, "but Condere son of Eochaid?"

"Why should Condere go?" said the others.

"Not hard to tell," said Conchobar. "If it is reason and eloquence he practises, then Condere is the proper person."

"I shall go to meet him," said Condere.

So Condere went just as the boy took the beach. "Thou hast come far enough, my good boy," said Condere, "for us to know whither thou goest and whence is thy race."

"I do not make myself known to any one man," said the lad, "nor do I avoid any man."

"Thou shalt not land," said Condere, "until thou hast made thyself known."

"I shall go whither I have set out," said the lad.

The boy turned away. Then said Condere: "Turn to me, my boy; Conchobar will protect thee. Turn to Conchobar, the valiant son of Nessa; to Sencha, the son of Coscra; to Cethern, the red-bladed son of Fintan, the fire that wounds battalions; to Amergin the poet; to Cumscraid of the great hosts. Welcome he whom Conall the Victorious protects."

"Thou hast met us well," said the lad. "Therefore shalt thou have thy answer. Turn back again!" said the lad. "For though thou hadst the strength of a hundred, thou art not able to check me."

"Well," said Condere, "let someone else go to speak to thee!" So Condere went to the men of Ulster and told them.

"It shall not be," said Conall the Victorious, "that the honor of Ulster be carried off while I am alive." Then he went towards the boy. "Thy play is pretty, my good boy," said Conall.

"It will not be less pretty against thee," said the lad. The lad put a stone in his sling. He sent it into the air, so that its noise and thunder as it went up reached Conall, and threw him on his back. Before he could rise, the lad put the strap of his shield upon his arms.

"Someone else against him!" said Conall. In that way the boy made mockery of the host of Ulster.

Cu Chulainn, however, was present at the time, going towards the boy, and the arm of Emer, Forgall's daughter, over his neck. "Do not go down!" said she. "It is a son of thine that is down there. Do not murder thy only son! It is not fair fight nor wise to rise up against thy son. Turn to me! Hear my voice! My advice is good. Let Cu Chulainn hear it! I know what name he will tell, if the boy down there is Connla, the only son of Aife," said Emer.

Then said Cu Chulainn: "Forbear, woman! Even though it were he who is there," said he, "I would kill him for the honor of Ulster."

Then he went down himself. "Delightful, my boy, is the play which thou makest," said he.

"*Your* play, though, is not so," said the little boy, "that two of you did not come, so that I may make myself known to them."

"It would have been necessary to bring a small boy along with me," said Cu Chulainn. "However, thou wilt die unless thou tellest thy name."

"Let it be so!" said the lad. The boy made for him. They exchanged blows. The lad, by a properly measured stroke with the sword, cropped off Cu Chulainn's hair. "The mockery has come to a head!" said Cu Chulainn. "Now let us wrestle!"

"I cannot reach thy belt," said the boy. He got upon two stones, and thrust Cu Chulainn thrice between two pillar-stones, while the boy did not move either of his feet from the stones until his feet went into the stones up to his ankles. The track of his feet is there still. Hence is the Strand of the Track (Tracht Eisi) in Ulster.

Then they went into the sea to drown each other, and twice the boy ducked him. Thereupon Cu Chulainn went at the boy from the water, and played him false with the *gae bulga;* for to no man had Scathach ever taught the use of that weapon save to Cu Chulainn alone. He sent it at the boy through the water, so that his bowels fell about his feet.

"Now, this is what Scathach never taught me!" cried the boy. "Woe that thou hast wounded me!"

"It is true," said Cu Chulainn. He took the boy between his arms, and carried him till he let him down before the men of Ulster. "Here is my son for you, men of Ulster," said he.

"Alas!" said the men; and "It is true," said the boy. "If I were among you to the end of five years, I should vanquish the men of the world before you on every side, and you would hold kingship as far as Rome. Since it is as it is, point out to me the famous men that are on the spot, that I may take leave of them!"

Thereupon he put his arms round the neck of one after another, bade farewell to his father, and forthwith died. Then his cry of lament was raised, his grave made, his stone set up, and to the end of three days no calf was let to their cows by the men of Ulster, to commemorate him.

THE SICK–BED OF CU CHULAINN

"The Sick-bed of Cu Chulainn," like numerous other early Irish sagas, is a compilation based on several versions of the same story. The tale in its earliest form probably told how a mortal hero, having fallen under a fairy spell, was lured by the fairy people to the Happy Otherworld, where he was healed of his malady or assisted the supernatural folk in their tribal feuds. In the present form of the story the double visits of the fairy messengers to the ailing Cu Chulainn, the double account of Loeg's experiences in the fairy realm, as well as other repetitions and inconsistencies are the result of the unskilled work of the compiler and interpolater to whom the oldest extant versions are due. Noteworthy also is the fact that here, as in "The Wooing of Emer" (see p. 153), Cu Chulainn's wife Emer plays a prominent part.

Every year the men of Ulster were accustomed to hold festival together; and the time when they held it was for three days before Samain, and for three days after that day, and upon Samain itself. And the time that is spoken of is that when the men of Ulster used to assemble in Mag Muirthemne, and there they used to hold the festival every year; nor was there anything in the world that they would do at that time except sports, and marketings, and splendors, and pomps, and feasting and eating; and it is from that custom of theirs that the Festival of Samain was descended, that is now held throughout the whole of Ireland.

Now once upon a time the men of Ulster held festival in Mag Muirthemne, and the reason that this festival was held was that every man of them should every Samain give account of the combats he had made and of his valor. It was their custom to hold that festival in order to give account of these combats, and the manner in which they gave that account was this: each man used to cut off the tip of the tongue of a foe whom he had killed, and carry it with him in a pouch. Moreover, in order to make more great the numbers of their contests, some used to bring with them the tips of the tongues of beasts, and each man publicly declared the fights he had fought, one man of them after the other. And they did this also: they laid their swords over their thighs when they related their combats, and their own

swords used to turn against them when the strife that they declared was false; nor was this to be wondered at, for at that time
it was customary for demons to scream from the weapons of men,
so that for this cause their weapons might be the more able to
guard them.

To that festival then came all the men of Ulster except two
alone, and these two were Fergus mac Roig, and Conall the
Victorious.

"Let the festival be held!" cried the men of Ulster.

"Nay," said Cu Chulainn, "it shall not be held until Conall
and Fergus come," and this he said because Fergus was the foster-
father of Cu Chulainn, and Conall was his comrade.

Then said Sencha, "Let us for the present engage in games of
chess; and let the druids sing, and let the jugglers perform their
feats"; and it was done as he had said.

Now while they were thus employed a flock of birds came down
and hovered over a neighboring lake; never were seen in Ireland
more beautiful birds than these. And a longing that these birds
should be given to them seized upon the women who were there;
and each of them began to boast of the prowess of her husband
at bird-catching.

"How I wish," said Ethne, Conchobar's wife, "that I could have
two of those birds, one of them upon each of my two shoulders."

"It is what we all long for," said the women.

"If any should have this gift, I should be the first one to have
it," said Ethne [1] Inguba, the wife of Cu Chulainn.

"What are we to do now?" said the women.

"It is easy to answer you," said Leborcham, the daughter of
Oa and Adarc; "I will go now with a message from you, and will
seek for Cu Chulainn." She then went to Cu Chulainn.

"The women of Ulster would be well pleased," she said, "if
yonder birds were given to them by thy hand."

Cu Chulainn reached for his sword to unsheathe it against her.
"Cannot the women of Ulster find any other but us," he said,
"to give them their bird-hunt to-day?"

"It is not seemly for thee to rage thus against them," said

---

[1] It will be noted that later in the story Emer is Cu Chulainn's wife. This
confusion results from the fact that this story is a combination of at least
two more ancient accounts.

Leborcham, "for it is on thy account that the women of Ulster have assumed one of their three blemishes, even the blemish of blindness." For there were three blemishes that the women of Ulster assumed, that of crookedness of gait, and that of a stammering in their speech, and that of blindness. Each of the women who loved Conall the Victorious had assumed a crookedness of gait; each woman who loved Cuscraid Menn, the Stammerer of Macha, Conchobar's son, stammered in her speech; each woman in like manner who loved Cu Chulainn, had assumed a blindness of her eyes, in order to resemble Cu Chulainn; for he, when his mind was angry within him, was accustomed to draw in one of his eyes so far that a crane could not reach it in his head, and would thrust out the other so that it was as great as a cauldron in which a calf is cooked.

"Yoke for us the chariot, O Loeg!" said Cu Chulainn. At that Loeg yoked the chariot, and Cu Chulainn went into the chariot, and he cast his sword at the birds with a cast like the cast of a boomerang, so that they flapped against the water with their claws and wings. And they seized upon all the birds, and they gave them and distributed them among the women; nor was there any one of the women, except Ethne alone, who had not a pair of those birds.

Then Cu Chulainn returned to his wife.

"Thou art angry," said he to her.

"I am in no way angry," answered Ethne, "for I deem it as being by me that the distribution was made. And thou hast done what was fitting," she said, "for there is not one of these women but loves thee; none in whom thou hast no share; but for myself, none has any share in me but thou alone."

"Be not angry," said Cu Chulainn, "if in the future any birds come to Mag Muirthemne or to the Boyne, the two birds that are the most beautiful among those that come shall be thine."

A little while after this they saw two birds flying over the lake, linked together by a chain of red gold. They sang a gentle song, and a sleep fell upon all the men who were there except Cu Chulainn. Cu Chulainn rose up to pursue the birds.

"If thou wilt listen to me," said Loeg (and so also said Ethne), "thou wilt not go against them; behind those birds is some special power. Other birds may be taken by thee at some future day."

"Is it possible that such claim as this should be made upon me?" said Cu Chulainn. "Place a stone in my sling, O Loeg!"

Loeg thereon took a stone, and he placed it in the sling, and Cu Chulainn launched the stone at the birds, but the cast missed. "Alas!" said he. He took another stone, and he launched this also at the birds, but the stone flew past them.

"Wretch that I am," he cried; "since the very first day that I assumed arms, I have never missed a cast until this day!" And he threw his spear at them, and the spear went through the shield of the wing of one of the birds, and the birds flew away, and went beneath the lake.

After this Cu Chulainn departed, and he rested his back against a stone pillar, and his soul was angry within him, and sleep fell upon him. Then saw he two women come to him; the one of them had a green mantle upon her, and upon the other was a purple mantle folded in five folds. And the woman in the green mantle approached him, and she laughed a laugh at him, and she gave him a stroke with a horsewhip. And then the other approached him, and she also laughed at him, and she struck him in the same way; and for a long time were they thus, each of them in turn coming to him and striking him, until he was all but dead; and then they departed from him.

Now the men of Ulster perceived the state in which Cu Chulainn was, and they cried out that he should be awakened; but "Nay," said Fergus, "you shall not move him, for he is seeing a vision"; and a little after that Cu Chulainn arose from his sleep.

"What has happened to thee?" said the men of Ulster; but he had no power to bid greeting to them.

"Let me be carried," he said, "to the sick-bed that is in Tete Brecc; not to Dun Imrith, nor yet to Dun Delgan."

"Wilt thou not be carried to Dun Delgan, thy stronghold, to seek for Emer?" said Loeg.

"Nay," said he, "my word is for Tete Brecc"; and thereon they bore him from that place, and he was in Tete Brecc until the end of one year, and during all that time he had speech with no one.

Now upon a certain day before the next Samain, at the end of a year, when the men of Ulster were in the house where Cu Chulainn was, Fergus being at the side-wall, and Conall the Victorious at his head, and Lugaid Red-Stripes at his pillow, and Ethne

Inguba at his feet;—when they were there in this manner, a man
came to them, and he seated himself near the entrance of the
chamber in which Cu Chulainn lay.

"What has brought thee here?" said Conall the Victorious.

"No hard question to answer," said the man. "If the man who
lies yonder were in health, he would be a good protection to all of
Ulster; in the weakness and the sickness in which he now is, so
much the more great is the protection that they have from him.
I have no fear of any of you," he said, "for it is to give to this
man a greeting that I come."

"Welcome to thee, then, and fear nothing," said the men of
Ulster; and the man rose to his feet, and he sang them the following
verses:

> O, Cu Chulainn! of thy illness
> Not great will be the length.
> They would heal thee if they were here,
> The daughters of Aed Abrat.

> Thus spoke Liban in Mag Cruach,
> By the side of Labraid the Swift:
> Love holds Fann's heart;
> She longs to be joined to Cu Chulainn.

> Goodly in truth would be the day
> When Cu Chulainn comes to my land.
> If he comes he shall have silver and gold;
> He shall have much wine to drink.

> Could he but love me enough for that,
> Cu Chulainn son of Sualtam!
> I have seen him in slumber,
> Without his arms, in very truth.

> 'Tis to Mag Muirthemne thou shouldst go,
> On the night of Samain, without injury to thyself.
> I will send thee Liban,
> To heal thy sickness, O Cu Chulainn!

> O, Cu Chulainn! of thy illness,
> Not great will be the length.
> They would heal thee if they were here,
> The daughters of Aed Abrat.

"Who art thou, then, thyself?" said the men of Ulster.

"I am Angus, the son of Aed Abrat," he answered; and the man
then left them, nor did any of them know whence it was he had
come, nor whither he went.

Then Cu Chulainn sat up, and he spoke to them. "Fortunate indeed is this!" said the men of Ulster; "tell us what it is that has happened to thee."

"Upon Samain night last year," he said, "I indeed saw a vision"; and he told them of all he had seen.

"What should now be done, Father Conchobar?" said Cu Chulainn.

"This hast thou to do," answered Conchobar; "rise, and go to the pillar where thou wert before."

Then Cu Chulainn went forth to the pillar, and then saw he the woman in the green mantle come to him. "This is good, O Cu Chulainn!" said she.

"It is no good thing in my thought," said Cu Chulainn. "Wherefore camest thou to me last year?" •

"It was indeed to do no injury to thee that we came," said the woman, "but to seek for thy friendship. I have come to greet thee," she said, "from Fann, the daughter of Aed Abrat; her husband, Manannan mac Lir (Son of the Sea), has abandoned her, and she has thereon set her love on thee. My own name is Liban, and I have brought to thee a message from my husband, Labraid the Swift Sword-Wielder, that he will give thee the woman Fann in exchange for one day's service to him in battle against Senach Siaborthe, and against Eochaid Iuil, and against Eogan Inber."

"I am in no fit state," he said, "to contend with men to-day."

"That will last but a little while," she said; "thou shalt be whole, and all that thou hast lost of thy strength shall be increased to thee. Labraid shall bestow on thee that gift, for he is the best of all warriors that are in the world."

"Where is it that Labraid dwells?" asked Cu Chulainn.

"In Mag Mell, the Plain of Delight," said Liban; "and now I desire to go to that other land," said she.

"Let Loeg go with thee," said Cu Chulainn, "that he may learn of the land from which thou hast come."

"Let him come, then," said Liban.

She and Loeg departed after that, and they went forward toward Mag Mell, the place where Fann was. And Liban turned to seek for Loeg, and she placed him beside her shoulder. "Thou wouldst never go hence, O Loeg!" said Liban, "wert thou not under a woman's protection."

"It is not a thing that I have most been accustomed to up to this time," said Loeg, "to be under a woman's guard."

"Shame, and everlasting shame," said Liban, "that Cu Chulainn is not where thou art."

"It were well for me," answered Loeg, "if it were indeed he who is here."

They passed on then, and went forward until they came opposite to the shore of an island, and there they saw a skiff of bronze lying upon the lake before them. They entered into the skiff, and they crossed over to the island, and came to the palace door, and there they saw a man, and he came towards them. And thus spoke Liban to the man whom they saw there:

> Where is Labraid, the swift sword-handler,
> The head of victorious troops?
> Victory is in his strong chariot;
> He stains with red the points of his spears.

And the man replied to her thus:

> Labraid, the swift sword-handler—
> He is not slow: he will be strong.
> They are gathering for the battle;
> They are making ready for the slaughter
> That will fill Mag Fidga.

They entered into the palace, and they saw there thrice fifty couches within the palace, and three times fifty women upon the couches; and the women all bade Loeg welcome, and it was in these words that they addressed him:

> Welcome to thee, O Loeg,
> Because of thy quest:
> Loeg, we also
> Hail thee as our guest!

"What wilt thou do now?" said Liban; "wilt thou go on without a delay, and hold speech with Fann?"

"I will go," he answered, "if I may know the place where she is."

"That is no hard matter to tell," she answered; "she is in her chamber apart." They went there, and they greeted Fann, and she welcomed Loeg in the same fashion as the others had done.

Fann was the daughter of Aed Abrat; Aed means fire, and he is the fire of the eye: that is, of the eye's pupil: Fann moreover

is the name of the tear that runs from the eye; it was on account
of the clearness of her beauty that she was so named, for there is
nothing else in the world except a tear to which her beauty could
be likened.

Now, while they were thus in that place, they heard the rattle
of Labraid's chariot as he approached the island, driving across
the water. "The spirit of Labraid is gloomy to-day," said Liban;
"I will go and greet him." And she went out, and she bade welcome
to Labraid, and she spoke as follows:

> Hail to Labraid, swift sword-handler!
> Heir to an army—small and armed with javelins.
> He hacks the shields—he scatters the spears,
> He cleaves the bodies—he slaughters free men;
> He seeks for bloodshed—bright is he in the conflict:
> To thee, who war against the hosts, Labraid, hail!
>
> Hail to Labraid, the swift sword-handler!
> Heir to an army—small and armed with javelins.

Labraid did not reply to her, and the lady spoke again thus:

> Hail to Labraid, swift sword-handler!
> Ready in giving,—generous to all,—eager for combat;
> Scarred thy side,—fair thy speech,—strong thy hand,
> Kindly in ruling,—hardy in judgments,—powerful in vengeance.
> He fights off the hosts.—Hail, Labraid!
>
> Hail to Labraid, swift handler of the battle-sword!

Labraid still made no answer, and she sang another lay thus:

> Hail, Labraid, swift sword-handler!
> Bravest of warriors,—more proud than the sea!
> He routs the armies,—he joins the combats;
> He tests the soldiers,—he raises up the weak,
> He humbles the strong. Hail, Labraid!
>
> Hail, Labraid, swift sword-handler!

"Thou speakest not rightly, O woman," said Labraid; and he
then addressed her thus:

> There is no pride or arrogance in me, oh wife!
> And no deluding spell can weaken my judgment.
> We are going now into a conflict of doubtful issue, decisive and severe,
> Where red swords strike in powerful hands,
> Against the multitudinous and united hosts of Eochaid Iuil.
> There is no presumption in me—no pride and no arrogance in me, oh wife!

"Let now thy mind be appeased," said the woman Liban to him. "Loeg, the charioteer of Cu Chulainn, is here; and Cu Chulainn has sent word to thee that he will come to join thy hosts."

Then Labraid bade welcome to Loeg, and he said to him: "Welcome, O Loeg! for the sake of the lady with whom thou comest, and for the sake of him from whom thou hast come. Go now to thine own land, O Loeg!" said Labraid, "and Liban shall accompany thee."

Then Loeg returned to Emain, and he gave news of what he had seen to Cu Chulainn, and to all others beside; and Cu Chulainn rose up, and he passed his hand over his face, and he greeted Loeg brightly, and his mind was strengthened within him for the news that Loeg had brought him.

(At this point occurs a break in the story, resulting from the fact that the narrative in its present form is made up of at least two earlier accounts. Into the gap are inserted a description of the Bull-Feast at which Lugaid Red-Stripes is elected king over all Ireland; also the exhortation that Cu Chulainn, supposed to be lying on his sick-bed, gives to Lugaid as to the duties of a king. After this insertion, which has no real connection with the narrative, the story itself proceeds, but from another point, for the thread is taken up at the place where Cu Chulainn has indeed awaked from his trance, but is still on his sick-bed; the message of Angus appears to have been given, but Cu Chulainn does not seem to have met Liban for the second time, and he lies at Emain Macha not at Tete Precc. Ethne has disappeared as an actor from the scene; her place is taken by Emer, Cu Chulainn's wife; and the whole style of the romance is altered for the better. Even if it were not for the want of agreement of the two versions, we could see that we have here two tales founded upon the same legend but by two different hands, the end of the first and the beginning of the second alike missing, and the gap filled in by the story of the election of Lugaid.)

Now as to Cu Chulainn, it has to be related thus: He called upon Loeg to come to him; and "Go, O Loeg!" said Cu Chulainn, "to the place where Emer is; and say to her that fairy women have come upon me, and that they have destroyed my strength; and say also to her that it goes better with me from hour to hour, and bid her to come and see me"; and the young man Loeg then spoke these words in order to hearten the mind of Cu Chulainn:

Little indeed is its use to a warrior—
The bed where he lies in sickness.
His illness is the work of the fairy folk,
Of the women of Mag Trogach.

They have beaten thee,
They have put thee into captivity;
They have led thee off the track.
The power of the women has rendered thee impotent.

Awake from the sleep in which thou art fighting
Against beings who are not soldiers;
The hour has come for thee to take thy place
Among heroes who drive their chariots to battle.

Place thyself upon the seat of thy war chariot.
Then will come the chance
To cover thyself with wounds,
To do great deeds.

When Labraid shows his power,
When the splendor of his glory shines,
Then must thou arise,
Then wilt thou be great.

Little indeed is its use to a warrior—
The bed where he lies in sickness.
His illness is the work of the fairy folk,
Of the women of Mag Trogach.

And Loeg, after that heartening, departed; and he went to the place where Emer was; and he told her of the state of Cu Chulainn.

"Ill has it been what thou hast done, O youth!" she said; "for although thou art known as one who dost wander in the lands where the fairy folk dwell, yet no virtue of healing hast thou found there and brought for the cure of thy lord. Shame upon the men of Ulster!" she said, "for they have not sought to do a great deed, and to heal him. Yet, had Conchobar thus been fettered, had it been Fergus who lost his sleep, had it been Conall the Victorious to whom wounds had been dealt, Cu Chulainn would have saved them." And she then sang a song, and in this fashion she sang it:

O Loeg mac Riangabra! alas!
Thou hast searched fairyland many times in vain;
Thou tarriest long in bringing thence
The healing of the son of Dechtire.

Woe to the high-souled Ulstermen!
Neither foster-father or foster-brother of Cu Chulainn
Has made a search through the wide world
To find the cure for his brave comrade.

If Fergus, foster-father of Cu Chulainn, were under this spell,
And if, to heal him, there was needed the knowledge of a druid,
The son of Dechtire would never take repose
Until Fergus had found a druid who could heal him.

If it were the foster-brother of Cu Chulainn, Conall the Victorious,
Who was afflicted with wounds,
Cu Chulainn would search through the whole world
Until he found a physician to heal him.

If Loegaire the Triumphant
Had been overborne in rugged combat,
Cu Chulainn would have searched through the green meads of all Ireland
To find a cure for the son of Connad mac Iliach.

Alas! sickness seizes upon me, too,
Because of Cu Chulainn, the Hound of Conchobar's smith!
The sickness that I feel at my heart creeps over my whole body!
Would that I might find a physician to heal thee!

Alas! death is at my heart!
For sickness has checked the warrior who rode his chariot across the plain,
And now he goes no more
To the assembly of Muirthemne.

Why does he go forth no more from Emain?
It is because of the fairy folk that he lingers.
My voice grows weak and dies.

Month, season, year, all have gone by,
And yet sleep has not taken up its accustomed course.
There is no one by him. Not one fair word
Doth ever come to his ears, O Loeg mac Riangabra.

And, after that she had sung that song, Emer went forward to Emain that she might visit Cu Chulainn; and she seated herself in the chamber where Cu Chulainn was, and thus she addressed him: "Shame upon thee!" she said, "to lie thus prostrate for a woman's love! well may this long sick-bed of thine cause thee to ail!" And it was in this fashion that she addressed him, and she chanted this lay:

> Arise, hero of Ulster!
> Awake joyful and sound.
> Look upon the king of Ulster, how great he is!
> Long enough hast thou slept.

It is ill sleeping too deep;
It is the weakness that follows defeat;
Sleeping too long is like milk to repletion;
It is the lieutenant of death; it has all death's power.

Awake! Sleep is the repose of the sot;
Throw it off with burning energy.
I have spoken much, but it is love that inspires me.
Arise, hero of Ulster!

Arise, hero of Ulster!
Awake joyful and sound.
Look upon the king of Ulster, how great he is!
Long enough hast thou slept.

And Cu Chulainn at her word stood up; and he passed his hand over his face, and he cast all his heaviness and his weariness away from him, and then he arose, and went on his way before him until he came to the enclosure that he sought; and in that enclosure Liban appeared to him. And Liban spoke to him, and she strove to lead him into fairyland; but "What place is that in which Labraid dwells?" said Cu Chulainn. "It is easy for me to tell thee!" she said:

Labraid's home is over a pure lake,
Where troops of women congregate.
Easy for thee to go there,
If thou wilt know swift Labraid.

His skilled arm strikes down hundreds;
Wise are they who describe his deeds:
Beautifully purple the colors
Which are on the cheeks of Labraid.

He shakes his head like a wolf in the battle
Before the thin blood-stained swords.
He shatters the arms of his impotent enemies;
He shatters the bucklers of the warriors.

. . . .

"I will not go thither at a woman's invitation," said Cu Chulainn.

"Let Loeg go then," said the woman, "and let him bring to thee tidings of all that is there."

"Let him depart, then," said Cu Chulainn; and Loeg rose up and departed with Liban, and they came to Mag Luada, and to Bile Buada, and over the fair green of Emain, and over the fair green of Fidga, and in that place dwelt Aed Abrat, and with him his daughters.

Then Fann bade welcome to Loeg, and "How is it," said she, "that Cu Chulainn has not come with thee?"

"It pleased him not," said Loeg, "to come at a woman's call; moreover, he desired to know whether it was indeed from thee that had come the message, and to have full knowledge of everything."

"It was indeed from me that the message was sent," she said; "and let now Cu Chulainn come swiftly to seek us, for it is for to-day that the strife is set."

Then Loeg went back to the place where he had left Cu Chulainn, and Liban with him; and "How appears this quest to thee, O Loeg?" said Cu Chulainn.

And Loeg answered, "In a happy hour shalt thou go," said he, "for the battle is set for to-day"; and it was in this manner that he spake, and described the fairy world thus:

> I went in the twinkling of an eye
> Into a marvellous country where I had been before.
> I reached a cairn of twenty armies,
> And there I found Labraid of the long hair.
>
> I found him sitting on the cairn,
> A great multitude of arms about him.
> On his head his beautiful fair hair
> Was decked with an apple of gold.
>
> Although the time was long since my last visit
> He recognized me by my five-fold purple mantle.
> Said he, "Wilt thou come with me
> Into the house where dwells Failbe the Fair?"
>
> Two kings are in the house,
> Failbe the Fair and Labraid.
> Three fifties of warriors are about them.
> For all their great number they live in the one house.
>
> On the right are fifty beds,
> And on the beds, as many warriors;
> On the left, fifty beds,
> And a warrior on every bed.
>
> The beds have round columns,
> Beautiful posts, adorned with gold.
> They gleam brightly in the light
> Which comes from a stone, precious and brilliant.

At the door toward the west
On the side toward the setting sun,
There is a troop of grey horses with dappled manes,
And another troop of horses, purple-brown.

At the door toward the east
Are three trees of purple glass.
From their tops a flock of birds sing a sweetly drawn-out song
For the children who live in the royal stronghold.

At the entrance to the enclosure is a tree
From whose branches there comes beautiful and harmonious music.
It is a tree of silver, which the sun illumines;
It glistens like gold.

There are thrice fifty trees.
At times their leaves mingle, at times, not.
Each tree feeds three hundred people
With abundant food, without rind.

There is a well in that noble palace of the fairy-mound.
There you will find thrice fifty splendid cloaks,
With a brooch of shining gold
To fasten each of the cloaks.

There is a cauldron of invigorating mead,
For the use of the inmates of the house.
It never grows less; it is a custom
That it should be full forever.

There is a woman in the noble palace.
There is no woman like her in Erin.
When she goes forth you see her fair hair.
She is beautiful and endowed with many gifts.

Her words, when she speaks to anyone,
Have a marvellous charm.
She wounds every man to the heart
With the love she inspires.

The noble lady said,
"Who is the youth whom we do not know?
Come hither if it be thou
That art the servant of the warrior of Muirthemne."

I yielded to her request with reluctance;
I feared for my honor.
She said to me, "Will he come,
The only son of the excellent Dechtire?"

It is a pity that thou hast not gone, O Cu Chulainn!
Everyone asks for you.
You yourself should see how it is built,
The grand palace that I have seen.

If I owned the whole of Erin,
With supreme sovereignty over its fair inhabitants,
I would give it up—the temptation would be irresistible—
I would go and live in the country where I have just been.

I went in the twinkling of an eye
Into a country where I had been before.
I reached a cairn of twenty armies,
And there I found Labraid of the long hair.

"The quest then is a good one," said Cu Chulainn.

"It is goodly indeed," said Loeg, "and it is right that thou shouldst go to attain it, and all things in that land are good." And thus further also spoke Loeg, as he told of the loveliness of the fairy dwelling:

They are beautiful women, victorious, never knowing the sorrow of the
    vanquished,
The daughters of Aed Abrat.
The beauty of Fann deserves glittering renown;
No king or queen is her equal.

I repeat what has been said to me:
She is a mortal daughter of Adam, without sin.
The beauty of Fann in our days,
Is beyond comparison.

I saw the glorious warriors
Armed with trenchant weapons,
With garments of bright colors;
These were not the garments of underlings.

I saw the women, joyous at the feast;
I saw the troop of maidens;
I saw the handsome boys
Walking about the trees on the hill.

In the house I heard the musicians
Playing for Fann.
If I had not made haste to go away
I would have got my hurt from that music.

I saw the hill where the house stands.
Ethne Inguba is a fair woman,
But the woman I speak of now,
Would drive entire armies to madness.

·   ·   ·   ·   ·   ·   ·   ·   ·

And Cu Chulainn, when he had heard that report, went on with Liban to that land, and he took his chariot with him. And they came to the island of Labraid, and there Labraid and all the women that were there bade them welcome; and Fann gave an especial welcome to Cu Chulainn.

"What is there now set for us to do?" said Cu Chulainn.

"No hard matter to answer," said Labraid; "we must go forth and make a circuit about the army."

They went out then, and they came to the army, and they let their eyes wander over it; and the host seemed to them to be innumerable. "Arise, and go hence for the present," said Cu Chulainn to Labraid; and Labraid departed, and Cu Chulainn remained confronting the army. And there were two ravens there, who spake, and revealed druid secrets, but the armies who heard them laughed.

"It must surely be the madman from Ireland who is there," said the army; "it is he whom the ravens would make known to us"; and the armies chased them away so that they found no resting-place in that land.

Now at early morn Eochaid Iuil went out in order to bathe his hands in the spring, and Cu Chulainn saw his shoulder through the hood of his tunic, and he hurled his spear at him, and he pierced him. And he by himself slew thirty-three of them, and then Senach Siaborthe assailed him, and a great fight was fought between them, and Cu Chulainn slew him; and after that Labraid approached, and he broke before him those armies.

Then Labraid entreated Cu Chulainn to stay his hand from the slaying; and "I fear now," said Loeg, "that the man will turn his wrath upon us; for he has not found a combat to suffice him. Go now," said Loeg, "and let there be brought three vats of cold water to cool his heat. The first vat into which he goes will boil over; after he has gone into the second vat, none will be able to bear the heat of it: after he has gone into the third vat, its water will have but a moderate heat."

And when the women saw Cu Chulainn's return, Fann sang thus:

> Stately the charioteer that steps the road;
> If he be beardless it is because he is young.
> Splendid the course he drives over the plain,
> At eve on Aenach Fidgai.

.   .   .   .

There is in each of his two cheeks
A red dimple like red blood,
A green dimple, a brown dimple,
A crimson dimple of light color.

There are seven lights in his eye,—
It is a fact not to be left unspoken,—
Eyebrows brown, of noblest set,
Eyelashes of chafer black.

. . . .

He outstrips all men in every slaughter;
He traverses the battle to the place of danger;
There is not one with a high hardy blade,
Not one like Cu Chulainn.

Cu Chulainn it is that comes hither,
The young champion from Muirthemne;
They who have brought him from afar
Are the daughters of Aed Abrat.

Dripping blood in long red streams,
To the sides of lofty spears he brings;
Haughty, proud, high for valor,
Woe be to him against whom he becomes angered.

Liban, moreover, bade a welcome to Cu Chulainn, and she sang
as follows:

Welcome to Cu Chulainn;
Relieving king;
A great prince of Mag Muirthemne;
Great his noble mind;
A battle-victorious champion;
A strong valor-stone;
Blood-red of anger;
Ready to arrange the champions of valor of Ulster;
Beautiful his complexion;
Dazzler of the eyes to maidens;
He is welcome.

"Tell us now of the deeds thou hast done, O Cu Chulainn!"
cried Liban; and Cu Chulainn replied to her thus:

. . . .

I threw a cast of my spear
Into the court of Eogan Inber.
I do not know—path of fame—
Whether it is good I have done, or evil.

. . . .

A host fair, red-complexioned, on backs of steeds,
They pierced me upon all sides;
The people of Manannan son of Lir,
Invoked by Eogan Inber.

. . . .

I heard the groan of Eochaid Iuil;
It is in good friendship his lips speak.
If the man has spoken true, it certainly won the battle,
The throw that I threw.

Now, after all these things had passed, Cu Chulainn slept with Fann, and he abode for a month in her company, and at the end of the month he came to bid her farewell. "Tell me," she said, "to what place I may go for our tryst, and I will be there"; and they made tryst at the yew tree by the strand that is known as Iubar Cinn Trachta (Newry).

Now word was brought to Emer of that tryst, and knives were whetted by Emer to slay the fairy woman; and she came to the place of the tryst, and fifty women were with her. And there she found Cu Chulainn and Loeg, and they were engaged in the chess-play, so that they did not perceive the women's approach. But Fann marked it, and she cried out to Loeg: "Look now, O Loeg!" she said, "and mark that sight that I see."

"What sight is that of which thou speakest?" said Loeg, and he looked and saw it, and thus it was that Fann addressed him:

> Loeg! look behind thee!
> > Close at hand
> > Wise, well-ranked women
> > > Press on us;
> > Bright on each bosom
> > > Shines the gold clasp;
> > Knives, with green edges
> > > Whetted, they hold.
> As for the slaughter chariot chiefs race,
> Comes Forgall's daughter; changed is her countenance.

"Have no fear," said Cu Chulainn, "thou shalt meet no foe;
Enter thou my strong car, with its bright seat:
I will set thee before me, will guard thee from harm
Against women, that swarm from Ulster's four quarters:
Though the daughter of Forgall vows war against thee,
Though her dear foster-sisters she rouses against thee,
Bold Emer will dare no deed of destruction,
Though she rageth against thee, for I will protect thee."

Moreover to Emer he said:

> I avoid thee, O lady, as heroes
>> Avoid to meet friends in battle;
> The hard spear thy hand shakes cannot injure,
>> Nor the blade of thy thin gleaming knife;
> For the wrath that rages within thee
>> Is but weak, nor can cause me fear:
> It were hard if the war my might wages
>> Must be quenched by a weak woman's power.

> "Speak! and tell me, Cu Chulainn," said Emer,
>> "Why thou wouldst lay this shame on my head?
> I stand dishonored before the women of Ulster,
> And all women who dwell in Erin,
>> And all folk who love honor beside:
> Though I came on thee secretly,
>> Though I remain oppressed by thy might,
> And though great is thy pride in the battle,
>> If thou leavest me, naught is thy gain:
> Why, dear youth, dost thou make such attempt?"

> "Speak thou, Emer, and say," said Cu Chulainn,
>> "Should I not remain with this lady?
> For she is fair, pure and bright, and well skilled,
> A fit mate for a monarch, filled with beauty,
>> And can ride the waves of ocean:
> She is lovely in countenance, lofty in race,
> And skilled in handicraft, can do fine needlework,
>> Has a mind that can guide with firmness."

"Truly," answered Emer, "the woman to whom thou dost cling is in no way better than am I myself! Yet fair seems all that's red; what's new seems glittering; and bright what's set o'erhead; and sour are things well known! Men worship what they lack; and what they have seems weak; in truth thou hast all the wisdom of the time! O youth!" she said, "once we dwelled in honor together, and we would so dwell again, if only I could find favor in thy sight!" and her grief weighed heavily upon her.

"By my word," said Cu Chulainn, "thou dost find favor, and thou shalt find it as long as I am in life."

"Desert me, then!" cried Fann.

"No," said Emer, "it is more fitting that I should be the deserted one."

"Not so, indeed," said Fann. "It is I who must go, and danger

rushes upon me from afar." And an eagerness for lamentation
seized upon Fann, and her soul was great within her, for it was
shame to her to be deserted and straightway to return to her home;
moreover, the mighty love that she bore to Cu Chulainn was
tumultuous in her, and in this fashion she lamented, and lamenting
sang this song:

> I it is that will go on the journey;
> I give assent with great affliction;
> Though there is a man of equal fame,
> I would prefer to remain.

> I would rather be here,
> To be subject to thee, without grief,
> Than to go, though you may wonder at it,
> To the sunny palace of Aed Abrat.

> O Emer! the man is thine,
> And well mayst thou wear him, thou good woman,—
> What my arm cannot reach,
> That I am forced to wish well.

> Many were the men that were asking for me,
> Both in the court and in the wilderness;
> Never with those did I hold a meeting,
> Because I it was that was righteous.

> Woe! to give love to a person,
> If he does not take notice of it;
> It is better for a person to turn away
> Unless he is loved as he loves.

> With fifty women hast thou come hither,
> O Emer of the yellow hair,
> To capture Fann—it was not well—
> And to kill her in her misery.

> There are thrice fifty, during my days,
> Of women, beautiful and unwedded,
> With me in my court together;
> They would not abandon me.

Now upon this it was discerned by Manannan that Fann the
daughter of Aed Abrat was engaged in unequal warfare with the
women of Ulster, and that she was like to be left by Cu Chulainn.
And thereon Manannan came from the east to seek for Fann, and
he was perceived by her, nor was there any other conscious of his
presence saving Fann alone. And when she saw Manannan, Fann

was seized by great bitterness of mind and by grief, and being thus, she made this song:

> Behold the valiant son of Lir,
> From the plains of Eogan Inber,—
> Manannan, lord over the world's fair hills,
> There was a time when he was dear to me.

> Even if to-day he were nobly constant,
> My mind loves not jealousy.
> Affection is a subtle thing;
> It makes its way without labor.

> One day I was with the son of Lir,
> In the sunny palace of Dun Inber;
> We then thought, without doubt,
> That we should never be separated.

> When Manannan, the great one, espoused me,
> I was a worthy wife for him;
> For his life he could not win from me
> The odd game at chess.

> When Manannan the great married me,
> I was a wife worthy of him;
> A wristband of doubly-tested gold
> He gave to me as the price of my blushes.

> I had with me at going over the sea
> Fifty maidens of many gifts.
> I gave to them fifty men,
> Without reproach, as their companions.

> Four fifties, without deceit,
> That was the assembly of one house;
> Twice fifty men, happy and perfect,
> Twice fifty women, fair and healthy.

> I see coming over the sea hither—
> No erring person sees him—
> The horseman of the crested wave;
> He stays not on his long boats.

> At thy coming, no one yet sees,
> Anyone but a dweller in the fairy-mound;
> Thy good sense is magnified by every gentle host,
> Though they be far away from thee.

> As for me, I would have cause for anger,
> Because the minds of women are silly;
> The person whom I loved exceedingly
> Has placed me here at a disadvantage.

I bid thee farewell, O beautiful Cu;
We depart from thee with a good heart;
Though we return not, be thy good will with us;
Everything is good, compared with going away.

It is now time for me to take my departure;
There is a person to whom it is not a grief;
It is, however, a great disgrace,
O Loeg, son of Riangabar.

I shall go with my own husband,
Because he will not show me disobedience.
Now that you may not say it is a secret departure,
If you desire it, now behold me.

Then Fann rose behind Manannan as he passed, and Manannan greeted her: "O woman!" he said, "which wilt thou do? wilt thou depart with me, or abide here until Cu Chulainn comes to thee?"

"In truth," answered Fann, "either of the two of you would be a fitting husband to adhere to; and neither of you is better than the other; yet, Manannan, it is with thee that I go, nor will I wait for Cu Chulainn, for he has betrayed me; and there is another matter, moreover, that weigheth with me, O noble prince!" said she, "and that is that thou hast no consort who is of worth equal to thine, but such a one hath Cu Chulainn already."

And Cu Chulainn saw Fann as she went from him to Manannan, and he cried out to Loeg: "What does this mean that I see?"

" 'Tis no hard matter to answer," said Loeg. "Fann is going away with Manannan mac Lir, since she hath not pleased thee!"

Then Cu Chulainn bounded three times high into the air, and he made three great leaps towards the south, and thus he came to Tara Luachra, and there he abode for a long time, having no meat and no drink, dwelling upon the mountains, and sleeping upon the high-road that runs through the midst of Luachra.

Then Emer went on to Emain, and there she sought out king Conchobar, and she told him of Cu Chulainn's state, and Conchobar sent out his learned men and his people of skill, and the druids of Ulster, to find Cu Chulainn, and to bind him fast, and bring him with them to Emain. And Cu Chulainn tried to kill the people of skill, but they chanted wizard and fairy spells against him, and they bound fast his feet and his hands until he came a little to his senses. Then he begged for a drink at their hands, and the druids gave him a drink of forgetfulness, so that afterwards he had no more remembrance of Fann nor of anything else that he had then done; and they also gave a drink of forgetfulness to Emer that she might forget her jealousy, for her state was in no way better than the state of Cu Chulainn. And Manannan shook his cloak between Cu Chulainn and Fann, so that they might never meet together again throughout eternity.

THE STORY OF MAC DATHO'S PIG

"The Story of Mac Datho's Pig" is a remarkably picturesque narrative. The action is swift, the dialogue spirited, and the climactic arrangement of the episodes highly effective. The plot is based on the ancient Celtic practice of assigning the choicest portion at feasts to the guest who could most successfully establish his superiority over his fellows (p. 254). It is of interest to note that the author, writing as early as the ninth or tenth century, thought of the enmity between Ulster and Connacht as extending back into remote antiquity. Incidentally, "The Story of Mac Datho's Pig" is one of the few sagas of the Ulster cycle in which Cu Chulainn does not appear. The scene, it will be noted, is laid in Leinster.

There was a famous land-holder of Leinster. Mac Datho (Son of the Two Mutes) was his byname. He had a hound that would run round all Leinster in one day. That hound's name was Ailbe, whence the Plain of Ailbe is called. And of him was said:

> Mesroida was Mac Datho's name,
> Who had the pig—no falsehood!
> And Ailbe, his famous cunning splendid hound,
> From whom is the renowned plain of Ailbe.

Now Ireland was full of the fame and renown of that hound. Then to Mac Datho came messengers from Medb and Ailill of Connacht to ask him for his hound. But at the same time came messengers of Ulster and Conchobar to ask for the same hound. Welcome was made to them, and they were taken into Mac Datho's stronghold.

This was one of the five chief hostels of Ireland at that time, and there used to be boiling water in it always. There was the hostel of Da Derga among the men of Cualu in Leinster, and the hostel of Forgall Monach beside Lusk, and the hostel of Da Reo in Brefne, and the hostel of Da Choga in Westmeath. Seven doors there were in each hostel, seven roads through it, and seven fire-places therein. Seven cauldrons in the seven fire-places. An ox and a salted pig would go into each of these cauldrons, and the man that came along the road would thrust the fleshfork into the cauldron, and whatever he brought up with the first thrust, that he would eat, and if nothing were brought up with the first thrust, there was nothing for him.

199

The messengers were taken to Mac Datho, who was in bed, to be asked their pleasure, before their ration was brought to them; and they said their messages. "We come to ask for the hound," said the messengers of Connacht, "from Ailill and from Medb, and in exchange for it there shall be given threescore hundred milch cows at once, and a chariot with the two horses that are best in Connacht, and as much again at the end of the year besides all that."

"We too have come to ask for it," said the messengers of Ulster and Conchobar, "and Conchobar is no worse friend than Ailill and Medb, and the same amount shall be given from the north, and be added to, and there will be good friendship from it continually."

Mac Datho fell into great silence, and was three days and nights without sleeping, nor could he eat food for the greatness of his trouble, but was always moving about from one side to another. It was then his wife addressed him and said: "Long is the fast thou art keeping," said she; "there is plenty of food by thee, though thou dost not eat it." And then she said:

> Sleeplessness is brought
> To Mac Datho into his house,
> There was something on which he deliberated,
> Though he speaks to none.
>
> He turns away from me to the wall,
> The hero of the Fene of fierce valor;
> His prudent wife observes
> That her mate is without sleep.

The man. Crimthann Nia Nair said:
> "Do not trust thy secret to women;
> A woman's secret is not well concealed,
> Wealth is not trusted to a slave."

The woman. Why wouldst thou talk to a woman
> If something were not amiss?
> A thing that thy mind will not penetrate,
> Someone else's mind will penetrate.

The man. The hound of Mesroida Mac Datho,
> Evil was the day when they came for him;
> Many fair men will fall for his sake,
> More than one can tell will be the fights for him.

> If to Conchobar it is not given,
> Certainly it will be a churlish deed;
> His hosts will not leave
> Any more of cattle or of land.
> If to Ailill it be refused,
> The son of Matach will carry it off.

The woman. I have advice for thee in this,
>The result of which will not be bad:
>Give it to them both,
>No matter who will fall because of it.

The man. The advice that thou givest,
>It does not make me glad,

.   .   .   .   .   .

After that Mac Datho arose, and gave himself a shake and said, "Now bring us food, and let us and the guests who have come here be merry." They stayed with him for three days and three nights, and he went aside with them: with the messengers of Connacht first, and said to them, "I was in great perplexity and doubt, and this is what has grown of it, that I have given the hound to Ailill and to Medb, and let them come for it splendidly and proudly with as many warriors and nobles as they can get, and they shall have drink and food and many gifts besides, and shall take the hound and be welcome." Those messengers departed and were thankful.

He also went to the messengers of Ulster and said to them, "After much doubting I have given the hound to Conchobar, and let him and the flower of the province come for it proudly, and they shall have many other gifts, and you shall be welcome."

But for one and the same day he had made his tryst with them all; nor was it neglected by them. So then two provinces of Ireland came and stopped in front of Mac Datho's hostel. He himself went to meet them and bade them welcome. "It is welcome you are, O warriors," said he. "Come within into the close." Then they went beyond into the hostel. One half of the house for the Connachtmen, and the other half for the men of Ulster. That house was not a small one. Seven doors in it, and fifty beds between each two doors. Those were not faces of friends at a feast, the people who were in that house, for many of them had injured another; for three hundred years before the birth of Christ there had been war between them. "Let the pig be killed for them!" said Mac

Datho. Threescore milch cows had been feeding it for seven years. But on venom that pig had been reared, since on its account a slaughter of the men of Ireland was made.

Then the pig was brought to them, and there were sixty oxen drawing that one pig, besides their other food. Mac Datho himself was attending on them. "A welcome to you," said he, "and there is not to be found the like of such a quantity of food. We have many pigs and beeves in Leinster, and what is wanting to your provision to-night, will be killed for you to-morrow."

"The provision is good," said Conchobar.

There were nine men under the hurdle on which was the tail of the pig, and they had their load therein.

"The pig is good," said Conchobar.

"It is good," said Ailill; "how shall the pig be divided, O Conchobar?"

"How would you divide it indeed," said Bricriu mac Carbaid from his couch, "where the valorous warriors of the men of Ireland are, but by contest of arms, and let each of you therefore give a blow on the other's nose."

"Let it be done so!" said Ailill.

"We are agreed," said Conchobar, "for we have lads in the house that have many a time gone round the border."

"There will be need of thy lads to-night, O Conchobar," said Senlaech Arad from Cruachan Conalath in the west; "they have often turned their backs on the road of Luachar Dedad. Many a fat beef too have they left with me."

"It was a fat beef thou leftest with me," said Munremur mac Gerrcind, "even thy own brother, Cruithne mac Ruaidlinde from Cruachan Conalath of Connacht."

"He was no better," said Lugaid son of Cu Roi, "than Irloth son of Fergus mac Leite, who was left dead by Echbel mac Dedad at Tara Luachra."

"What sort of man was Congancnes mac Dedad, do you think," said Celtchar mac Uthecair, "whom I slew myself and cut off his head?"

Each of them brought up his exploits in the face of the other, till at last it came to one man who beat every one, even Cet mac Matach of Connacht. He raised his weapon above the host, and took his knife in his hand and sat down by the pig. "Now let

there be found among the men of Ireland," said he, "one man able
to oppose me, or let me divide the pig."

There was not at that time found a warrior among the men of
Ulster to stand up to him, and a great silence fell upon them then.
"Stop this for me, O Loegaire," said Conchobar.

"It shall be stopped," said Loegaire; "Cet must not carve the
pig before the face of us all."

"Wait a little, O Loegaire," said Cet, "that I may speak to thee.
It is a custom with you Ulstermen that every youth among you
who takes arms makes us his first goal. Thou too didst come to the
border, and we met at the border, and thou didst leave charioteer
and chariot and horses with me; and thou didst then escape with a
lance through thee. Thou wilt not get at the pig in that manner!"
Loegaire sat down on his couch.

"It shall not be," said a tall, fair warrior of Ulster, stepping forth
from his couch, "that Cet carve the pig."

"Who is this?" said Cet.

"A better warrior than thou," said all, "even Angus son of Lam-
Gabaid ('Hand-wail') of Ulster."

"Why is his father called Hand-wail?" said Cet.

"We know not indeed," said all.

"But *I* know," said Cet. "Once I went eastward. An alarm
was raised around me, and Hand-wail came up with me like every
one else. He made a cast with a large lance at me. I cast back the
same lance at him which struck off his hand, so that it lay on the
field before him. What brings the son of that man to stand up to
me?" said Cet. Then Angus sat down on his couch.

"Still keep up the contest," said Cet, "or let me carve the pig."

"It is not right that thou carve it, O Cet," said another tall, fair
warrior of Ulster.

"Who is this?" said Cet.

"Eogan Mor mac Durthacht," said all, "king of Fernmag."

"I have seen him before," said Cet.

"Where hast thou seen me?" said Eogan.

"In front of thy own house, when I took a drove of cattle from
thee. The alarm was raised in the land around me. Thou metst
me and castest a spear at me so that it stood out of my shield.
I cast the same spear at thee, which passed through thy head
and struck thy eye out of thy head. And the men of Ireland

see thee with one eye ever since." Eogan sat down in his seat after that.

"Still keep up the contest, men of Ulster," said Cet, "or allow me to carve the pig."

"Thou shalt not carve it yet," said Munremur mac Gerrcind.

"Is that Munremur?" said Cet.

"It is he," said the men of Ireland.

"It was I that last cleaned my hands in thee, O Munremur," said Cet. "It is not three days yet since out of thy own land I carried off three warriors' heads from thee together with the head of thy first-born son." Munremur sat down in his seat.

"Continue the contest," said Cet, "or I shall carve the pig."

"Indeed, thou shalt have it," said a tall, gray, very terrible warrior of the men of Ulster.

"Who is this?" said Cet.

"That is Celtchar mac Uthecair," said all.

"Wait a little, Celtchar," said Cet, "unless thou wishest to come to blows at once. I came, O Celtchar, to the front of thy house. The alarm was raised around me. Every one went after me. Thou camest like every one else, and going into a gap before me didst throw a spear at me. I threw another spear at thee which went through thy loins and through the upper part of thy testicles, so that thou hast had a sickness of urine ever since, nor have either son or daughter been born to thee since." After that Celtchar sat down in his seat.

"Continue the contest," said Cet, "or I shall carve the pig."

"Thou shalt have it," said Menn son of Sword-heel.

"Who is this?" said Cet.

"Menn," said all.

"What means it," said Cet, "that the sons of churls with nick-names should come to contend with me? For it was I who chris-tened thy father by that name, since it is I that cut off his heel, so that he carried but one heel away with him. What should bring the son of such a man to contend with me?" Menn sat down in his seat.

"Continue the contest," said Cet, "or I shall carve the pig."

"Thou shalt have it," said Cuscraid the Stammerer of Macha son of Conchobar.

"Who is this?"

"This is Cuscraid," said all.

"He has the making of a king with respect to his figure, but he earns no thanks from me," said Cet. "Thou madest thy first raid upon us. We met on the border. Thou didst leave a third of thy people with me, and thus camest away, with a spear through thy throat, so that no word comes rightly over thy lips, since the sinews of thy throat were wounded, so that Cuscraid the Stammerer is thy byname ever since."

In that way he laid disgrace on the whole province.

While he made ready with the pig and had his knife in his hand, they saw Conall the Victorious coming towards them into the house. And he sprang on to the floor of the house. The men of Ulster gave great welcome to Conall the Victorious at that time. It was then Conchobar threw his helmet from his head and shook himself in his own place. "We are pleased," said Conall, "that our portion is in readiness for us. Who carves for you?" said Conall.

"One man of the men of Ireland has obtained by contest the carving of it, Cet mac Matach."

"Is that true, O Cet?" said Conall. "Art thou carving the pig?"

"It is true indeed," said Cet.

Then said Cet to Conall:

> Welcome Conall, heart of stone,
> Fierce glow of fire, glitter of ice,
> Red strength of anger under a hero's breast,
> Wound-inflicter, triumphant in battle, I see the son of Finnchoem!

Then said Conall to Cet:

> Welcome Cet,
> Cet mac Matach, . . .
> Heart of ice, strong chariot-chief of battle,
> Battling sea, fair shapely bull,
> Cet mac Matach!

" The decision will be clear in our meeting and in our parting," said Conall. "It shall be a famous tale even with the slave who drives oxen, our meeting to-night."

"Get up from the pig, O Cet!" said Conall.

"What brings thee to it?" said Cet.

"It is true," said Conall, "I will be the challenger. I will give you competition," said Conall, "for I swear what my people swear, since I first took spear and weapons, I have never been a day without having slain a Connachtman, or a night without plundering, nor have I ever slept without the head of a Connachtman under my knee."

"It is true," said Cet, "thou art even a better warrior than I; but if Anluan mac Matach (my brother) were in the house, he would match thee contest for contest, and it is a shame that he is not in the house to-night."

"But he *is*," said Conall, taking Anluan's head out of his belt and throwing it at Cet's chest, so that a gush of blood broke over his lips. After that Conall sat down by the pig, and Cet went from it.

"Now let them come to the contest," said Conall. Truly, there was not then found among the men of Connacht a warrior to stand up to him in contest, for they were loath to be slain on the spot. The men of Ulster made a cover around him with their shields, for there was an evil custom in the house, the people of one side throwing stones at the people of the other side. Then Conall went to carve the pig and took the end of its tail in his mouth until he had finished dividing it. He sucked up the whole tail, and a load for nine was in it, so that he did not leave a bit of it, and he cast its skin and membrane from him, as the poet said:

· · · · · · ·

> A load for nine its heavy tail.
> While he was at the brave prosperous carving,
> Conall the Victorious consumed it

However, to the men of Connacht he gave no more but a quarter of the pig, or the two fore-legs of the pig. Their share of the pig seemed small to the men of Connacht. They rose up. Then from the other side arose the men of Ulster until each of them reached the other. Then there were blows over ear and head, so that the heap of the warriors' bodies on the floor was as high as the side of the house. For there were slain one thousand and four hundred armed men both of Ulster and Connacht, so that seven streams of blood and gore burst through the seven doors. Then the hosts burst through those doors and raised a great shout in the middle of the close, and each one was striking and slaying the other. Then Fergus took the great oak that was in the middle of the close to the men of Connacht, after having torn it from its roots. Others say that it was Cu Roi mac Dairi who took the oak to them, and that it was then that he came to them, for there was no man of

Munster there before, except Lugaid son of Cu Roi, and Cetin Pauci, and that when Cu Roi came to them, he carried off alone one half of the pig with its back from Leth Cuinn. Then they broke forth from the close into the field. They continued to fight in front of the close.

Then Mac Datho came out with the hound in his hand, and let him in amongst them to see which side he would choose; and the hound chose Ulster and set to tearing the men of Connacht greatly. Ailill and Medb went into their chariot, and their charioteer with them, and Mac Datho let the hound after them, and they say it was in the Plain of Ailbe that the hound seized the pole of the chariot that was under Ailill and Medb. Then the charioteer of Ailill and Medb dealt the hound a blow so that he sent its body aside and that the head of the hound remained on the pole of the chariot at Ibar Cinn Chon (the Yew-tree of the Hound's Head), whence Connacht takes its name. And they also say that from that hound Mag Ailbe (the Plain of Ailbe) is called, for Ailbe was the name of the hound.

This now is the road which the men of Connacht went southward, to wit, over Belach Mugna, past Roiriu, past Ath Midbine in Maistiu, past Kildare, past Raith Imgan into Feeguile, to Ath Mic Lugna, past Druim Da Maige over Drochat Cairpri. There, at Ath Cinn Chon (Hound's Head Ford) in Fir Bili the head of the hound fell from the chariot. As they were going along Froechmag of Meath eastward, Fer Loga, the charioteer of Ailill, lying in wait in the heather, jumped on to the chariot behind Conchobar and seized his head from behind. "Methinks," said he, "O Conchobar, thou wilt not get hence."

"Thou shalt have thy wish," said Conchobar.

"Truly, I do not want much from thee," said Fer Loga, "for I want to be taken by thee to Emain Macha, and the women of Ulster and their maiden daughters shall sing their chorus around me every evening and shall all say: 'Fer Loga is my darling,' etc."

"Thou shalt have that," said Conchobar. That the maidens of Emain Macha had to do, for they did not dare to do otherwise for fear of Conchobar. And on that day a year gone Conchobar let him go back to the west at Athlone, and he had two horses of Conchobar's with him, with their golden bridles. But he did not get the women's song though he got the horses. And this is how Ulster and Connacht fell out about the hound of Mac Datho and about his pig.

THE DEBILITY OF THE ULSTERMEN

"The Debility of the Ulstermen" was composed ostensibly to explain the fact that when Queen Medb, with her allies, sought to invade Ulster all the warriors of Ulster except Cu Chulainn were unable to fight. It also accounts for the origin of the name Emain Macha by one of those fanciful etymologies common in the "Dinnshenchas." Essentially, it is typical of a large class of early Irish tales which deal with the love between mortals and fairy beings.

There lived on the heights and in the solitudes of the hills a rich cow-lord of the Ulstermen, Crunnchu mac Agnoman by name. In his solitude great wealth accumulated to him. He had four sons around him. His wife, the mother of his children, died. For a long time he lived without a wife. As he was one day alone on the couch in his house, he saw coming into the mansion a young stately woman, distinguished in her appearance, clothing, and demeanor. Macha was the woman's name, as scholars say. She sat herself down on a chair near the hearth, and stirred the fire. She passed the whole day there, without exchanging a word with any one. She fetched a kneading-trough and a sieve and began to prepare food. As the day drew to an end she took a vessel and milked the cow, still without speaking.

When she returned to the house, she turned right about, went into his kitchen and gave directions to his servants; then she took a seat next to Crunnchu. Each one went to his couch; she remained to the last and put out the fire, turned right about again and laid herself down beside him, laying her hand on his side. For a long time they dwelt together. Through his union with her, he increased yet more in wealth. His handsome appearance was delightful to her.

Now the Ulstermen frequently held great assemblies and meetings. All, as many as could go, both of men and women, went to the gathering. "I, too," said Crunnchu, "will go like every one else to the assembly."

"Go not," said his wife, "lest thou run into danger by speaking of us; for our union will continue only if thou dost not speak of me in the assembly."

"I will not utter a word," said Crunnchu.

The Ulstermen gathered to the festival, Crunnchu also going with the rest. It was a brilliant festival, not alone in regard to the people, but as to horses and costumes also. There took place races and combats, tournaments, games, and processions.

At the ninth hour the royal chariot was brought upon the ground, and the king's horses carried the day in the contests. Then bards appeared to praise the king and the queen, the poets and the druids, his household, the people and the whole assembly. The people cried: "Never before have two such horses been seen at the festival as these two horses of the king: in all Ireland there is not a swifter pair!"

"My wife runs quicker than these two horses," said Crunnchu.

"Seize the man," said the king, "and hold him until his wife can be brought to the race-contest!"

He was made fast, and messengers were despatched from the king to the woman. She bade the messengers welcome, and asked them what had brought them there. "We have come for you that you may release your husband, kept prisoner by the king's command, because he boasted that you were swifter of foot than the king's horses."

"My husband has spoken unwisely," said she; "it was not fitting that he should say so. As for me, I am ill, and about to be delivered of a child."

"Alas for that," said the messengers, "for thy husband will be put to death if thou dost not come."

"Then I must needs go," she said.

Forthwith she went to the assembly. Every one crowded round to see her. "It is not becoming," said she, "that I should be gazed at in this condition. Wherefore am I brought hither?"

"To run in contest with the two horses of the king," shouted the multitude.

"Alas!" she cried, "for I am close upon my hour."

"Unsheath your swords and hew yonder man to death," said the king.

"Help me," she cried to the bystanders, "for a mother hath borne each one of you. Give me, O King, but a short delay, until I am delivered."

"It shall not be so," replied the king.

"Then shame upon you who have shown so little respect for me," she cried. "Because you take no pity upon me, a heavier infamy will fall upon you."

"What is thy name?" asked the king.

"My name," said she, "and the name of that which I shall bear, will for ever cleave to the place of this assembly. I am Macha, daughter of Sainreth mac Imbaith (Strange son of Ocean). Bring up the horses beside me!" It was done, and she outran the horses and arrived first at the end of the course. Then she gave vent to a cry in her pain, but God helped her, and she bore twins, a son and a daughter, before the horses reached the goal. Therefore is the place called Emain Macha, " the Twins of Macha."

All who heard that cry were suddenly seized with weakness, so that they had no more strength than the woman in her pain. And she said, "From this hour the ignominy that you have inflicted upon me will redound to the shame of each one of you. When a time of oppression falls upon you, each one of you who dwells in this province will be overcome with weakness, as the weakness of a woman in child-birth, and this will remain upon you for five days and four nights; to the ninth generation it shall be so."

Thus it was. It continued from the days of Crunnchu to the days of Fergus mac Donnell, or till the time of Forc, son of Dallan, son of Mainech, son of Lugaid. Three classes there were upon whom the debility had no power, namely, the children and the women of Ulster, and Cu Chulainn, because he was not descended from Ulster; none, also, of those who were outside the province were afflicted by it.

This is the cause of the Noinden Ulad, or the Debility of the Ulstermen.

THE CATTLE–RAID OF REGAMNA

(Cu Chulainn and the Morrigu)

"The Cattle-Raid of Regamna" is one of a number of early Irish romances called *remscéla*, or foretales, designed to explain the central epic. It also belongs to a group of sagas called "cattle-raids" (*tána bó*), of which the most important is "The Cattle-Raid of Cooley" (p. 281). In the present instance the title has little appropriateness, as only one cow instead of a herd is stolen and no person called Regamna (or, perhaps, Regaman) appears in the story.

Besides "The Cattle-Raid of Regamna" there are several other ancient Irish episodic narratives dealing with one or both of the two famous bulls that figure in "The Cattle-Raid of Cooley"—the Donn of Cooley and the White-Horned of Connacht. According to one account the two animals were originally fairy swine-herds who were at enmity with each other and who assumed a series of transformations until they finally appeared as the two bulls. See also "The Adventures of Nera," p. 248.

When Cu Chulainn lay asleep in Dun Imrith, he heard a cry sounding out of the north, a cry terrible and fearful to his ears. Out of a deep slumber he was aroused by it so suddenly, that he fell out of his bed upon the ground like a sack, in the east wing of the house.

He rushed forth without weapons, until he gained the open air, his wife following him with his armor and his garments. He perceived Loeg in his harnessed chariot coming towards him from Ferta Laig in the North. "What brings thee here?" said Cu Chulainn.

"A cry that I heard sounding across the plain," said Loeg.

"From which direction?" said Cu Chulainn.

"From the north-west," said Loeg, "across the great highway leading to Caill Cuan."

"Let us follow the sound," said Cu Chulainn.

They went forward as far as Ath da Ferta (Ford of the Two Chariot Poles). When they arrived there, they heard the rattle of a chariot from the loamy district of Culgaire. They saw before them a chariot harnessed with a chestnut horse. The horse had but one leg, and the pole of the chariot passed through its body,

211

so that the peg in front met the halter passing across its forehead. Within the chariot sat a woman,[1] her eye-brows red, and a crimson mantle around her. Her mantle fell behind her between the wheels of the chariot so that it swept along the ground. A big man went along beside the chariot. He also wore a coat of crimson, and on his back he carried a forked staff of hazelwood, while he drove a cow before him.

"The cow is not pleased to be driven on by thee," said Cu Chulainn.

"She does not belong to thee," said the woman; "the cow is not owned by any of thy friends or associates."

"The cows of Ulster belong to me," said Cu Chulainn.

"Thou wouldst give a decision about the cow!" said the woman; "you are taking too much upon yourself, O Cu Chulainn!"

"Why is it the woman who accosts me?" said Cu Chulainn. "Why is it not the man?"

"It is not the man to whom thou didst address thyself," said the woman.

"Oh yes," said Cu Chulainn, "but it is thou who dost answer for him."

"He is Uar-gaeth-sceo Luachar-sceo."

"Well, to be sure, the length of the name is astonishing!" said Cu Chulainn. "Talk to me then thyself, for the man does not answer. What is thy own name?"

"The woman to whom you speak," said the man, "is called Faebor beg-beoil cuimdiuir folt scenb-gairit sceo uath."

"Thou art making a fool of me!" said Cu Chulainn. And he made a leap into the chariot. He put his two feet on her two shoulders, and his spear on the parting of her hair.

"Do not play thy sharp weapons on me!" she said.

"Then tell thy true name," said Cu Chulainn.

"Go further off from me then," said she. "I am a female satirist, and he is Daire mac Fiachna of Cooley; I carry off this cow as a reward for a poem."

"Let us hear thy poem," said Cu Chulainn.

"Only move further off," said the woman. "Thy shaking of thy weapons over my head will not influence me." Then he moved

[1] The woman is the Morrigu, usually identified as an ancient Irish goddess of battle.

off until he was between the two wheels of the chariot. Then she
sang to him.[1]

.   .   .   .

Cu Chulainn prepared to spring again into the chariot; but
horse, woman, chariot, man, and cow, all had disappeared. Then
he perceived that she had been transformed into a black bird on
a branch close by him. "A dangerous enchanted woman you are!"
said Cu Chulainn.

"Henceforth this *grellach* 'clayey place' shall bear the name of
the 'enchanted place' (*dolluid*)," said the woman; and Grellach
Dolluid was it called.

"If I had only known that it was thou," said Cu Chulainn,
"we should not have parted thus."

"Whatever thou hast done," said she, "will bring thee ill-
luck."

"Thou canst not harm me," said he.

"Certainly I can," said the woman. "I am guarding thy death-
bed, and I shall be guarding it henceforth. I brought this cow
out of the fairy-mound of Cruachan so that she might breed by
the bull of Daire mac Fiachna, namely the Donn of Cooley.
So long as her calf shall be a yearling, so long shall thy life be;
and it is this that shall cause the Cattle-Raid of Cooley."

"My name shall be all the more renowned in consequence of
this Cattle-Raid," said the hero:

> I shall strike down their warriors,
> I shall fight their battles,
> I shall survive the Cattle-Raid!

"How wilt thou manage that?" said the woman; "for, when
thou art engaged in a combat with a man as strong, as victorious,
as dexterous, as terrible, as untiring, as noble, as brave, as great
as thyself, I will become an eel, and I will throw a noose round
thy feet in the ford, so that heavy odds will be against thee."

"I swear by the god by whom the Ulstermen swear," said
Cu Chulainn, "that I will bruise thee against a green stone of
the ford; and thou never shalt have any remedy from me if thou
leavest me not."

"I shall also become a gray wolf, and I will take strength from
thy right hand, as far as to thy left arm."

[1] The song of the Morrigu has not been translated.

"I will encounter thee with my spear," said he, "until thy left or right eye is forced out; and thou shalt never have help from me, if thou leavest me not."

"I will become a white, red-eared cow," said she, "and I will go into the pond beside the ford, in which thou art in deadly combat with a man as skilful in feats as thyself, and a hundred white, red-eared cows behind me; and I and all behind me will rush into the ford, and the 'faithfulness of men' will be brought to a test that day, and thy head shall be cut off from thee."

"I will with my sling make a cast against thee," said he, "so that thy right or thy left leg will be broken, and thou shalt never have help from me, if thou dost not leave me."

Thereupon the Morrigu departed into the fairy-mound of Cruachan in Connacht, and Cu Chulainn returned to his dwelling.

This, then, is one of the foretales to the "Cattle-Raid of Cooley."

THE INTOXICATION OF THE ULSTERMEN

"The Intoxication of the Ulstermen" is an excellent example of a class of Irish tales in which the author, instead of following a definite plot, gives free reign to his imagination, using a slender narrative as a thread on which to hang a bewildering array of descriptive and other details that had long been familiar to professional story-tellers. There are few wilder scenes in any literature than that of the drunken chariot heroes of Ulster losing their way and careering southward across country from Ulster to Kerry, only to find themselves at length trapped in an iron house concealed within wooden walls under which raging fires are lighted by their enemies.

When the sons of Mil of Spain reached Erin, their sagacity circumvented the Tuatha De Danann, so that Erin was left to the partition of Amergin Glunmar, son of Mil; for he was a king-poet and a king-judge. And he divided Erin into two parts, and gave the part that was underground to the Tuatha De Danann, and the other part to the sons of Mil, his own mortal people.

The Tuatha De Danann went into the hills and fairy places, so that they spoke with the fairy folk underground. They left five of their number before the five provinces of Erin, to excite war and conflict and valor and strife between the sons of Mil. They left five of them before the province of Ulster in particular. The names of these five were: Brea son of Belgan, in Dromana-Breg; Redg Rotbel in the slopes of Mag Itha; Tinnel the son of Boclachtna, in Sliab Edlicon; Grici in Cruachan Aigle; Gulbann the Grey son of Grac, in the Ben of Gulban Gort son of Ungarb.

They excited a quarrel amongst the sections of Ulster, regarding its division into three parts, when the province was at its best, to wit, during the time of Conchobar son of Fachtna Fathach. They who shared the province with Conchobar were his own fosterling, Cu Chulainn mac Sualtach, and Fintan son of Niall Niamglonnach, from Dun-da-Benn.

The partition that was made of the province was this: from the hills of Uachtar Forcha, which is called Usnech of Meath, to the middle of Traig Baile, was Cu Chulainn's portion of the province. Conchobar's third, moreover, was from Traig Baile to Traig Thola, in Ulster. Fintan's third was from Traig Thola to Rinn Seimne and Latharna.

A year was the province thus, in three divisions, until the feast of Samain was made by Conchobar in Emain Macha. The extent of the banquet was a hundred vats of every kind of ale. Conchobar's officers said that all the nobles of Ulster would not be too many to partake of the banquet, because of its excellence.

The resolution formed by Conchobar was to send his woman messenger, Leborcham, for Cu Chulainn to Dun Delgan, and Findchad Fer Benduma son of Traglethan, for Fintan son of Niall Niamglonnach, to Dun-da-Benn.

Leborcham reached Dun Delgan, and told Cu Chulainn to go and speak with his fair guardian, to Emain Macha. Cu Chulainn was then giving a great banquet for the people of his own territory in Dun Delgan; and he said that he would not go, but that he would attend the people of his own country. His wife, the fair-haired Emer, daughter of Forgall Monach, the sixth best woman that Erin contained, said that he should go and speak with his guardian Conchobar.

"Harnessed are the horses, and yoked is the chariot," said Loeg; "wait not for the evil hour, that thou mayest not be hindered of thy valor. Jump into it when thou likest."

Cu Chulainn took his warlike apparel around him; and he leaped into his chariot, and proceeded on by the most direct road, and shortest way to Emain Macha. And Sencha mac Ailill came to bid welcome to Cu Chulainn on the green of Emain Macha. This is the welcome he offered to him:

"Welcome, ever welcome thy coming, thou glorious head of the host of Ulster; thou gem of valor and bravery of the Gael; thou dear, subduing, purple-fisted son of Dechtire."

"That is the welcome of a gift-asking man," said Cu Chulainn.

"It is indeed," said Sencha mac Ailill.

"Name the gift thou requirest," said Cu Chulainn.

"I will, provided there be fit securities regarding it."

"Say what are the securities thou dost require, in consideration of a counter-gift for me."

"The two Conalls and Loegaire, viz. Conall Anglonnach son of Iriel Glunmar, and Conall the Victorious son of Amergin, and the furious Loegaire the Triumphant."

The boon was secured upon these guarantees, in consideration of a counter-gift for Cu Chulainn.

"What are the securities thou dost desire regarding the counter-gift?" asked Sencha.

"The three young, noble, distinguished gillies: Cormac Conlonges son of Conchobar, Mesdead son of Amergin, and Eochaid Cenngarb son of Celtchar."

"What I ask," said Sencha mac Ailill, "is that thou wouldst cede to Conchobar, for a year, the third of Ulster which is in thy hand."

"If the province were the better for his having it for a year, it is not hard; for he is the fountain in its proper site that cannot be stained or defiled, the descendant of the kings of Erin and Alba. Therefore if the province were the better for its being in his possession for a year, it is not hard that he should have it; but if it is not the better, we will insist that he must be placed upon his own third at the end of a year."

Fintan son of Niall Niamglonnach arrived. The illustrious good druid Cathbad met him and bade him welcome.

"Welcome thy coming, O beautiful, illustrious youth; thou mighty warrior of the great province of Ulster, against whom neither plunderers nor spoilers nor pirates can contend; thou border-man of the province of Ulster."

"That is the welcome of a man that asks a boon," said Fintan.

"It is, truly," said Cathbad.

"Speak, that it may be given thee," said Fintan.

"I will speak, provided that I have my fit securities regarding it."

"Say, what securities requirest thou, in consideration of a return boon for me?" said Fintan.

"Celtchar son of Uthecar; Uma, son of Remanfisech, from the brooks of Cooley; and Ergi Echbel from Bri Ergi."

They bound upon those guarantees.

"Speak now, O Fintan; what securities wilt thou accept regarding thy return boon?"

"The three sons of the valiant Usnech; the three torches of valor of Europe: Naisi, Anli, and Ardan."

Those guarantees were ratified on both sides.

They came into the house in which Conchobar was, to wit, into the Tete Brecc.

"Conchobar is now king of Ulster," said Cathbad, "if Fintan will give him his third."

"Yes," said Sencha, "for Cu Chulainn has given his."

"If so," said Cu Chulainn, "let him come to drinking and delight with me; for that is my counter-request."

"Where are my securities and bonds," asked Fintan, "when that is permitted to be said?"

The guarantees of each of them advanced savagely; and such was the fierceness of the uprising, that nine were covered with wounds, and nine with blood, and nine in death agonies, amongst them on one side and the other.

Sencha mac Ailill arose, and waved the peaceful branch of Sencha, so that the Ulstermen were quiet.

"Too much have you quarrelled," said Sencha, "for Conchobar is not King of Ulster until the end of a year."

"We will agree," said Cu Chulainn, "provided that you come not between us at the end of a year."

"I will not do so, truly," said Sencha.

Cu Chulainn bound him to this.

They remained during three days and nights, drinking that banquet of Conchobar until it was finished. They went then to their houses and forts and good residences.

He that came at the end of a year found the province a fountain of desire and of wealth with Conchobar; so that there was not a residence waste or empty from Rinn Seimne and Latharna to the hill of Uachtar Forcha and to Dub and to Drobais, without a son in the place of his father and his grandfather, serving his hereditary lord.

At this time a conversation occurred between Cu Chulainn and Emer.

"Methinks," said Emer, "Conchobar is now High-King of Ulster."

"Not sad, if it were so," said Cu Chulainn.

"It is time to prepare his banquet of sovereignty for him now," said Emer, "because he is a king forever."

The banquet was prepared; and there were a hundred vats of every kind of ale in it.

It was at the same time that Fintan son of Niall Niamglonnach decided to prepare his banquet; and there were a hundred vats of every kind of ale in it. And it was prepared and ready. On the same day both were begun, and on the same day they were ready. On the same day their horses were harnessed for them, and their chariots yoked. Cu Chulainn arrived the first at Emain. He had only unyoked his horses when Fintan arrived. Cu Chulainn was there, inviting Conchobar to his banquet, when Fintan arrived.

"Where are my bonds and guarantees, when that is permitted to be said?" asked Fintan.

"Here we are," said the sons of Usnech, rising up together.

"Even I," said Cu Chulainn, "am not without guarantees."

The Ulstermen advanced furiously to their arms; and because Sencha did not dare to come between them, they were so quarrelsome that Conchobar could do nothing for them but leave to them the royal hall in which they were. And a son of his followed him, whose name was Furbaide, whom Cu Chulainn had fostered. And Conchobar looked upon him.

"Good, O my son," said Conchobar, "if it pleased thee, the pacification of the Ulstermen would come through thee."

"How is that?" said the youth.

"By weeping and grieving in the presence of thy fair guardian, Cu Chulainn; for he was never in any difficulty of battle or conflict, that his mind would not be fixed on thee."

The boy went back and wept and grieved in the presence of his guardian, Cu Chulainn. Cu Chulainn asked what ailed him. The youth said to Cu Chulainn that "Just when the province is a fountain of desire, thou shouldst be disturbing and spoiling it, for the sake of the exchange of one night."

"I have pledged my word regarding it," said Cu Chulainn, "and it shall not be transgressed."

"I have sworn my oath," said Fintan, "that the Ulstermen shall come with me tonight."

"I would find an excellent counsel for you," said Sencha mac Ailill: "the first half of the night to Fintan, and the last half to Cu Chulainn, in order to appease the little boy's grief."

"I will allow it," said Cu Chulainn.

"I will agree, too," said Fintan.

The Ulstermen then rose up about Conchobar; and he sent messengers throughout the province, to muster the people of the province to Fintan's banquet. Conchobar himself went, with the company of the Craeb Ruad (Red Branch) around him, to Dun-da-Benn, to the house of Fintan son of Niall Niamglonnach.

The Ulstermen arrived at the festival assembly, so that there was not a man from a village in Ulster that did not come there. The way in which they came was, each noble with his lady; each king with his queen; each musician with his accompaniments; each hunter with his huntress. As if only a company of nine had reached the place—so were they attended to. There were fair-formed, bright-shaped sleeping-places prepared for them. There were splendid, lofty pavilions, littered with bent and fresh rushes, and long houses for the multitude, and immense, wide, capacious cooking-houses; and a variegated, wide-mouthed hall, which was broad and capacious, protective, square, four-doored, in which the nobles of Ulster, both men and women, might be accommodated at drinking and enjoyment. Provisions of food and ale were poured out for them, so that the allowance of a hundred of food and ale reached every nine of them.

The drinking house was afterwards arranged by Conchobar according to deeds, and parts, and families; according to grades, and arts, and customs, with a view to the fair holding of the banquet. Distributors came to distribute, and cup-bearers to deal, and door-keepers for door-keeping. Their music, and their minstrelsy, and their harmonies were played. Their lays, and their poesies, and their eulogies were chanted for them; and jewels and valuables and treasures were distributed to them.

It was then that Cu Chulainn said to Loeg mac Riangabra: "Go out, my master Loeg; observe the stars of the air and ascertain when the midnight comes; for often hast thou been watching and waiting for me in far distant countries."

Loeg went out. He continued watching and observing until midnight came. As midnight came Loeg proceeded to the place where Cu Chulainn was.

"It is midnight now, O Cu of the Feats," said he.

When Cu Chulainn heard this, he informed Conchobar, who was then in the hero-seat in front of him. Conchobar stood up with a speckled-bright bugle-horn. Mute and silent were the Ulstermen when they saw the king standing. Such was the silence that if a needle fell from the roof to the floor it would be heard.

One of the prohibitions of the Ulstermen was to speak before the king; and one of the prohibitions of the king was to speak before his druids.

It was then the excellent druid Cathbad asked, "What is it, O magnificent High-King of Ulster, O Conchobar?"

"Cu Chulainn here; he thinks it time to go and drink his banquet."

"Does he wish to merit the blessings of the assembled Ulstermen, and leave our weaklings and our women and our youths behind?"

"I should like it," said Cu Chulainn, "provided that our fighters, our champions, our warriors, our musicians, our poets, and our minstrels come with us."

The Ulstermen advanced as the advance of one man out upon the hard-surfaced green. "Good, O my master Loeg," said Cu Chulainn, "give a light course to the chariot." The charioteer possessed the three virtues of charioteering in that hour; to wit, turning around and straight backing and "leap over gap."

"Good, O my master Loeg," said Cu Chulainn, "give ardor of speed to the horses."

Cu Chulainn's horses broke into a furious sudden start. The horses of the Ulstermen followed their example. And where they went was into the green of Dun-da-Benn, to Cathar Osrin, to Li Thuaga, to Dun-Rigain, to Ollarbi, and by the shores of Ollarbi, into Mag Macha, into Sliab Fuait, and into Ath an Foraire, to Port Not of Cu Chulainn, into Mag Muirthemne, into Crich Saithi, across Dubid, across the stream of the Boyne, into Mag Breg and Meath, into Mag Lena, into Cliather Cell, across the Brosnas of Bladma; their left towards the gap of Mer daughter of Treg, which is to-day called Bernan Ele; their right to the Hills of Eblinne, daughter of Guaire, across the fair stream which is called the river of Ua Cathbad, into the great plain of Munster, through the middle of Artine, and into Smertaini; their right toward the rocks of Loch Gair; across the pool-stream of Maig, to Cliu Mail maic Ugaine, into the territory of Deise Beg, into the land of Cu Roi mac Dairi. Every hill over which they passed they leveled, so that they left it in low glens; every wood through which they passed, the iron wheels of the chariots cut the roots of the great trees, so that it was open country after them; the streams and fords and pools which they crossed were

fully-dry flags after them for a long time, and for long periods,
from the quantity which the cavalcades carried away with their
own bodies out of the contents of cascade, ford, and pool.

Then it was that Conchobar King of Ulster said, "We have
not found this way between Dun-da-Benn and Dun Delgan (Cu
Chulainn's stronghold)."

"We pledge our word truly," said Bricriu; "but it is more dig-
nified for us to whisper than for another to cry out loud. It seems
to us that it is not in the territory of Ulster that we are at all."

"We give our word," said Sencha mac Ailill, "that it is not
in the territory of Ulster at all we are."

"We give our word," said Conall the Victorious, "that it is
true."

It was then that the charioteers of the Ulstermen tightened the
bits in the mouths of their horses, from the first charioteer to the
last charioteer; whereupon Conchobar said, "Who will ascertain
for us in what territory we are?"

"Who should ascertain it for thee but Cu Chulainn?" said
Bricriu, "for it is he it is that has said that there was not a district
in which he had not committed the slaughter of a hundred."

"Of me it comes, O Bricriu," said Cu Chulainn; "I will go."

Cu Chulainn proceeded into Drum Colchailli, which is called
Ani Cliach.

"Say, my master Loeg, knowest thou in what territory we are?"

"I know not, indeed," said Loeg.

"But I know," said Cu Chulainn. "This is to the south of
Cenn Abrat of Sliab Cain. The mountains of Eblinne are these
to the north-east. That bright lake which thou see is the linn of
Limerick. This is Drum Colchailli in which we are, which is
called Ani Cliach, in the territory of the Deise Beg. Before us,
to the south, is the host, in Cliu Mail maic Ugaine, in the land
of Cu Roi mac Dairi maic Dedad."

While they were so engaged, tremendous heavy snow poured
upon the Ulstermen, until it reached to their shoulders, and to
the shafts of the chariots. Defences were made by the charioteers
of the Ulstermen, who between them raised stone columns to
shelter their horses, between them and the snow; so that the
echlasa of the horses of Ulster remain still, from that time to this.
And these are the proofs of the story.

Cu Chulainn and his charioteer Loeg advanced to the place where the Ulstermen were.

"Query, then," asked Sencha mac Ailill; "what is the territory in which we are?"

"We are," said Cu Chulainn, "in the territory of the Deise Beg, in the land of Cu Roi mac Dairi; to wit, in Cliu Mail maic Ugaine."

"Woe to us in that case," said Bricriu, "and woe to the Ulstermen."

"Say not so, O Bricriu," answered Cu Chulainn, "for I will give guidance to the Ulstermen in the return of the same way, so that we will reach our enemies before it be day."

"Woe to the Ulstermen," said Celtchar mac Uthecair, "that the one was born who gives this counsel."

"We have never known thee to have, O Cu Chulainn," said Fergna, a valor-chief of the Ulstermen, "a counsel of weakness, timidity, or cowardice for the Ulstermen until this night."

"Alas! that the person who gives the counsel should go," said red-hand Lugaid, son of Leit, king of Dal Araide, "without making him a mark of darts and arms and edges."

"Query, however," said Conchobar; "what do you wish?"

"We desire," said Celtchar mac Uthecair, "to be a day and a night in the territory in which we are, because it would be a sign of defeat for us to go out of it; for it is not 'a fox's track' with us in valley or waste or wood."

"Speak then, O Cu Chulainn," said Conchobar; "what is the proper place of encampment for us during this day and night?"

"The fair-green of Senchlochar is here," said Cu Chulainn; "and this rough winter season is not fair-time. And Tara Luachra is on the slopes of eastern Luachar; and in it are residences and houses."

"To go to Tara Luachra, then, is what is right," said Sencha mac Ailill.

They went on in the straight direction of the road to Tara Luachra, and Cu Chulainn as a guide before them.

Now Tara Luachra, if it were empty before or after, it is not that night it was empty. No wonder, indeed, for a son had been born to Ailill and Medb, whose name was Maine Mo Epert, and he was given in fosterage to Cu Roi mac Dairi; and Ailill and Medb had come that night, accompanied by the chieftains of their province, to drink at the end of that son's first month. Though these were all there, Eochaid mac Luchta likewise was there with the men of his province; and Cu Roi mac Dairi was there also, with all the Clan Dedad. And though these were all there, a provident woman was the amazonian Medb, daughter of the High-King of Erin, that is, Eochaid Fedlech; there were two observers and druids guarding her. Their names were Crom Deroil and Crom Darail, two foster-sons of the good, illustrious druid Cathbad.

It happened to them, then, to be on the wall of Tara Luachra at that time, looking and guarding, observing and viewing, on every side from them. It was then that Crom Deroil said, "Have you seen the thing which has appeared to me?"

"What thing?" said Crom Darail.

"It seems to me that it is swords of crimson warfare and the tread of multitudes that I perceive coming over the side of Ir Luachair from the east," answered the other druid.

"I would not think a clot of gore and blood too much in the mouth of him that utters that," said Crom Darail; "for that is not an army or a multitude, but the gigantic oaks past which we came yesterday."

"If it were they, why the immense royal chariots under them?"

"They are not chariots," said Crom Darail, "but the royal strongholds past which we came."

"If they are strongholds, why are those splendid all-white shields on them?"

"They are not shields at all," said Crom Darail, "but the columns that are in the doors of those royal strongholds."

"If they are columns," said Crom Deroil, "what is the cause of the profusion of red-armed spears above the great black breasts of the mighty host?"

"They are not spears, either," said Crom Darail, "but the stags and wild beasts of the country, with their horns and antlers above them."

"If they are stags and wild beasts," said Crom Deroil, "what causes the quantity of sods which their horses send from their shoes, so that it is pitch dark to the mighty air over their heads?"

"They are not horses," said Crom Darail, "but the herds and flocks and cattle of the country, after being let out of their sheds, for it is in those pastures the birds and winged animals alight in the snow."

"My conscience, if they are birds and winged animals, they are not a flock of one bird.

> If they are flocks, with the hue of a flock,
>   They are not the flock of one bird.
> A white-speckled, golden garment
>   Is, you would think, about each bird.
>
> If they are flocks of a rough glen,
>   From out of the black clefts,
> Not few are the angry spears
>   Above the fierce darts.
>
> Methinks they are not snow showers,
>   But stout, active men,
> Who are in threatening bands
>   Above the adjusted darts;
> A man under each hard, purple shield.
>   Prodigious is the flock.

"And reprove me not therefore," said Crom Deroil, "for it is I that speak the truth. As they come past the points of the trees of Ir Luachair from the east, what would make them stoop, unless they were men?"

. . . .

The fair-visaged Cu Roi mac Dairi heard the dispute of the two druids on the walls of Tara Luachra before him. "It is not at one these druids outside are," said the King of the World, the fair-visaged Cu Roi mac Dairi.

It was then the sun rose over the orb of the earth. "Visible to us now is the host," said Crom Deroil.

. . . .

Not long were they there, the two watchers, the two druids, until a full, fierce rush of the first band broke thither past the glen. Such was the fury with which they advanced, that there was not left a spear on a rack, nor a shield on a spike, nor a sword in an armory in Tara Luachra, that did not fall down. From every house on which was thatch in Tara Luachra, the thatch fell in immense flakes. One would think that it was the sea that had come over the walls and over the recesses of the world to them.

The forms of countenances were changed, and there was chattering
of teeth in Tara Luachra within. The two druids fell in fits and
in faintings and in paroxysms; one of them, Crom Darail, fell
over the wall outside, and Crom Deroil over the wall inside. And
notwithstanding, Crom Deroil got up, and cast an eye over the
first band that came into the green.

The host alighted on the green, and sat in one band on the
green. The snow dissolved and melted thirty feet on either side
of them, from the ardor of the great powerful warriors of Ulster.

Crom Deroil came into the house in which were Medb and Ailill
and Cu Roi and Eochaid mac Luchta; and Medb asked whence
came the clamor that occurred; whether it was down from the
air, or across the sea from the west, or from Erin, from the east.

"It is from Erin, from the east, across the slopes of the Ir
Luachair, undoubtedly," said Crom Deroil. "I see a barbaric
host, and I know not whether they are Irishmen or foreigners;
but if they are Irishmen, and if they are not foreigners, they are
Ulstermen."

"Should not the descriptions of the Ulstermen be known to
Cu Roi there?" asked Medb; "for often has he been on raids,
and on hostings, and on journeyings along with them."

"I would know them," said Cu Roi, "if I could obtain a description of them."

"The description of the first band that came into the place I
have, indeed," said Crom Deroil.

"Give it to us then," said Medb.

"I saw before the stronghold to the east, outside," said Crom
Deroil, "a royal, immense band; the equal of a king was every
man in the band. There were three in front of the band, and a
broad-eyed, royal, gigantic warrior between them in the middle.
Comparable to a moon in its great fifteenth was his countenance,
his visage, and his face. His beard was fair, forked, and pointed;
his bushy, reddish-yellow hair was looped to the slope of his hood.
A purple-bordered garment encircled him, a brooch of wrought
gold being in the garment over his white shoulder. Next to his
white skin was a shirt of kingly satin. A purple-brown shield,
with rims of yellow gold, was over him. He had a gold-hilted,
embossed sword; a purple-bright, well-shaped spear in his white
firm right hand, accompanied by its forked dart. At his right

stood a true warrior; brighter than snow was his countenance, his visage, and his face. At his left side a little black-browed man, greatly resplendent. A fair, very-brilliant man was playing the edge-feat over them; his sharp inlaid sword in the one hand, his large warrior-like sword in the other hand. These he sent up and down past one another, so that they would touch the hair and forehead of the great central hero; but before they could reach the ground, the same man would catch their points, both backs and edges."

"Regal is the description," said Medb.

"Regal is the band whose description it is," said Cu Roi.

"What, then; who are they?" asked Ailill.

"Not hard to tell," said Cu Roi. "That great central hero is Conchobar, son of Fachtna Fathach, the lawful, worthy king of Ulster, descendant of the kings of Erin and Alba. On his right side is Fintan, son of Niall Niamglonnach, the man of the third of Ulster, whose countenance and face is more bright than snow. The little black-browed man is Cu Chulainn son of Sualtam. Ferchertne, son of Corpre, son of Ilia, is the fair beaming man who is playing warlike feats over them. A king-poet of the king-poets of Ulster is he, and a rear-guard of Conchobar when he goes into his enemies' country. Whoever would wish to solicit or speak to the king, it is not permitted until that man is appeased."

"Here before these to the east, outside," said Crom Deroil, "I saw a splendid, active trio, clothed in warrior's dress. Two of them were young, child-like; the third had a forked, purple-brown beard. They would not remove the dew from the grass, for the celerity and lightness with which they came; as if not one of the great host perceived them, and they see the whole host."

"Gentle and light and peaceful is the description," said Medb.

"Gentle and peaceful is the band whose description it is," said Cu Roi.

"Who are they?" asked Ailill.

"Not hard to tell," said Cu Roi. "Three noble youths of the Tuatha De Danann are there: Delbaeth son of Ethliu, and Angus Oc son of the Dagda, and Cermat Honey-mouth. They came at the end of night this day, to excite valor and battle, and they have mixed themselves through the host. And it is true that the hosts do not perceive them; but they see the hosts."

"Here before them to the east, outside," said Crom Deroil, "I see a warlike, valorous company, with three distinguished persons advancing in front of them. A wrathful brown hero is there; and a fair truly-splendid hero; and a valiant, king-stout, mighty champion, with thick red-yellow hair; and comparable to a honey-comb at the end of harvest, or clasps of fair gold, is the bright glistening of his hair; two-forked, black-brown is his beard, which is equal to the measure of a hero's hand in length; like the purple hue of the gilly-flower, or sparkles of fresh fire, his countenance, his visage, and his face. They bear three knightly, brown-red shields; three immense, whizzing, warlike spears; three heavy, stout-striking swords. Three shapely suits of purple apparel about them."

"Heroic and knightly, by our conscience, is the description," said Medb.

"Heroic and knightly is the band whose description it is," said Cu Roi.

"What, then; who are they?" said Ailill.

"Not hard to tell," said Cu Roi. "Three prime heroes of Ulster are they—the two Conalls and Loegaire—viz., Conall Anglonnach son of Iriel Glunmar, and Conall the Victorious son of Amergin, and Loegaire the Triumphant from Rath Immil."

"Here before them to the east, outside," said Crom Deroil, "I saw a hideous, unknown trio in the front of the band, with three linen shirts girding their bodies; three hairy, dark-gray garments in folds about them; three iron pins in the garments over their bosoms; three coarse dark-brown heads of hair on them; three bright-grey shields, with hard ozier bindings upon them; three broad-bladed lances with them; three gold-hilted swords have they. Like the baying of a foreign hound in the chase is the loud heart-bellowing of each warrior of them when hearing of their enemies in this fortress."

"Fierce and warlike is the description," said Medb.

"Fierce is the band whose description it is," said Cu Roi.

"What, then; who are they?" said Ailill.

"Not hard to tell," said Cu Roi. "Three leaders of battle of the Ulstermen are they—Uma son of Remanfisech, from Fedan of Cooley; Ergi Echbel, from Bri Ergi; and Celtchar the Great, son of Uthecar, from Rath Celtchar, from Dun da Lethglas."

"Here in front of them to the east, outside," said Crom Deroil, "I saw a large-eyed, large-thighed, noble-great, immensely-tall man, with a splendid gray garment about him; with seven short, black, equally-smooth cloaklets around him; shorter was each upper one, longer each lower. At either side of him were nine men. In his hand was a terrible iron staff, on which were a rough end and a smooth end. His play and amusement consisted in laying the rough end on the heads of the nine, whom he would kill in the space of a moment. He would then lay the smooth end on them, so that he would reanimate them in the same time."

"Wonderful is the description," said Medb.

"Great is the person whose description it is," said Cu Roi.

"What, then; who is he?" said Ailill.

"Not hard to tell," said Cu Roi. "The great Dagda son of Ethliu, the good god of the Tuatha De Danann. To magnify valor and conflict he wrought confusion upon the host in the morning this day; and no one in the host sees him."

.   .   .   .

"Here before them, to the east, outside," said Crom Deroil, "I saw a band of their rabble. One man in their midst, with a black, pointed thick head of hair, having large, subtle, all-white eyes in his head, and a smooth-blue Ethiopian countenance; a ribbed garment in folds about him; a brazen clasp in his garment, over his breast; a large bronze wand in his hand, and a melodious little bell beside him, which he touches with his wand before the host, so that it gives pleasure and delight to the High-King and to the whole host."

"Laughable and amusing is the description," said Medb.

"Laughable is the person whose description it is," said Cu Roi.

"Who is he?" said Ailill.

"Not hard to tell," said Cu Roi. "That is the royal fool Roimid, Conchobar's fool. There never was fatigue or sorrow on any man of the Ulstermen that he would heed, if only he saw the royal fool, Roimid."

.   .   .   .

"Here before them, to the east, outside," said Crom Deroil, "I saw a prodigious royal band. One man in front of it, with coarse, black hair. An expression of gentleness in one of his eyes;

foam of crimson blood in the other eye; that is, at one time a gentle, friendly aspect, at another time a fierce expression. An open-mouthed otter on each of his two shoulders. A smooth, white-surfaced shield upon him. A white-hilted sword with him. A large, warrior-like spear to the height of his shoulder. When its spear-ardor seized it, he would deal a blow of the handle of the mighty spear upon his hand when the full measure of a sack of fiery particles would burst over its side and edge. A blood-black cauldron of horrid, noxious liquid before him, composed, through sorcery, of the blood of dogs, cats, and druids. And the head of the spear was plunged in that poisonous liquid when its spear-ardor came."

"By our conscience, the description is venomous," said Medb.

"Venomous is he whose description it is," said Cu Roi.

"Who, then, is he?" asked Ailill.

"That is Dubtach Chafertongue, of Ulster," said Cu Roi; "a man who never merited thanks from anyone; and when a prey falls to the Ulstermen, a prey falls to him alone. The quick, deedful spear (*Luin*) of Celtchar is in his hand, on loan, and a cauldron of crimson blood is before it, for it would burn its handle, or the man that is bearing it, unless it was bathed in the cauldron of noxious blood. And foretelling battle it is."

"Here before them, to the east, outside," said Crom Deroil, "I see another band there. A sedate, gray-haired man in front thereof. A fair bright garment about him, with borders of all-white silver. A beautiful white shirt next to the surface of his skin; a white-silver belt around his waist; a bronze branch at the summit of his shoulder; the sweetness of melody in his voice; his utterance loud but slow."

"Judicial and sage, by our conscience, is the description," said Medb.

"Sage and judicial the person whose description it is," said Cu Roi.

"Who, then, is he?" asked Ailill.

"Not hard to tell. Sencha the Great, son of Ailill son of Mael-chloid, from Carn Mag of Ulster; the most eloquent man of the men of earth, and the peace-maker of the hosts of the Ulstermen. The men of the world, from the rising to the setting, he would pacify with his three fair words."

.   .   .   .

That is the description of the first division that came into the fair-green. The great druid was not able to describe them further.

"They are the Ulstermen," said Medb.

"They are indeed," said Cu Roi.

"Was it imagined before or after; or is it in prediction or prophecy with you?"

"That we know not," said Cu Roi.

"Is there in the stronghold any one that knows?" asked Medb.

"There is," said Cu Roi, "the senior of the Clan Dedad, to wit, Gabalglinni son of Dedad, who has been, and he blind, maintained thirty years in this stronghold."

"Let some one go and ask him if they were expected; and let it be asked of him what preparation was made for them."

"Who shall go there?" asked Cu Roi.

"Let Crom Deroil and Faenglinni, son of Dedad, go."

They went to the house where Gabalglinni was maintained.

"Who is this?" asked he.

"Crom Deroil and Faenglinni, son of Dedad, are here," said they, "to inquire of thee if the coming of the Ulstermen was in prediction or in prophecy; or if so, whether there is any preparation for them?"

"Long has their coming been in prophecy. That they may be attended to, this is the provision. An iron house, and two wooden houses about it; and a subterranean house under it, and a strong iron flag upon that; and all the faggots and inflammable materials and coal that were found were collected into the subterranean house, so that it is quite full. It is what was prophecied for us, that the nobles of Ulster would be congregated in one night in that house. There are seven chains of good iron here under the feet of this bed. Let them be firmly fastened to the seven pillar-stones that are on the green outside."

Then Crom Deroil and Faenglinni came into the house in which were Medb and Ailill of Connacht and the nobles of the province of Munster, and related to them how the Ulstermen were awaited.

"Let one from me and one from thee go to bid them welcome, O Cu Roi," said Medb.

"Who shall go there?" asked Cu Roi.

"These same two," said Medb, "that welcome may be given to

them from me with the nobles of the province of Connacht, and from thee with the nobles of the two provinces of Munster."

"I shall know," said Cu Roi, "by the person that answers whether they come with peace or with battle; for if it is Dubtach Chafertongue of Ulster that answers, it is with discord they come; if it is Sencha mac Ailill that answers, it is with peace they come."

The messengers went on to the place where the Ulstermen were on the green.

"Welcome, ever-welcome, thy coming, O high-puissant, high-noble High-King of Ulster, from Medb and from Ailill, and from the chieftains of the province of Connacht along with them," said Crom Deroil.

"Welcome, ever-welcome, thy coming, O high-puissant, high-noble High-King of Ulster, from Cu Roi mac Dairi, with the nobles of the two provinces of Munster, who are yonder in the stronghold," said Faenglinni mac Dedad.

"It is pleasing to us and pleasing to the king," said Sencha mac Ailill; "and it was not to commit injury or conflict the Ulstermen came but in a drunken escapade, from Dun-da-Benn to Cliu Mail maic Ugaine; and they deemed it not honorable to get out of the district until they should be a night encamped in it."

The messengers proceeded to the place in which were Medb and Ailill and Cu Roi and Eochaid, with the nobles of the three provinces, and they related the news to them.

The poets, the minstrels, and the entertainers were sent to the Ulstermen, while a house was being arranged for them, to furnish amusement for them.

Messengers were then sent to them, to inform them that the best hero of the Ulstermen might select the choicest house for them. A quarrel arose about that among the Ulstermen. A hundred powerful warriors rose up together upon their arms; but Sencha mac Ailill pacified them.

"Let Cu Chulainn go there," said Sencha; "about the measure of his house you have come; and you shall be under his guarantee until you return again."

Cu Chulainn went. The Ulstermen advanced as one man after Cu Chulainn. Cu Chulainn looked upon the largest house that was in the place; it happened to be the iron house, about which the two wooden houses were.

Their attendants came to them, and an enormous bonfire was lighted for them; and provisions of food and ale were dealt to them. As night approached, their attendants and servants stole away from them one by one, until the last man, who closed the door after him. And the seven chains of iron were fixed upon the house, and fastened to the seven pillars that were upon the green outside. Thrice fifty smiths were brought, with their smith's-bellows, to blow the fire. Three circles were made around the house; and the fire was ignited from above and from below, in the house, until the heat from the fire came through the house from below. Then the hosts shouted loudly about the house, so that the Ulstermen were silent, speechless, until Bricriu said, "What, O Ulstermen, is the great heat that seizes our feet? But it is fitter that I should know than any other person. It seems to me they are burning us from below, and from above; and the house is closed fast."

"There will be a means by which we shall know," said Triscatal Strongman, getting up and delivering a blow with his foot on the iron door. But the door neither creaked nor resounded nor was injured.

"Not well hast thou made thy banquet for the Ulstermen, O Cu Chulainn," said Bricriu; "thou hast brought them into an enemy's pen."

"Say not so, O Bricriu," answered Cu Chulainn. "I will do my hero feat, a deed through which the Ulstermen will all get out."

Cu Chulainn plunged his sword up to the hilt through the iron house, and through the two houses of boards.

"An iron house here," said Cu Chulainn, "between two houses of boards."

"Worse than all, alas!" said Bricriu.

(The conclusion of this form of the story is lost. There is, however, another version, the beginning of which is lost, in one of our oldest manuscripts, which dates from the eleventh century. This fragment begins with the dispute of the Ulstermen over which of them should lead the way into the enclosure. There is apparently no iron house in this version. The visitors are lodged in a wooden house and besieged by the hosts of the Erna. Ailill and his sons try to protect the Ulstermen.)

" 'Tis I," said Triscoth.[1] "Any man of them whom I shall look fiercely at—his lips shall die."

" 'Tis I," said the fool Reorda.[2]

---

[1] Triscatal in the other version.   [2] Roimid in the other version.

" 'Tis I," said Nia na Trebuin-cro.

" 'Tis I," said Daeltenga (Chafertongue.)

"Either of us shall go," said Dub and Rodub.

Each man rose against the other, regarding it.

"Can you not decide that thing?" asked Sencha. "The man whom the Ulstermen honor, though he were not the best warrior here, 'tis he should go."

"Which of us is that?" asked the Ulstermen.

"Cu Chulainn there; even though he were not the best warrior here, 'tis he should go."

They then advanced into the enclosure of the fort, and Cu Chulainn in front of them.

"Is this the youth that is the best warrior among the Ulstermen?" asked Fintan.

Thereupon Cu Chulainn jumped up until he was on the summit of the enclosure, and leaped valorously on the bridge, so that the weapons that were in the stronghold fell from their racks. The Ulstermen were afterwards taken into a secure oaken house, with a yew door, three feet thick, having two iron hooks, and an iron spit through them. The house was furnished with flock-beds and bed-clothes. Crom Deroil sent their weapons after them; and they sat down; and Cu Chulainn's weapons were elevated over them.

"Let water for washing be heated for them," said Ailill. And ale and food were given them until they were intoxicated. Crom Deroil visited them again, to know if there was anything they would wish.

When they were merry drunk Sencha clapped his hands. They all listened to him. "Give now your blessing on the prince who has protected you, who has been generous to you. It is not 'a hand in a poor, garnered field.' Plentiful are food and ale for you with the prince who has protected you. It was not necessary to wait for cooking."

"It is true," said Chafertongue. "I swear by my people's gods that there shall never reach your country anything but what birds may carry away of you in their claws; but the men of Erin and Alba will possess your land, and take your women and treasures and break your children's heads against stones."

It was of him Fergus said thus in the "Cattle-Raid":

> Let off Dubtach Chafertongue,
> Behind the host drag him;
> No good has he done.
> He slew the maiden-band.
>
> He did a hateful, hideous act—
> The killing of Fiacha, Conchobar's son.
> Not more famous for him, it was heard,
> The killing of Maine son of Fedlimid.
>
> The kingship of Ulster he contests not—
> The son of Lugaid son of Casruba;
> What he does against men is,
> To attack them when they sit.

"That is not false, however," said Dubtach. "Observe the strength of the house and the fastening that is on the house. See you not that though you be anxious to leave it, you cannot? I am now deceived, unless there is a contest about our being brought out. However, that hero who is the best warrior among the Ulstermen—let him bring some news from the opponents."

Cu Chulainn advanced, and made a somersault upwards, carried away the upper roof of the house, and was on the roof of another house, when he saw the multitude down below. They formed into a battle-throng to attack the Ulstermen inside. Ailill placed his back to the door to protect them. His seven sons joined hands with him before the door. The multitude burst into the middle of the enclosure; Cu Chulainn returned to his people, and gave the door a kick, so that his leg went through it up to the knee. "If it were to a woman that was given," said Chafertongue, "she would be in her bed." Cu Chulainn delivered another kick, and the door fell down before him. "May I be saved," said Sencha; "it is Cu Chulainn that is here this time. Every virtue that is a virtue to heroes fighting, you shall have. Your companions are coming to you here.

"What is your counsel?" asked Sencha.

"Put your backs, all, against the wall, and let everyone have his weapons in front of him; and send one man to speak with them."

Heavy as it was, they threw the house from off them.

"Who shall speak to them?" asked Sencha.

"I will speak to them," said Triscoth. "Any one of them that I look upon—his lips shall die."

The others were holding their council outside.

"Query: who shall speak to them, and go the first to them into the house?" said the warriors outside.

"I shall go," said Lopan.

Lopan then went into the house to them, accompanied by nine persons. "Is that pleasant, O heroes?" asked he.

"Yes," said the heroes.

"Man against man?" said Triscoth.

"True, true."

"Triscoth here, speaking for the Ulstermen! They have not good speakers besides."

Triscoth looked fiercely at him so that he fainted.

Fer Caille came into the house; nine men with him. "Is that pleasant, O warriors?" said he.

"The full pleasure," said Triscoth, "is one man against another."

Triscoth looked fiercely at him, and he fainted.

Mianach "the unknown" came into the house; nine men with him.

"Pale to us," said he, "appear the sick that are on the floor." Triscoth looked at him.

"Look at me," said Mianach, "and see if I would die of it."

The other took him by the leg and dashed him against the three nines that were in the house, so that not one of them escaped alive.

The multitude outside gathered around the house, to take it against the Ulstermen. But the Ulstermen upset the house, so that three hundred of the host outside it fell under the house. The battle closed between them. They were engaged in battle until mid-day on the morrow. The Ulstermen were wounded, however, and they were fewer in number.

Ailill was on the rampart of the stronghold, looking at them. "The stories of the Ulstermen were stories worth telling me until today," said he. "It was told me that not in Erin were there heroes equal to them. But I perceive that they do nought but treachery today. It has long been a proverb 'no battle should be fought without a king.' If it were about me that battle were going on, it would not continue long. You see," said Ailill to the Ulstermen, "I am not able for them; and I have been profaned regarding you."

Thereupon Cu Chulainn dashed suddenly through the multitude and assailed them thrice. Furbaide Ferbenn son of Conchobar attacked them also all around. The others would not wound him because of his beauty.

"Why do you not wound this warrior?" said one of them. "Not agreeable the deeds he performs. I swear by my people's gods, though it were a head of gold he had, I would slay him when he slew my brother." Furbaide pierced him with a spear and he died thereof. The battle was subsequently gained over the Erna; only three of them escaped from it.

The Ulstermen then plundered the entire stronghold, but protected Ailill and his seven sons, because they were not in the battle against them. From that time forth Tara Luachra was not inhabited.

Crimthann Nia Nair of the Erna escaped from the battle. He met with Richis, a female satirist, westwards of the Laune. "Was my son lost?" asked she.

"Yes," said Crimthann.

"Come with me," said she, "until you avenge him."

"What revenge?" asked Crimthann.

"That you slay Cu Chulainn for his sake," replied she.

"How can that be done?" asked Crimthann.

"Not difficult. If you only use your two hands upon him, you will need nothing more; for you will find him unprepared."

They then went in pursuit of the host of the Ulstermen, and found Cu Chulainn on a ford before them in the country of Owney. Richis took off her clothes in presence of Cu Chulainn, who hid his face downwards, that he might not see her nakedness. "Attack him now, O Crimthann," said Richis.

"The man approaches thee," said Loeg.

"Not so, indeed," said Cu Chulainn. "Whilst the woman is in that condition I shall not rise up."

Loeg took a stone out of the chariot and cast it at her, which hit her across the *luthan*, so that her back was broken in two; and she died thereof afterwards.

Cu Chulainn then advanced against Crimthann and fought with him and carried away his head and spoils.

Then Cu Chulainn and his charioteer went after the host until all arrived at Cu Chulainn's stronghold, where they rested that night. They were all entertained to the end of forty nights on the same feast by Cu Chulainn. And they afterwards departed from him and left a blessing with him.

Ailill came from the south towards the Ulstermen and remained as a friend with them. The width of his face was given to him of gold and silver and the worth of seven bondmaids was given to each of his sons. He subsequently went to his own country in peace and unity with the Ulstermen.

Conchobar was afterward without destruction of his kingship whilst he lived.

THE EXILE OF THE SONS OF USNECH

"The Exile of the Sons of Usnech" is one of the best known ancient Irish sagas. It is also one of the few stories of the Ulster cycle that have been preserved on the lips of the folk down to modern times. Versions composed as early as the eighth or ninth century exist in mediaeval manuscripts, and variants of the story are still to be heard in the remote country districts of Ireland and Scotland. Folk versions of the story have been especially popular in the Gaelic-speaking districts of Scotland, a fact perhaps due to the complimentary references to Scotland in certain forms of the narrative.

"The Exile of the Sons of Usnech" owes its popularity to the fact that it tells the tragic love story of the beautiful but ill-starred Derdriu (Deirdre), the Helen of ancient Irish tradition. Fated from birth to bring misfortune to others, this primitive epic woman flees from the court of the elderly and uxorious King Conchobar with the handsome young Naisi, one of the three "sons of Usnech," only to involve herself, her lover, and his brothers in sorrow and disaster. Though not so well known as her Greek counterpart, Derdriu still deserves to rank as one of the great tragic heroines of literature.

As regards its connection with the Ulster cycle, this tale explains how Dubtach, Fergus mac Roig, Conchobar's son Cormac, and other Ulstermen are arrayed among the forces of Connacht, the traditional enemy of their native province, during the Cattle-Raid of Cooley. In revenge for the murder of the "sons of Usnech," Fergus, Dubtach, and Cormac slay many of their fellow-tribesmen and betake themselves with three thousand followers to the court of Ailill and Medb of Connacht, whom they assist on the Cattle-Raid of Cooley and other raids upon Ulster.

The Deirdre story is the theme of several recent Anglo-Irish dramas, notably J. M. Synge's "Deirdre of the Sorrows."

In the house of Fedlimid, the son of Dall, who was the narrator of stories to Conchobar the king of Ulster, the men of Ulster sat at their ale; and before the men, in order to attend upon them, stood the wife of Fedlimid, and she great with child. Round about the board went drinking-horns, and portions of food; and the revellers shouted in their drunken mirth. And when the men desired to lay themselves down to sleep, the woman also went to her couch; and, as she passed through the midst of the house, the child cried out in her womb, so that its shriek was heard throughout the whole house, and throughout the outer court that lay about it.

239

And at that shriek, all the men sprang up; and, head to head, they thronged together in the house, whereupon Sencha mac Ailill rebuked them: "Let none of you stir!" cried he, "and let the woman be brought before us, that we may learn what is the meaning of that cry." Then they brought the woman before them, and thus spoke to her Fedlimid, her husband:

> What is that, of all cries far the fiercest,
> In thy womb raging loudly?
> Through all ears thou piercest with that clamor;
> With that scream, from sides swollen and strong:
> Of great woe, for that cry, is foreboding to my heart;
> That is torn through with terror, and sore with grief.

Then the woman turned, and she approached Cathbad the druid, for he was a man of knowledge, and thus she spoke to him:

> Give thou ear to me, Cathbad, thou fair one of face,
> Thou great crown of our honor, and royal in family;
> Let the man so exalted be set still higher,
> Let the druid draw knowledge, that druids can obtain.
> For I want words of wisdom, and none can I express;
> Nor to Fedlimid a torch of sure knowledge can stretch:
> As no wit of a woman knows what she bears,
> I know naught of that cry that sounds forth from within me.

And then said Cathbad:

> It is a maid who screamed wildly just now,
> Fair and curling locks shall flow round her,
> Blue-centred and stately her eyes;
> And her cheeks shall glow like the foxglove.
> For the tint of her skin, we commend her,
> In its whiteness, newly fallen like snow;
> And her teeth are faultless in splendor;
> And her lips are red like coral:
> A fair woman is she, for whom heroes, that fight
> In their chariots for Ulster, shall be doomed to death.
> It is a woman who hath given that shriek,
> Golden-haired, with long tresses, and tall;
> For whose love many chiefs shall strive,
> And great kings shall ask for her favors.
> To the west she shall hasten, beguiling
> A great host, that shall march from Ulster:
> Red as coral, her lips shall be smiling,
> As they reveal her teeth, white as pearls:
> That woman is fair, and great queens shall be fain
> Of her form, that is faultless, unflawed.

Then Cathbad laid his hand upon the womb of the woman; and the little child cried out beneath his hand: "Aye, indeed," he said, "it is a woman child who is here: Deirdre shall be her name, and evil shall come from her."

Now some days after that the girl child was born; and then thus sang Cathbad:

> O Deirdre! thou art great cause of ruin;
>   Though famous, and fair, and pale:
> Before Fedlimid's daughter shall part from life,
>   All Ulster shall wail her deeds.
>
> Yes, mischief shall come, in the after-time,
>   Thou fair shining maid, on thy account;
> Hear ye this: Usnech's sons, the three noble chiefs,
>   Shall be forced into banishment.
>
> While thou art in life, shall a fierce wild deed
>   Be done in Emain, though late:
> Later yet, it shall mourn it refused to heed
>   The guard of Rog's powerful son.[1]
>
> O noble lady! it is through thy fault
>   That Fergus to exile flees;
> That a son of king Conchobar shall be in sorrow,
>   When Fiachna is injured, and dies.
>
> O noble lady! the guilt is all thine!
>   Gerre son of Illadan is slain;
> And when Eogan mac Durthacht's great life is destroyed,
>   Not less shall be found our sorrow.
>
> A grim deed shalt thou do, and shalt be in anger
>   Against the king of glorious Ulster:
> In whatever place men shall dig thee thy little grave,
>   Of Deirdre they long shall sing.

"Let that maiden be slain!" cried out the young men of Ulster. "Not so!" said Conchobar; "let her in the morning be brought to me, and she shall be reared according to my will, and she shall be my wife, and in my companionship shall she be."

The men of Ulster were not so hardy as to turn him from his purpose, and thus it was done. The maiden was reared according to Conchobar's will, and she grew up to be the fairest maid in all Erin. She was brought up in a house apart; so that none of the men of Ulster might see her till the time came when she

---

[1] *I.e.*, Fergus mac Roig.

should sleep with Conchobar: none of mankind was permitted to enter the house where she was reared, save only her foster-father, and her foster-mother; and in addition to these Leborcham, to whom naught could be refused, for she was a woman-satirist.

Now it chanced upon a certain day in the time of winter that the foster-father of Deirdre was outside the house, skinning a calf upon the snow, in order to cook it for her, and the blood of the calf lay upon the snow, and she saw a black raven which came down to drink it. "Leborcham," said Deirdre, "that man only will I love, who hath the three colors that I see yonder,—his hair as black as the raven, his cheeks red like the blood, and his body as white as the snow."

"Blessing and good fortune to thee!" said Leborcham; "that man is not far away. He is yonder in the stronghold of Emain Macha, which is nigh; and the name of him is Naisi, the son of Usnech."

"I shall never be in good health again," said Deirdre, "until the time comes when I may see him."

It befell that Naisi was upon a certain day alone upon the rampart of the stronghold of Emain, and he uttered his musical warrior-cry: well did the music ring out that was sung by the sons of Usnech. Each cow and every beast that heard them, gave two-thirds more of milk than its wont; and each man by whom that cry was heard deemed it to be a sufficiency of pleasure to him. Goodly, moreover, was the play that these men made with their weapons; if the whole province of Ulster had been assembled together against them in one place, and they three only had been able to set their backs against one another, the men of Ulster would not have borne away victory from those three: so well were they skilled in parry and defence. And they were swift of foot when they hunted the game, and with them it was the custom to catch their quarry by swiftness of foot alone.

Now while this Naisi was alone on the rampart, Deirdre also soon escaped outside her house to him, and she ran past him, and at first he knew not who she might be.

"Fair is the young heifer that springs past me!" he cried.

"Well may the young heifers be great," she said, "in a place where no bulls are."

"Thou hast, as thy bull," said he, "the bull of the whole province of Ulster, even Conchobar, the king of Ulster."

"I would choose between you two," she said, "and I would take for myself a younger bull, even such as thou art."

"Not so, indeed," said Naisi, "for I fear the prophecy of Cathbad."

"Sayest thou this, as meaning to refuse me?" said she.

"Yea, indeed," he said; and she sprang upon him, and she seized him by his two ears. "Two ears of shame and of mockery shalt thou have," she cried, "if thou take me not with thee."

"Release me, woman!" said he.

"That will I not."

Then Naisi raised his musical warrior-cry, and the Ulstermen heard it, and each of them sprang up: and the sons of Usnech hurried out to their brother.

"What is it," they said, "that thou dost? let it not be by any fault of thine that war is stirred up between us and the men of Ulster."

Then he told them all that had been done; and "There shall evil come on thee from this," said they; "moreover thou shalt lie under the reproach of shame so long as thou dost live; but we will go with her into another land, for there is no king in all Ireland who will refuse us welcome if we come to him."

Then they took counsel together, and that same night they departed, three times fifty warriors, and three times fifty women, and dogs, and servants, and Deirdre with them.

And for a long time they wandered about Ireland, in vassalage to this chieftain or that; and often Conchobar sought to slay them, either by ambuscade or by treachery; from round about Es Ruad, near to Ballyshannon in the west, they journeyed, and they turned them back to Benn Etar, in the north-east, which men to-day call the Hill of Howth. Nevertheless the men of Ulster drove them from the land, and they came to the land of Alba (Scotland), and in its wildernesses they dwelt. And when the chase of the wild beasts of the mountains failed them, they made raids upon the cattle of the men of Alba, and took them for themselves; and the men of Alba gathered themselves together with intent to destroy them. Then they took shelter with the king of Alba, and the king took them into his following, and they served him in war. And they made for themselves houses of their own on the green of the king of Alba's stronghold: it was on account of Deirdre that these houses were made, for they feared that men might see her, and that on her account they might be slain.

Now one day the high-steward of the king of Alba went out in the early morning, and he took a turn about Naisi's house, and saw Naisi and Deirdre sleeping therein. He hurried back to the king, and waked him: "Up to this day," said he, "we have found no wife for thee fit for thyself. Naisi the son of Usnech has a wife of worth sufficient for the emperor of the western world! Let Naisi be slain, and let the woman sleep with thee."

"Not so!" said the king; "but do thou go each day to her house, and woo her for me secretly."

Thus was it done; but Deirdre, whatever the steward told her, used straightway to recount it each evening to her husband; and since nothing was obtained from her, the sons of Usnech were sent into dangers, and into wars, and into strifes that thereby they might be slain. Nevertheless they showed themselves to be stout in every strife, so that the king gained no advantage from them by such attempts as these.

The men of Alba were gathered together to destroy the sons of Usnech, and this also was told to Deirdre. And she told her news to Naisi: "Depart hence!" said she, "for if you depart not this night, upon the morrow you will be slain!" And they departed that night, and they betook themselves to an island of the sea.

Now the news of what had passed was brought to the men of Ulster. "It is a pity, O Conchobar!" said they, "that the sons of Usnech should die in the land of enemies, for the sake of an evil woman. It is better that they should come under thy protection, and that they should come into their own land, rather than that they should fall at the hands of foes."

"Let them come to us then," said Conchobar, "and let men go as securities to them." The news was brought to them.

"This is welcome news for us," they said; "we will indeed come, and let Fergus come as our surety, and Dubtach, and Cormac the son of Conchobar." These then went to them, and they moved them to pass over the sea. But at the instigation of Conchobar, Fergus was pressed to join in an ale-feast, while the sons of Usnech were pledged to eat no food in Erin, until they had eaten the food of Conchobar in Emain. So Fergus, with Dubtach and Cormac, tarried behind; and the sons of Usnech went on, accompanied by Fiacha, Fergus' son; until they came to the fair-green before Emain.

Now at that time Eogan son of Durthacht king of Fernmag had come to Emain to make his peace with Conchobar, for they had for a long time been at enmity; and to him, and to certain mercenaries of Conchobar, the charge was given that they should slay the sons of Usnech. The sons of Usnech stood upon the fair-green of Emain, and the women were sitting upon the ramparts of Emain. And Eogan came with his band of mercenaries across the meadow, and the son of Fergus took his place by Naisi's side. And Eogan greeted them with a mighty thrust of his spear, and the spear broke Naisi's back, and passed through it. The son of Fergus made a spring, and he threw both arms around Naisi, and he brought him beneath himself to shelter him, while he threw himself down above him; and it was thus that Naisi was slain, through the body of the son of Fergus. Then there began a slaughter throughout the fair-green, so that none escaped who did not fall by the points of the spears, or the edge of the sword. And Deirdre was brought to Conchobar to be in his power, and her arms were bound behind her back.

Now the sureties who had remained behind heard what had been done; that is, Fergus and Dubtach and Cormac. And thereon they came, and they forthwith performed great deeds. Dubtach slew, with the one thrust of his spear, Maine a son of Conchobar, and Fiachna the son of Fedelm, Conchobar's daughter; and Fergus struck down Traigtren the son of Traiglethan, and his brother. And Conchobar was wrathful at this, and a fight took place; so that upon that day three hundred of the men of Ulster fell. And Dubtach slew the maidens of Ulster; and, ere the day dawned, Fergus set Emain on fire. Then they went away into exile, and betook them to the land of Connacht to find shelter with Ailill and Medb, for they knew that that royal pair would give them welcome. To the Ulstermen the exiles showed no love: three thousand stout men went with them; and for sixteen years never did they allow cries of lamentation and of fear among the Ulstermen to cease: each night their vengeful forays caused men to quake and to wail.

Deirdre lived on for a year in the household of Conchobar; and during all that time she smiled not a smile of laughter, she took not her sufficiency of food or sleep, and she raised not her head from her knee. And if any one brought before her entertainers, she used to speak thus:

> Though troops brave and fair to see,
>> May return home and ye await them;
> When Usnech's sons came home to me in Alba,
>> They came more heroically.
>
> With abundant mead my Naisi stood:
>> And near our fire his bath I poured;
> On Anli's stately back wood;
>> On Ardan's an ox or a goodly boar.
>
> Though ye think the mead sweet
>> That warlike Conchobar drinks,
> I oft have known a sweeter drink,
>> Often on the edge of a spring.
>
> Our board was spread beneath the tree,
>> And Naisi kindled the cooking fire;
> Meat, prepared from Naisi's game
>> Was more sweet to me than honey.
>
> Though well your horns may blow music,
>> Though sweetly your pipes may sound,
> I say without fear, that I know well
>> I have often heard a sweeter strain.
>
> Though horns and pipes sound clear,
>> Though Conchobar's mind rejoice in these,
> A more magic strain, more sweet, more dear
>> Were the voices of the sons of Usnech.
>
> Like sound of wave, Naisi's bass rolled;
>> We heard him long, he sang so sweet:
> And Ardan's voice took middle place;
>> And Anli's tenor rang clear.
>
> Now Naisi lies in his tomb:
>> A poor guard his friends gave;
> They poured his cup of doom,
>> The poisoned cup, which caused his death.
>
> Ah! Dear fair lands of Berthan;
>> Thy men are proud, though thy hills be barren:
> Ohon! to-day I do not rise there
>> To wait for the return of Usnech's sons.

That one firm, just mind, loved,
  The dear shy, yet proud youth,
I loved to pass with him through woods,
  To gird up my dress and run with him at morn.

When bent on foes, those dear gray eyes,
  That maids adored, boded ill;
When, spent with toil, he lay still,
  Through the dark woods his voice soared.

For this cause, no more I sleep;
  No more I stain my nails with pink:
No joy can break the watch I keep;
  For Usnech's sons come not again.

For half the night no sleep I find;
  No bed can beguile me to rest:
My mind wanders among crowds of thoughts;
  I find no time to eat or smile.

No time to joy is left for me
  In the proud array of Emain in the east of Ireland;
For gorgeous house, and garments gay,
  There can be neither peace, nor joy, nor rest.

"Whom dost thou hate the most," said Conchobar, "of these whom thou now seest?"

"Thee thyself," she answered, "and with thee Eogan the son of Durthacht."

"Then," said Conchobar, "thou shalt live with Eogan for a year"; and he gave Deirdre over into Eogan's hand.

Now upon the morrow they went away across the fair-green of Macha, and Deirdre stood behind Eogan in the chariot; and the two husbands who were with her were the two men whom she had sworn never to see together upon the earth, and as she looked upon them, "Ha, Deirdre," said Conchobar, "it is the same glance that a ewe gives when between two rams that thou sharest now between me and Eogan!" Now there was a great rock of stone in front of them, and Deirdre struck her head upon that stone, and she shattered her head, and so she died.

This then is the tale of the exile of the sons of Usnech, and of the exile of Fergus, and of the death of Deirdre.

THE ADVENTURES OF NERA

"The Adventures of Nera," apparently also known in ancient times as the "Cattle-Raid of Aingen," is one of the wildest tales in early Irish literature. In its present form, unfortunately, it is the result of two unskillfully combined parallel accounts of Nera's excursion into the fairy world; hence the confused state of the latter part of the text. The scene is laid in Connacht, not in Ulster. The story is connected, at least superficially, with the two famous bulls that figure in the "Cattle-Raid of Cooley" (p. 281). The compiler was acquainted not only with the central epic, but also with the "Cattle-Raid of Regamna" (p. 211) and "The Exile of the Sons of Usnech" (p. 239). The reference to the opening of the fairy-mounds on Hallowe'en is a piece of ancient folk-lore which has come down even to the present day. The royal family preparing food in the midst of the great hall at Cruachan, the hanging of the captives before the door, and the emphasis upon the terrors of the night are touches of primitive barbarism and superstition which point to the antiquity of the traditions underlying the tale. The cave of Cruachan, known in Christian tradition as "Ireland's gate to Hell," was, according to pagan belief, an entrance to fairyland.

One Samain Ailill and Medb were in Rath Cruachan with their whole household. They set about cooking food. Two captives had been hanged by them the day before. Then Ailill said: "He who would put a withe round the foot of either of the two captives that are on the gallows, shall have a prize for it from me, as he may choose."

Great was the darkness of that night and its horror, and demons would appear on that night always. Each man of them went out in turn to try that night, and quickly would he come back into the house. "I will have the prize from thee," said Nera, "and I shall go out."

"Truly thou shalt have this my gold-hilted sword here," said Ailill.

Then Nera went out towards the captives, and put good armor on him. He put a withe round the foot of one of the two captives. Thrice it sprang off again. Then the captive said to him that unless he put a proper peg on it, though he be at it till the morrow, he would not fix it. So Nera put a proper peg on it.

248

Said the captive from the gallows to Nera: "That is manly, O Nera!"

"Manly indeed!" said Nera.

"By the truth of thy valor," said the captive, "take me on thy neck, that I may get a drink; I was very thirsty when I was hanged."

"Come on my neck then!" said Nera. So the captive went onto his neck.

"Whither shall I carry thee?" said Nera.

"To the house which is nearest to us," said the captive.

So they went to that house. Then they saw something—a lake of fire round that house. "There is no drink for us in this house," said the captive; "let us therefore go to the other house, which is nearest to us." They went to it and saw a lake of water around it. "Do not go to that house!" said the captive; "there is never a washing- nor a bathing-tub, nor a slop-pail in it at night after sleeping. Let us still go on to the other house." Nera let him down at the door. He went into the house. There were tubs for washing and bathing in it, and a drink in either of them. Also a slop-pail on the floor of the house. The captive then drank a draught of either of them and scattered the last sip from his lips at the faces of the people that were in the house, so that they all died. Henceforth it is not good to have either a tub for washing or bathing, or a slop-pail in a house after sleeping.

Thereupon Nera carried the captive back to his torture, and then returned to Cruachan. Then he saw something. The stronghold of Cruachan seemed to be burnt before him, and he beheld a heap of heads of his people cut off by the warriors of the fairy-mound. He went after the fairy host into the cave of Cruachan. "There is a man on our track here!" said the last man to Nera. "The heavier is the track," said his comrade to him, and each man said that word to his mate from the last man to the first man. Thereupon they reached the fairy-mound of Cruachan and went into it. Then the heads were displayed to the king in the fairy-mound. "What shall be done to the man that came with you?" said one of them.

"Let him come hither, that I may speak with him," said the king. Then Nera came to them and the king said to him: "What brought thee with the warriors into the fairy-mound?"

"I came in the company of thy army," said Nera.

"Go now to yonder house," said the king. "There is a lone woman there, who will make thee welcome. Tell her it is from me thou art sent to her, and come every day to this house with a load of firewood."

Then Nera did as he was told. The woman bade him welcome and said: "Welcome to thee, if it is the king of the fairy folk that sent thee hither."

"It is he, truly," said Nera. Every day Nera used to go with a burden of firewood to the stronghold of the king. He saw every day a blind man, and a lame man on his neck, coming out of the stronghold before him. They would go until they were at the brink of a well before the stronghold. "Is it there?" said the blind man. "It is indeed," said the lame one. "Let us go away," said the lame man.

Nera then asked the woman about this. "Why do the blind man and the lame man visit the well?"

"They visit the crown, which is in the well," said the woman; " namely, a diadem of gold, which the king wears on his head. It is there it is kept."

"Why do those two go?" said Nera.

"Not hard to tell," said she, "because it is they that are trusted by the king to visit the crown. One of them was blinded, the other lamed."

"Come hither a little," said Nera to the woman, his wife, "that thou mayst explain my adventures now."

"What has appeared to thee?" said the woman.

"Not hard to tell," said Nera. "When I was going into the fairy-mound, methought the fortress of Cruachan was destroyed and Ailill and Medb with their whole household had fallen in it."

"That is not true, indeed," said the woman, "but a fairy host came to thee. That will come true, however," said she, "unless thou revealest it to thy friends."

"How shall I give warning to my people?" said Nera.

"Rise and go to them," said she. "They are still around the same cauldron and the charge has not yet been removed from the fire." Yet it had seemed to him three days and three nights that he had been in the fairy-mound. "Tell them to be on their guard at next Samain, unless they come and destroy the fairy-mound. For I warn them of this: that the fairy-mound must be destroyed by Ailill and Medb, and the crown of Briun must be carried off by them."

These are the three things which were found there: the mantle of Loegaire in Armag, and the crown of Briun in Connacht, and the shirt of Dunlaing in Leinster in Kildare.

"How will it be believed of me, that I have gone into the fairy-mound?" said Nera.

"Take fruits of summer with thee," said the woman. So he took wild garlic with him and primrose and golden fern. "And I shall be pregnant by thee," said she, "and shall bear thee a son. Send a message to the fairy-mound, when thy people are coming to destroy it, that thou mayest take away thy family and thy cattle from the fairy-mound."

Thereupon Nera went to his people, and found them around the same cauldron; and he related his adventures to them. And then his sword was given to him, and he staid with his people to the end of a year. That was the very year in which Fergus mac Roig came as an exile from the land of Ulster to Ailill and Medb at Cruachan. "Thy time has come, O Nera," said Ailill to Nera. "Arise and bring thy people and thy cattle from the fairy-mound, that we may go to destroy it."

Then Nera went to his wife in the fairy-mound, and she bade him welcome. "Arise and go out to the stronghold now," said the woman to Nera, "and take a burden of firewood with thee. I have gone to it for a whole year with a burden of firewood on my neck every day in thy place, and I said thou wert in sickness. And there is also thy son yonder."

Then he went out to the stronghold, and carried a burden of firewood with him on his neck. "Welcome alive from the sickness in which thou wast!" said the king. "I am displeased that the woman should sleep with thee without asking."

"Thy will shall be done about this," said Nera.

"It will not be hard for thee," said the king.

He went back to his house. "Now tend thy cows today!" said the woman; "I gave one of the cows to thy son at once after his birth." So Nera went with his cattle that day.

Then while he was asleep the Morrigu took his son's cow, and the Donn Bull of Cooley bulled her in the east in Cooley. She (the Morrigu) then went again westward with her cow. Cu Chulainn overtook them in the plain of Muirthemne as they passed across it. For it was one of Cu Chulainn's taboos that even a woman should leave his land without his knowledge. It was one of his taboos that birds should feed on his land, unless they left something with him. It was one of his taboos that fish should remain in the bays, unless they were caught by him. It was one of his taboos that warriors of another tribe should be in his land without his challenging them, before morning if they came at night, or before night if they came in the day. Every maiden and every single woman that was in Ulster, they were in his ward till they were ordained for husbands. These are the taboos of Cu Chulainn. Cu Chulainn overtook the Morrigu with her cow, and he said: "This cow must not be taken."

Nera went back then to his house with his cows in the evening. "My son's cow is missing," said he.

"I did not deserve that thou shouldst go and tend cows in that way," said his wife to him. Thereupon the cow returned.

"A wonder now! Whence does this cow come?" said Nera.

"Truly, she comes from Cooley, after being bulled by the Donn of Cooley," said the woman. "Go out now, lest thy warriors come," she said. "This host cannot go for a year till Samain next. They will come on Samain next, for the fairy-mounds of Erin are always opened about Samain."

Nera went to his people. "Whence comest thou?" said Ailill and Medb to Nera, "and where hast thou been since thou didst go from us?"

"I was in fair lands," said Nera, "with great treasures and precious things, with plenty of garments and food, and wonderful treasures. They would have come to slay you on the next Samain, unless it had been revealed to you."

"We shall certainly go against them," said Ailill.

So they remained there till the end of the year. "Now if thou hast anything in the fairy-mound," said Ailill to Nera, "bring it away." So Nera went on the third day before Samain and brought his drove out of the fairy-mound. Now as the bull calf went out of the fairy-mound, that is, the calf of the cow of Aingen (Aingen was the name of his son), it bellowed thrice. At that same hour Ailill and Fergus were playing drafts, when they heard the bellowing of the bull calf in the plain. Then said Fergus:

> I like not the calf
> Bellowing in the plain of Cruachan,
> The son of the Donn Bull of Cooley, which approaches,
> The young son of the bull from Loch Laig.
>
> There will be calves without cows
> On Bairche in Cooley,
> The king will go a fateful march
> Through this calf of Aingen.

Then the bull calf and the Whitehorned met in the plain of Cruachan. A night and a day they were there fighting, until at last the bull calf was beaten. Then the bull calf bellowed when it was beaten. "What did the calf bellow?" Medb asked of her cow-herd, whose name was Buaigle.

"I know that, my good father Fergus," said Bricriu, "it is the strain which thou sangest in the morning." On that Fergus glanced aside and struck with his fist at Bricriu's head, so that the five men of the draft-board that were in his hand, went into Bricriu's head, and it was a lasting hurt to him.

"Tell me, O Buaigle, what did the bull say?" said Medb.

"Truly, it said," answered Buaigle, "if its father came to help it, that is the Donn of Cooley, the Whitehorned would not be seen in Ai, and it would be beaten throughout the whole plain of Ai on every side."

Then said Medb in the manner of an oath: "I swear by the gods that my people swear by, that I shall not lie down, nor sleep on down or flockbed, nor shall I drink buttermilk nor nurse my side, nor drink red ale nor white, nor shall I taste food, until I see those two bulls fighting before my face."

Thereafter the men of Connacht and the black host of exile went into the fairy-mound, and destroyed it, and took out what there was in it. And then they brought away the crown of Briun—that is the third wonderful gift in Erin—and the mantle of Loegaire in Armag, and the shirt of Dunlaing in Leinster in Kildare. Nera was left with his people in the fairy-mound, and has not come out until now, nor will he come till Doom.

BRICRIU'S FEAST

"Bricriu's Feast" is one of the longest narratives of the Ulster cycle. It exists in several versions, the oldest of which is based on an original composed probably as early as the eighth century. Though somewhat marred by repetitions and contradictions, the story, taken as a whole, is one of the best in early Irish literature. It consists of a series of episodes describing various tests of valor which the three bravest warriors of Ulster—Cu Chulainn, Conall, and Loegaire—undergo in order to determine who is most worthy to receive the choicest portion of a feast prepared by Bricriu of the Poison Tongue, the Thersites of the cycle. The antiquity of the motif around which the narrative centers is vouched for by a Greek writer who relates that at ancient Celtic feasts the choicest titbit, or "Champion's portion," was assigned to the bravest warrior present, whose pre-eminence was sometimes established by a fight on the spot. Cu Roi, who figures in several episodes, is a semi-supernatural being who probably belonged originally, not to the Ulster cycle, but to the legendary history of the south of Ireland.

Bricriu Poison-tongue held a great feast for Conchobar mac Nessa and for all the Ulstermen. The preparation of the feast took a whole year. For the entertainment of the guests a spacious house was built by him. He erected it at Dun Rudraige after the likeness of the Red Branch in Emain Macha. Yet it surpassed the buildings of that period entirely for material, for artistic design, and for beauty of architecture—its pillars and frontings splendid and costly, its carving and lintel-work famed for magnificence. The house was made in this fashion: on the plan of Tara's Mead-Hall, having nine compartments from fire to wall, each fronting of bronze thirty feet high, overlaid with gold. In the fore part of the palace a royal couch was erected for Conchobar high above those of the whole house. It was set with carbuncles and other precious stones which shone with a luster of gold and silver, radiant with every hue, making night like day. Around it were placed the twelve couches of the twelve tribes of Ulster. The nature of the workmanship was on a par with the material of the edifice. It took a wagon team to carry each beam, and the strength of seven Ulstermen to fix each pole, while thirty of the chief artificers of Erin were employed on its erection and arrangement.

Then a balcony was made by Bricriu on a level with the couch of Conchobar and as high as those of the heroes of valor. The decorations of its fittings were magnificent. Windows of glass were placed on each side of it, and one of these was above Bricriu's couch, so that he could view the hall from his seat, as he knew the Ulstermen would not allow him within.

When Bricriu had finished building the hall and the balcony, supplying it with both quilts and blankets, beds and pillows, providing meat and drink, so that nothing was lacking, neither furnishings nor food, he straightway went to Emain Macha to meet Conchobar and the nobles of Ulster.

It fell upon a day when there was a gathering of the Ulstermen in Emain. He was at once made welcome, and was seated by the shoulder of Conchobar. Bricriu addressed himself to him as well as to the body of Ulstermen. "Come with me," said Bricriu, "to partake of a banquet with me."

"Gladly," rejoined Conchobar, "if that please the men of Ulster."

Fergus mac Roig and the nobles of Ulster made answer, "No; for if we go our dead will outnumber our living, when Bricriu has incensed us against each other."

"If ye come not, worse shall ye fare," said Bricriu.

"What then," asked Conchobar, "if the Ulstermen go not with thee?"

"I will stir up strife," said Bricriu, "between the kings, the leaders, the heroes of valor, and the yeomen, till they slay one another, man for man, if they come not to me to share my feast."

"That shall we not do to please thee," said Conchobar.

"I will stir up enmity between father and son so that it will come to mutual slaughter. If I do not succeed in doing so, I will make a quarrel between mother and daughter. If that does not succeed, I will set each of the Ulster women at variance, so that they come to deadly blows till their breasts become loathsome and putrid."

"Sure it is better to come," said Fergus.

"Do ye straightway take counsel with the chief Ulstermen," said Sencha son of Ailill.

"Unless we take counsel against this Bricriu, mischief will be the consequence," said Conchobar.

Thereupon all the Ulster nobles assembled in council. In discussing the matter Sencha counselled them thus: "Take hostages from Bricriu, since ye have to go with him, and set eight swordsmen about him so as to compel him to retire from the house as soon as he has laid out the feast."

Furbaide Ferbenn son of Conchobar brought Bricriu their reply and explained the whole matter.

"It is happily arranged," said Bricriu.

The men of Ulster straightway set out from Emain Macha, host, battalion, and company, under king, chieftain, and leader. Excellent and admirable the march of the brave and valiant heroes to the palace.

The hostages of the nobles had gone security on his behalf, and Bricriu accordingly considered how he should manage to set the Ulstermen at variance. His deliberation and self-scrutiny being ended, he betook himself to the presence of Loegaire the Triumphant son of Connad mac Iliach. "Hail now, Loegaire the Triumphant, thou mighty mallet of Breg, thou hot hammer of Meath, flame-red thunderbolt, thou victorious warrior of Ulster, what hinders the championship of Ulster being thine always?"

"If so I choose, it shall be mine," said Loegaire.

"Be thine the sovereignty of the nobles of Erin," said Bricriu, "if only thou act as I advise."

"I will indeed," said Loegaire.

"Sooth, if the Champion's Portion of my house be thine, the championship of Emain is thine forever. The Champion's Portion of my house is worth contesting, for it is not the portion of a fool's house," said Bricriu. "Belonging to it is a caldron full of generous wine, with room enough for three of the valiant heroes of Ulster; furthermore a seven-year-old boar; nought has entered its mouth since it was little save fresh milk and fine meal in springtime, curds and sweet milk in summer, the kernel of nuts and wheat in autumn, beef and broth in winter; a cow-lord full seven-year-old; since it was a little calf neither heather nor twig-tops have passed its lips, nought but sweet milk and herbs, meadow-hay and corn. Add to this five-score cakes of wheat cooked in honey. Five-and-twenty bushels, that is what was supplied for these five-score cakes—four cakes from each bushel. Such is the champion's portion of my house. And since thou art the best hero among the men of Ulster, it is but just to give it to thee, and so I wish it. By the end of the day, when the feast is spread out, let thy charioteer get up, and it is to him the champion's portion will be given."

"Among them shall be dead men if it is not done so," said Loegaire. Bricriu laughed at that, for it pleased him well.

When he had done inciting Loegaire the Triumphant to enmity, Bricriu went to Conall the Victorious. "Hail to thee, Conall the Victorious! Thou art the hero of victories and of combats; great are the victories thou hast already scored over the heroes of Ulster. By the time the Ulstermen go into foreign bounds thou art three days and three nights in advance over many a ford; thou protectest their rear when returning so that an assailant may not spring past thee nor through thee nor over thee; what then should hinder the Champion's Portion of Emain being thine always?" Though great his treachery with regard to Loegaire, he showed twice as much with Conall the Victorious.

When he had satisfied himself with inciting Conall the Victorious to quarrel, he went to Cu Chulainn. "Hail to thee, Cu Chulainn! Thou victor of Breg, thou bright banner of the Liffey, darling of Emain, beloved of wives and of maidens, for thee today Cu Chulainn is no nickname, for thou art the champion of the Ulstermen. Thou wardest off their great feuds and forays; thou seekest justice for each man of them; thou attainest alone to what all the Ulstermen fail in; all the men of Ulster acknowledge thy bravery, thy valor, and thy achievements surpassing theirs. What meaneth therefore thy leaving of the Champion's Portion for some one else of the men of Ulster, since no one of the men of Erin is capable of contesting it against thee?"

"By the gods of my tribe," said Cu Chulainn, "his head shall he lose who comes to contest it with me." Thereafter Bricriu severed himself from them and followed the host as if no contention had been made among the heroes.

Whereupon they entered Bricriu's stronghold, and each one occupied his couch therein, king, prince, noble, yeoman, and young hero. The half of the hall was set apart for Conchobar and his retinue of valiant Ulster heroes; the other half was reserved for the ladies of Ulster attending on Mugan daughter of Eochaid Fedlech, wife of Conchobar. Those who attended on Conchobar were the chief Ulster warriors with the body of youths and entertainers.

While the feast was being prepared for them, the musicians and players performed. The moment Bricriu spread the feast with its savories he was ordered by the hostages to leave the hall. They straightway got up with their drawn swords in their hands to expell him. Whereupon Bricriu and his wife went out to the balcony. As he arrived at the threshold of the stronghold he called out, "That Champion's Portion, such as it is, is not the portion of a fool's house; do ye give it to the Ulster hero ye prefer for valor." And then he left them.

Then the waiters got up to serve the food. The charioteer of Loegaire the Triumphant, that is, Sedlang mac Riangabra, rose up and said to the distributors: "Give to Loegaire the Triumphant the Champion's Portion which is by you, for he alone is entitled to it before the other young heroes of Ulster."

Then Id mac Riangabra, charioteer to Conall the Victorious, got up and spoke to like effect. And Loeg mac Riangabra spoke as follows: "Bring it to Cu Chulainn; it is no disgrace for all the Ulstermen to give it to him; it is he that is most valiant among you."

"That's not true," said Conall the Victorious and Loegaire the Triumphant.

They got up upon the floor and donned their shields and seized their swords. They hewed at one another until half the hall was an atmosphere of fire with the clash of sword- and spear-edge, the other half one white sheet from the enamel of the shields. Great alarm got hold upon the stronghold; the valiant heroes shook; Conchobar himself and Fergus mac Roig were furious on seeing the injury and injustice of two men attacking one, namely Conall the Victorious and Loegaire the Triumphant attacking Cu Chulainn. There was no one among the Ulstermen who dared separate them until Sencha spoke to Conchobar: "Part the men," said he.

Thereupon Conchobar and Fergus intervened; the combatants immediately let drop their hands to their sides. "Execute my wish," said Sencha.

"Your will shall be obeyed," they responded.

"My wish, then," said Sencha, "is to-night to divide the Champion's Portion there among all the host, and after that to decide with reference to it according to the will of Ailill mac Matach, for it is accounted unlucky among the Ulstermen to close this assembly unless the matter be adjudged in Cruachan."

The feasting was then resumed; they made a circle about the fire and got drunken and merry.

Bricriu, however, and his queen were in their balcony. From his couch the condition of the palace was visible to him, and how things were going on. He exercised his mind as to how he should contrive to get the women to quarrel as he had the men. When Bricriu had done searching his mind, it just chanced as he could have wished that Fedelm Fresh-Heart came from the stronghold with fifty women in her train, in jovial mood. Bricriu observed her coming past him. "Hail to thee to-night, wife of Loegaire the Triumphant! Fedelm Fresh-Heart is no nickname for thee with respect to thy excellence of form and wisdom and of lineage. Conchobar, king of a province of Erin, is thy father, Loegaire the Triumphant thy husband; I should deem it but small honor to thee that any of the Ulster women should take precedence of thee in entering the banqueting-hall; only at thy heel should all the Ulster women tread. If thou comest first into the hall to-night, the sovereignty of the queenship shalt thou enjoy over all the ladies of Ulster forever." Fedelm at that takes a leap over three ridges from the hall.

Thereafter came Lendabair daughter of Eogan mac Durthacht, wife of Conall the Victorious. Bricriu addressed her, saying, "Hail to thee, Lendabair! For thee that is no nickname; thou art the darling and pet of all mankind on account of thy splendor and of thy luster. As far as thy husband hath surpassed all the heroes of mankind in valor and in comeliness, so far hast thou distinguished thyself above the women of Ulster." Though great the deceit he applied in the case of Fedelm, he applied twice as much in the case of Lendabair.

Then Emer came out with half a hundred women in her train. "Greeting and hail to thee, Emer daughter of Forgall Monach, wife of the best man in Erin! Emer of the Fair Hair is no nickname for thee; Erin's kings and princes contend for thee in jealous rivalry. As the sun surpasseth the stars of heaven, so far dost thou outshine the women of the whole world in form and shape and lineage, in youth and beauty and elegance, in good name and wisdom and address." Though great his deceit in the case of the other ladies, in that of Emer he used thrice as much.

The three companies thereupon went out until they met at a

spot three ridges from the hall. None of them knew that Bricriu had incited them one against the other. To the hall they straightway return. Even and easy and graceful their carriage on the first ridge; scarcely did one of them raise one foot before the other. But on the ridge following, their steps were shorter and quicker. On the ridge next to the house it was with difficulty each kept up with the other; so they raised their robes to the rounds of their hips to complete the attempt to go first into the hall. For what Bricriu had said to each of them with regard to the other was that whosoever entered first should be queen of the whole province. The amount of confusion then occasioned by the competition was as it were the noise of fifty chariots approaching. The whole stronghold shook and the warriors sprang to their arms and tried to kill one another within.

"Stay," cried Sencha; "they are not enemies who have come; it is Bricriu who has set to quarrelling the women who have gone out. By the gods of my tribe, unless the door be closed against them, our dead will outnumber our living." Thereupon the doorkeepers closed the doors. Emer, the daughter of Forgall Monach, wife of Cu Chulainn, by reason of her speed, outran the others and put her back against the door, and straightway called upon the doorkeepers before the other ladies came, so that the men within got up, each of them to open the door for his own wife that she might be the first to come in. "Bad outlook to-night," said Conchobar. He struck the silver scepter that was in his hand against the bronze pillar of the couch, and the company sat down.

"Stay," said Sencha; "it is not a warfare of arms that shall be held here; it will be a warfare of words." Each woman went out under the protection of her husband, and then followed the "Ulster Women's War of Words."

(The series of rhetorical speeches in which the women enumerate the virtues of their respective husbands is omitted.)

Thus did the men in the hall behave on hearing the laudatory addresses of the women—Loegaire and Conall each sprang into his hero's light, and broke a stave of the palace at a like level with themselves, so that in this way their wives came in. Cu Chulainn upheaved the palace just over against his bed, till the stars of heaven were to be seen from underneath the wattle. By that opening came his own wife with half a hundred of her attendants in her train, as also a hundred in waiting upon the other twain. Other ladies could not be compared with Emer, while no one at all was to be likened to Emer's husband. Thereupon Cu Chulainn let the palace down until seven feet of the wattle entered the ground; the whole stronghold shook, and Bricriu's balcony was laid flat to the earth in such a way that Bricriu and his queen toppled down until they fell into the ditch in the middle of the courtyard among the dogs. "Woe is me," cried Bricriu, as he hastily got up, "enemies have come into the palace." He took a turn round and saw how it was lop-sided and inclined entirely to one side. He wrung his hands, then betook himself within, so bespattered that none of the Ulstermen could recognize him.

Then from the floor of the house Bricriu made speech: "Alas! that I have prepared you a feast, O Ulstermen. My house is more to me than all my other possessions. Upon you, therefore, it is taboo to drink, to eat, or to sleep until you leave my house as you found it upon your arrival."

Thereupon the valiant Ulstermen went out of the house and tried to tug it, but they did not raise it so much that even the wind could pass between it and the earth. That matter was a difficulty for the Ulstermen. "I have no suggestion for you," said Sencha, "except that you entreat of him who left it lop-sided to set it upright."

Whereupon the men of Ulster told Cu Chulainn to restore the house to its upright position, and Bricriu made a speech: "O King of the heroes of Erin, if thou set it not straight and erect, none in the world can do so." All the Ulstermen then entreated Cu Chulainn to solve the difficulty. That the banqueters might not be lacking for food or for ale, Cu Chulainn got up and tried to lift the house at a tug and failed. A distortion thereupon got hold of him, whilst a drop of blood was at the root of each single hair, and he drew his hair into his head, so that, looked on from above, his dark-yellow curls seemed as if they had been shorn with scissors, and taking upon himself the motion of a millstone he strained himself until a warrior's foot could find room between each pair of ribs.

His natural resources and fiery vigor returned to him, and he then heaved the house aloft and set it so that it reached its former level. Thereafter the consumption of the feast was pleasant to them, with the kings and the chieftains on the one side round about Conchobar the illustrious, the noble high-king of Ulster.

Again it was their hap to quarrel about the Champion's Portion. Conchobar with the nobles of Ulster interposed with the view of judging between the heroes. "Go to Cu Roi mac Dairi, the man who will undertake to intervene," said Conchobar.

. . . .

"I accept that," said Cu Chulainn.

"I agree," said Loegaire.

"Let us go, then," said Conall the Victorious.

"Let horses be brought and thy chariot yoked, O Conall," said Cu Chulainn.

"Woe is me!" cried Conall.

"Every one," said Cu Chulainn, "knows the clumsiness of thy horses and the unsteadiness of thy going and thy turnout; thy chariot's movement is most heavy; each of the two wheels raises turf every way thy big chariot careers, so that for the space of a year there is a well-marked track easily recognized by the warriors of Ulster."

"Dost thou hear that, Loegaire?" said Conall.

"Woe is me!" said Loegaire. "But I am not to blame or reproach. I am nimble at crossing fords, and more, to breast the storm of spears, out-stripping the warriors of Ulster. Put not on me the pretence of kings and champions against single chariots in strait and difficult places, in woods and on confines, until the champion of a single chariot tries not to career before me."

Thereupon Loegaire had his chariot yoked and he leaped into it. He drove over the Plain-of-the-Two-Forks, of the Gap-of-the-Watch, over the Ford of Carpat Fergus, over the Ford of the Morrigu, to the Rowan Meadow of the Two Oxen in the Fews of Armagh, by the Meeting of the Four Ways past Dundalk, across Mag Slicech, westwards to the slope of Breg. A dim, dark, heavy mist overtook him, confusing him in such a way that it was impossible for him to fare farther. "Let us stay here," said Loegaire to his charioteer, "until the mist clears up." Loegaire alighted from his chariot, and his gillie put the horses into the meadow that was near at hand.

While there, the gillie saw a huge giant approaching him. Not beautiful his appearance: broad of shoulder and fat of mouth, with sack eyes and a bristly face; ugly, wrinkled, with bushy eyebrows; hideous and horrible and strong; stubborn and violent and haughty; fat and puffing; with big sinews and strong forearms; bold, audacious, and uncouth. A shorn black patch of hair on him, a dun covering about him, a tunic over it to the ball of his rump; on his feet old tattered brogues, on his back a ponderous club like the wheel-shaft of a mill.

"Whose horses are these, gillie?" he asked, as he gazed furiously at him.

"The horses of Loegaire the Triumphant."

"Yes! a fine fellow is he!" And as he thus spoke he brought down his club on the gillie and gave him a blow from top to toe.

The gillie gave a cry, whereupon Loegaire came up. "What is this you are doing to the lad?" asked Loegaire.

"It is by way of penalty for damage to the meadow," said the giant.

"I will come myself, then," said Loegaire; and they struggled together until Loegaire fled to Emain leaving his horses and gillie and arms.

Not long thereafter Conall the Victorious took the same way and arrived at the plain where the druidical mist overtook Loegaire. The like hideous black, dark cloud overtook Conall the Victorious, so that he was unable to see either heaven or earth. Conall thereupon leapt out and the gillie unharnessed the horses in the same meadow. Not long thereafter he saw the same giant coming towards him. He asked him whose servant he was.

"I am the servant of Conall the Victorious," he said.

"A good man he!" said the giant, and he raised his hands and gave the gillie a blow from top to toe. The fellow yelled. Then came Conall. He and the giant came to close quarters. Stronger were the wrestling turns of the giant, and Conall fled, as Loegaire had done, having left behind his charioteer and his horses, and came to Emain.

Cu Chulainn then went by the same way till he came to the same place. The like dark mist overtook him as fell upon the two preceding. Cu Chulainn sprang down, and Loeg brought the horses into the meadow. He had not long to wait until he saw the same man coming towards him. The giant asked him whose servant he was.

"Servant to Cu Chulainn."

"A good man he!" said the giant, plying him with the club.

Loeg yelled. Then Cu Chulainn arrived. He and the giant came to close quarters and either rained blows upon the other. The giant was worsted. He forfeited horses and charioteer, and Cu Chulainn brought along with him his fellows' horses, charioteers, and accoutrements, till he reached Emain in triumph.

"Thine is the Champion's Portion," said Bricriu to Cu Chulainn, and to the others, "well I know from your deeds that you are in no way on a par with Cu Chulainn."

"Not true, Bricriu," said they, "for we know it is one of his friends from the fairy world that came to him to play us mischief and coerce us with regard to the championship. We shall not forego our claim on that account."

The men of Ulster, with Conchobar and Fergus, failed to effect a settlement. And the conclusion the nobles in Conchobar's following arrived at was, to accompany the heroes and have the difficulty adjudged at the abode of Ailill mac Matach and of Medb of Cruachan Ai with reference to the Champion's Portion and the mutual rivalry of the women. Fine and lovely and majestic the march of the Ulstermen to Cruachan. Cu Chulainn, however, remained behind the host entertaining the Ulster ladies, performing nine feats with apples and nine with knives, in such wise that one did not interfere with the other.

Loeg mac Riangabra then went to speak to him in the featstead and said: "You sorry simpleton, your valor and bravery have passed away, the Champion's Portion has gone from you; the Ulstermen have reached Cruachan long since."

"Indeed we had not at all perceived it, my Loeg. Yoke us the chariot, then," said Cu Chulainn. Loeg accordingly yoked it and off they started. By that time the Ulstermen had reached Mag Breg, Cu Chulainn, having been incited by his charioteer, travelled with such speed from Dun Rudraige, the Grey of Macha and the Black Sainglenn racing with his chariot across the whole province of Conchobar, across Sliab Fuait and across Mag Breg, that the third chariot arrived first in Cruachan.

In virtue then of the swiftness and impetuous speed with which all the valiant Ulstermen reached Cruachan under the lead of Conchobar and the body of chiefs, a great shaking seized Cruachan,

till the war-arms fell from the walls to the ground, seizing likewise
the entire host of the stronghold, till the men in the royal keep
were like rushes in a stream. Medb thereupon spoke: "Since the
day I took up home in Cruachan I have never heard thunder,
there being no clouds." Thereupon Finnabair, daughter of Ailill
and Medb, went to the balcony over the high porch of the stronghold. "Mother dear," said she, "I see a chariot coming along the
plain."

"Describe it," said Medb, " its form, appearance, and style; the
color of the horses; how the hero looks, and how the chariot
courses."

(Here follows a conventional description in highly embroidered rhetoric
of the chariots and personal appearance of Loegaire and Conall. This,
as well as the description of Cu Chulainn's chariot, is omitted. The narrative is resumed with the description of Cu Chulainn himself, long famous
with Gaelic literary men and professional story-tellers.)

"In the chariot a dark, melancholy man, comeliest of the men
of Erin. Around him a soft crimson pleasing tunic fastened across
the breast, where it stands open, with a salmon-brooch of inlaid
gold, against which his bosom heaves, beating in full strokes. A
long-sleeved linen kirtle with a white hood, embroidered red with
flaming gold. Set in each of his eyes eight red dragon gem-stones.
His two cheeks blue-white and blood-red. He emits sparks of
fire and burning breath, with a ray of love in his look. A shower
of pearls, it seems, has fallen into his mouth. Each of his two
eyebrows as black as the side of a black spit. On his two thighs
rests a golden-hilted sword and fastened to the copper frame of
the chariot is a blood-red spear with a sharp mettlesome blade
on a shaft of wood well fitted to his hand. Over both his shoulders
a crimson shield with a rim of silver, chased with figures of animals
in gold. He leaps the hero's salmon-leap into the air and does
many like swift feats besides. Such is the chief of a chariot-royal.
Before him in that chariot is a charioteer, a very slender, tall,
much-freckled man. On his head very curled bright-red hair,
with a fillet of bronze upon his brow which prevents the hair from
falling over his face. On both sides of his head patins of gold
confine the hair. A shoulder-mantle about him with sleeves
opening at the two elbows, and in his hand a goad of red gold with
which he guides the horses.

"Truly, it is a drop before a shower; we recognize the man from his description," said Medb.

> An ocean fury, a whale that rages, a fragment of flame and fire;
> A bear majestic, a grandly moving billow,
>   A beast in maddening anger:
> In the crash of glorious battle
>   Through the hostile foe he leaps,
>   His shout the fury of doom;
> A terrible bear, he is death to the herd of cattle:
> Feat upon feat, head upon head he piles:
> Praise ye the hearty one, he who is completely victor.
> As fresh malt is ground in the mill shall we be ground by
>   Cu Chulainn.

"By the god of my people," said Medb, "I swear if it be in fury Cu Chulainn comes to us, like as a mill of ten spokes grinds very hard malt, so he alone will grind us into mould and gravel, should the whole province attend on us in Cruachan, unless his fury and violence are subdued."

"How do they come this time?" said Medb.

> Wrist to wrist and palm to palm,
>   Tunic to tunic they advance,
> Shield to shield and frame to frame.
>   A shoulder-to-shoulder band,
> Wood to wood and car to car,
>   This they all are, fond mother.
>
> As thunder when crashing on the roof,
>   With speed the chargers dash,
> As heavy seas which storms are shaking,
>   The earth in turn they pound;
> Anon it vibrates as they strike,
> Their strength and weight are like and like.
>   Their name is noble,
>   No ill fame!

Then Medb made speech:

> Women to meet them, and many, half naked,
> Full-breasted and bare and beautiful, numerous;
> Bring vats of cold water where wanting, beds ready for rest,
> Fine food bring forth, and not scanty, but excellent,
> Strong ale and sound and well malted, warriors' keep;
> Let the gates of the stronghold be set open, open the enclosure.
> The batallion that is rushing on won't kill us, I hope.

Thereupon Medb went out by the high door of the palace into the court, thrice fifty maidens in her train, with three vats of cold water for the three valiant heroes in front of the hosts, in order to alleviate their heat. Choice was straightway given them so as to ascertain whether a house apiece should be allotted them or one house among the three. "To each a house apart," said Cu Chulainn. Thereafter such as they preferred of the thrice fifty girls were brought into the house, fitted up with beds of surprising magnificence. Finnabair in preference to any other was brought by Cu Chulainn into the apartment where he himself was. On the arrival of the Ulstermen, Ailill and Medb with their whole household went and bade them welcome. "We are pleased," said Sencha son of Ailill, responding.

Thereupon the Ulstermen came into the stronghold, and the palace is left to them as recounted, viz., seven circles and seven compartments from fire to partition, with bronze frontings and carvings of red yew. Three stripes of bronze in the arching of the house, which was of oak, with a covering of shingles. It had twelve windows with glass in the openings. The couch of Ailill and Medb in the center of the house, with silver frontings and stripes of bronze round it, with a silver wand by the partition facing Ailill, that would reach the mid hips of the house so as to check the inmates unceasingly. The Ulster heroes went round from one door of the palace to the other, and the musicians played while the guests were being prepared for. Such was the spaciousness of the house that it had room for the hosts of valiant heroes of the whole province in the retinue of Conchobar. Moreover, Conchobar and Fergus mac Roig were in Ailill's apartment with nine valiant Ulster heroes besides. Great feasts were then prepared for them and they were there until the end of three days and three nights.

Thereafter Ailill inquired of Conchobar with his Ulster retinue what was the purpose of his visit. Sencha related the matter on account of which they had come, viz., the three heroes' rivalry as to the Champion's Portion, and the ladies' rivalry as to precedence at feasts—"They could not stand being judged anywhere else than here by thee." At that Ailill was silent and was not in a happy mood. "Indeed," said he, "it is not to me this decision should be given as to the Champion's Portion, unless it be done from hatred."

"There is really no better judge," said Sencha.

"Well," said Ailill, "I require time to consider. For that then three days and three nights suffice for me," said Ailill.

"That would not forfeit friendship," answered Sencha.

The Ulstermen straightway bade farewell; being satisfied, they left their blessing with Ailill and Medb and their curse with Bricriu, for it was he who had incited them to strife. They then departed from the territory of Medb, having left Loegaire and Conall and Cu Chulainn to be judged by Ailill. The like supper as before was given to each of the heroes every night.

One night as their portion was assigned to them, three cats from the cave of Cruachan were let loose to attack them, that is, three beasts of magic. Conall and Loegaire made for the rafters, leaving their food with the beasts. In that wise they slept until the morrow. Cu Chulainn fled not from the beast which was attacking him. When it stretched its neck out for eating, Cu Chulainn gave a blow with his sword on the beast's head, but the blade glided off as it were from stone. Then the cat set itself down. Under the circumstances Cu Chulainn neither ate nor slept, but he kept his place. As soon as it was early morning the cats were gone. In such condition were the three heroes seen on the morrow.

"Does not that trial suffice for adjudging you?" asked Ailill.

"By no means," said Conall and Loegaire, "it is not against beasts we are striving but against men."

Ailill, having gone to his chamber, set his back against the wall. He was disquieted in mind, for he took the difficulty that faced him to be fraught with danger. He neither ate nor slept till the end of three days and three nights. "Coward!" Medb then called him; "if you do not decide, I will."

"Difficult for me to judge them," Ailill said; "it is a misfortune for one to have to do it."

"There is no difficulty," said Medb, "for Loegaire and Conall Cernach are as different as bronze and white bronze; and Conall Cernach and Cu Chulainn are as different as white bronze and red gold."

It was then, after she had pondered her advice, that Loegaire the Triumphant was summoned to Medb. "Welcome, O Loegaire the Triumphant," said she; "it is meet to give thee the Champion's Portion. We assign to thee the sovereignty of the heroes of Erin

from this time forth, and the Champion's Portion, and a cup of
bronze with a bird chased in silver on its bottom. In preference
to every one else, take it with thee as a token of award. No one
else is to see it until, at the day's end, thou hast come to the Red
Branch of Conchobar. On the Champion's Portion being exhibited
among you, then shalt thou bring forth thy cup in the presence of
all the Ulster nobles. Moreover, the Champion's Portion is therein.
None of the valiant Ulster heroes will dispute it further with thee.
For the thing thou art to take away with thee shall be a token of
genuineness in the estimation of all the Ulstermen." Thereupon
the cup with its full of luscious wine was given to Loegaire the
Triumphant. On the floor of the palace he swallowed the contents
at a draught. "Now you have the feast of a champion," said
Medb; "I wish you may enjoy it a hundred years at the head of
all Ulster."

Loegaire thereupon bade farewell. Then Conall Cernach was
likewise summoned to the royal presence. "Welcome," said Medb,
"O Conall Cernach; proper it is to give thee the Champion's
Portion, with a cup of white bronze besides, having a bird on the
bottom of it chased in gold." Thereafter the cup was given to
Conall with its full of luscious wine.

Conall bade farewell. A herald was then sent to fetch Cu Chulainn. "Come to speak with the king and queen," said the messenger. Cu Chulainn at the time was busy playing chess with
Loeg mac Riangabra, his own charioteer. "No mocking!" he
said; "you might try your lies on some other fool." He hurled
one of the chessmen, and it pierced the center of the herald's
brain. He got his death blow therefrom, and fell between Ailill
and Medb.

"Woe is me," said Medb; "sorely doth Cu Chulainn work on
us his fury when his fit of rage is upon him." Whereupon Medb
got up and came to Cu Chulainn and put her two arms round his
neck.

"Try a lie upon another," said Cu Chulainn.

"Glorious son of the Ulstermen and flame of the heroes of Erin,
it is no lie that is to our liking where thou art concerned. Were all
Erin's heroes to come, to thee by preference would we grant the
quest, for, in regard to fame, bravery, and valor, distinction, youth,
and glory, the men of Erin acknowledge thy superiority."

Cu Chulainn got up. He accompanied Medb into the palace, and Ailill bade him a warm welcome. A cup of gold was given him full of luscious wine, and having on the bottom of it birds chased in precious stone. With it, in preference to every one else there was given him a lump, as big as his two eyes, of dragon-stone. "Now you have the feast of a champion," said Medb. "I wish you may enjoy it a hundred years at the head of all the Ulster heroes." "Moreover, it is our verdict," said Ailill and Medb, "inasmuch as thou art not to be compared with the Ulster warriors, neither is thy wife to be compared with their women. Nor is it too much, we think, that she should always precede all the Ulster ladies when entering the Mead Hall." At that Cu Chulainn drank at one draught the full of the cup, and then bade farewell to the king, queen, and whole household.

Thereafter he followed his charioteer. "My plan," said Medb to Ailill, "is to keep those three heroes with us again to-night, and to test them further."

"Do as thou deemest right," said Ailill. The men were then detained and brought to Cruachan and their horses unyoked.

Their choice of food was given them for their horses. Conall and Loegaire told them to give oats two years old to theirs. But Cu Chulainn chose barley grains for his. They slept there that night. The women were apportioned among them. Finnabair, with a train of fifty damsels, was brought to the place of Cu Chulainn. Sadb the Eloquent, another daughter of Ailill and Medb, with fifty maids in attendance was ushered into the presence of Conall Cernach. Concend, daughter of Cet mac Matach, with fifty damsels along with her, was brought into the presence of Loegaire the Triumphant. Moreover, Medb herself was accustomed to visit the couch of Cu Chulainn. They slept there that night.

On the morrow they arose early in the morning and went to the house where the youths were performing the wheel-feat. Then Loegaire siezed the wheel until it reached half up the sidewall. Upon that the youths laughed and cheered him. It was in reality a jeer, but it seemed to Loegaire a shout of applause. Conall then took the wheel. It was on the ground. He tossed it as high as the ridge-pole of the hall. The youths raised a shout at that. It seemed to Conall that it was a shout of applause and victory.

To the youths it was a shout of scorn. Then Cu Chulainn took the wheel—it was in mid-air he caught it. He hurled it aloft till it cast the ridge-pole from off the hall; the wheel went a man's cubit into the ground in the outside enclosure. The youths raised a shout of applause and triumph in Cu Chulainn's case. It seemed to Cu Chulainn, however, it was a laugh of scorn and ridicule they then gave vent to.

Cu Chulainn then sought out the womenfolk and took thrice fifty needles from them. These he tossed up one after the other. Each needle went into the eye of another, till in that wise they were joined together. He returned to the women, and gave each her own needle into her own hand. The young warriors praised Cu Chulainn. Whereupon they bade farewell to the king, the queen, and household as well.

On the arrival of Loegaire, Conall, and Cu Chulainn at Emain Macha, the heroes of Ulster ceased their discussions and their babblings and fell to eating and enjoying themselves. It was Sualtam mac Roig, father of Cu Chulainn himself, who that night attended upon the Ulstermen. Moreover, Conchobar's ladder-vat was filled for them. Their portion having been brought into their presence, the waiters began to serve, but at the outset they withheld the Champion's Portion from distribution. "Why not give the Champion's Portion," said Dubtach Chafertongue, "to some one of the heroes; those three have not returned from the King of Cruachan, bringing no sure token with them, whereby the Champion's Portion may be assigned to one of them."

Thereupon Loegaire the Triumphant got up and lifted on high the bronze cup having the silver bird chased on the bottom. "The Champion's Portion is mine," said he, "and none may contest it with me."

"It is not," said Conall Cernach. "Not alike are the tokens we brought off with us. Yours is a cup of bronze, whereas mine is a cup of white bronze. From the difference between them the Champion's Portion clearly belongs to me."

"It belongs to neither of you," said Cu Chulainn as he got up and spoke. "You have brought no token that procures you the Champion's Portion. Yet the king and the queen whom you visited were loath in the thick of distress to intensify the strife. But no less than your deserts have you received at their hands.

The Champion's Portion remains with me, seeing I have brought a token distinguished above the rest."

He then lifted on high a cup of red gold having a bird chased on the bottom of it in precious dragon-stone, the size of his two eyes. All the Ulster nobles in the train of Conchobar mac Nessa saw it. "Therefore it is I," he said, "who deserve the Champion's Portion, provided I have fair play."

"To thee we all award it," said Conchobar and Fergus and the Ulster nobles as well. "By the verdict of Ailill and Medb the Champion's Portion is yours."

(At this point there is introduced a short episode in which the three competitors go to be tested by a strange personage called Ercol. The scene then shifts to the banqueting hall of Conchobar.)

"I swear by my people's god," said Loegaire the Triumphant and Conall the Victorious, "that the cup you have brought is purchased. Of the jewels and the treasures in your possession you have given to Ailill and Medb for it in order that a defeat might not be on record against you, and that the Champion's Portion might be given to no one else by preference. By my people's god, that judgment shall not stand; the Champion's Portion shall not be yours."

They then sprang up one after the other, their swords drawn. Straightway Conchobar and Fergus intervened, whereupon they let down their hands and sheathed their swords.

"Hold!" said Sencha, "do as I bid."

"We will," they said.

(The heroes are then sent to Budi mac m-Bain [Yellow son of Fair], and by him to Uath mac Imomain [Terror son of Great Fear]. The episode of Uath consists of a short version of the beheading incident which is recited in more detail later in the part called The Champion's Covenant [see below].)

The Ulstermen advised them to go to Cu Roi for judgment. To that too they agreed.

On the morning of the morrow the three heroes—Cu Chulainn, Conall, and Loegaire—set off to Cu Roi's stronghold (Cathair Con Roi). They unyoked their chariots at the gate of the hold, then entered the court. Whereupon Blathnat, Minn's daughter, wife of Cu Roi mac Dairi, bade them a warm welcome. That night on their arrival Cu Roi was not at home, but knowing they would come, he counselled his wife regarding the heroes until he should return from his Eastern expedition into Scythia. From the age of seven years, when he took up arms, until his death, Cu Roi had not reddened his sword in Erin, nor ever had the food of Erin passed his lips. Nor could Erin retain him for his haughtiness, renown, and rank, overbearing fury, strength, and gallantry. His wife acted according to his wish in the matter of bathing and washing, providing them with refreshing drinks and beds most excellent. And they liked it well.

When bedtime was come, she told them that each was to take his night watching the fort until Cu Roi should return. "And, moreover, thus said Cu Roi, that you take your turn watching according to seniority." In whatsoever quarter of the globe Cu Roi should happen to be, every night he chanted a spell over his stronghold, so that the fort revolved as swiftly as a mill-stone. The entrance was never to be found after sunset.

The first night, Loegaire the Triumphant took the watch, inasmuch as he was the eldest of the three. As he kept watch into the later part of the night, he saw a giant approaching him as far as his eyes could see from the sea westwards. Exceedingly huge and ugly and horrible Loegaire thought him, for, in height, it seemed to him, he reached into the sky, and the reflection of the sea was visible between his legs. Thus did he come, his hands full of stripped oaks, each of which would form a burden for a wagon-team of six, at whose root not a stroke had been repeated after a single sword-stroke. One of the stakes he cast at Loegaire, who let it pass him. Twice or thrice he repeated it, but the stroke reached neither the skin nor the shield of Loegaire. Then Loegaire hurled a spear at him but it did not hit him.

The giant stretched his hand toward Loegaire. Such was its length that it reached across the three ridges that were between them as they were throwing at each other, and thus in his grasp the giant seized him. Though Loegaire was big and imposing, he fitted like a year-old child into the clutch of his opponent, who then ground him between his two palms as a chessman is turned in a groove. In that state, half-dead, the giant tossed him out over the fort, so that he fell into the mire of the ditch at the gate. The fort had no opening there, and the other men and inmates of the hold thought Loegaire had leapt outside over the fort, as a challenge for the other men to do likewise.

There they were until the day's end. When the night-watch began, Conall went out as sentry, for he was older than Cu Chulainn. Everything occurred as it did to Loegaire the first night.

The third night Cu Chulainn went on watch. That night the three Greys of Sescind Uarbeil, the three Ox-feeders of Breg, and the three sons of Big-fist the Siren met by appointment to plunder the stronghold. This too was the night of which it was foretold that the Spirit of the Lake by the fort would devour the whole population of the hold, man and beast.

Cu Chulainn, while watching through the night, had many uneasy forebodings. When midnight came he heard a terrific noise drawing near to him. "Holloa, holloa," Cu Chulainn shouted, "who is there? If friends they be, let them not stir; if foes, let them flee." Then they raised a terrific shout at him. Whereupon Cu Chulainn sprang upon them, so that the nine of them fell dead to the earth. He heaped their heads in disorder into the seat of watching and resumed his post. Another nine shouted at him. In like manner he killed three nines, making one cairn of them, heads and accoutrements.

While he was there far on into the night, tired and sad and weary, he heard the rising of the lake on high as if it were the booming of a very heavy sea. However deep his dejection, he could not resist going to see what caused the great noise he heard. He then perceived the upheaving monster, and it seemed to him to be thirty cubits in curvature above the loch. It raised itself on high into the air and sprang towards the fort, opening its mouth so that one of the halls could go into its gullet.

Then Cu Chulainn called to mind his swooping feat, sprang on high, and was as swift as a winnowing riddle right round the monster. He entwined his two arms about its neck, stretched his hand into its gullet, tore out the monster's heart, and cast it from him on the ground. Then the beast fell from the air and rested on the earth, after having sustained a blow on the shoulder. Cu Chulainn then plied it with his sword, hacked it to bits, and took the head with him into the sentry-seat along with the other heap of skulls.

While there, depressed and miserable in the morning dawn, he saw the giant approaching him westwards from the sea. "Bad night," says he.

"It will be worse for thee, thou oaf," said Cu Chulainn. Then the giant cast one of the branches at Cu Chulainn, who let it pass him. He repeated it twice or thrice, but it reached neither the skin nor the shield of Cu Chulainn. Cu Chulainn then hurled his spear at the giant, but it did not reach him. Whereupon the giant stretched out his hand towards Cu Chulainn to grip him as he had the others. Cu Chulainn leapt the hero's salmon-leap and called to mind his swooping feat with his sword drawn over the giant's head. As swift as a hare he was, and in mid-air circling round the giant, until he made a water-wheel of him.

"Life for life, O Cu Chulainn," he said.

"Give me my three wishes," said Cu Chulainn.

"Thou shalt have them as they come at a breath," he said.

> The sovereignty of Erin's heroes be henceforth mine,
> The Champion's Portion without dispute,
> The precedence to my wife over the Ulster ladies forever.

"It shall be thine," he said at once. Then he who had been talking with Cu Chulainn vanished, he knew not whither.

Then Cu Chulainn mused to himself as to the leap his fellows had leapt over the fort, for their leap was big and broad and high. Moreover, it seemed to him that it was by leaping that the valiant heroes had gone over it. He tried it twice and failed. "Alas!" said Cu Chulainn, "my exertions for the Champion's Portion have exhausted me, and now I lose it through not being able to take the leap the others took." As thus he mused, he assayed the following feats: he would spring backwards in mid-air a shot's distance from the fort, and then he would rebound from there until his forehead struck the fort. Then he would spring on high until all that was within the fort was visible to him, and again he would sink up to his knees in the earth owing to the pressure of his vehemence and violence. At another time he would not take the dew from off the tip of the grass by reason of his buoyancy of mood, vehemence of nature, and heroic valor. What with the fit and fury that raged upon him he stepped over the fort outside and alighted at the door of the hall. His two footprints are in the flag on the floor of the hold at the spot where

the royal entrance was.   Thereafter he entered the house and
heaved a sigh.

Then Minn's daughter, Blathnat, wife of Cu Roi, spoke: "Truly
not the sigh of one dishonored, but a victor's sigh of triumph."
The daughter of the king of the Isle of the Men of Falga (*i.e.*,
Blathnat) knew full well of Cu Chulainn's evil plight that night.
They were not long there when they beheld Cu Roi coming towards
them, carrying into the house the standard of the three nines
slain by Cu Chulainn, along with their heads and that of the
monster. He put the heads from off his breast on to the floor of
the stead, and spoke: "The gillie whose one night's trophies are
these is a fit lad to watch the king's stronghold forever.   The
Champion's Portion, over which you have fallen out with the
gallant youths of Erin, truly belongs to Cu Chulainn. The bravest
of them, were he here, could not match him in number of trophies."
Cu Roi's verdict upon them was:

The Champion's Portion to be Cu Chulainn's,
With the sovereignty of valor over all the Gael,
And to his wife the precedence on entering the Mead Hall before all the
    ladies of Ulster.

And the value of seven bond-maidens in gold and silver Cu Roi
gave to Cu Chulainn in reward for his one night's performance.

The three heroes of Ulster straightway bade Cu Roi farewell
and kept on until they were seated in Emain Macha before the
day closed. When the waiters came to deal and divide, they took
the Champion's Portion with its share of ale out of the distribution
that they might have it apart. "Indeed, sure are we," said Dubtach
Chafertongue, "you think not tonight of contending for the
Champion's Portion. Perhaps the man you sought out has under-
taken to pass judgment."

Whereupon said the other folk to Cu Chulainn, "The Champion's Portion was not assigned to one of you in preference to
the other. As to Cu Roi's judgment upon these three, not a whit
did he concede to Cu Chulainn upon their arriving at Emain."
Cu Chulainn then declared that he by no means coveted the winning of it; for the loss thence resulting to the winner would be on
a par with the profit got from it. The championship was therefore
not fully assigned until the advent of the Champion's Covenant
in Emain, which follows.

One day as the Ulstermen were in Emain Macha, fatigued after the gathering and the games, Conchobar and Fergus mac Roig, with the Ulster nobles as well, proceeded from the playing field outside and seated themselves in the Red Branch of Conchobar. Neither Cu Chulainn nor Conall the Victorious nor Loegaire the Triumphant were there that night. But the hosts of Ulster's heroes were there. As they were seated, it being eventide, and the day drawing toward the close, they saw a big uncouth fellow of exceeding ugliness drawing nigh them into the hall. To them it seemed as if none of the Ulstermen would reach half his height. Horrible and ugly was the carle's disguise. Next his skin he wore an old hide with a dark dun mantle around him, and over him a great spreading club-tree branch the size of a winter-shed under which thirty bullocks could find shelter. Ravenous yellow eyes he had, protruding from his head, each of the twain the size of an ox-vat. Each finger was as thick as a person's wrist. In his left hand he carried a stock, a burden for twenty yoke of oxen. In his right hand was an axe weighing thrice fifty glowing molten masses of metal. Its handle would require a yoke of six to move it. Its sharpness such that it would lop off hairs, the wind blowing them against its edge.

In that guise he went and stood by the fork-beam beside the fire. "Is the hall lacking in room for you," said Dubtach Chafertongue to the uncouth clodhopper (*bachlach*), "that ye find no other place than by the fork-beam, unless ye wish to be an illumination to the house?—only sooner will a blaze be to the house than brightness to the household."

"Whatever property may be mine, you will agree that no matter how big I am the household will be lighted, while the hall will not be burned. That, however, is not my sole function; I have others as well. But neither in Erin nor in Alba nor in Europe nor in Africa nor in Asia, including Greece, Scythia, the Isles of Gades, the Pillars of Hercules, and Bregon's Tower have I accomplished the quest on which I have come, nor a man to do me fair play regarding it. Since ye Ulstermen have excelled all the peoples of those lands in strength, prowess and valor; in rank, magnanimity, and dignity; in truth, generosity, and worth, get one among you to grant the boon I ask."

"In truth it is not just that the honor of a province be carried off," said Fergus mac Roig, "because of one man who fails in keeping his word of honor. Death certainly is not a whit nearer to him than to you."

"It is not I that shun it."

"Make thy quest known to us, then," said Fergus.

"Only if fair play is offered me will I tell it."

"It is right to give fair play," said Sencha son of Ailill, "for it is not seemly for a great people to break a mutual covenant over any unknown individual. It seems to us, furthermore, that if you at last find a person such as you seek, you will find him here."

"Conchobar I put aside," said he, "for the sake of his sovereignty, and Fergus mac Roig also on account of his like privilege. These two excepted, come whosoever of you that may dare, that I may cut off his head tonight, he mine tomorrow night."

"Sure then there is no warrior here," said Dubtach, "after these two."

"By my troth there will be at this moment," cried Munremur mac Gerrcind as he sprung on to the floor of the hall. The strength of Munremur was as the strength of a hundred warriors, each arm having the might of a hundred "centaurs." "Bend down, bachlach," said Munremur, "that I may cut off thy head tonight, thou to cut off mine tomorrow."

"Were that the object of my quest I could get it anywhere," said the bachlach; "let us act according to our covenant—I to cut off your head tonight, you to avenge it tomorrow night."

"By my people's gods," said Dubtach Chafertongue, "death is thus for thee no pleasant prospect, should the man killed tonight attack thee on the morrow. It is given to thee alone if thou hast the power, being killed night after night, and to avenge it the next day."

"Truly I will carry out what you all as a body agree upon by way of counsel, strange as it may seem to you," said the bachlach. He then pledged the other to keep his troth in this contention as to fulfilling his tryst on the morrow.

With that Munremur took the axe from the bachlach's hand. Seven feet apart were its two angles. Then the bachlach put his neck across the block. Munremur dealt a blow across it with the axe until it stood in the block beneath, cutting off the head so that it lay by the base of the fork-beam, the house being filled with the blood.

Straightway the bachlach rose, recovered himself, clasped his head, block, and axe to his breast, and made his exit from the hall with the blood streaming from his neck. It filled the Red Branch on every side. Great was the people's horror, wondering at the marvel that had appeared to them. "By my people's gods," said Dubtach Chafertongue, "if the bachlach, having been killed tonight, come back tomorrow, he will not leave a man alive in Ulster."

The following night he returned, and Munremur shirked him. Then the bachlach began to urge his pact with Munremur. "Truly it is not right for Munremur not to fulfill his covenant with me."

That night, however, Loegaire the Triumphant was present. "Who of the warriors that contest Ulster's Champion's Portion will carry out a covenant with me tonight? Where is Loegaire the Triumphant?" said he.

"Here," said Loegaire. He pledged him, too, yet Loegaire did not keep his agreement. The bachlach returned on the morrow and similarly pledged Conall Cernach, who came not as he had sworn.

The fourth night the bachlach returned, and fierce and furious was he. All the ladies of Ulster came that night to see the strange marvel that had come to the Red Branch. That night Cu Chulainn was there also. Then the bachlach began to upbraid them. "Ye men of Ulster, your valor and your prowess are gone. Your warriors greatly covet the Champion's Portion, yet are unable to contest it. Where is the mad fellow called Cu Chulainn? I would like to know whether his word is better than the others."

"No covenant do I desire with you," said Cu Chulainn.

"Likely is that, thou wretched fly; greatly dost thou fear to die." Whereupon Cu Chulainn sprang towards him and dealt him a blow with the axe, hurling his head to the top rafter of the Red Branch until the whole hall shook. Cu Chulainn then again caught up the head and gave it a blow with the axe and smashed it. Thereafter the bachlach rose up.

On the morrow the Ulstermen were watching Cu Chulainn to see whether he would shirk the bachlach as the other heroes had done. As Cu Chulainn was awaiting the bachlach, they saw that great dejection seized him. It would have been fitting had they sung his dirge. They felt sure that his life would last only until the bachlach came. Then said Cu Chulainn with shame to Conchobar, "Thou shalt not go until my pledge to the bachlach is fulfilled; for death awaits me, and I would rather have death with honor."

They were there as the day was closing and they saw the bachlach approaching. "Where is Cu Chulainn?" said he.

"Here I am," he replied.

"Thou art dull of speech tonight, unhappy one; greatly you fear to die. Yet, though great your fear, death you have not shirked."

Thereafter Cu Chulainn stretched his neck across the block, which was of such size that his neck reached but half way. "Stretch out thy neck, thou wretch," cried the bachlach.

"Thou art keeping me in torment," said Cu Chulainn; "dispatch me quickly. Last night, by my troth, I tormented thee not. Verily I swear that if thou torment me I will make myself as long as a crane above you."

"I cannot slay thee," said the bachlach, "what with the shortness of your neck and your side and the size of the block."

Then Cu Chulainn stretched out his neck so that a warrior's foot would have fitted between any two of his ribs; his neck he stretched until his head reached the other side of the block. The bachlach raised his axe until it reached the roof-tree of the house. The creaking of the old hide that was about him and the crashing of the axe—both his arms being raised aloft with all his might— were as the loud noise of a wood tempest-tossed in a night of storm. Down it came then on his neck—its blunt side below, all the nobles of Ulster gazing upon them.

"O Cu Chulainn, arise! Of the warriors of Ulster and Erin, no matter their mettle, none is found to compare with thee in valor, bravery, and truthfulness. The sovereignty of the heroes of Erin to thee from this hour forth and the Champion's Portion undisputed, and to thy wife the precedence always of the ladies of Ulster in the Mead-Hall. And whosoever shall lay wager against thee from now, as my tribe swears I swear, all his life he will be in danger." Then the bachlach vanished. It was Cu Roi mac Dairi who in that guise had come to fulfill the promise he had given to Cu Chulainn.

THE CATTLE-RAID OF COOLEY

(Táin Bó Cualgne)

"The Cattle-Raid of Cooley" is the central epic of the Ulster cycle.
It exists in several versions, the oldest of which goes back probably to
the eighth century. The tale opens with the famous "Pillow-Talk"—a
racy dialogue between Queen Medb of Connacht and her hen-pecked
husband, Ailill. The queen, on finding that her possessions equal those
of her husband, except for one bull, the White-Horned of Connacht,
determines to make up the deficiency by gaining possession of the most
famous bull in Ireland, the Donn of Cooley, which is the property of
Daire, a chieftain of Ulster. When Medb learns that she cannot obtain
the Donn as a loan, she determines to take the animal by force and gathers
an army to invade Ulster. Owing to the temporary debility of all the
adult warriors of Ulster (p. 208), the seventeen-year-old Cu Chulainn
undertakes to oppose Medb's host single-handed. When Medb hears of
Cu Chulainn, she inquires about him from the Ulster exiles in her army
(p. 239) and learns of his boyish exploits (p. 137). As the result of an
agreement between Medb and Cu Chulainn, the Ulster champion meets at
a ford on the border of the two provinces a single Connacht warrior each
day over a period extending from Samain (the beginning of winter) till the
beginning of spring. The men of Connacht finally succeed in invading
Ulster and carrying off the Donn of Cooley, but they are later defeated by
the Ulstermen, now restored to their normal strength. The Donn of Cooley,
after slaying the White-Horned of Connacht, returns to his native district
and utters mad bellowings of triumph till his heart bursts and he dies.

In spite of obvious imperfections, "The Cattle-Raid of Cooley" is a
splendid example of an epic in the making. It shows many evidences of
literary artistry and is not without passages of marked power and impres-
siveness. The combat between Cu Chulainn and his friend Ferdiad is
one of the most famous passages in early Irish literature.

THE PILLOW-TALK

Once on a time, when Ailill and Medb had spread their royal bed
in Cruachan, the stronghold of Connacht, such was the pillow-talk
betwixt them:

Said Ailill, "True is the saying, O woman, 'She is a well-off
woman that is a rich man's wife.'"

"Aye, that she is," answered the wife; "but wherefore say'st
thou so?"

"For this," Ailill replied, "that thou art this day better off than the day that first I took thee."

Then answered Medb, "As well-off was I before I ever saw thee."

" It was a wealth, indeed, we never heard nor knew of," said Ailill; "but a woman's wealth was all thou hadst, and foes from lands next thine were wont to carry off the spoil and booty that they took from thee."

"Not so was I," said Medb; "the High King of Erin himself was my father, Eochaid Feidlich son of Finn son of Finnen son of Finnguin son of Rogen Ruad son of Rigen son of Blathacht son of Beothacht son of Enna Agnech son of Angus Turbech. Of daughters had he six: Derbriu, Ethne and Ele, Clothru, Mugain and Medb, myself, that was the noblest and seemliest of them all. It was I was the goodliest of them in bounty and gift-giving, in riches and treasures. It was I was best of them in battle and strife and combat. It was I that had fifteen hundred royal mercenaries of the sons of aliens exiled from their own land, and as many more of the sons of freemen of the land. These were as a standing house-hold-guard," continued Medb; "hence hath my father bestowed one of the five provinces of Erin upon me, that is, the province of Cruachan; wherefore 'Medb of Cruachan' am I called. Men came from Finn son of Ross Ruad, king of Leinster, to seek me for a wife, and I refused him; and from Cairbre Niafer son of Ross Ruad, king of Tara, to woo me, and I refused him; and they came from Conchobar son of Fachtna Fathach, king of Ulster, and I refused him likewise. They came from Eochaid Bec, and I went not; for it is I that exacted a peculiar bride-gift, such as no woman ever required of a man of the men of Erin, namely, a husband without avarice, without jealousy, without fear. For should he be mean, the man with whom I should live, we were ill-matched together, inasmuch as I am great in largess and gift-giving, and it would be a disgrace for my husband if I should be better at spending than he, and for it to be said that I was superior in wealth and treasures to him, while no disgrace would it be were one as great as the other. Were my husband a coward, it were as unfit for us to be mated, for I by myself and alone break battles and fights and combats, and it would be a reproach for my husband should his wife be more full of life than himself, and no reproach our being equally bold.

Should he be jealous, the husband with whom I should live, that too would not suit me, for there never was a time that I had not one man in the shadow of another. Howbeit, such a husband have I found, namely thyself, Ailill son of Ross Ruad of Leinster. Thou wast not churlish; thou wast not jealous; thou wast not a sluggard. It was I plighted thee, and gave purchase price to thee, which of right belongs to the bride—of clothing, namely, the raiment of twelve men, a chariot worth thrice seven bondmaids, the breadth of thy face of red gold, the weight of thy left forearm of white bronze. Whoso brings shame and sorrow and madness upon thee, no claim for compensation or satisfaction hast thou therefor that I myself have not, but it is to me the compensation belongs," said Medb, "for a man dependent upon a woman's maintenance is what thou art."

"Nay, not such was my state," said Ailill; "but two brothers had I; one of them over Tara, the other over Leinster; namely Finn over Leinster and Cairbre over Tara. I left the kingship to them because they were older but not superior to me in largess and bounty. Nor heard I of a province in Erin under woman's keeping but this province alone. And for this I came and assumed the kingship here as my mother's successor; for Mata of Muresc, daughter of Matach of Connacht, was my mother. And who could there be for me to have as my queen better than thyself, being, as thou wert, daughter of the High King of Erin?"

"Yet so it is," pursued Medb, "my fortune is greater than thine."

"I marvel at that," Ailill made answer, "for there is none that hath greater treasures and riches and wealth than I: indeed, to my knowledge there is not."

THE OCCASION OF THE CATTLE-RAID

Then were brought to them the least precious of their possessions, that they might know which of them had the more treasures, riches, and wealth. Their pails and their cauldrons and their iron-wrought vessels, their jugs and their pots and their eared pitchers were fetched to them.

Likewise their rings and their bracelets and their thumb-rings and their golden treasures were fetched to them, and their apparel, both purple and blue and black and green.

Their numerous flocks of sheep were led in from fields and meadows and plains. These were counted and compared, and found to be equal, of like size, of like number; however, there was one uncommonly fine ram over Medb's sheep, and he was worth a bondmaid, but a corresponding ram was over the ewes of Ailill.

Their horses and steeds and studs were brought from pastures and paddocks. There was a noteworthy horse in Medb's herd and he was of the value of a bondmaid; a horse to match was found among Ailill's.

Then were their numerous droves of swine driven from woods and shelving glens and wolds. These were numbered and counted and claimed. There was a noteworthy boar with Medb, and yet another with Ailill.

Next they brought before them their droves of cattle and their herds and their roaming flocks from the brakes and the wastes of the province.

These were counted and numbered and claimed, and were the same for both, equal in size, equal in number, except only there was an especial bull of the bawn of Ailill, and he was the calf of one of Medb's cows, and Finnbennach (the White-Horned) was his name. But he, deeming it no honor to be in a woman's possession, had left and gone over to the herd of the king. And it was the same to Medb as if she owned not a pennyworth, forasmuch as she had not a bull of his size amongst her cattle.

Then it was that Mac Roth the messenger was summoned to Medb, and Medb strictly bade Mac Roth learn where might be found a bull of that likeness in any of the provinces of Erin. "In truth," said Mac Roth, "I know where the bull is that is best and better again, in the province of Ulster, in the district of Cooley, in the house of Daire mac Fiachna; the Donn of Cooley he is called."

"Go thou to him, Mac Roth, and ask for me of Daire the loan for a year of the Donn of Cooley, and at the year's end he shall have a reward for the loan, to wit, fifty heifers and the Donn of Cooley himself. And bear a further boon with thee, Mac Roth: should the borderfolk and those of the country grudge the loan of that rare jewel that is the Donn of Cooley, let Daire himself come with his bull, and he shall get a measure equalling his own land of the smooth Mag Ai and a chariot of the worth of thrice seven bondmaids and he shall enjoy my own closest intimacy."

Thereupon the foot-messengers went to the house of Daire mac Fiachna. This was the number wherewith Mac Roth went, namely, nine members of Medb's court. Welcome was lavished on Mac Roth in Daire's house—fitting welcome it was—chief messenger of all was Mac Roth. Daire asked of Mac Roth what had brought him upon the journey and why he had come. The messenger announced the cause for which he had come, and related the contention between Medb and Ailill.

"And it is to beg the loan of the Donn of Cooley to match the White-Horned of Connacht that I have come," said he; "and thou shalt receive the hire of his loan, that is, fifty heifers and the Donn of Cooley himself. And yet more I may add: come thyself with thy bull and thou shalt have of the land of the smooth soil of Mag Ai as much as thou ownest here, and a chariot of the worth of thrice seven bondmaids, and enjoy Medb's favors besides."

At these words Daire was well pleased, and he leaped for joy so that the seams of his flock-bed rent in twain beneath him.

"By the truth of our conscience," said he, "however the Ulstermen take it, whether well or ill, this time this jewel shall be delivered to Ailill and to Medb, the Donn of Cooley shall go into the land of Connacht." Well pleased was Mac Roth at the words of Daire son of Fiachna.

Thereupon the messengers were served, and straw and fresh rushes were spread under them. The choicest of food was brought to them and a feast was served to them and soon they were noisy and intoxicated. And a discourse took place between two of the messengers.

" 'Tis true what I say," spoke the one; "good is the man in whose house we are."

"Of a truth, he is good."

"Nay, is there one among all the men of Ulster better than he?" persisted the first.

"In truth, there is," answered the second messenger. "Better is Conchobar whose man he is, Conchobar who holds the kingship of the province. And though all the Ulstermen gathered around him, it were no shame for them. Yet is it passing good of Daire that what had been a task for the four mighty provinces of Erin to bear away from the land of Ulster, that is the Donn of Cooley, is surrendered so freely to us nine footmen."

Hereupon a third messenger had his say: "What is this ye dispute about?" he asked.

"That messenger says, 'A good man is the man in whose house we are.'"

"Yea, he is good," said the other.

"Is there among all the Ulstermen any that is better than he?" demanded the first messenger further.

"Aye, there is," answered the second messenger; "better is Conchobar whose man he is; and though all the Ulstermen gathered around him, it were no shame for them. Yet truly good it is of Daire, that what had been a task for four of the great provinces of Erin to bear away out of the borders of Ulster is handed over even to us nine footmen."

"I would not grudge to see a retch of blood and gore in the mouth whereout that was said; for were not the bull given willingly, yet should he be taken by force."

At that moment it was that Daire mac Fiachna's chief steward came into the house and with him a man with drink and another with food, and he heard the foolish words of the messenger; and anger came upon him and he set down their food and drink for them and he neither said to them, "Eat," nor did he say, "Eat not."

Straightway he went into the house where was Daire mac Fiachna and said, "Is it thou that hast given that notable jewel to the messengers, the Donn of Cooley?"

"Yea, it was I," Daire made answer.

"Indeed it was not the part of a king to give him. For it is true what they say: Unless thou hadst bestowed him of thy own free will, so wouldst thou yield him against thy will by the host of Ailill and Medb and the great cunning of Fergus mac Roig."

"I swear by the gods I worship," said Daire, "they shall in no wise take by foul means what they cannot take by fair!"

There they abode until morning. Early in the morning the messengers arose and proceeded to the house where Daire was. "Tell us, lord, how we may reach the place where the Donn of Cooley is kept."

"Nay then," said Daire; "if it were my custom to deal foully with messengers or with travelling folk or with them that go by the road, not one of you would depart alive!"

"How sayest thou?" said Mac Roth.

"Great cause there is," replied Daire: "ye said, unless I yielded willingly, I should yield to the might of Ailill's host and Medb's and the great cunning of Fergus."

"Even so," said Mac Roth, "whatever the runners drunken with thine ale or thy viands have said, it is not for thee to heed or mind, nor yet to be charged on Ailill and on Medb."

"For all that," answered Daire, "this time I will not give my bull, if I can help it!"

Back then the messengers went until they arrived at Cruachan, the stronghold of Connacht. Medb asked their tidings, and Mac Roth told them: that they had not brought the bull from Daire.

"And the reason?" demanded Medb.

Mac Roth recounted to her how the dispute arose. "There is no need to polish knots over such affairs as that, Mac Roth; for it was known," said Medb, "if the Donn of Cooley would not be given with their will, he would be taken in their despite, and taken he shall be!"

So far is recounted the Occasion of the Cattle-Raid.

.   .   .   .

THE COMBAT OF CU CHULAINN AND FERDIAD

The four great provinces of Erin were side by side and against Cu Chulainn from Monday before Samain (Hallowe'en) to Wednesday after Spring-beginning, and without leave to work harm or vent their rage on the province of Ulster, while yet all the Ulstermen were sunk in their nine days' pains, and Conall Cernach sought out battle in strange foreign lands paying the tribute and tax of Ulster. Sad was the plight and strait of Cu Chulainn during that time, for he was not a day or a night without fierce, fiery combat waged on him by the men of Erin, until he killed Calatin with his seven and twenty sons and Fraech son of Fidach and performed many deeds and successes which are not enumerated here. Now this was sore and grievous to Medb and to Ailill.

Then the men of Erin took counsel who should be fit to send to the ford to fight and do battle with Cu Chulainn to drive him off from them.

With one accord they declared that it should be Ferdiad son of Daman son of Daire, the great and valiant warrior of the Fir

Domnann, the horn-skin from Irrus Domnann, the irresistible force, and the battle-rock of destruction, the own dear foster-brother of Cu Chulainn. And fitting it was for him to go thither, for well-matched and alike was their manner of fight and of combat. Under the same instructress had they done skillful deeds of valor and arms, when learning the art with Scathach and with Uathach and with Aife.[1] Yet was it the felling of an oak with one's fists, and the stretching of the hand into a serpent's den, and a going into the lair of a lion, for hero or champion in the world, aside from Cu Chulainn, to fight or combat with Ferdiad on whatever ford or river or mere he set his shield. And neither of them overmatched the other, save in the feat of the *gae bulga* (bag-spear) which Cu Chulainn possessed. Howbeit against this, Ferdiad was horn-skinned when fighting and in combat with a warrior on the ford; and they thought he could avoid the *gae bulga* and defend himself against it, because of the horn about him of such kind that neither arms nor multitude of edges could pierce it.

Then were messengers and envoys sent from Medb and Ailill to Ferdiad. Ferdiad denied them their request, and dismissed and sent back the messengers, and he went not with them, for he knew wherefore they would have him, to fight and combat with his friend, with his comrade and his fosterbrother, Cu Chulainn.

Then did Medb despatch to Ferdiad the druids and the poets of the camp, and lampooners and hard-attackers to the end that they might make the three satires to stay him and the three scoffing speeches against him, to mock at him and revile and disgrace him, that they might raise three blisters on his face,—Blame, Blemish, and Disgrace, that he might not find a place in the world to lay his head, if he came not with them to the tent of Medb and Ailill.

Ferdiad came with them for the sake of his own honor and for fear of their bringing shame on him, since he deemed it better to fall by the shafts of valor and bravery and skill than to fall by the shafts of satire, abuse, and reproach. And when Ferdiad was come into the camp, Medb and Ailill beheld him, and great and most wonderful joy possessed them, and they sent him to where their trusty people were, and he was honored and waited on, and choice, well-flavored strong liquor was poured out for him until he became drunken and merry. Finnabair, daughter of Ailill and Medb, was

[1] See p. 162.

seated at his side. It was Finnabair that placed her hand on every goblet and cup Ferdiad quaffed. She it was that gave him three kisses with every cup that he took. She it was that passed him sweet-smelling apples over the bosom of her tunic. This is what she ceased not to say, that her darling and her chosen sweetheart of the world's men was Ferdiad. And when Medb got Ferdiad drunken and merry, great rewards were promised him if he would make the fight and combat.

When now Ferdiad was satisfied, happy and joyful, Medb spoke, "Hail now, Ferdiad. Dost thou know the occasion wherefor thou art summoned to this tent?"

"I know not, in truth," Ferdiad replied; "unless it be that the nobles of the men of Erin are here. Why is it a less fitting time for me to be here than any other good warrior?"

"It is not that, indeed," answered Medb, "but to give thee a chariot worth four times seven bondmaids, and the apparel of two men and ten men, of cloth of every color, and the equivalent of Mag Muirthemne of the rich soil of Mag Ai, and that thou shouldst be at all times in Cruachan, and wine be poured out for thee there; the freedom of thy descendants and thy race forever, free of tribute, free of rent, without constraint to encamp or take part in our expeditions, without duress for thy son, or for thy grandson, or for thy great-grandson, till the end of time and existence; this leaf-shaped golden brooch of mine shall be thine, wherein are ten-score ounces, and ten-score half-ounces, and ten-score scruples, and ten-score quarters; Finnabair, my daughter and Ailill's, to be thy own wife, and my own most intimate friendship, if thou exactest that withal."

"He needs it not," they cried, one and all; "great are the rewards and gifts!"

Such were the words of Medb, and she spoke them here and Ferdiad responded:

Medb.   Great rewards in arm-rings,
                 Share of plain and forest,
                 Freedom of thy children
                     From this day till Doom!
                 Ferdiad son of Daman,
                 More than thou couldst hope for,
                 Why shouldst thou refuse it,
                     That which all would take?

Ferdiad.   Naught I'll take without bond—
No ill spearman am I—
Hard on me to-morrow:
  Great will be the strife!
He called Hound of Culann,
How his thrust is grievous!
No soft thing to stand him;
  Rude will be the wound!

Medb.   Champions will be surety,
Thou needst not keep hostings.
Reins and splendid horses
  Shall be given as pledge!
Ferdiad, good, of battle,
For that thou art dauntless,
Thou shalt be my lover,
  Past all, free of pain!

Ferdiad.   Without bond I'll not go
To engage in ford-feats;
It will live till doomsday
  In full strength and force.
Ne'er will I yield—who hears me,
Whoe'er counts upon me—
Without sun- and moon-oath,
  Without sea and land!

Medb.   Why then dost thou delay it?
Bind it as it please thee,
By kings' hands and princes',
  Who will stand for thee!
Lo, I will repay thee,
Thou shalt have thine asking,
For I know thou wilt slaughter
  Man that meets thee!

Ferdiad.   Nay, without six sureties—
It shall not be fewer—
Ere I do my exploits
  There where hosts will be!
Should my will be granted,
I expect, though unequal,
That I'll meet in combat
  Cu Chulainn the brave!

Medb.   Domnall, then, or Cairbre,
Niaman famed for slaughter,
Or even poets,
  Natheless, thou shalt have.

Bind thyself on Morann,
Wouldst thou its fulfillment,
Bind on smooth Man's Cairbre,
    And our two sons, bind!

Ferdiad.

Medb, with wealth of cunning,
Whom no spouse can bridle,
Thou it is that guardest
    Cruachan of the mounds!
High thy fame and wild power!
Mine the fine pied satin;
Give thy gold and silver,
    Which were proffered me!

Medb.

To thee, foremost champion,
I will give my ringed brooch.
From this day till Sunday,
    Shall thy respite be!
Warrior, mighty, famous,
All the earth's fair treasures
Shall to thee be given;
    Everything be thine!

Finnabair of the champions,
Queen of western Erin,
When thou hast slain the Smith's Hound,
Ferdiad, she is thine!

Ferdiad.

Should I have Finnabair to wife,
All of Ai and Cruachan too,
And to dwell for alway there,
I would not seek the deedful Cu Chulainn!

Equal skill to me and him—
Thus spoke Ferdiad—
The same nurses reared us both,
And with them we learned our art.

Not for fear of battle hard,
Noble Eochaid Fedlech's daughter,
Would I shun the Blacksmith's Hound,
But my heart bleeds for his love!

Medb.

Thou shalt have, dear bright-scaled man,
One swift, proud, high-mettled steed.
Thou shalt have domains and land
And shalt stay not from the fight!

Fordiad.

But that Medb entreated so
And that poets' tongues did urge,
I'd not go for hard rewards
To contend with my own friend!

Medb.   Son of Daman of white cheeks,
    Shouldst thou check this heroes' Hound,
    For ever thy fame will live,
    When thou comest from Ferdiad's Ford!

Then said they, one and all, those gifts were great.

" 'Tis true, they are great. But though they are," said Ferdiad, "with Medb herself I will leave them, and I will not accept them if it be to do battle or combat with my fosterbrother, the man of my alliance and affection, and my equal in skill of arms, namely, with Cu Chulainn"; and he said:

> Greatest toil, this, greatest toil,
> Battle with the Hound of gore!
> Liefer would I battle twice
> With two hundred men of Fal (Ireland)!
>
> Sad the fight, and sad the fight,
> I and Hound of feats shall wage!
> We shall hack both flesh and blood;
> Skin and body we shall hew!
>
> Sad, O god, yea, sad, O god,
> That a woman us should part!
> My heart's half, the blameless Hound;
> Half the brave Hound's heart am I!
>
> .   .   .   .
>
> Liefer would I, liefer far,
> Arms should slay me in fierce fight,
> Than the death of the heroes' Hound
> Should be food for ravenous birds!
>
> Tell him this, O tell him this,
> To the Hound of beauteous hue,
> Fearless Scathach hath foretold
> My fall on a ford through him!
>
> Woe to Medb, yea, woe to Medb,
> Who hath used her guile on us;
> She hath set me face to face
> 'Gainst Cu Chulainn—hard the toil!

"Ye men," said Medb, in the wonted fashion of stirring up disunion and dissension, as if she had not heard Ferdiad at all, "true is the word Cu Chulainn speaks."

"What word is that?" asked Ferdiad.

"He said, then," replied Medb, "he would not think it too much if thou shouldst fall by his hands in the choicest feat of his skill in arms, in the land whereto he should come."

"It was not just for him to speak so," said Ferdiad; "for it is not cowardice or lack of boldness that he hath ever seen in me by day or night. And I speak not so of him, for I have it not to say of him. And I swear by my arms of valor, if it be true that he spoke so, I will be the first man of the men of Erin to contend with him on the morrow, how loath soever I am to do so!"

And he gave his word in the presence of them all that he would go and meet Cu Chulainn. For it pleased Medb, if Ferdiad should fail to go, to have them as witnesses against him, in order that she might say that it was fear or dread that caused him to break his word.

"Blessing and victory upon thee for that!" said Medb; "it pleaseth me more than for thee to show fear and lack of boldness. For every man loves his own land, and how is it better for him to seek the welfare of Ulster, because his mother was descended from the Ulstermen, than for thee to seek the welfare of Connacht, as thou art the son of a king of Connacht?"

Then it was that Medb obtained from Ferdiad the easy surety of a covenant to fight and contend on the morrow with six warriors of the champions of Erin, or to fight and contend with Cu Chulainn alone, if to him this last seemed lighter. Ferdiad obtained of Medb the easy surety, as he thought, to send the aforesaid six men for the fulfillment of the terms which had been promised him, should Cu Chulainn fall at his hands.

There was a wonderful warrior of the Ulstermen present at that covenant, and that was Fergus mac Roig. Fergus betook him to his tent. "Woe is me, for the deed that will be done on the morning of the morrow!"

"What deed is that?" his tent-folk asked.

"My good fosterling Cu Chulainn will be slain!"

"Alas! who makes that boast?"

"Not hard to say: None other but his dear, devoted foster-brother, Ferdiad son of Daman. Why bear ye not my blessing," Fergus continued, "and let one of you go with a warning and mercy to Cu Chulainn, if perchance he will leave the ford on the morn of the morrow?"

"As we live," said they, "though it were thyself was on the ford of battle, we would not go near him to seek thee."

"Come, my lad," cried Fergus, "get our horses for us, and yoke the chariot."

Then were Fergus's horses fetched for him and his chariot was yoked, and he came forward to the place of combat where Cu Chulainn was, to inform him of the challenge, that Ferdiad was to fight with him.

"A chariot comes hither towards us, O Cu Chulainn!" cried Loeg. For in this wise was the gillie, with his back towards his lord as the two played chess. He used to win every other game of draughts and chess from his master. Watch and guard of the four points of the compass was he besides.

"What manner of chariot is it?" asked Cu Chulainn.

"A chariot like to a royal fort, huge, with its yoke, strong, golden; with its great board of copper; with its shafts of bronze; with its two horses, black, swift, stout, strong-forked, thick-set, under beautiful shafts. One kingly, broad-eyed warrior is the combatant in the chariot. A curly, forked beard he wears that reaches below outside over the smooth lower part of his soft tunic, which would shelter fifty warriors on a day of storm and rain under the heavy shield of the warrior's beard. A bent buckler, white, beautiful, of many colors, he bears, with three stout-wrought chains, so that there is room from edge to edge for four troops of ten behind the leather of the shield which hangs upon the broad back of the warrior. A long, hard-edged, broad, red sword in a sheath woven and twisted of white silver. A strong, three-ridged spear, wound and banded with all-gleaming white silver he has lying across the chariot."

"Not difficult to recognize him," said Cu Chulainn; "it is my master Fergus that comes hither with a warning and with compassion for me, before all the four provinces of Erin."

Fergus drew nigh and sprang from his chariot. Cu Chulainn bade him welcome. "Welcome is thy coming, O master Fergus!" cried Cu Chulainn. "If a flock of birds comes into the plain, thou shalt have a duck with the half of another. If a fish comes into the river-mouth, thou shalt have a salmon with the half of another. A handful of water-cress and a bunch of laver and a sprig of sea-grass and a drink of cold water from the sand thou shalt have thereafter."

"It is an outlaw's portion, that," said Fergus.

" 'Tis true; 'tis an outlaw's portion is mine," answered Cu Chulainn.

"Truly intended, methinks, the welcome, O fosterling," said Fergus. "But were it for this I came, I should think it better to leave it. It is for this I am here, to inform thee who comes to fight and contend with thee at the morning hour early on the morrow."

"Even so we will hear it from thee," said Cu Chulainn.

"Thine own friend and comrade and fosterbrother, the man thine own equal in feats and in skill of arms and in deeds, Ferdiad son of Daman son of Daire, the great and mighty warrior of the Fir Domnann."

"As my soul liveth," replied Cu Chulainn, "it is not to an encounter we wish our friend to come, and not for fear, but for love and affection of him; and almost I would prefer to fall by the hand of that warrior than for him to fall by mine."

"It is just for that," answered Fergus, "that thou shouldst be on thy guard and prepared. Say not that thou hast no fear of Ferdiad, for it is fitting that thou shouldst have fear and dread before fighting with Ferdiad. For unlike to all whom it fell to fight and contend with thee on the Cattle-Raid of Cooley on this occasion is Ferdiad son of Daman son of Daire, for he has a horny skin about him in battle against a man, a belt, equally strong, victorious in battle, and neither points nor edges are reddened upon it in the hour of strife and anger. For he is the fury of the lion, and the bursting of wrath, and the blow of doom, and the wave that drowns foes."

"Speak not thus!" cried Cu Chulainn, "for I swear by my arms of valor, the oath that my people swear, that every limb and every joint will be as a pliant rush in the bed of a river under the point of the sword, if he show himself to me on the ford! Truly I am here," said Cu Chulainn, "checking and staying four of the five grand provinces of Erin from Monday at Samain till the beginning of spring, and I have not left my post for a night's disport, through stoutly opposing the men of Erin on the Cattle-Raid of Cooley. And in all this time, I have not put foot in retreat before any one man nor before a multitude, and methinks just as little will I turn in flight before him."

And thus spoke he, that it was not fear of Ferdiad that caused his anxiety regarding the fight, but his love for him. And, on his part, so spoke Fergus, putting him on his guard because of Ferdiad's strength, and he said these words and Cu Chulainn responded:

Fergus. O Cu Chulainn—splendid deed—
Lo, it is time for thee to rise.
Here in rage against thee comes
Ferdiad, red-faced Daman's son!

Cu Chulainn. Here am I—no easy task—
Holding Erin's men at bay;
A foot I have never turned in flight
In my fight with single foe!

· · · · · · ·

Fergus. Fierce the man with scores of deeds;
No light thing him to subdue.
Strong as hundreds—brave his mien—
Point pricks not, edge cuts him not!

Cu Chulainn. If we clash upon the ford,
I and Ferdiad of known skill,
We'll not part until we know;
Fierce will be our weapon fight!

· · · · · · ·

Fergus. Greatest deed awaits thy hand:
Fight with Ferdiad, Daman's son.
Hard stern arms with stubborn edge,
Shalt thou have, thou Culann's Hound!

After that, Fergus returned to the camp and halting-place of the men of Erin, lest the men of Erin should say he was betraying them or forsaking them, if he should remain longer than he did conversing with Cu Chulainn. And they took farewell of each other.

Now as regards the charioteer of Cu Chulainn after Fergus went from them: "What wilt thou do to-night?" asked Loeg.

"What, indeed?" said Cu Chulainn.

"It will be thus," said the charioteer: "Ferdiad will come to attack thee, with new beauty of plaiting and dressing of hair, and washing and bathing, and the four provinces of Erin with him to look at the combat. I would that thou shouldst go where thou wilt get a like adorning for thyself, to the place where is Emer Foltchain (Emer of the Beautiful Hair), thy wife, daughter of Forgall Monach, at Cairthenn in Cluan da Dam (Two Oxen's Meadow) in Sliab Fuait, where thou wilt get even such an adorning for thyself."

"It is fitting to do so," said Cu Chulainn. Then Cu Chulainn went thither that night to Dun Delgan, his own stronghold, and passed the night with his wife. His doings from that time are not related here now.

As for Ferdiad, he betook himself to his tent and to his people, and imparted to them the easy surety which Medb had obtained from him to do combat and battle with six warriors on the morrow, or to do combat and battle with Cu Chulainn alone, if he thought it a lighter task. He made known to them also the fair terms he had obtained from Medb of sending the same six warriors for the fulfillment of the covenant she had made with him, should Cu Chulainn fall by his hands.

The folk of Ferdiad were not joyful, blithe, cheerful, or merry that night, but they were sad, sorrowful, and downcast, for they knew that here were the two champions and the two bulwarks in a gap for a hundred, the two pillars of battle and strife of the men of Erin of that time met in combat; one or the other of them would fall there or both would fall, and if it should be one of them, they believed it would be their king and their own lord that would fall there, for it was not easy to contend and do battle with Cu Chulainn on the Cattle-Raid of Cooley.

Ferdiad slept right heavily the first part of the night, but when the end of the night was come, his sleep and his heaviness left him. And the anxiousness of the combat and the battle came upon him. But most troubled in spirit was he that he should allow all the treasures to pass from him, and the maiden, by reason of the combat with one man. Unless he fought with that one man, he must needs fight with six champions on the morrow. What tormented him more than that was, should he once show himself on the ford to Cu Chulainn, he was certain he would never have power of head or of life ever after. And Ferdiad arose early on the morrow. And he charged his charioteer to take his horses and to yoke his chariot. The charioteer sought to dissuade him from that journey. "By our word," said the gillie, "it would be better for thee to remain than to go thither," said he; "for, not more do I commend it for thee than I condemn it."

"Hold thy peace about us, boy!" said Ferdiad, "for we will brook no interference from any one concerning this journey. For the promise we gave to Medb and Ailill in the presence of

the men of Erin, it would shame us to break it; for they would
say it was fear or dread that caused us to break it. And, by my
conscience, I would almost liefer fall myself by Cu Chulainn's
hand than that he should fall by mine on this occasion. And should
Cu Chulainn fall by my hand on the ford of combat, then shall
Medb and many of the men of Erin fall by my hand because of
the pledge they extorted from me, and I drunken and merry."

And in this manner he spoke, conversing with the charioteer,
and he uttered these words, the little lay that follows, urging on
the charioteer, and the servant responded:

Ferdiad.   Let us haste to the encounter,
      To battle with this man;
      The ford we will come to,
       Over which Badb will shriek!
      To meet with Cu Chulainn,
      To wound his slight body,
      To thrust the spear through him
       So that he may die!

The Henchman. To stay it were better;
      Thy threats are not gentle;
      Death's sickness will one of you have,
       And sad will ye part!
      To meet Ulster's noblest,
      To meet whence ill cometh;
      Long will men speak of it.
       Alas, for thy course!

Ferdiad.   Not fair what thou speakest;
      No fear has the warrior;
      We owe no one meekness;
       We stay not for thee!
      Hush, gillie, about us!
      The time will bring strong hearts;
      More meet strength than weakness;
       Let us on to the tryst!

Ferdiad's horses were now brought forth and his chariot was
hitched, and he set out from the camp for the ford of battle when
yet day with its full light had not come there for him. "My lad,"
said Ferdiad, "it is not fitting that we make our journey without
bidding farewell to the men of Erin. Turn the horses and the
chariot for us toward the men of Erin." Thrice the servant turned
the heads of the horses and the chariot towards the men of Erin.

Then he came upon Medb, letting her water from her on the floor of the tent. "Ailill, sleepest thou still?" asked Medb.

"Not so!" replied Ailill.

"Dost hear thy new son-in-law taking farewell of thee?"

"Is that what he does?" asked Ailill.

"It is that, truly," Medb answered; "but I swear by what my tribe swears, not on the same feet will the man who makes that greeting come back to you."

"Howbeit, we have profited by a happy alliance of marriage with him," said Ailill; "if only Cu Chulainn falls by his hand. I should be pleased if they both fell, yet I would prefer that Ferdiad should escape."

Ferdiad came to the ford of combat. "Look, my lad!" said Ferdiad, "is Cu Chulainn on the ford?"

"That he is not," replied the gillie.

"Look well for us," said Ferdiad.

"Cu Chulainn is not a little speck where he would be in hiding," answered the gillie.

"It is true, then, my lad; till this day Cu Chulainn has not heard of a goodly warrior coming to meet him on the Cattle-Raid of Cooley, and now when he has heard of one, he has left the ford."

"Shame for thee to slander Cu Chulainn in his absence. Rememberest thou not when ye gave battle to German Garbglas above the borders of the Tyrrhene Sea, thou leftest thy sword with the hosts and it was Cu Chulainn who slew a hundred warriors till he reached it and brought it to thee? And mindest thou well where we were that night?" the gillie asked further.

"I know not," Ferdiad answered.

"At the house of Scathach's steward," said the other; "and thou wentest proudly in advance of us all into the house. The churl gave thee a blow with his three-pointed fork in the small of the back, so that thou flewest like a bolt out over the door. Cu Chulainn came in and gave the churl a blow with his sword, so that he made two pieces of him. I was their house-steward while you were in that place. If it were that day, thou wouldst not say thou wast a better warrior than Cu Chulainn."

"Wrong is what thou hast done, O gillie," said Ferdiad; "for I would not have come to the combat, hadst thou spoken thus to

me at first. Why dost thou not lay the chariot-poles at my side
and the skin-coverings under my head, so that I may sleep now?"

"Alas," said the gillie, "it is a sorry sleep before deer and a
pack of wolves here!"

"How so, gillie? Art thou not able to keep watch and guard
for me?"

"I am," the gillie answered; "unless they come in clouds or in
the air to attack thee, they shall not come from east or from west
to attack thee without warning, without notice."

"Come, gillie," said Ferdiad, "unharness the horses and spread
for me the cushions and skins of my chariot under me here, so
that I sleep off my heavy fit of sleep and slumber here, for I slept
not the last part of the night with the anxiousness of the battle
and combat."

The gillie unharnessed the horses; he unfastened the chariot
under him, and spread beneath Ferdiad the chariot-cloths. He
slept off the heavy fit of sleep that was on him. The gillie remained
on watch and guard for him.

Now how Cu Chulainn fared is related here: He arose not till
the day with its bright light had come to him, lest the men of
Erin might say it was fear or fright of the champion he had, if
he should arise early. And when the day with its full light had
come, he passed his hand over his face and bade his charioteer
take his horses and yoke them to his chariot. "Come, gillie," said
Cu Chulainn, "take out our horses for us and harness our chariot,
for an early riser is the warrior appointed to meet us, Ferdiad
son of Daman son of Daire. If Ferdiad awaits us, he must needs
think it long."

"The horses are taken out," said the gillie; "the chariot is
harnessed. Mount, and be it no shame to thy valor to go thither!"

Cu Chulainn stepped into the chariot and they pressed forward
to the ford. Then it was that the cutting, feat-performing, battle-
winning, red-sworded hero, Cu Chulainn son of Sualtam, mounted
his chariot, so that there shrieked around him the goblins and
fiends and the sprites of the glens and the demons of the air; for
the Tuatha De Danann were wont to set up their cries around
him, to the end that the dread and the fear and the fright and the
terror of him might be so much the greater in every battle and on
every field, in every fight and in every combat wherein he went.

Not long had Ferdiad's charioteer waited when he heard something: a rush and a crash and a hurtling sound, and a din and a thunder, a clatter and a clash, namely, the shield-cry of feat-shields, and the jangle of javelins, and the deed-striking of swords, and the thud of the helmet, and the ring of spears, and the clang of the cuirass, and the striking of arms, the fury of feats, the straining of ropes, and the whirr of wheels, and the creaking of the chariot, the tramping of horses' hoofs, and the deep voice of the hero and battle-warrior in grave speech with his servant on his way to the ford to attack his opponent.

The servant came and touched his master with his hand and awakened him. "Ferdiad, master," said the youth, "rise up! They are here to meet thee at the ford." Then Ferdiad arose and girt his body in his war-dress of battle and combat. And the gillie spoke these words:

> The roll of a chariot,
> Its fair yoke of silver;
> A great man and stalwart
>   Overtops the strong car!
> Over Bri Ross, over Brane
> Their swift path they hasten;
> Past Old-tree Town's tree-stump,
>   Victorious they speed!
>
> A sly Hound that driveth,
> A fair chief that urgeth,
> A free hawk that speedeth
>   His steeds towards the south!
> Gore-coloured, the Cua,
> It is sure he will take us;
> We know—vain to hide it—
>   He brings us defeat!
>
> Woe to him on the hillock,
> The brave Hound before him;
> Last year I foretold it,
>   That some time he'd come!

"Come, gillie," said Ferdiad; "for what reason praisest thou this man ever since I am come from my house? And it is almost a cause for strife with thee that thou hast praised him thus highly. But Ailill and Medb have prophecied to me that this man will fall by my hand; and since it is for a reward, he shall quickly be torn asunder by me. Make ready the arms on the ford against his coming."

"Should I turn my face backward," said the gillie, "methinks the poles of that chariot yonder will pass through the back of my neck."

"Too much, my lad," said Ferdiad, "dost thou praise Cu Chulainn, for not a reward has he given thee for praising, but it is time to fetch help."

.   .   .   .

It was not long that Ferdiad's charioteer remained there when he saw something: "How beholdest thou Cu Chulainn?" asked Ferdiad of his charioteer.

"I behold," said he, "a beautiful, five-pointed chariot, broad above, of white crystal, with a thick yoke of gold, with stout plates of copper, with shafts of bronze, with wheel-bands of bronze covered with silver, approaching with swiftness, with speed, with perfect skill; with a green shade, with a thin-framed, dry-bodied box surmounted with feats of cunning, straight-poled, as long as a warrior's sword. On this is room for a hero's seven arms, the fair seat for its lord; two wheels, dark, black; a pole of tin, with red enamel, of a beautiful color; two inlaid, golden bridles. This chariot is placed behind two fleet steeds, nimble, furious, small-headed, bounding, large-eared, small-nosed, sharp-beaked, red-chested, gaily prancing, with inflated nostrils, broad-chested, quick-hearted, high-flanked, broad-hoofed, slender-limbed, over-powering and resolute. A grey, broad-hipped, small-stepping, long-maned horse, whose name is Liath (the Gray) of Macha, is under one of the yokes of the chariot; a black, crisp-maned, swift-moving, broad-backed horse, whose name is Dub (the Black) of Sainglenn, under the other. Like unto a hawk after its prey on a sharp tempestuous day, or to a tearing blast of wind of spring on a March day over the back of a plain, or unto a startled stag when first roused by the hounds in the first of the chase, are Cu Chulainn's two horses before the chariot, as if they were on glowing, fiery flags, so that they shake the earth and make it tremble with the fleetness of their course.

"In the front of this chariot is a man with fair, curly, long hair. There is around him a cloak, blue, Parthian purple. A spear with red and keen-cutting blades, flaming-red in his hand. The semblance of three heads of hair he has, namely, brown hair next to the skin of his head, blood-red hair in the middle, a crown of gold is the third head of hair.

"Beautiful is the arrangement of that hair so that it makes three coils down behind over his shoulders. Even as a thread of gold it seems, when its hue has been wrought over the edge of an anvil; or like to the yellow of bees whereon shines the sun on a summer's day is the shining of each single hair of his head. Seven toes he has on each of his feet and seven fingers on each of his hands and the brilliance of a very great fire is around his eye.

"Befitting him is the charioteer beside him, with curly, jet-black hair, shorn broad over his head. A cowled garment around him, open at the elbows. A horsewhip, very fine and golden in his hand, and a light-grey cloak wrapped around him, and a goad of white silver in his hand. He plies the goad whatever way would go the deed-renowned warrior that is in the chariot."

And Cu Chulainn reached the ford. Ferdiad waited on the south side of the ford; Cu Chulainn stood on the north side. Ferdiad bade welcome to Cu Chulainn. "Welcome is thy coming, O Cu Chulainn!" said Ferdiad.

"Truly spoken has seemed thy welcome always till now," answered Cu Chulainn; "but to-day I put no more trust in it. And, O Ferdiad," said Cu Chulainn, "it were fitter for me to bid thee welcome than that thou should'st welcome me; for it is thou that art come to the land and the province wherein I dwell; and it is not fitting for thee to come to contend and do battle with me, but it were fitter for me to go to contend and do battle with thee. For before thee in flight are my women and my boys and my youths, my steeds and my troops of horses, my droves, my flocks and my herds of cattle."

"Good, O Cu Chulainn," said Ferdiad; "what has ever brought thee out to contend and do battle with me? For when we were together with Scathach and with Uathach and with Aife, thou wast not a man worthy of me, for thou wast my serving-man, even for arming my spear and dressing my bed."

"That was indeed true," answered Cu Chulainn; "because of my youth and my littleness did I so much for thee, but this is by no means my mood this day. For there is not a warrior in the

world I would not drive off this day in the field of battle and
combat."

It was not long before they met in the middle of the ford. And
then it was that each of them cast sharp-cutting reproaches at
the other, renouncing his friendship; and Ferdiad spoke these
words there, and Cu Chulainn responded:

Ferdiad.   What led thee, O Cu,
                    To fight a strong champion?
                    Thy flesh will be gore-red
                        Over smoke of thy steeds!
                    Alas for thy journey,
                    A kindling of firebrands;
                    In sore need of healing,
                    If home thou shouldst reach!

Cu Chulainn.   I have come before warriors
                    Around the herd's wild Boar,
                    Before troops and hundreds,
                        To drown thee in deep.
                    In anger, to prove thee
                    In hundred-fold battle,
                    Till on thee come havoc,
                        Defending thy head!

Ferdiad.   Here stands one to crush thee,
                    'Tis I will destroy thee,

                    .   .   .   .   .   .

                    From me there shall come
                    The flight of their warriors
                    In the presence of Ulster,
                    That long they'll remember
                    The loss that was theirs!

Cu Chulainn.   How then shall we combat?
                    For wrongs shall we heave sighs?
                    Despite all, we'll go there,
                        To fight on the ford!
                    Or is it with hard swords,
                    Or even with red spear-points,
                    Before hosts to slay thee,
                        If thy hour hath come?

Ferdiad.   Before sunset, before nightfall—
                    If need be, then guard thee—
                    I'll fight thee at Bairche,
                        Not bloodlessly fight!

The Ulstermen call thee,
"He has him!" Oh, hearken!
The sight will distress them
   That through them will pass!

Cu Chulainn.   In danger's gap fallen,
At hand is thy life's term;
On thee plied be weapons,
   Not gentle the skill!
One champion will slay thee;
We both will encounter;
No more shall lead forays,
   From this day till doom!

Ferdiad.   Away with thy warnings,
Thou world's greatest braggart;
Nor guerdon nor pardon,
   Low warrior, for thee!
It is I that well know thee,
Thou heart of a cageling—
This lad merely tickles—
   Without skill or force!

Cu Chulainn.   When we were with Scathach,
For wonted arms' training,
Together we'd fare forth,
   To seek every fight.
Thou wast my heart's comrade,
My clan and my kinsman;
Never found I one dearer;
   Thy loss would be sad!

Ferdiad.   Thou wager'st thine honor
Unless we do battle;
Before the cock crows,
   Thy head on a spit!
Cu Chulainn of Cooley,
Mad frenzy hath seized thee;
All ill we'll wreak on thee,
   For thine is the sin!

"Come now, O Ferdiad," cried Cu Chulainn, "not meet was it for thee to come to contend and do battle with me, because of the instigation and intermeddling of Ailill and Medb, and because of the false promises that they made thee. Because of their deceitful terms and of the maiden Finnabair have many good men been slain. And all that came because of those promises of deceit, neither profit nor success did it bring them, and they have fallen by me. And none the more, O Ferdiad, shall it win victory or increase of fame for thee; and, as they all fell, shalt thou too fall by my hand!" Thus he spake, and he further uttered these words, and Ferdiad hearkened to him:

> Come not nigh me, noble chief,
> Ferdiad, comrade, Daman's son.
> Worse for thee than it is for me;
> Thou wilt bring sorrow to a host!
>
> Come not nigh me against all right;
> Thy last bed is made by me.
> Why shouldst thou alone escape
> From the prowess of my arms?
>
> Shall not great feats thee undo,
> Though thou art purple, horny-skinned?
> And the maid thou boastest of,
> Shall not, Daman's son, be thine!
>
> Finnabair, Medb's fair daughter,
> Great her charms though they may be,
> Fair as is the damsel's form,
> She is not for thee to enjoy!
>
> Finnabair, the king's own child,
> Is the lure, if truth be told;
> Many they whom she has deceived
> And undone as she has thee!
>
> Break not, foolish one, oath with me;
> Break not friendship, break not bond;
> Break not promise, break not word;
> Come not nigh me, noble chief!
>
> Fifty chiefs obtained in plight
> This same maid, a proffer vain.
> Through me went they to their graves;
> Spear-right all they had from me!
>
> .   .   .   .
>
> Were she my affianced wife,
> Smiled on me this fair land's head,
> I would not thy body hurt,
> Right nor left, in front nor behind!

"Good, O Ferdiad," cried Cu Chulainn, " a pity it is for thee to abandon my alliance and my friendship for the sake of a woman that has been trafficked to fifty other warriors before thee, and it would be long before I would forsake thee for that woman.

Therefore it is not right for thee to come to fight and combat with me; for when we were with Scathach and Uathach and Aife, we were together in practice of valor and arms of the world, and it was together we were used to seek out every battle and every battle-field, every combat and every contest, every wood and every desert, every covert and every recess." And thus he spoke and he uttered these words:

Cu Chulainn.   We were heart-companions once;
We were comrades in the woods;
We were men that shared one bed,
When we slept the heavy sleep,
After hard and weary fights.
Into many lands, so strange,
Side by side we sallied forth,
And we ranged the woodlands through,
When with Scathach we learned arms!

Ferdiad.   O Cu Chulainn, rich in feats,
Hard the trade we both have learned;
Treason hath overcome our love;
Thy first wounding hath been brought;
Think not of our friendship more,
Cu, it avails thee not!

"Too long are we now in this way," said Ferdiad; "and what arms shall we resort to to-day, O Cu Chulainn?"

"With thee is thy choice of weapons this day until night-time," answered Cu Chulainn, "for thou art he that first didst reach the ford."

"Rememberest thou at all," asked Ferdiad, "the choice of arms we were wont to practice with Scathach and with Uathach and with Aife?"

"Indeed, and I do remember," answered Cu Chulainn.

"If thou rememberest, let us begin with them."

They betook them to their choicest deeds of arms. They took upon them two equally-matched shields for feats, and their eight-edged targets for feats, and their eight small darts, and their eight straight swords, with ornaments of walrus-tooth, and their eight lesser ivoried spears which flew from them and to them like bees on a day of fine weather.

They cast no weapons that struck not. Each of them was busy casting at the other with those missiles from morning's early twilight until noon at mid-day, the while they overcame their various feats with the bosses and hollows of their feat-shields. However great the excellence of the throwing on either side, equally great was the excellence of the defence, so that during all that time neither bled nor reddened the other.

"Let us cease now from this bout of arms, O Cu Chulainn," said Ferdiad; "for it is not by such our decision will come."

"Yea, surely, let us cease, if the time hath come," answered Cu Chulainn.

Then they ceased. They threw their feat-tackle from them into the hands of their charioteers.

"To what weapons shall we resort next, O Cu Chulainn?" asked Ferdiad.

"Thine is the choice of weapons until nightfall," answered Cu Chulainn, "for thou art he who didst first reach the ford."

"Let us begin, then," said Ferdiad, "with our straight-cut, smooth-hardened throwing-spears, with cords of full-hard flax on them."

"Aye, let us begin then," assented Cu Chulainn.

Then they took on them two hard shields, equally strong. They fell to their straight-cut, smooth-hardened spears with cords of full-hard flax on them. Each of them was engaged in casting at the other with the spears from the middle of noon till yellowness came over the sun at the hour of evening's sundown. However great the excellence of the defense, equally great was the excellence of the throwing on either side, so that each of them bled and reddened and wounded the other during that time.

"Wouldst thou fain make a truce, O Cu Chulainn?" asked Ferdiad.

"It would please me," replied Cu Chulainn; "for whoso begins with arms has the right to desist."

"Let us leave off from this now, O Cu Chulainn," said Ferdiad.

"Aye, let us leave off, if the time has come," answered Cu Chulainn.

So they ceased; and they threw their arms from them into the hands of their charioteers.

Thereupon each of them went toward the other in the middle of the ford, and each of them put his hand on the other's neck and gave him three kisses in remembrance of his fellowship and friendship. Their horses were in one and the same paddock that night, and their charioteers at one and the same fire; and their charioteers made ready a litter-bed of fresh rushes for them with pillows for wounded men on them. Then came healing and curing folk to heal and cure them, and they laid healing herbs and grasses and a curing charm on their cuts and stabs, their gashes and many wounds. Of every healing herb and grass and curing charm that was brought from the fairy-mounds of Erin to Cu Chulainn and was applied to the cuts and stabs, to the gashes and many wounds of Cu Chulainn, a like portion thereof he sent across the ford westward to Ferdiad, to put on his wounds and his pools of gore, so that the men of Erin should not have it to say, should Ferdiad fall at his hands, it was more than his share of care had been given to him.

Of every food and of every savory, soothing and strong drink that was brought by the men of Erin to Ferdiad, a like portion thereof he sent over the ford northwards to Cu Chulainn; for the purveyors of Ferdiad were more numerous than the purveyors of Cu Chulainn. All the men of Erin were purveyors to Ferdiad, to the end that he might keep Cu Chulainn off from them. But only the inhabitants of Mag Breg were purveyors to Cu Chulainn. They were wont to come daily, that is, every night, to converse with him.

They bided there that night. Early on the morrow they arose and went to the ford of combat.

"To what weapons shall we resort on this day, O Ferdiad?" asked Cu Chulainn.

"Thine is the choosing of weapons till night-time," Ferdiad made answer, "because it was I had my choice of weapons yesterday."

"Let us take, then," said Cu Chulainn, "to our great, well-tempered lances to-day, for we think that the thrusting will bring nearer the decisive battle to-day than did the casting of yesterday. Let our horses be brought to us and our chariots yoked, to the end that we engage in combat over our horses and chariots on this day."

"Good, let us do so," Ferdiad assented.

Thereupon they took full-firm broad-shields on them for that day. They took to their great, well-tempered lances on that day. Either of them began to pierce and to drive, to throw and to press down the other, from early morning's twilight till the hour of evening's close. If it were the wont of birds in flight to fly through the bodies of men, they could have passed through their bodies on that day and carried away pieces of blood and flesh through their wounds and their sores into the clouds and the air all around. And when the hour of evening's close was come, their horses were spent and the drivers were wearied, and they themselves, the hero warriors of valor, were exhausted.

"Let us give over now, O Ferdiad," said Cu Chulainn, "for our horses are spent and our drivers tired, and when they are exhausted, why should we too not be exhausted?" And in this manner he spoke, and uttered these words at that place:

> We need not our chariots break—
> This, a struggle fit for giants.
> Place the hobbles on the steeds,
> Now that the din of arms is over!

"Yea, we will cease, if the time has come," replied Ferdiad. They ceased then. They threw their arms away from them into the hands of their charioteers. Each of them came towards his fellow. Each laid his hand on the other's neck and gave him three kisses. Their horses were in the one pen that night, and their charioteers at one fire. . . . etc.

They abode there that night. Early on the morrow they arose and repaired to the ford of combat. Cu Chulainn marked an evil mien and a dark mood that day beyond every other on Ferdiad.

"It is evil thou appearest to-day, O Ferdiad," said Cu Chulainn; "thy hair has become dark to-day, and thine eye has grown drowsy and thine upright form and thy features and thy gait have gone from thee!"

"Truly not for fear nor for dread of thee has that happened to me to-day," answered Ferdiad; "for there is not in Erin this day a warrior I could not repel!"

"Alas! O Ferdiad," said Cu Chulainn, "a pity it is for thee to oppose thy fosterbrother and comrade and friend on the counsel of any woman in the world!"

"A pity it is, O Cu Chulainn," Ferdiad responded. "But, should I part without a struggle with thee, I should be in ill repute for-ever with Medb and with the nobles of the four great provinces of Erin."

"A pity it is, O Ferdiad," said Cu Chulainn; "not on the counsel of all the men and women of the world would I desert thee or would do thee harm. And almost would it make a clot of gore of my heart to be combating with thee!"

And Cu Chulainn lamented and moaned, and he spoke these words and Ferdiad responded:

Cu Chulainn.	Ferdiad, ah, if it be thou, Well I know thou art doomed to die! To have gone at a woman's hest, Forced to fight thy sworn comrade!
Ferdiad.	O Cu Chulainn—wise decree— Loyal champion, hero true, Each man is constrained to go Beneath the sod that hides his grave!
Cu Chulainn.	Finnabair, Medb's fair daughter, Stately maiden though she be, Not for love they'll give to thee, But to prove thy kingly might!
Ferdiad.	Proved was my might long since, Thou Cu of gentle spirit. Of one braver I've not heard, Till to-day I have not found!
Cu Chulainn.	Thou art he provoked this fight, Son of Daman, Daire's son, To have gone at woman's word, Swords to cross with thine old friend!
Ferdiad.	Should we then unfought depart, Brothers though we are, bold Hound, Ill would be my word and fame With Ailill and Cruachan's Medb!
Cu Chulainn.	Food has not yet passed his lips, Nay, nor has he yet been born, Son of king or blameless queen, For whom I would work thee harm!
Ferdiad.	Culann's Hound, with floods of deeds, Medb, not thou, hath us betrayed; Fame and victory thou shalt have; Not on thee we lay our fault!
Cu Chulainn.	Clotted gore is my stout heart, Near I am parted from my soul; Wrongful it is—with hosts of deeds— Ferdiad, dear, to fight with thee!

After this colloquy Ferdiad spoke. "How much soever thou findest fault with me to-day," said Ferdiad, "for my ill-boding mien and evil doing, it will be as an offset to my prowess." And then he said, "To what weapons shall we resort to-day?"

"With thyself is the choice of weapons to-day until night-time come," replied Cu Chulainn, "for it was I that chose on the day gone by."

"Let us resort, then," said Ferdiad, "to our heavy, hard-smiting swords this day, for we trust that the smiting each other will bring us nearer to the decision of battle to-day than did our piercing each other yesterday."

"Let us go, then, by all means," responded Cu Chulainn.

Then they took two full-great long-shields upon them for that day. They turned to their heavy, hard-smiting swords. Each of them fell to strike and to hew, to lay low and cut down, to slay and undo his fellow, till as large as the head of a month-old child was each lump and each cut, each clutter and each clot of gore that each of them took from the shoulders and thighs and shoulder-blades of the other.

Each of them was engaged in smiting the other in this way from the twilight of the early morning till the hour of evening's close. "Let us leave off from this now, O Cu Chulainn!" said Ferdiad.

"Aye, let us leave off if the hour is come," said Cu Chulainn.

They parted then, and threw their arms away from them into the hands of their charioteers. Though in comparison it had been the meeting of two happy, blithe, cheerful, joyful men, their parting that night was of two that were sad, sorrowful, and full of suffering. They parted without a kiss, a blessing, or any other sign of friendship, and their servants disarmed the steeds and the heroes; no healing nor curing herbs were sent from Cu Chulainn to Ferdiad that night, and no food nor drink was brought from Ferdiad to him. Their horses were not in the same paddock that night. Their charioteers were not at the same fire.

They passed that night there. It was then that Ferdiad arose early on the morrow and went alone to the ford of combat, and dauntless and vengeful and mighty was the man that went thither that day, Ferdiad the son of Daman. For he knew that that day would be the decisive day of the battle and combat; and he knew that one or the other of them would fall there that day, or that

they both would fall. It was then he donned his battle-garb of
battle and fight and combat. He put his silken, glossy trews with
its border of speckled gold next to his white skin. Over this,
outside, he put his brown-leathern, well-sewed kilt. Outside of
this he put a huge, goodly flagstone, the size of a millstone, the
shallow stone of adamant which he had brought from Africa, and
which neither points nor edges could pierce. He put his solid,
very deep, iron kilt of twice molten iron over the huge goodly
flag as large as a millstone, through fear and dread of the *gae
bulga* on that day. About his head he put his crested war-cap of
battle and fight and combat, whereon were forty carbuncle-gems
beautifully adorning it and studded with red-enamel and crystal
and rubies and with shining stones of the Eastern world. His
angry, fierce-striking spear he seized in his right hand. On his
left side he hung his curved battle-sword, which would cut a hair
against the stream with its keenness and sharpness, with its gold
pommel and its rounded hilt of red gold. On the arch-slope of his
back he slung his massive, fine, buffalo shield of a warrior whereon
were fifty bosses, wherein a boar could be shown in each of its
bosses, apart from the great central boss of red gold. Ferdiad
performed divers brilliant manifold marvellous feats on high that
day, unlearned of any one before, neither from foster-mother
nor from foster-father, neither from Scathach nor from Uathach
nor from Aife, but he found them of himself that day in the face
of Cu Chulainn.

Cu Chulainn likewise came to the ford, and he beheld the various,
brilliant, manifold, wonderful feats that Ferdiad performed on
high. "Thou seest yonder, O Loeg my master, the divers bright,
numerous, marvellous feats that Ferdiad performs one after the
other, and therefore, O Loeg," cried Cu Chulainn, "if defeat be
my lot this day, do thou prick me on and taunt me and speak evil
to me, so that the more my spirit and anger shall rise in me. If,
however, before me his defeat takes place, say thou so to me and
praise me and speak me fair, to the end that greater may be my
courage."

"It certainly shall be done so, if need be, O Cucuc," Loeg
answered.

Then Cu Chulainn, too, girded on his war-harness of battle and
fight and combat about him, and performed all kinds of splendid,

manifold, marvellous feats on high that day which he had not learned from anyone before, neither with Scathach nor with Uathach nor with Aife.

Ferdiad observed those feats, and he knew they would be plied against him in turn.

"What weapons shall we resort to to-day?" asked Cu Chulainn.

"With thee is the choice of weapons till night-time," Ferdiad responded.

"Let us go to the Feat of the Ford, then," said Cu Chulainn.

"Aye, let us do so," answered Ferdiad. Albeit Ferdiad spoke that, he deemed it the most grievous thing whereto he could go, for he knew that Cu Chulainn used to destroy every hero and every battle-soldier who fought with him in the Feat of the Ford.

Great indeed was the deed that was done on the ford that day. The two horses, the two champions, the two chariot-fighters of the west of Europe, the two bright torches of valor of the Gael, the two hands of dispensing favor and of giving rewards and jewels and treasures in the west of the northern world, the two veterans of skill and the two keys of bravery of the Gael, the man for quelling the variance and discord of Connacht, the man for guarding the cattle and herds of Ulster, to be brought together in an encounter as from afar, set to slay or to kill each other, through the sowing of dissension and the incitement of Ailill and Medb.

Each of them was busy hurling at the other in those deeds of arms from early morning's gloaming till the middle of noon. When mid-day came, the rage of the men became wild, and each drew nearer to the other.

Thereupon Cu Chulainn gave one spring once from the bank of the ford till he stood upon the boss of Ferdiad son of Daman's shield, seeking to reach his head and to strike it from above over the rim of the shield. Straightway Ferdiad gave the shield a blow with his left elbow, so that Cu Chulainn went from him like a bird onto the brink of the ford. Again Cu Chulainn sprang from the brink of the ford, so that he lighted upon the boss of Ferdiad's shield, that he might reach his head and strike it over the rim of the shield from above. Ferdiad gave the shield a thrust with his left knee, so that Cu Chulainn went from him like an infant onto the bank of the ford.

Loeg espied that. "Woe, then, O Cu Chulainn," cried Loeg, "it seems to me the battle-warrior that is against thee hath shaken thee as a woman shakes her child. He has washed thee as a cup is washed in the tub. He hath ground thee as a mill grinds soft malt. He hath pierced thee as a tool bores through an oak. He hath bound thee as the bindweed binds the trees. He hath pounced on thee as a hawk pounces on little birds, so that no more hast thou right or title or claim to valor or skill in arms till the very day of doom and of life, thou little imp of an elf-man!"

Thereat for the third time Cu Chulainn arose with the speed of the wind, and the swiftness of a swallow, and the dash of a dragon, and the strength of a lion into the clouds of the air, till he alighted on the boss of the shield of Ferdiad son of Daman, so as to reach his head that he might strike it from above over the rim of his shield. Then it was that the warrior gave the shield a violent powerful shake, so that Cu Chulainn flew from it into the middle of the ford, the same as if he had not sprung at all.

It was then the first distortion of Cu Chulainn took place, so that a swelling and inflation filled him like breath in a bladder, until he made a dreadful, many-colored, wonderful bow of himself, so that as big as a giant or a sea-man was the hugely-brave warrior towering directly over Ferdiad.

Such was the closeness of the combat they made, that their heads encountered above and their feet below and their hands in the middle over the rims and bosses of their shields.

Such was the closeness of the combat they made, that their shields burst and split from their rims to their centers.

Such was the closeness of the combat they made, that their spears bent and turned and shivered from their tips to their rivets.

Such was the closeness of the combat they made, that the boccanach and the bannanach (the puck-faced sprites and the white-faced sprites) and the spirits of the glens and the uncanny beings of the air screamed from the rims of their shields and from the guards of their swords and from the tips of their spears.

Such was the closeness of the combat they made, that the steeds of the Gael broke loose affrighted and plunging with madness and fury, so that their chains and their shackles, their traces and their tethers snapped, and the women and children and the undersized, the weak and the madmen among the men of Erin broke out through the camp southwestward.

At that time they were at the edge-feat of the swords. It was then Ferdiad caught Cu Chulainn in an unguarded moment, and he gave him a thrust with his tusk-hilted blade, so that he buried it in his breast, and his blood fell into his belt, till the ford became crimsoned with the clotted blood from the battle-warrior's body. Cu Chulainn endured it not under Ferdiad's attack, with his death-bringing, heavy blows, and his long strokes and his mighty middle slashes at him.

Then Cu Chulainn bethought him of his friends from the fairy-mound and of his mighty folk who would come and defend him and of his scholars to protect him, whenever he would be hard-pressed in the combat. It was then that Dolb and Indolb arrived to help and to succor their friend, namely Cu Chulainn, and one of them went on either side of him and they smote Ferdiad, the three of them, and Ferdiad did not perceive the men from the fairy-mound. Then it was that Ferdiad felt the onset of the three together smiting his shield against him, and thence he called to mind that, when they were with Scathach and Uathach, learning together, Dolb and Indolb used to come to help Cu Chulainn out of every stress wherein he was.

Ferdiad spoke; "Not alike are our foster-brothership and our comradeship, O Cu Chulainn."

"How so, then?" asked Cu Chulainn.

"Thy friends of the fairy-folk have succored thee, and thou didst not disclose them to me before," said Ferdiad.

"Not easy for me were that," answered Cu Chulainn, "for if the magic veil be once revealed to one of the sons of Mil, none of the Tuatha De Danann will have power to practice concealment or magic. And why complainest thou here, O Ferdiad?" said Cu Chulainn; "thou hast a horn skin whereby to multiply feats and deeds of arms on me, and thou hast not shown me how it is closed or how it is opened."

Then it was they displayed all their skill and secret cunning to one another, so that there was not a secret of either of them kept from the other except the *gae bulga*, which was Cu Chulainn's alone. Howbeit, when the fairy friends found Cu Chulainn had been wounded, each of them inflicted three great, heavy wounds on Ferdiad. It was then that Ferdiad made a cast to the right, so that he slew Dolb with that goodly cast. Then followed the two woundings and the two throws that overcame him, till Ferdiad made a second throw toward Cu Chulainn's left, and with that throw he stretched low and killed Indolb dead on the floor of the ford. Hence it is that the story-teller sang the verse:

> Why is this called Ferdiad's Ford,
> Even though three men on it fell?
> None the less it washed their spoils—
> It is Dolb's and Indolb's Ford!

What need to relate further! When the devoted, equally great sires and warriors, and the hard, battle-victorious wild champions that fought for Cu Chulainn had fallen, it greatly strengthened the courage of Ferdiad, so that he gave two blows for every blow of Cu Chulainn's. When Loeg mac Riangabra saw his lord being overcome by the crushing blows of the champion who oppressed him, Loeg began to stir up and rebuke Cu Chulainn, in such a way that a swelling and inflation filled Cu Chulainn from the top to the ground, so that he made a dreadful, wonderful bow of himself like a rainbow in a shower of rain, and he made for Ferdiad with the violence of a dragon or with the strength of a blood-hound.

And Cu Chulainn called for the *gae bulga* from Loeg mac Riangabra. This was its nature: in the stream it was made ready, and from between the fork of the foot it was cast; the wound of a single spear it gave when it entered the body, and thirty barbs it had when it opened, and it could not be drawn out of a man's flesh till the flesh had been cut about it.

Thereupon Loeg came forward to the brink of the river and to the place where the fresh water was dammed, and the *gae bulga* was sharpened and set in position. He filled the pool and stopped the stream and checked the tide of the ford. Ferdiad's charioteer watched the work, for Ferdiad had said to him early in the morning, "Now, gillie, do thou hold back Loeg from me to-day, and I will hold back Cu Chulainn from thee and thy men forever."

"This is a pity," said Ferdiad's charioteer; "no match for him am I; for a man to combat a hundred is he amongst the men of Erin, and that am I not. Still, however slight his help, it shall not come to his lord past me."

Thus were the charioteers: two brothers were they, namely, Id mac Riangabra and Loeg mac Riangabra. As for Id mac Riangabra, he was then watching his brother thus making the dam till he filled the pools and went to set the *gae bulga* downwards. It was then that Id went up and released the stream and opened the dam and undid the fixing of the *gae bulga*. Cu Chulainn became deep purple and red all over when he saw the setting undone of the *gae bulga*. He sprang from the top of the ground so that he alighted light and quick on the rim of Ferdiad's shield. Ferdiad gave a strong shake of the shield, so that he hurled Cu Chulainn the measure of nine paces out to the westward over the ford. Then Cu Chulainn called and shouted to Loeg to set about preparing the *gae bulga* for him. Loeg hastened to the pool and began the work. Id ran and opened the dam and released it before the stream. Loeg sprang at his brother and they grappled on the spot. Loeg threw Id and handled him sorely, for he was loath to use weapons on him. Ferdiad pursued Cu Chulainn westwards over the ford. Cu Chulainn sprang on the rim of the shield. Ferdiad shook the shield, so that he sent Cu Chulainn the space of nine paces eastwards over the ford. Cu Chulainn called and shouted to Loeg and bade him stop the stream and make ready the spear. Loeg attempted to come nigh it, but Ferdiad's charioteer opposed him, so that Loeg turned upon him and left him on the sedgy bottom of the ford. He gave him many a heavy blow with clenched fist on the face and countenance, so that he broke his mouth and his nose and put out his eyes and his sight, and left him lying wounded and full of terror. And forthwith Loeg left him and filled the pool and checked the stream and stilled the noise of the river's voice, and set in position the *gae bulga*. After some time Ferdiad's charioteer arose from his death-cloud, and set his hands on his face and countenance, and he looked away towards the ford of combat and saw Loeg fixing the *gae bulga*. He ran again to the pool and made a breach in the dike quickly and speedily, so that the river burst out in its booming, bounding, bellying, bank-breaking billows making its own wild course. Cu Chulainn became purple and red all over when he saw the setting of the *gae bulga* had been disturbed, and for the third time he sprang from the top of the ground and alighted on the edge of Ferdiad's shield, so as to strike him over the shield from above.

Ferdiad gave a blow with his left knee against the leather of the bare shield, so that Cu Chulainn was thrown into the waves of the ford.

Thereupon Ferdiad gave three severe woundings to Cu Chulainn. Cu Chulainn cried and shouted loudly to Loeg to make ready the *gae bulga* for him. Loeg attempted to get near it, but Ferdiad's charioteer prevented him. Then Loeg grew very wroth at his brother, and he made a spring at him, and he closed his long, full-valiant hands over him, so that he quickly threw him to the ground and straightway bound him. And then he went from him quickly and courageously, so that he filled the pool and stayed the stream and set the *gae bulga*. And he cried out to Cu Chulainn that it was ready, for it was not to be discharged without a quick word of warning before it. Hence it is that Loeg cried out:

> Ware! beware the *gae bulga*,
> Battle-winning Culann's Hound! and the rest.

And he sent it to Cu Chulainn along the stream.

Thus it was that Cu Chulainn let fly the white *gae bulga* from the fork of his irresistible right foot. Ferdiad began to defend the ford against Cu Chulainn, so that the noble Cu Chulainn arose with the swiftness of a swallow and the wail of the storm-play in the rafters of the firmament, so that he laid hold of the breadth of his two feet of the bed of the ford, in spite of the champion. Ferdiad prepared for the feat according to the report thereof. He lowered his shield, so that the spear went over its edge into the watery, water-cold river. And he looked at Cu Chulainn, and he saw all his various venomous feats made ready, and he knew not to which of them he should first give answer, whether to the " Fist's breast-spear," or to the " Wild shield's broad-spear," or to the " Short spear from the middle of the palm," or to the white *gae bulga* over the fair, watery river.

When Ferdiad saw that his gillie had been thrown and heard the *gae bulga* called for, he thrust his shield down to protect the lower part of his body. Cu Chulainn gripped the short spear that was in his hand, cast it off the palm of his hand over the rim of the shield and over the edge of the corselet and hornskin, so that its farther half was visible after piercing Ferdiad's heart in his bosom. Ferdiad gave a thrust of his shield upwards to protect the upper part of his body, though it was help that came too late. Loeg sent the *gae bulga* down the stream, and Cu Chulainn caught it in the fork of his foot, and when Ferdiad raised his shield Cu Chulainn threw the *gae bulga* as far as he could cast underneath at Ferdiad, so that it passed through the strong, thick, iron apron of wrought iron, and broke in three parts the huge, goodly stone the size of a millstone, so that it cut its way through the body's protection into him, till every joint and every limb was filled with its barbs.

"Ah, that blow suffices," sighed Ferdiad. "I am fallen of that! But, yet one thing more: mightily didst thou drive with thy right *foot*. And it was not fair of thee for me not to fall by thy *hand*." And he yet spoke and uttered these words:

> O Cu of grand feats,
> Unfairly I am slain!
> Thy guilt clings to me;
> My blood falls on thee!
>
> No meed for the wretch
> Who treads treason's gap,
> Now weak is my voice;
> Ah, gone is my bloom!
>
> My ribs' armor bursts,
> My heart is all gore;
> I battled not well;
> I am smitten, O Cu!
>
> Unfair, side by side,
> To come to the ford.
> 'Gainst my noble ward
> Hath Medb turned my hand!
>
> There will come rooks and crows
> To gaze on my arms,
> To eat flesh and blood.
> A tale, Cu, for thee!

Thereupon Cu Chulainn hastened towards Ferdiad and clasped his two arms about him, and bore him with all his arms and his armor and his dress northwards over the ford, so that it would be with his face to the north of the ford, in Ulster, the triumph took place and not to the west of the ford with the men of Erin. Cu Chulainn laid Ferdiad there on the ground, and a cloud and a faint and a swoon came over Cu Chulainn there by the head of Ferdiad. Loeg espied it and the men of Erin all arose for the attack upon him.

"Come, O Cucuc," cried Loeg; "arise now from thy trance, for the men of Erin will now come to attack us, and it is not single combat they will allow us, now that Ferdiad son of Daman son of Daire is fallen by thee."

"What availeth it me to arise, O gillie," said Cu Chulainn, "now that this one is fallen by my hand?" In this wise the gillie spoke, and he uttered these words and Cu Chulainn responded:

Loeg.	Now arise, O Emain's Hound; Now most fits thee courage high. Ferdiad hast thou thrown—of hosts— God's fate! How thy fight was hard!
Cu Chulainn.	What avails me courage now? I'm oppressed with rage and grief, For the deed that I have done On his body sworded sore.
Loeg.	It becomes thee not to weep; Fitter for thee to exult! That red-speared one thee hath left Plaintful, wounded, steeped in gore!
Cu Chulainn.	Even had he cleaved my leg, And one hand had severed, too; Woe, that Ferdiad—who rode steeds— Shall not ever be in life!
Loeg.	Liefer far what has come to pass, To the maidens of the Red Branch; He to die, thou to remain; They grudge not that ye should part!
Cu Chulainn.	From the day I left Cooley, Seeking high and splendid Medb, Carnage has she had—with fame— Of her warriors whom I've slain!
Loeg.	Thou hast had no sleep in peace, In pursuit of thy great Cattle-Raid; Though thy troop was few and small, Oft thou wouldst rise at early morn!

Cu Chulainn began to lament and bemoan Ferdiad, and he spoke these words:

"Alas, O Ferdiad," said he, "it was thine ill fortune thou didst not take counsel with any of those that knew my real deeds of valor and arms, before we met in clash of battle!

"Unhappy for thee that Loeg mac Riangabra did not make thee blush in regard to our comradeship!

"Unhappy for thee that the truly faithful warning of Fergus thou did not take.

"Unhappy for thee that dear, trophied, triumphant, battle-victorious Conall counselled thee not in regard to our comradeship!

"For those men would not have spoken in obedience to the messages or desires or orders or false words of promise of the fair-haired woman of Connacht.

"For well do those men know that there will not be born a being that will perform deeds so tremendous and so great among the Connachtmen as I, till the very day of doom and of ever-lasting life, whether at handling of shield and buckler, at plying of spear and sword, at playing at draughts and chess, at driving of steeds and chariots."

And he spoke these warm words, sadly, sorrowfully in praise of Ferdiad:

"There shall not be found the hand of a hero that will wound warrior's flesh, like the cloud-colored Ferdiad!

"There shall not be heard from the gap of danger the cry of the red-mouthed Badb to the winged shade-speckled flocks of phantoms!

"There shall not be one that will contend for Cruachan that will obtain covenants equal to thine, till the very day of doom and of life henceforward, O red-cheeked son of Daman!" said Cu Chulainn.

Then it was that Cu Chulainn arose and stood over Ferdiad. "Ah, Ferdiad," said Cu Chulainn, "greatly have the men of Erin deceived and abandoned thee, to bring thee to contend and do battle with me. For no easy thing is it to contend and do battle with me on the Cattle-Raid of Cooley! And yet never before have I found combat that was so sore or distressed me so as thy combat, save the combat with Oenfer Aife, mine own son." [1] Thus he spoke and he uttered these words:

[1] See p. 172.

Ah, Ferdiad, betrayed to death,
Our last meeting, oh, how sad!
Thou to die, I to remain.
Ever sad our long farewell!

When we over yonder dwelt
With our Scathach, steadfast, true,
This we thought, that till the end of time,
Our friendship never would end!

Dear to me thy noble blush;
Dear thy comely, perfect form;
Dear thine eye, blue-grey and clear;
Dear thy wisdom and thy speech!

Never strode to rending fight,
Never wrath and manhood held,
Nor slung shield across broad back,
One like thee, Daman's red son!

Never have I met till now,
Since I slew Aife's only son,
One thy peer in deeds of arms,
Never have I found, Ferdiad!

Finnabair, Medb's daughter fair,
Beauteous, lovely though she be,
As a gad round sand or stones,
She was shown to thee, Ferdiad!

Then Cu Chulainn turned to gaze on Ferdiad. "Ah, my master
Loeg," cried Cu Chulainn, "now strip Ferdiad and take his armor
and garments off him, that I may see the brooch for the sake of
which he entered on the combat and fight with me."

Loeg came up and stripped Ferdiad. He took his armor off him
and he saw the brooch and he placed the brooch in Cu Chulainn's
hand, and Cu Chulainn began to lament and mourn over Ferdiad,
and he spoke these words:

Alas, golden brooch;
Ferdiad of the hosts,
O good smiter, strong,
Victorious thy hand!

Thy hair blond and curled,
A wealth fair and grand.
Thy soft, leaf-shaped belt
Around thee till death!

Our comradeship dear;
Thy noble eye's gleam;
Thy golden-rimmed shield;
Thy sword, worth treasures!

Thy white-silver torque
Thy noble arm binds.
Thy chess-board worth wealth;
Thy fair, ruddy cheek!

To fall by my hand,
I own was not just!
It was no noble fight!
Alas, golden brooch!

Thy death at Cu's hand
Was dire, O dear calf!
Unequal the shield
Thou hadst for the strife!

Unfair was our fight,
Our woe and defeat!
Fair the great chief;
Each host overcome
And put under foot!
Alas, golden brooch!

"Come, O Loeg, my master," cried Cu Chulainn; "now cut open Ferdiad and take the *gae bulga* out, because I may not be without my weapons."

Loeg came and cut open Ferdiad and he took the *gae bulga* out of him. And Cu Chulainn saw his weapons bloody and red-stained by the side of Ferdiad, and he uttered these words:

O Ferdiad, in gloom we meet.
Thee I see both red and pale.
I myself with unwashed arms;
Thou liest in thy bed of gore!

Were we yonder in the East,
With Scathach and our Uathach,
There would not be pallid lips
Twixt us two, and arms of strife!

Thus spoke Scathach trenchantly,
Words of warning, strong and stern:
"Go ye all to furious fight;
German, blue-eyed, fierce will come!"

Unto Ferdiad then I spoke,
And to Lugaid generous,
To the son of fair Baetan,
German we would go to meet!

We came to the battle-rock,
Over Loch Linn Formait's shore,
And four hundred men we brought
From the Isles of the Athissech!

As I and Ferdiad brave stood
At the gate of German's fort,
I slew Rinn the son of Nel;
He slew Ruad son of Fornel!

Ferdiad slew upon the slope
Blath, son of Colba Red-sword.
Lugaid, fierce and swift, then slew
Mugairne of the Tyrrhen Sea!

I slew, after going in,
Four times fifty grim, wild men.
Ferdiad killed—a furious horde—
Dam Dremenn and Dam Dilenn!

We laid waste shrewd German's fort
O'er the broad bespangled sea.
German we brought home alive
To our Scathach of broad shield!

Then our famous nurse made fast
Our blood-pact of amity,
That our angers should not rise
Amongst the tribe of noble Elg!

Sad the morn, a day in March,
Which struck down weak Daman's son.
Woe is me, the friend is fallen
Whom I pledged in red blood's draught!

Were it there I saw thy death,
Midst the great Greeks' warrior-bands,
I'd not live on after thee,
But together we would die!

Woe, what us befell therefrom,
Us, dear Scathach's fosterlings,
Sorely wounded me, stiff with gore,
Thee to die the death for ever!

> Woe, what us befell therefrom,
> Us, dear Scathach's fosterlings,
> Thee in death, me, strong, alive.
> Valor is an angry strife!

"Good, O Cucuc," said Loeg, "let us leave this ford now; too long are we here!"

"Aye, let us leave it, O my master Loeg," replied Cu Chulainn. "But every combat and battle I have fought seems a game and a sport to me compared with the combat and battle of Ferdiad." Thus he spoke, and he uttered these words:

> All was play, all was sport,
> Till Ferdiad came to the ford!
>   One task for both of us,
>   Equal our reward.
>   Our kind gentle nurse
>   Chose him over all!
>
> All was play, all was sport,
> Till Ferdiad came to the ford!
>   One our life, one our feat,
>   One our skill in arms.
>   Two shields gave Scathach
>   To Ferdiad and me!
>
> All was play, all was sport,
> Till Ferdiad came to the ford!
>   Dear the shaft of gold
>   I smote on the ford.
>   Bull-chief of tribes,
>   Braver he than all!
>
> Only games and only sport,
> Till Ferdiad came to the ford!
> Loved Ferdiad seemed to me,
> After me would live for ever!
> Yesterday, a mountain's size—
> He is but a shade to-day!
>
> Only games and only sport,
> Till Ferdiad came to the ford!
> Lion, furious, flaming, fierce;
> Swollen wave that wrecks like doom!
>
> Three things countless on the Cattle-Raid
> Which have fallen by my hand:
> Hosts of cattle, men and steeds,
> I have slaughtered on all sides!

Though the hosts were great,
That came out of Cruachan wild,
More than a third and less than half,
Slew I in my direful sport!

Never trod in battle's ring;
Banba nursed not on her breast;
Never sprang from sea or land,
King's son that had larger fame!

Thus far the Combat of Ferdiad with Cu Chulainn and the Tragic Death of Ferdiad.

THE TRAGIC DEATH OF CU ROI MAC DAIRI

"The Tragic Death of Cu Roi mac Dairi" is one of a group of sagas which belong to the oldest parts of the Ulster cycle and which center around Cu Roi mac Dairi, a half demonic personage with magic powers, who, according to tradition, resided in the south of Ireland. He is associated especially with Kerry, where the remains of a prehistoric fortification in the Slemish Mountains are still known as Caher Conree, "Cu Roi's City." It is not surprising that the composers of the Ulster cycle should conceive the idea of representing their beloved hero, Cu Chulainn, as victorious over this great southern champion. Cu Chulainn, being only a beardless youth, usually wins by strategem rather than by open warfare. The story told in "The Tragic Death of Cu Roi mac Dairi" must have been widespread; there are numerous versions of it in early Irish and its fame even spread across the channel into Wales.

Why did the men of Ulster slay Cu Roi mac Dairi? Easy to say. Because of Blathnat who was carried off from the siege of the Fir Falgae, because of the three cows of Iuchna and the "three men of Ochain," that is, the little birds that used to be on the ears of Iuchna's cows. And a cauldron was carried off with the cows. This cauldron was their calf. Thirty cows' milking was the capacity of the cauldron, and the full of it was milked from them every time while the birds were singing to them. Hence said Cu Chulainn in the Siaburcharpat: [1]

> There was a cauldron in the fort:
> The calf of the three cows,
> Thirty cows within its gullet,
> That was its portion.
>
> They used to go to that cauldron,
> Delightful was the struggle,
> Nor did they come away from it again
> Until they left it full.
>
> There was much gold and silver in it,
> It was a goodly find.
> I carried off that cauldron
> With the daughter of the king.

[1] *I.e.*, "The Phantom Chariot of Cu Chulainn," p. 347.

Cu Roi mac Dairi went with the men of Ulster then to the siege, and they did not recognize him, that is, they called him the man in the grey mantle. Every time a head was brought out of the fort, "Who slew that man?" Conchobar would say. "I and the man in the grey mantle," each answered in turn.

When, however, they were dividing the spoil, they did not give Cu Roi a share, for justice was not granted him. He then ran in among the cows and gathered them before him, collected the birds in his girdle, thrust the woman under one of his armpits, and went from them with the cauldron on his back. And none among the men of Ulster was able to get speech with him save Cu Chulainn alone. Cu Roi turned upon the latter, thrust him into the earth to his armpits, cropped his hair with his sword, rubbed cow-dung into his head, and then went home.

After that Cu Chulainn was a whole year avoiding the Ulstermen. One day, however, when he was on the peaks of Bairche, he saw a great flock of black birds coming towards him over the sea. He killed one of them forthwith. After that he killed one of the flock in every land he passed through until he came to Srub Brain (Raven's Beak) in the west of Ireland, that is, the black bird's head which he cut off. Srub Brain is named therefrom. This took place west of Cu Roi's stronghold; and then Cu Chulainn knew that it was he who had brought him to shame; and he held converse with the woman Blathnat, for he had loved her even before she was brought over sea; she was a daughter of Iuchna king of the Fir Falgae (Men of Falga), that is, they were a "sea-wall" in the islands of the sea. He made a tryst with her again in the west on the night of Samain. Moreover, a province of the Erainn set forth to go with Cu Chulainn. It was on that day Blathnat advised Cu Roi that he should build a splendid enclosure for his stronghold of every pillar-stone standing or lying in Ireland. The Clan Dedad set out one day for the building of the stronghold, so that he was all alone in his fortress on that day. There was an agreement between Blathnat and Cu Chulainn, namely, to pour the milk of Iuchna's cows down the river in the direction of the Ulstermen, so that the river might be white when she was bathing Cu Roi. So it was done. It was poured down to them, and the river then became "Finnglas (White Flecked)."

She then began lousing his head in front of the stronghold.

"Come into the stronghold," said she, "and get washed before the hosts come back with their burdens of stones."

Just then he lifted up his head and saw the host of Ulster coming towards him along the glen, both foot and horse.

"Who are those yonder, woman?" said Cu Roi.

"Thy people," said Blathnat, "with the stones and oak for building the stronghold."

"If they are oaks, 'tis swiftly they travel; it is a triumph, if they are stones," said Cu Roi.

He raised his head again and continued to scan them.

"Who are these?" said he.

"Herds of kine and cattle," said she.

> If they are cattle, so that they are cattle,
> They are not herds of lean kine.
> There is a little man brandishing a sword
> On the back of every cow.

Thereupon Cu Roi went inside, and the woman bathed him, and she bound his hair to the bedposts and rails, and took his sword out of its scabbard and threw open the stronghold. He heard naught, however, until the Ulstermen had filled the house, and had fallen upon him. He rose up straightway against them, and slew a hundred of them with kicks and blows of his fists. An attendant who was within rose up against them and slew thirty of them. Thereof it was sung:

> Though the attendant of the prince,
> He was skilled at the battle-game,
> He slew thirty armed men,
> Then he let himself be slain.

Senfiacal first came at the cry, whereof it was said:

> Senfiacal came first;
> He slew a hundred men of the host.
> Though great was the might of his combat,
> He got his death through Cu Chulainn.

Then Cairbre Cuanach came upon them:

> Cairbre Cuanach came upon them.
> He slew a hundred men, a mighty encounter,
> He would have grappled with Conchobar,
> If the monster-abounding sea had not drowned him.

That is to say, when he was contending with Conchobar, he saw his stronghold in flames to the north of the sea. So he went into the sea to save it. His swim was great, and he was drowned there.

> The fight of Eochaid son of Daire
> From the promontory to the glen.
> He slew a hundred men, it was a great achievement.
> It was to avenge his good king.

Then it was the Clan Dedad cast from them every pillar-stone which was standing or lying in Ireland, when they heard the shouting, and came up to the slaughter around the fortress, whereof it was said:

> After that came the Clan Dedad
> To seek their king,
> Five score and three hundred,
> Ten hundred and two thousand.

When, however, they were slaying one another by the fortress, and Cu Chulainn had cut off Cu Roi's head, and the fortress was aflame, Ferchertne, Cu Roi's poet, was by his horses in the glen, and he said:

> Who is the youth that fights
> By the side of Cu Roi's fortress?
> If Daire's son were alive,
> It would not burn.

Fer Becrach, however, Cu Roi's charioteer, had made submission to Cairbre son of Conchobar, and he went into his chariot with him. He drove the horses against the rock, and the rock crushed both horses and men, whereof it was said:

> Fer Becrach . . .
> Perchance it is no lie thou sayest?
> He bore Cairbre son of Conchobar
> Under the bitter sea waves.

Then Ferchertne came. "Art not thou Ferchertne?" said Conchobar.

"I am, indeed," said he.

"Was Cu Roi kind to thee?" said Conchobar.

"He was kind, indeed," said he.

"Tell us somewhat of his bounty."

"I cannot now," said he. "My heart is sad after the slaying of my king, for mine own hand shall slay me, if no one else slay me!" Then Ferchertne the poet said: [1]

.   .   .   .

"That was a kingly gift," said Conchobar.

"It was little from him," said Ferchertne.

"Where is Blathnat?" said he.

"She is here," said the youths; "but it was only by striking off Cu Roi's head that we obtained her deliverance."

It was after that she was crushed against the rock, that is, the promontory of Cenn Bera. For the man Ferchertne made a rush towards her and caught her between his arms, so that her ribs broke in her back; and he hurled her down the cliff before him, so that the rock crushed them both, and their grave is on the strand under the rock. Hence it was sung:

> Sad was the struggle together
> Of Blathnat and Ferchertne,
> And the graves of them both are
> In the powerful land of Cenn Bera.

Nevertheless the slaughter increased on them every day from Samain to the middle of spring. The Ulstermen made a count of their forces, going and coming, and a half or a third of their heroes they left behind, as was said:

> Blathnat was slain
> In the slaughter above Argat-glenn.
> A grievous deed for a woman to betray her husband.

.   .   .   .

Now that is the tragic death of Cu Roi mac Dairi.

[1] The poem is omitted because of the difficulties of translation.

DEATH TALES OF THE ULSTER HEROES

In spite of the embarrassment attendant upon representing the unconquerable champion of Ulster as falling in battle, the ancient Irish saga writers could not resist the temptation to depict his death. The result was "The Great Rout of Muirthemne" (*Brislech mór Maige Muirthemne*), generally known as "The Death of Cu Chulainn." "The Death of Cu Chulainn" was composed, probably as early as the eighth century, by a writer of unusual ability. It is one of the most striking pieces of early Irish literature. The closing passage describing Cu Chulainn's death is genuinely heroic in conception and in style. Fully conscious that his end is near, Cu Chulainn goes forth to battle despite the omens that warn him; like Conaire in "The Destruction of Da Derga's Hostel" (p. 93), he is forced to break the taboos upon which his life depends, and at length he falls fighting single-handed against a band of vengeful but cowardly enemies.

The other two death tales given below, although written more or less to order, contain some interesting motifs, among the most instructive of them being the attachment of the pagan king Conchobar to Christian tradition. This particular phase of the story is obviously an afterthought added at a fairly late date to a narrative of undoubtedly primitive content. Because of Cu Chulainn's position as the central figure of the Ulster cycle, the account of his death is placed first, though the death of Celtchar is represented by the author as preceding it.

THE DEATH OF CU CHULAINN

When Cu Chulainn's foes came for the last time against him, his land was filled with smoke and flame, the weapons fell from their racks, and the day of his death drew nigh. The evil tidings were brought to him, and the maiden Leborcham bade him arise, though he was worn out with fighting in defence of the plain of Muirthemne, and Niam, wife of Conall the Victorious, also spoke to him; so he sprang to his arms, and flung his mantle around him; but the brooch fell and pierced his foot, forewarning him. Then he took his shield and ordered his charioteer Loeg to harness his horse, the Gray of Macha.

"I swear by the gods by whom my people swear," said Loeg, "though the men of Conchobar's province were around the Gray of Macha, they could not bring him to the chariot. I never refused thee till today. If thou wilt, come thou, and speak with the Gray himself."

Cu Chulainn went to him. And thrice did the horse turn his left side to his master. On the night before, the Morrigu had broken the chariot, for she liked not Cu Chulainn's going to the battle, for she knew that he would not come again to Emain Macha. Then Cu Chulainn reproached his horse, saying that he was not wont to deal thus with his master.

Thereat the Gray of Macha came and let his big round tears of blood fall on Cu Chulainn's feet. And then Cu Chulainn leaped into the chariot, and drove it suddenly southwards along the Road of Midluachar.

And Leborcham met him and besought him not to leave them; and the thrice fifty queens who were in Emain Macha and who loved him cried to him with a great cry. And when he turned his chariot to the right, they gave a scream of wailing and lamentation, and smote their hands, for they knew that he would not come to them again.

The house of his nurse that had fostered him was before him on the road. He used to go to it whenever he went driving past her southwards and from the south. And she kept for him always a vessel with drink therein. Now he drank a drink and fared forth, bidding his nurse farewell. Then he saw three Crones, blind of the left eye, before him on the road. They had cooked on spits of rowantree a dog with poisons and spells. And one of the things that Cu Chulainn was bound not to do, was going to a cooking-hearth and consuming the food.[1] And another of the things that he must not do, was eating his namesake's flesh.[2] He sped on and was about to pass them, for he knew that they were not there for his good.

Then said a Crone to him: "Visit us, O Cu Chulainn."

"I will not visit you in sooth," said Cu Chulainn.

"The food is only a hound," said she. "Were this a great cooking-hearth thou wouldst have visited us. But because what is here is little, thou comest not. Unseemly are the great who endure not the little and poor."

Then he drew nigh to her, and the Crone gave him the shoulder-blade of the hound out of her left hand. And then Cu Chulainn ate it out of his left hand, and put it under his left thigh. The hand that took it and the thigh under which he put it were seized from trunk to end, so that the normal strength abode not in them.

[1] Because of his *gesa*, or taboos.
[2] Since his name was *Cu* (hound), he was forbidden to eat dog's flesh.

Then he drove along the Road of Midluachar around Sliab
Fuait; and his enemy Erc son of Cairbre saw him in his chariot,
with his sword shining redly in his hand, and the light of valor
hovering over him, and his three-hued hair like strings of golden
thread over the edge of the anvil of some cunning craftsman.

"That man is coming towards us, O men of Erin!" said Erc;
"await him." So they made a fence of their linked shields, and at
each corner Erc made them place two of their bravest feigning to
fight each other, and a satirist with each of these pairs, and he told
the satirists to ask Cu Chulainn for his spear, for the sons of
Calatin had prophesied of his spear that a king would be slain by
it, unless it were given when demanded. And he made the men of
Erin utter a great cry. And Cu Chulainn rushed against them in
his chariot, performing his three thunder-feats; and he plied his
spear and sword; so that the halves of their heads and skulls and
hands and feet, and their red bones were scattered broadcast
throughout the plain of Muirthemne, in number like to the sands
of the sea and stars of heaven and dewdrops of May, flakes of
snow, hailstones, leaves in the forest, buttercups on Mag Breg,
and grass under the hoofs of herds on a day in summer. And gray
was the field with their brains after that onslaught and plying of
weapons which Cu Chulainn dealt unto them.

Then he saw one of the pairs of warriors contending together,
and the satirist called on him to intervene, and Cu Chulainn leaped
at them, and with two blows of his fist dashed out their brains.

"That spear to me!" said the satirist.

"I swear what my people swear," said Cu Chulainn, "thou dost
not need it more than I do. The men of Erin are upon me here and
I am attacking them."

"I will revile thee if thou givest it not," said the satirist.

"I have never yet been reviled because of my niggardliness or my
churlishness."

With that Cu Chulainn flung the spear at him with its handle
foremost, and it passed through his head and killed nine on the
other side of him.

And Cu Chulainn drove through the host, but Lugaid son of
Cu Roi [1] got the spear.

[1] Cu Chulainn had slain Cu Roi (p. 331) as well as kinsmen of others who
took part in his death.

"What will fall by this spear, O sons of Calatin?" asked Lugaid.

"A king will fall by that spear," said the sons of Calatin.

Then Lugaid flung the spear at Cu Chulainn's chariot, and it reached the charioteer, Loeg mac Riangabra, and all his bowels came forth on the cushion of the chariot.

Then said Loeg, "Bitterly have I been wounded," etc.

Thereafter Cu Chulainn drew out the spear, and Loeg bade him farewell. Then said Cu Chulainn: "Today I shall be warrior and I shall be charioteer also."

Then he saw the second pair contending, and one of them said it was a shame for him not to intervene. And Cu Chulainn sprang upon them and dashed them into pieces against a rock.

"That spear to me, O Cu Chulainn!" said the satirist.

"I swear what my people swear, thou dost not need the spear more than I do. On my hand and my valor and my weapons it rests today to sweep the four provinces of Erin today from the plain of Muirthemne."

"I will revile thee," said the satirist.

"I am not bound to grant more than one request this day, and, moreover, I have already paid for my honor."

"I will revile Ulster for thy default," said the satirist.

"Never yet has Ulster been reviled for my refusal nor for my churlishness. Though little of my life remains to me, Ulster shall not be reviled this day."

Then Cu Chulainn cast his spear at him by the handle and it went through his head and killed nine behind him, and Cu Chulainn drove through the host even as he had done before.

Then Erc son of Cairbre took the spear. "What shall fall by this spear, O sons of Calatin?" said Erc son of Cairbre

"Not hard to say: a king falls by that spear," said the sons of Calatin.

"I heard you say that a king would fall by the spear which Lugaid long since cast."

"And that is true," said the sons of Calatin. "Thereby fell the king of the charioteers of Erin, namely Cu Chulainn's charioteer, Loeg mac Riangabra."

Now Erc cast the spear at Cu Chulainn, and it lighted on his horse, the Gray of Macha. Cu Chulainn snatched out the spear. And each of them bade the other farewell. Thereat the Gray of

Macha left him with half the yoke under his neck and went into the Gray's Linn in Sliab Fuait.

Thereupon Cu Chulainn again drove through the host and saw the third pair contending, and he intervened as he had done before, and the satirist demanded his spear and Cu Chulainn at first refused it.

"I will revile thee," said the satirist.

"I have paid for my honor today. I am not bound to grant more than one request this day."

"I will revile Ulster for thy fault."

"I have paid for Ulster's honor," said Cu Chulainn.

"I will revile thy race," said the satirist.

"Tidings that I have been defamed shall never reach the land I have not reached. For little there is of my life remaining."

So Cu Chulainn flung the spear to him, handle foremost, and it went through his head and through thrice nine other men.

" 'Tis grace with wrath, O Cu Chulainn," said the satirist.

Then Cu Chulainn for the last time drove through the host, and Lugaid took the spear, and said:

"What will fall by this spear, O sons of Calatin?"

"I heard you say that a king would fall by the spear that Erc cast this morning."

"That is true," said they, "the king of the steeds of Erin fell by it, namely the Gray of Macha."

Then Lugaid flung the spear and struck Cu Chulainn, and his bowels came forth on the cushion of the chariot, and his only horse, the Black Sainglenn, fled away, with half the yoke hanging to him, and left the chariot and his master, the king of the heroes of Erin, dying alone on the plain.

Then said Cu Chulainn, "I would fain go as far as that loch to drink a drink thereout."

"We give thee leave," said they, "provided that thou come to us again."

"I will bid you come for me," said Cu Chulainn, "if I cannot come myself."

Then he gathered his bowels into his breast, and went forth to the loch.

And there he drank his drink, and washed himself, and came forth to die, calling on his foes to come to meet him.

Now a great mearing went westwards from the loch and his eye lit upon it, and he went to a pillar-stone which is in the plain, and he put his breast-girdle round it that he might not die seated nor lying down, but that he might die standing up. Then came the men all around him, but they durst not go to him, for they thought he was alive.

"It is a shame for you," said Erc son of Cairbre, "not to take that man's head in revenge for my father's head which was taken by him."

Then came the Gray of Macha to Cu Chulainn to protect him so long as his soul was in him and the "hero's light" out of his forehead remained. And the Gray of Macha wrought three red routs all around him. And fifty fell by his teeth and thirty by each of his hoofs. This is what he slew of the host. And hence is the saying, "Not keener were the victorious courses of the Gray of Macha after Cu Chulainn's slaughter."

And then came the battle goddess Morrigu and her sisters in the form of scald-crows and sat on his shoulder. "That pillar is not wont to be under birds," said Erc son of Cairbre.

Then Lugaid arranged Cu Chulainn's hair over his shoulder, and cut off his head. And then fell the sword from Cu Chulainn's hand, and smote off Lugaid's right hand, which fell on the ground. And Cu Chulainn's right hand was cut off in revenge for this. Lugaid and the hosts then marched away, carrying with them Cu Chulainn's head and his right hand, and they came to Tara, and there is the "Sick-bed" of his head and his right hand, and the full of the cover of his shield of mould.

From Tara they marched southwards to the river Liffey. But meanwhile the hosts of Ulster were hurrying to attack their foes, and Conall the Victorious, driving in front of them, met the Gray of Macha streaming with blood. Then Conall knew that Cu Chulainn had been slain. And he and the Gray of Macha sought Cu Chulainn's body. They saw Cu Chulainn at the pillar-stone. Then went the Gray of Macha and laid his head on Cu Chulainn's breast And Conall said, "A heavy care to the Gray of Macha is that corpse."

And Conall followed the hosts meditating vengeance, for he was bound to avenge Cu Chulainn. For there was a comrades' covenant between Cu Chulainn and Conall the Victorious, namely, that whichever of them was first killed should be avenged by the other. "And if *I* be the first killed," Cu Chulainn had said, "how soon wilt thou avenge me?"

"The day on which thou shalt be slain," said Conall, "I will avenge thee before that evening. And if I be slain," said Conall, "how soon wilt thou avenge me?"

"Thy blood will not be cold on earth," said Cu Chulainn, "before I shall avenge thee." So Conall pursued Lugaid to the Liffey.

Then was Lugaid bathing. "Keep a lookout over the plain," said he to his charioteer, "that no one come to us without being seen."

The charioteer looked. "One horseman is here coming to us," said he, "and great are the speed and swiftness with which he comes. Thou wouldst deem that all the ravens of Erin were above him. Thou wouldst deem that flakes of snow were specking the plain before him."

"Unbeloved is the horseman that comes there," said Lugaid. "It is Conall the Victorious, mounted on the Dewy-Red. The birds thou sawest above him are the sods from that horse's hoofs. The snow-flakes thou sawest specking the plain before him are the foam from that horse's lips and from the curbs of his bridle. Look again," said Lugaid, "what road is he coming?"

"He is coming to the ford," said the charioteer, "the path that the hosts have taken."

"Let that horse pass us," said Lugaid. "We desire not to fight against him." But when Conall reached the middle of the ford he spied Lugaid and his charioteer and went to them.

"Welcome is a debtor's face!" said Conall. "He to whom he oweth debts demands them of him. I am thy creditor for the slaying of my comrade Cu Chulainn, and here I am suing thee for this."

They then agreed to fight on the plain of Argetros, and there Conall wounded Lugaid with his javelin. Thence they went to a place called Ferta Lugdach.

"I wish," said Lugaid, "to have the truth of men from thee."

"What is that?" asked Conall the Victorious.

"That thou shouldst use only one hand against me, for one hand only have I."

"Thou shalt have it," said Conall the Victorious.

So Conall's hand was bound to his side with ropes. There for the space between two of the watches of the day they fought, and neither of them prevailed over the other. When Conall found that he prevailed not, he saw his steed the Dewy-Red by Lugaid. And the steed came to Lugaid and tore a piece out of his side.

"Woe is me!" said Lugaid, "that is not the truth of men, O Conall."

"I gave it only on my own behalf," said Conall. "I gave it not on behalf of savage beasts and senseless things."

"I know now," said Lugaid, "that thou wilt not go till thou takest my head with thee, since we took Cu Chulainn's head from him. So take," said he, "my head in addition to thine own, and add my realm to thy realm, and my valor to thy valor. For I prefer that thou shouldst be the best hero in Erin."

Thereat Conall the Victorious cut off Lugaid's head. And Conall and his Ulstermen then returned to Emain Macha. That week they entered it not in triumph. But the soul of Cu Chulainn appeared there to the thrice fifty queens who had loved him, and they saw him floating in his phantom chariot over Emain Macha, and they heard him chant a mystic song of the coming of Christ and the Day of Doom.

THE DEATH OF CELTCHAR MAC UTHECAIR

Whence is the death of Celtchar mac Uthecair? Not hard to tell. There was a famous man of the men of Ulster, Blai Briuga. He owned seven herds of cattle, seven score cows in each herd. He also kept a guest-house. Now it was taboo for him that a woman should come in a company to his house without his sleeping with her, unless her husband were in her company. Then Brig Bretach, the wife of Celtchar, went to his house. "Not good is what thou hast done, woman," said Blai Briuga. "Thy coming as thou hast come is taboo to me."

"It is a wretched man," said the woman, "that violates his own taboos."

"It is true. I am an old man, and moreover you are inciting me," said he.

That night he slept with her.

Celtchar came to know that; and he went to seek his wife. Blai Briuga went to Conchobar in the royal house. Celtchar also went to the royal house. There were Conchobar and Cu Chulainn playing a game of chess; and Blai Briuga's chest was over the playboard between them. And Celtchar planted a spear through him so that it stuck in the wattle of the wall behind him, so that a drop of blood fell from the point of the spear on the board.

"Truly, Cu Chulainn!" said Conchobar.

"Indeed, then, Conchobar!" said Cu Chulainn.

The board was measured from the drop hither and thither to know to which of them it was nearer. Now the drop was nearer to Conchobar, and it was the longer till revenge. Blai Briuga, however, died.

Celtchar escaped and went to the land of the Desi of Munster in the south. "This is bad, O Conchobar!" said the men of Ulster. "This means the ruin of the Desi. It was enough that we should lose the man who has died, and let Celtchar come back to his land."

"Let him come, then," said Conchobar; "and let his son go for him, and let him be his safeguard." At that time with the men of Ulster a father's crime was not laid upon his son, nor a son's crime upon the father. So Celtchar's son went to summon him until he was in the south.

"Wherefore have you come, my lad?" said Celtchar.

"That you may come to your land," said the boy.

"What is my safeguard?"

"I," said the lad.

"True," said he. "Subtle is the treachery that the men of Ulster practice on me, that I should go on my son's guarantee."

"Subtle (séim) shall be his name and the name of his offspring," said the druid.

"Wait, lad," said Celtchar, "and I will go with you."

This was done, and hence is Semuine in the land of the Desi.

However, this is the fine that was demanded for Blai Briuga,—to free them from the three worst pests that would come to Ulster in his time.

Then Conganchnes (Horn-skin) mac Dedad went to avenge his brother, Cu Roi mac Dairi maic Dedad, upon the men of Ulster. He devastated Ulster greatly. Spears or swords hurt him not, but sprang from him as from horn.

"Free us from this pest, O Celtchar!" said Conchobar.

"I will surely," said Celtchar. And on a certain day he went to converse with Conganchnes so that he beguiled him, promising him his daughter Niam, as well as a dinner for a hundred every afternoon to be supplied him.

Then the woman beguiled him, saying to him, "Tell me," said she, "how you may be killed."

"Red-hot iron spits have to be thrust into my soles and through my shins," he said.

Then she told her father that he should have two large spits made, and a sleeping spell put on them, and that he should gather a large host. And so it was done. And they went on their bellies, and the spears were thrust into his soles with sledge-hammers, and right through his marrow, so that he died by them. And Celtchar cut off his head, over which a cairn was raised; that is, a stone was placed by every man that came there.

And this was the second pest, the Mouse Brown; that is, a whelp which the son of a widow had found in the hollow of an oak, and which the widow reared until it was big. At last then it turned upon the sheep of the widow, and it killed her cows, and her son, and killed herself, and then went to the Glen of the Great Sow. Every night it would devastate a stronghold in Ulster and every day it lay asleep.

"Free us from it, O Celtchar!" said Conchobar. And Celtchar went into a wood and brought out a log of alder; and a hole was dug in it as long as his arms, and he boiled it in fragrant herbs and in honey and in grease until it was soft yet tough. Celtchar went toward the cave in which the Mouse Brown used to sleep, and he entered the cave early, before the hound came after the slaughter. It came, with its snout raised high in the air at the smell of the wood. And Celtchar pushed the wood out through the cave towards it. The hound took it in his jaws and put his teeth into it, and the teeth stuck in the tough wood. Celtchar pulled the wood toward him, and the hound pulled on the other side; and Celtchar put his arm along the log inside and took its heart out through its jaws so that he had it in his hand. And he took its head with him.

And that day, at the end of a year afterwards, cow-herds were by the side of the cairn of Conganchnes, and heard the squealing of whelps in the cairn. And they dug up the cairn and found three whelps in it, namely, a dun hound, and a speckled hound, and a black hound. The speckled hound was given as a present to Mac Datho of Leinster; and for its sake multitudes of the men of Ireland fell in the house of Mac Datho, and Ailbe was the name of that hound.[1] And it would be to Culann the smith that the dun hound was given,[2] and the black hound was Celtchar's own Doelchu. It let no man take hold of it save Celtchar. Once upon a time when Celtchar was not at home, and the hound was let out, the people of the household could not catch it; and it turned among the cattle and the flocks, and at last it destroyed a living creature every night in Ulster.

"Free us from that pest, O Celtchar!" said Conchobar. Celtchar went toward the glen in which the hound was, and a hundred warriors with him, and three times he called the hound until they saw it coming towards them, making straight for Celtchar until it was licking his feet.

"It is sad indeed, what the hound does," said all.

"I will no longer be incriminated on your account!" said Celtchar, giving it a blow with the Luin (spear) of Celtchar, so that he brought out its heart, whereupon it died.

"Woe!" cried everybody.

" 'Tis true," said he, as he raised the spear, when a drop of the hound's blood ran along the spear and went through him to the ground, so that he died of it. And his lament was set up and his stone and tomb were raised there. So this is the Tragical Death of Blai Briuga, and of Conganchnes, and of Celtchar mac Uthecair.

THE DEATH OF CONCHOBAR

Once upon a time the men of Ulster were greatly intoxicated in Emain Macha. Thence there arose great contentions and comparisons of trophies between them, especially between Conall and Cu Chulainn and Loegaire. "Bring me," said Conall, "the brain of Mesgegra, so that I may talk to the competing warriors." At that time it was a custom with the men of Ulster to take the brains out of the head of every warrior whom they slew in single combat, and to mix lime with them, so that they were made into hard balls. And whenever they were in contention or at comparison of trophies, these were brought to them, so that they had them in their hands.

[1] See p. 199.　　　　　　　　　　[2] See p. 140.

"Well, O Conchobar," said Conall, "until the competing warriors perform a deed like this in single combat, they are not capable of comparing trophies with me."

"That is true," said Conchobar.

Then the brain was put on the shelf where it was always kept. On the morrow every one went his way to his sport. Then Cet mac Matach of Connacht went upon a round of adventures in Ulster. This Cet was the most troublesome pest that was in Ireland. This is the way he went, across the green of Emain, having with him three warriors' heads of the men of Ulster.

While the jesters of Emain were at play with the brain of Mesgegra, one of them mentioned to the other what it was. Cet heard it, and snatched the brain out of the hand of one of them and carried it off; for he knew that it had been foretold of Mesgegra that he would avenge himself after his death. In every battle and in every combat which the men of Connacht had with the men of Ulster, Cet used to carry the brain in his girdle to see whether he could compass a famous deed by slaying a man of Ulster with it.

Once then Cet went eastwards until he took a drove of cows from the Men of Ros. The men of Ulster overtook him in pursuit. Then the men of Connacht came up from the other side to rescue him, and a battle was fought between them. Conchobar himself went into the battle. It was then that the women of Connacht begged Conchobar to come aside so that they might see his shape. For there was not on earth the shape of a human being like the shape of Conchobar, both for beauty and figure and dress, for size and symmetry and proportion, for eye and hair and whiteness, for wisdom and manner and eloquence, for raiment and nobleness and equipment, for weapons and wealth and dignity, for bearing and valor and race. Conchobar was faultless indeed. However, it was by the advice of Cet that the women importuned Conchobar. Then he went aside alone to be seen by the women.

Cet went into the midst of the crowd of women. He adjusted the brain of Mesgegra in the sling and threw it so that it hit the crown of Conchobar's head, so that two-thirds of it entered his head, and he fell upon his head forward to the ground. The men of Ulster ran towards him, and carried him off from Cet. On the brink of the Ford of Daire Da Baeth it was that Conchobar fell. His grave is there where he fell, and a pillar-stone at his head, and another at his feet.

The men of Connacht were then routed to Sce Aird na Con. The men of Ulster were driven eastwards again to the Ford of Daire Da Baeth. "Let me be carried out of this," said Conchobar. "I shall give the kingship of Ulster to any one who will carry me as far as my house."

"I will carry you," said Cenn Berraide, his own attendant. He put a cord around him and carried him on his back to Ardachad in Sliab Fuait. The attendant's heart broke within him. Hence the saying "Cenn Barraide's kingship over Ulster," to wit, the king upon his back for half the day.

However, the fight was kept up after the king from one hour of the day to the same hour of the next day, after which the men of Ulster were routed.

In the meantime Conchobar's physician Fingen was brought to him. It was he who would know from the smoke that arose from a house how many were ill in that house, and every disease that was in it.

"Well," said Fingen, "if the stone is taken out of your head, you will be dead forthwith. If it is not taken out, however, I would heal you, but it will be a blemish for you."

"It is easier for us," said the men of Ulster, "to bear the blemish than his death."

His head was then healed; and it was stitched with thread of gold, for the color of Conchobar's hair was the same as the color of gold. And the physician said to Conchobar that he should be on his guard lest anger should come on him, and that he should not mount a horse, that he should not have connection with a woman, that he should not eat food greedily, and that he should not run.

In that doubtful state, then, he was as long as he lived, seven years; and he was not capable of action, but remained in his seat only, until he heard that Christ had been crucified by the Jews. At that time a great trembling came over the elements, and the heavens and earth shook with the enormity of the deed that was then done, Jesus Christ, the son of the living God, to be crucified without guilt.

"What is this," said Conchobar to his druid. "What great evil is being done on this day?"

"That is true, indeed," said the druid (who then tells the story of the Crucifixion).

"Awful is that deed," said Conchobar.

"That man now," said the druid, "was born in the same night in which you were born, on the eighth before the calends of January, though the year was not the same."

It was then that Conchobar believed. And he was one of the two men that believed in God in Ireland before the coming of the Faith, Morann being the other man.

(The story, which ends with a piece of rhetorical fantasy supposed to have been uttered by Conchobar, is clearly incomplete, for it does not tell of Conchobar's death. The following paragraph, taken from another version, gives the conclusion.)

And thereupon Conchobar said, "The men of the world would know what I can do in fighting against the Jews for the sake of the crucifixion of Christ, if I were near Him."

Then he rose and made the onslaught, until Mesgegra's brain jumped out of his head, so that Conchobar died forthwith. Hence the Gaels say that Conchobar was the first pagan who went to Heaven in Ireland, for the blood that sprang out of his head was a baptism to him. And then Conchobar's soul was taken out of Hell until Christ encountered it as He brought the captive host out of Hell, so that Christ took the soul of Conchobar with Him to Heaven.

THE PHANTOM CHARIOT OF CU CHULAINN

The Christian writers of early Ireland were more kindly disposed toward their native pagan traditions than were the other newly converted peoples of medieval Europe. Holy men associate freely with fairy beings, St. Patrick listens with delight to the exploits of Finn and Oisin (p. 457), and he even uses his divine power to call back Cu Chulainn from the grave that the stiff-necked Loegaire, pagan high-king of Ireland, may be led to accept the new faith. Whoever conceived the idea of bringing together the most distinguished ancient pagan champion and the most beloved of Christian saints had a truly poetic imagination.

Patrick went to Tara to enjoin belief upon the King of Erin, that is, upon Loegaire, son of Niall, who was King of Erin at the time; for he would not believe in the Lord though He had been preached unto him.

Loegaire said to Patrick: "By no means will I believe in thee, nor yet in God, until thou shalt call up Cu Chulainn in all his dignity, as he is recorded in the old stories, that I may see him, and that I may address him in my presence here; after that I will believe in thee."

"Even this thing is possible for God," said Patrick.

Then a messenger came from God to Patrick, and he said that Patrick and Loegaire should remain until the morrow on the rampart of the rath of Tara, and that Cu Chulainn would appear to him there.

After the appearance of Cu Chulainn to him in his chariot, Loegaire went to converse with Patrick. Patrick said to Loegaire: "Has something indeed appeared to thee?"

"Something has indeed appeared to me," said Loegaire; "but I have not power to relate it, unless thou wilt sign and consecrate my mouth."

"I will not sign thy mouth," said Patrick, "until I have my demand. I will, however, make a sign on the air that comes out of thy mouth, in order that thou mayest describe the apparition which was shown to thee."

"As I was going," said Loegaire, "over the Slope of the Chariot to the Hill of the Fairy-mound of the Plain, in the Plateau of the Assembly in the plain of Mac Oc, I saw the cold piercing wind, like a double-barbed spear. It hardly spared to take the hair from our heads, and to go through us to the earth. I asked of Benen the meaning of the wind. Benen said to me, 'That is the wind of hell after its opening before Cu Chulainn.' We saw then the heavy fog which dropped upon us. I asked also of Benen the meaning of the heavy fog. Benen said that the fog was the breath of men and of horses that were traversing the plain before me.

"Then we saw a great raven-flock on high above us. The country was full of birds, and in height they reached to the clouds of heaven. I asked of Benen about these and he said they were sods thrown up by the hoofs of the horses that were yoked to Cu Chulainn's chariot. After that we saw the forms of the horses through the mist, and of men in the easy chariot; a charioteer on high behind them; a spirit-chieftain; horses that rode paths.

"I observed after this the two horses; equal in size and beauty were they, and only unlike in form and color; in swiftness, in symmetry, in action, equal. Broad were their hoofs and broad their backs; in color beautiful; in height, in vehemence, remarkable. Their heads were small: large-lipped, bright-eyed. Red of chest, sleek and well-knit, they yielded promptly to the yoke; they attracted attention by the lofty dignity of their movements; their manes and tails hung down in curls.

"Behind the pair a wide-spaced chariot. Beneath it, two black solid wheels; above it, two symmetrical, overlapping reins; its shafts firm and straight as swords; the reins adorned and pliant; the pole, white silver with a withe of white bronze; the yoke, firm, ridged, and made of gold; the hood, purple; the fittings, green.

"Within the chariot a warrior was visible. His hair was thick and black, and smooth as though a cow had licked it. In his head his eye gleamed swift and grey. About him was flung a tunic of purple-blue, its borders of white gold lacing. It was clasped with a brooch of red gold upon his breast; it floated out over each of his two shoulders. A white hooded cloak hung about him with a border of flaming red. A sword with a hilt of gold lying in a rest on his two thighs; and in his hand a broad gray spear on a shaft of wild ash. Beside it lay a sharp venomous dart. Across his shoulders he bore a purple shield surrounded by an even circle of silver; upon it were chased loop-animals in gold. Into his mouth a shower of pearls seemed to have been thrown. Blacker than the side of a black cooking-spit each of his two brows, redder than ruby his lips.

"Before him in the chariot was the charioteer; a very slender, tall and lank, stooped, very freckled man. Very curly red hair on the top of his head; a band of white bronze on his forehead, that prevented his hair from falling about his face. Above his two ears spheres of gold, into which his hair was gathered. About him was a winged little cloak, with an opening at its two elbows. He held in his hand a small whip of red gold with which he urged on his horses. It seemed to me that it was Cu Chulainn and Loeg, his charioteer, who were within the chariot, and that it was the Black of Sainglenn and the Gray of Macha that were yoked to it."

"Dost thou believe in God henceforth, O Loegaire," said Patrick, "since Cu Chulainn came to converse with thee?"

"If it were Cu Chulainn that I saw, it seems to me that he stayed too short a time conversing with me."

"God is powerful," said Patrick. "If it were indeed Cu Chulainn, he will return and converse with thee again."

Now they remained still in the same place, and they perceived the chariot coming across the plain towards them drawn by its two horses. Within rode Cu Chulainn garbed as a warrior, and Loeg mac Riangabra as his charioteer. Then in mid-air Cu Chulainn performed twenty-seven feats of skill above them. The Noise-feat of Nine, that is the Feat of Cat, the Feat of Cuar, and the Feat of Daire, the Blind-feat of Birds, the Leap over Poison, the Bed-folding of a Brave Champion, the Bellows-dart, the Stroke with Quickness, the Ardor of Shout, the Hero's Scream, the Wheel-feat, the Edge-feat, the Apple-feat, and the Noise-feat; the Ascent by rope, the Straightening of Body on Spear-point, the Binding of a Noble Champion, the Return-stroke, and the Stroke with Measure.

As for the charioteer, the management of the reins confounds all speech: he was above the evaporations and breathings of the horses.

Then Cu Chulainn went to converse with Patrick and saluted him, saying:

> I beseech, O holy Patrick,
>   In thy presence that I may be,
> That thou wouldst bring me with thy faithful ones,
>   Into the Land of the Living.

Then he addressed the king thus: "Believe in God and in holy Patrick, O Loegaire, that earth's surface may not come over thee; for it is not a demon that has come to thee: it is Cu Chulainn mac Sualtaim. A world for every champion is law of earth, every quiet one's is concealment, every hero's is earth, every holy one's is heaven: for of the order of demons is everything thou ponderest on: it is the world of each in turn that thou chariotest."

Cu Chulainn was silent, and Loegaire did not speak.

"Who chariots the Men of Breg, O Loegaire? Who sits their slopes? Who watches their fords? Whom do their wives elope with? Whom do their daughters love?"

"What is that inquiry to me and to thee?" asked Loegaire.

"There was a time, O Loegaire, when it was I who used to go among them, who used to go around them, who used to keep them together. I was their little champion whom they used to love: whom with high spirits they used to play about. There was a time, O Loegaire, when it was I who used to go to their great attacks, who used to burst their great contests. I was the battle-victorious, loud-shouting, red-wristed, broad-palmed, brave Cu Chulainn, who used to be on the rich plain of Muirthemne. Believe in God and in Patrick, O Loegaire, for it is not a demon that has come to thee, but Cu Chulainn son of Sualtam."

"If it is Cu Chulainn that is here present," said Loegaire, "he will tell us of his great deeds."

"That is true, O Loegaire," said Cu Chulainn. "I was the destroyer of hostageship in the reception of the fords of my territories; I was heavy of hand on heroes and great hosts. I used to hunt the fleet herds of my enemies in the full rushries, and left their flocks live-dead upon the mountains after the slaying in equal combat of the men who were over them."

"If thou didst indeed those deeds that thou recountest, the deeds of a hero were with thee; but they were not the deeds of Cu."

"That is true, O Loegaire," said Cu Chulainn.

> I was not a hound of taking of a fort,
> I was a hound of taking of a deer:
> I was not a hound of a forbidden trotter,
> I was a hound strong for combat:
> I was not a hound of round lickings of leavings,
> I was a hound who visited the troops:
> I was not a hound to watch over calves,
> I was a hound to guard Emain Macha.

"If those deeds are as thou recountest them, the deeds of a hero were with thee."

"That is true, O Loegaire," said Cu Chulainn: "the deeds of a hero were with me."

> I was a hero, I was a leader;
> I was the charioteer of a great chariot;
> I was gentle to the gentle,
> But against dishonor I wrought vengeance.

"I was not the poison-tongue of my territories; I was the casket of every secret for the maidens of Ulster. I was a child with children; I was a man with men. It was for correction I used to labor. I was good in spite of satirizing; I was better for praising."

"If it be Cu Chulainn that is here," said Loegaire, "he will tell us a portion of the great risks he risked."

"That is true, O Loegaire," said Cu Chulainn.

> I used to hunt their great flocks
> With hardy Conchobar:
> It was in a foreign territory,
> I used to behold each victory.

> I played on breaths
> Above the horses' steam:
> Before me on every side
> Great battles were broken.

> I broke contests
> On the champions of the territories:
> I was the sword-red hero
> After the slaying of hosts.

> I broke edge-feats
> On the points of their swords:
> I reached their great spoils,
> Were it through drivings of fire!

(The next stanzas describe a journey in which Cu Chulainn waged
battles in Lochlann on the north, and slew a giant. He continues:)

A journey I went, O Loegaire,
  When I went into the Land of Scath:
Dun Scaith in it with its locks of iron—
  I laid hand upon it.

Seven walls about that city—
  Hateful was the fort:
A palisade of irons on each wall,
  On which were nine heads.

Doors of iron on each side—
  Not strong defences against us:
I struck them with my foot,
  And drove them into fragments.

There was a pit in the dun,
  Belonging to the king, so it is said:
Ten serpents burst
  Over its border—it was a great deed!

After that I attacked them,
  Though vast the throng,
Until I made bits of them
  Between my two fists

There was a house full of toads,
  That were let loose upon us;
Sharp, beaked monsters
  That clave to my snout.

Fierce dragon-like monsters
  Were sent against us;
Strong were their witcheries

    .   .   .   .   .   .

After that I attacked them;
  When a rush was made on me,
I ground them into small pieces
  Between my two palms.

There was a cauldron in that dun; [1]
  The calf of the three cows:
Thirty joints of meat in its girth
  Were not a charge for it.

The cows used to frequent that cauldron,
  Delightful was the contest;
They would not go from it on any side,
  Until they left it full.

[1] See p. 328.

There was much gold and silver in it—
   Wonderful was the find:
That cauldron was given to us
   By the daughter of the king.

The three cows we carried off—
   They swam boldly over the sea:
There was a load of gold for two men
   To each of them on her neck.

After we had come upon the ocean,
   Which spread out towards the north,
The crew of my currach was engulfed
   By the fierce storm.

After this I floated them—
   Though it was a sharp danger—
Nine men on each of my hands,
   Thirty on my head.

Eight upon my two sides
   Clung to my body.
Thus I swam the ocean
   Until I reached the harbor.

What I suffered of trouble,
   O Loegaire, by sea and land:—
Yet more severe was a single night,
   When the demon was wrathful.

My little body was scarred—
   With Lugaid the victory:
Demons carried off my soul
   Into the red charcoal.

I played the swordlet on them,
   I plied on them the *gae bulga;*
I was in my complete victory
   With the demon in pain.

Great as was my heroism,
   Hard as was my sword,
The devil crushed me with one finger
   Into the red charcoal!

(Cu Chulainn endeavors to persuade King Loegaire to believe in God and Patrick, by dwelling on the pains of hell, in which are lying the champions of Ulster. He extols Patrick's power in having conjured him up. He concludes:)

> Though thine were a perpetual life
>   Of earth, with its beauty,
> Better is a single reward in heaven
>   With Christ, Son of the living God.
>
> I beseech, O holy Patrick,
>   In thy presence, that I may come,
> That thou wouldst bring me with thy faithful ones
>   Unto the land which thou drivest about.

"Believe in God and holy Patrick, O Loegaire, that a wave of earth may not come over thee. It will come, unless thou believest in God and in holy Patrick, for it is not a demon that has come to thee: it is Cu Chulainn son of Sualtam."

Now, that thing indeed happened: earth came over Loegaire; Heaven was decreed for Cu Chulainn. Loegaire believed in Patrick in consequence.

Great was the power of Patrick in awakening Cu Chulainn after being nine times fifty years in the grave; that is, from the reign of Conchobar mac Nessa,—it is he that was born in co-birth with Christ—to the end of the reign of Loegaire, son of Niall, son of Eochaid Muigmedoin, son of Muiredach Tirech, son of Fiachra Roptine, son of Cairbre Liffechar, son of Cormac Ulfada, son of Art Oenfer, son of Conn the Hundred-Fighter, son of Feradach Rechtmar, son of Tuathal Techtmar, son of Feradach Finnfachtnach, son of Crimthann Niadnar, son of Lugaid of the Red Stripes. And he (*i.e.*, Lugaid) was a foster-son to Cu Chulainn son of Sualtam.

THE CYCLE OF FINN, OSSIAN, AND THEIR COMPANIONS

The third of the great cycles of Irish heroic literature is known as the Finn, or Ossianic cycle. According to the Irish annals, Finn flourished during the third century after Christ, but the earliest references to him in literature do not appear until several hundred years later, and the vast majority of the tales about him are found in manuscripts dating from the twelfth and later centuries. These accounts, composed at various times from the Middle Ages down to the nineteenth century, differ greatly in their conceptions of Finn. Though all regard him as the chief of a *fián*, or warrior band, among whom the most distinguished heroes are his son Oisin (Ossian) and his grandson Oscar, one group of tales represents him as the head of a sort of national militia in the employ of one of the high-kings of Ireland, usually Conn the Hundred-Fighter (p. 488); another, as powerful enough to oppose the high-king; while a third, perhaps the latest, elevates him to a position superior to all opponents, portraying him as a slayer of monsters, a general benefactor of his country, and, above all, a national defender of Ireland against foreign invaders, especially the dreaded Vikings.

The Finn cycle differs markedly from that of Ulster. The tales are much more numerous and were in general written down at a much later date than those of Ulster. Moreover, few of them furnish linguistic evidence of having been composed before the twelfth century, nor do they as a rule contain references to ancient manners and customs such as those that give the Ulster epics their value as pictures of pre-Christian culture. Whereas the Ulster tales, as we have seen, are usually written in prose interspersed with semi-lyric passages in verse, the Finn material contains not only narratives in prose but also many poems of the ballad type. Though few tales of the Ulster cycle have been preserved in modern Irish folk-lore, the exploits of Finn and his companions have formed a part of the popular literature of Gaelic-speaking Ireland and Scotland from the Middle Ages to the present day. In other words, the Ulster epic appears to have been from the eighth or ninth century the literary property of the aristocracy, while the Finn material was perhaps from the beginning the literature of the folk and consequently was more or less modernized by each succeeding generation of folk poets and popular story-tellers.

As to the origin of the Finn epic, much remains yet to be learned. It appears from early references in the annals and other sources that Finn's company was only one of many *fiána*, or bands of warriors which existed in ancient Ireland and were a recognized feature of the social system. Since the oldest traditions represent Finn as having his chief stronghold on the hill of Almu, the modern Allen, near Kildare, it has been inferred that his *fián* belonged to Leinster. Opposed to Finn are other *fiána*, especially the *fián* of Goll mac Morna, which is identified with Connacht. According to one view, the *fiána* of Finn and his opponents were bands of soldiers levied by the ruling Milesian high-kings upon the older subject peoples of Ireland. These bands were forced to be ready to take up arms at any time and consequently were prevented from earning a livelihood by continuous application to the occupations of peace. Hence they lived in war times by depredation and in peace by hunting. Professor Eoin MacNeill calls the Finn epic the "epic of a subject race" and thus explains the scarcity of Finn material in the earliest Irish manuscripts as well as the continued popularity of the Finn ballads and stories among the folk. As a hunter and a popular hero Finn resembles Robin Hood more nearly than he does any other figure in English tradition.

THE CAUSE OF THE BATTLE OF CNUCHA

The parentage of Finn and the beginning of the hereditary feud between him and Goll mac Morna are related in this story. The battle is supposed to have taken place toward the end of the second century of the Christian era. The date of composition is at least as early as the eleventh century, and may be considerably earlier, for the short, dry succession of factual statements is a trait which is distinctly reminiscent of the earlier style.

When Cathar Mor son of Fedlimid Fir Urglais son of Cormac Gelta-gaith was in the kingship of Tara, and Conn the Hundred-Fighter in Kells, in the rigdonna's land, Cathar had a celebrated druid, Nuada son of Achi son of Dathi son of Brocan son of Fintan, of Tuath Dathi in Breg. The druid was soliciting land in Leinster from Cathar; for he knew that it was in Leinster his inheritance would be. Cathar gave him his choice of land. The land the druid chose was Almu in Leinster. She that was wife to Nuada was Almu, daughter of Becan.

A stronghold was built by the druid then in Almu, and *alamu* (lime) was rubbed to its wall, until it was all white; and perhaps it was from that the name " Almu " was applied to it; of which was said:

> All-white is the stronghold of battle renown
> As if it had received the lime of Ireland;
> From the *alamu* which he gave to his house,
> Hence it is that "Almu" is applied to Almu.

Nuada's wife, Almu, begged that her name might be given to the hill; and her request was granted, and it was in it she was to be buried, hence it was said:

> Almu—beautiful was the woman!—
> Wife of Nuada the great, son of Achi;
> She entreated—the division was just—
> That her name should be on the perfect hill.

Nuada had a distinguished son, named Tadg. Rairiu, daughter of Donn-Duma, was his wife. A celebrated druid also was Tadg. Death came to Nuada; and he left his stronghold, as it was, to his son; and it is Tadg that was druid to Cathar in the place of his father.

357

Rairiu bore a daughter to Tadg; her name was Muirne of the fair neck. This maiden grew up in great beauty, so that the sons of the kings and mighty lords of Ireland were wont to be courting her.

Cumall, son of Trenmor, king-warrior of Ireland, was then in the service of Conn, and he, like every other youth, was demanding the maiden. Nuada gave him a refusal, for he knew that it was on account of Cumall he would have to leave Almu. The same woman was mother to Cumall and to Conn's father, to wit, Fedlimid Rechtaide.

Cumall, however, came and took Muirne by force, since she had not been given to him. Tadg went to Conn, told him what Cumall had done, and he began to incite Conn and to reproach him.

Conn dispatched messengers to Cumall, and ordered him to leave Ireland, or to restore Muirne to Tadg. Cumall said he would not give her up; everything else he would give but not the woman. Conn sent his soldiers, and Urgriu son of Lugaid Corr king of the Luagni, and Daire the Red son of Eochaid, and his son Aed (who was afterwards called Goll) to attack Cumall. Cumall assembled his army against them; and the battle of Cnucha was fought between them, and Cumall was slain along with many of his people.

Cumall fell by Goll son of Morna. Luchet wounded Goll in his eye, so that he destroyed it. And hence it is that the name Goll (the One-eyed) attached to him; whereof was said:

> Aed was the name of Daire's son,
> Until Luchet of fame wounded him;
> Since the heavy lance wounded him,
> Therefore, he has been called Goll.

Goll killed Luchet. It is because of this battle, moreover, that a hereditary feud existed between the sons of Morna and Finn mac Cumaill. Daire had two names, to wit, Morna and Daire.

Muirne went, after that, to Conn; for her father, Tadg the druid, rejected her and would not let her come to him, because she was pregnant; he ordered his people to burn her. Nevertheless, he dared not compass her destruction against the will of Conn, who, when the girl asked him how she should act, said, "Go to Fiacal son of Conchenn, to Tara Mairci, and let thy delivery be effected there." This was because a sister to Cumall was Fiacal's wife,

Bodball the druidess. Connla, Conn's servant, went with her, to escort her, until she came to Fiacal's house, to Tara Mairci. Muirne was welcomed by Fiacal and his wife and bore a son, to whom the name Demne was given.

Demne stayed at Tara Mairci until he was able to raid all who were his enemies. He then declared war or offered single combat against Tadg, unless the full eric (fine) for his father be given to him. Tadg said that he would give him judgment therein, which was that Almu, as it was, should be ceded to him for ever, and Tadg was to leave it. So it was done. Tadg abandoned Almu to Demne, afterwards called Finn, and came to Tuath Dathi, to his own hereditary land; and he abode in Cnoc Rein, which is called Tadg's Tulach to this day. So that hence was said this:

. . . .

> Finn demands from Tadg of the towers,
> For killing Cumall the great,
> Battle, without respite, without delay,
> Or that he should obtain single combat.
> Because Tadg was not able to sustain battle
> Against the high prince,
> He abandoned to him—it was for him enough—
> Almu altogether, as it stood.

Finn went afterwards to Almu, and abode in it. And it is it that was his principal residence whilst he lived. Finn and Goll concluded peace after that; and the eric of his father was given by the Clan Morna to Finn. And they lived peacefully, until a quarrel occurred between them in Tara Luachra, regarding the Slanga-pig, when Banb Sinna son of Maelenaig was slain; of which was said:

> Afterwards they made peace—
> Finn and Goll of mighty deeds—
> Until Banb Sinna was slain
> Regarding the pig, in Tara Luachra.

THE BOYHOOD DEEDS OF FINN

The following story gives the reasons for the long enmity between Finn and the sons of Urgriu, the tragic outcome of which is related in "The Death of Finn" (p. 424). Stories of the boyhood of traditional characters, in Irish as well as in other heroic literature, are the natural result of the public demand for more material concerning favorite national heroes. "The Boyhood Deeds of Finn," unfortunately, comes down to us incomplete. It contains a number of striking passages of nature poetry, done in the best bardic tradition of the second period (about 1200 to 1350), as yet unmarred by the exaggerated piling up of epithets that characterizes much later Irish poetry. The reader will notice some similarity between this story and "The Boyhood Deeds of Cu Chulainn" (p. 137). He will also observe that "The Boyhood Deeds of Finn" differs in certain respects from the parallel account given in "The Cause of the Battle of Cnucha" (p. 357). The two represent two different streams of tradition, one older than the other.

There befell a meeting of valor and a contest of battle about the chieftaincy of the fian (national militia) and about the high-stewardship of Ireland between Cumall son of Trenmor, and Urgriu son of Lugaid Corr of the Luagni. Cumall was of the Corco Oche of Cuil Contuinn, for to these the Ui Tairrsig, Cumall's tribe, belonged. Torba, daughter of Eochaman of the Erne, was the wife of Cumall, until he married Muirne of the fair neck.

Then the battle of Cnucha was fought between them, between Cumall and Urgriu. Daire the Red, son of Eochaid the Fair son of Cairbre the Valorous son of Muiredach, and his son Aed fought the battle along with Urgriu. Another name for that Daire was Morna Wry-neck. Luchet and Aed, son of Morna, met in the battle. Luchet wounded Aed, and destroyed one of his eyes, whence the name of Goll, the One-eyed, stuck to him from that time forth. Luchet fell by Goll. The man who kept Cumall's treasure-bag wounded Cumall in the battle. Cumall fell in the battle by Goll mac Morna, who carried off his spoils and his head, whence there was a hereditary feud between Finn mac Cumaill and the sons of Morna.

Hence sang the shanachie:

Goll, son of Daire the Red, with fame,
Son of Eochaid the Fair, of valor excellent,
Son of Cairbre the Valorous with valor,
Son of Muiredach from Finnmag.

Goll slew Luchet of the hundreds
In the battle of Cnucha, it is no falsehood:
Luchet the Fair of prowess bright
Fell by the son of Morna.

By him fell great Cumall
In the battle of Cnucha of the hosts.
It is for the chieftaincy of Erin's fian
That they waged the stout battle.

The children of Morna were in the battle
And the Luagni of Tara,
Since to them belonged the leadership of the men of Ireland
By the side of every valorous king.

Victorious Cumall had a son,
Finn, bloody, of weapons hard:
Finn and Goll, great their fame,
Mightily they waged war.

Afterwards they made peace,
Finn and Goll of the hundred deeds,
Until Banb Sinna fell
About the pig at Tara Luachra.

Aed was the name of the son of Daire
Until Luchet with glory wounded him:
Since the fierce lance had wounded him,
Therefore was he called Goll.

Cumall left his wife Muirne pregnant. And she brought forth
a son, to whom the name of Demne was given. Fiacal mac Conchinn, and Bodball the druidess, and the Gray one of Luachar
came to Muirne, and carried away the boy, for his mother durst
not let him be with her. Muirne afterwards slept with Gleor
Red-hand, king of the Lamraige, whence the saying, "Finn, son
of Gleor." Bodball, however, and the Gray one, and the boy
with them, went into the forest of Sliab Bladma. There the boy
was secretly reared. That was indeed necessary, for many a
sturdy stalwart youth, and many a venomous hostile warrior
and angry fierce champion of the warriors of the Luagni and of
the sons of Morna were lying in wait for that boy, and for Tulcha

the son of Cumall. In that manner then those two women-warriors reared him for a long time.

Then, at the end of six years, his mother came to visit her son, for she had been told that he was in that place, and besides, she was afraid of the sons of Morna for him. However, she passed from one wilderness to another, until she reached the forest of Sliab Bladma. She found the hunting-booth and the boy asleep in it. And then she lifted the boy to her bosom, and pressed him to her, and she pregnant at the time. It was then she made the quatrains, fondling her son:

Sleep in peaceful slumber, etc.

Thereupon the woman bade farewell to the women-warriors, and told them to take charge of the boy till he should be fit to be a fighter. And so the boy grew up till he was able to hunt.

On a certain day the boy went out alone, and saw ducks upon a lake. He sent a shot among them, which cut off the feathers and wings of one, so that a trance fell upon her; and then he seized her and took her with him to the hunting-booth. And that was Finn's first chase.

Later he went with certain cairds (men of art) to flee from the sons of Morna, and was with them about Crotta. These were their names: Futh and Ruth and Regna of Mag Fea, and Temle and Olpe and Rogein. There scurvy came upon him, and therefrom he became scald-headed, whence he used to be called Demne the Bald. At that time there was a robber in Leinster, Fiacal, the son of Codna. Then in Feeguile Fiacal came upon the cairds, and killed them all save Demne alone. After that he was with Fiacal, the son of Codna, in his house in Sescenn Uairbeoil. The two women-warriors came southwards to the house of Fiacal, the son of Codna, in search of Demne, and he was given to them. And then they took him with them from the south to Sliab Bladma.

One day he went out alone until he reached Mag Life, and a certain stronghold there; and he saw the youths playing hurly upon the green of the stronghold. He went to contend in running or in hurling with them. He came again the next day, and they put one-fourth of their number against him. Again they came with one-third of their number against him. However, at last they all went against him, and he won his game from them all.

"What is thy name?" they said.

"Demne," said he.

The youths told that to the chief of the stronghold. "Then kill him, if you know how to do it—if you are able to do it," said he.

"We should not be able to do anything to him," said they.

"Did he tell you his name?" asked he.

"He said," said they, "that his name was Demne."

"What does he look like?" said he.

"A shapely fair (*finn*) youth," said they.

"Then Demne shall be named Finn, 'the Fair,'" said he. Whence the youths used to call him Finn.

He came to them on the next day, and went to them at their game. All together they threw their hurlies at him. He turned among them, and threw seven of them to the ground. He went from them into the forest of Sliab Bladma.

Then, at the end of a week, he came back to the stronghold. The youths were swimming in a lake that was close by. The youths challenged him to come and try to drown them. Thereupon he jumped into the lake to them, and drowned nine of them. After that he went to Sliab Bladma.

"Who drowned the youths?" everybody asked.

"Finn," said they.

So that henceforth the name Finn stuck to him.

Once he went forth across Sliab Bladma, and the two women-warriors together with him, when a fleet herd of wild deer was seen by them on the ridge of the mountain. "Alas!" said the two old women, "that we cannot get hold of one of those!"

"*I* can," said Finn, and he dashed upon them, laying hold of two bucks among them, and brought them with him to their hunting-booth. After that he would hunt for them constantly.

"Go from us now, lad," said the women-warriors to him, "for the sons of Morna are watching to kill thee."

Alone he went from them until he reached Loch Lene, above Luachar, and there he took military service with the king of Bantry. At that place he did not make himself known. However, there was not at that time a hunter his equal. Thus said the king to him:

"If Cumall had left a son," said he, "one would think thou wast he. However, we have not heard of his leaving a son, except

Tulcha son of Cumall, and he is in military service with the king of Scotland."

Later he bade farewell to the king, and went from them to Carbrige, which at this day is called Kerry, where he took military service with the king of that land. Then, on a certain day, the king came to play chess. He was prompted by Finn, and won seven games one after another.

"Who art thou?" said the king.

"The son of a peasant of the Luagni of Tara," said he.

"No," said the king; "thou art the son whom Muirne bore to Cumall; stay here no longer, lest thou be slain while under my protection."

Then he went forth to Cullen of the Ui Cuanach, to the house of Lochan, a chief smith, who had a very beautiful daughter, Cruithne by name. She fell in love with the youth.

"I shall give thee my daughter, though I know not who thou art." Thereupon the girl slept with the youth.

"Make spears for me," said the youth to the smith. So Lochan made two spears for him. He then bade farewell to Lochan, and went away.

"My boy," said Lochan, "do not go upon the road on which is the sow called the Beo." She it was that devastated the midlands of Munster. But what happened to the youth was to go upon the very road on which the sow was. Then the sow charged him; but he thrust his spear at her, so that it went through her, and left her without life. Then he took the head of the sow with him to the smith as a bridal gift for his daughter. Hence is Sliab Muck (Pig Mountain) in Munster.

After that the youth went onwards into Connacht to seek Crimall, the son of Trenmor. As he was on his way, he heard the wail of a woman. He went towards it, and saw a woman; and now it was tears of blood, and now a gush of blood, so that her mouth was red. "Thou art red-mouthed, woman!" said he.

"Good cause have I," said she, "for my only son has been slain by a tall, very terrible warrior who came in my way."

"What was thy son's name?" said he.

"Glonda was his name," said she. Hence is the Ford of Glonda and the Causeway of Glonda on Moinmoy, and from that redness of mouth the Ford of the Red Mouth has been so called ever since. Then Finn went in pursuit of the warrior, and they fought a combat, and Finn slew the warrior. This is how he was: he had the treasure-bag with him, the treasures of Cumall. He who had fallen there was the Gray one of Luachar, who had dealt the first wound to Cumall in the battle of Cnucha.

Thereupon Finn went into Connacht, and found Crimall as an old man in a desert wood there, and a number of the old fian together with him; and it is they who did the hunting for him. Then he showed him the bag and told him his story from beginning to end; how he had slain the man of the treasures. Finn bade farewell to Crimall, and went to learn poetry from Finneces, who was on the Boyne. He durst not remain in Ireland else, until he took to poetry, for fear of the sons of Urgriu, and of the sons of Morna.

Seven years Finneces had been on the Boyne, watching the salmon of Fec's Pool; for it had been prophesied of him that he would eat the salmon of Fec, after which nothing would remain unknown to him. The salmon was found, and Demne was then ordered to cook it; and the poet told him not to eat anything of the salmon. The youth brought him the salmon after cooking it. "Hast thou eaten any of the salmon, my lad?" said the poet.

"No," said the youth, "but I burned my thumb, and put it into my mouth afterwards."

"What is thy name, my lad?" said he.

"Demne," said the youth. "Finn is thy name, my lad," said he; "and to thee was the salmon given to be eaten, and indeed thou art the Finn." Thereupon the youth ate the salmon. It is that which gave the knowledge to Finn, so that, whenever he put his thumb into his mouth and sang through *teinm laida*,[1] then whatever he had been ignorant of would be revealed to him.

He learnt the three things that constitute a poet: *teinm laida, imbas forosna,* and *dichetul dichennaib.*[2] It is then Finn made this lay to prove his poetry:

May-day, season surpassing! Splendid is color then. Blackbirds sing a
    full lay, if there be a slender shaft of day.
The dust-colored cuckoo calls aloud: Welcome, splendid summer! The
    bitterness of bad weather is past, the boughs of the wood are a thicket.
Summer cuts the river down, the swift herd of horses seeks the pool, the
    long hair of the heather is outspread, the soft white bog-down grows.

[1] Apparently a magic formula.   [2] Magic gifts or formulae of some sort.

Panic startles the heart of the deer, the smooth sea runs apace—season when ocean sinks asleep—blossom covers the world.

Bees with puny strength carry a goodly burden, the harvest of blossoms; up the mountain-side kine take with them mud, the ant makes a rich meal.

The harp of the forest sounds music, the sail gathers—perfect peace. Color has settled on every height, haze on the lake of full waters.

The corncrake, a strenuous bard, discourses; the lofty virgin waterfall sings a welcome to the warm pool; the talk of the rushes is come.

Light swallows dart aloft, loud melody reaches round the hill, the soft rich mast buds, the stuttering quagmire rehearses.

The peat-bog is as the raven's coat, the loud cuckoo bids welcome, the speckled fish leaps, strong is the bound of the swift warrior.

Man flourishes, the maiden buds in her fair strong pride; perfect each forest from top to ground, perfect each great stately plain.

Delightful is the season's splendor, rough winter has gone, white is every fruitful wood, a joyous peace in summer.

A flock of birds settles in the midst of meadows; the green field rustles, wherein is a brawling white stream.

A wild longing is on you to race horses, the ranked host is ranged around: a bright shaft has been shot into the land, so that the water-flag is gold beneath it.

A timorous tiny persistent little fellow sings at the top of his voice, the lark sings clear tidings: surpassing May-day of delicate colors!

However, Finn went to Cethern, the son of Fintan, further to learn poetry with him. At that time there was a very beautiful maiden in Bri Ele, that is to say, in the fairy-knoll of Bri Ele, and the name of that maiden was Ele. The men of Ireland were at feud about that maiden. One man after another went to woo her. Every year on Samain the wooing used to take place; for the fairy-mounds of Ireland were always open about Samain; for on Samain nothing could ever be hidden in the fairy-mounds. To each man that went to woo her this used to happen: one of his people was slain. This was done to mark the occasion, nor was it ever found out who did it.

Like everybody else, the poet Cethern went to woo the maiden. However, Finn did not like the poet's going on that errand. As they went to the wooing they formed themselves into three bands. There were nine in each band. As they went towards the fairy-mound, a man of their people was slain between them; and it was not known who had slain him. Oircbel the poet was the name of the man that was slain there. Hence is Fert Oircbeil, the Grave of Oircbel, in Clonfad. Thereupon they separated, and Finn went from them. . . . However, Finn thought it a grievance and a great disgrace.

He went until he came to the house of the champion Fiacal mac Conchinn, at Sliab Mairge. It is there his dwelling was at that time. To him, then, Finn made his complaint, and told him how the man had been slain among them in the fairy-mound. Fiacal told him to go and sit down by the two Paps of Anu, behind Luachar. So he went and sat down between the two strongholds which are between the two Paps of Anu.

Now, when Finn was there between them, on Samain night, he saw the two fairy-mounds opened around him, even the two strongholds, their ramparts having vanished before them. And he saw a great fire in either of the two strongholds; and he heard a voice from one of them, which said: "Is your sweet-root good?"

"Good, indeed!" said a voice in the other fairy-mound.

"Question: shall anything be taken from us to you?"

"If that be given to us, something will be given to you in return."

While Finn was there he saw a man coming out of the fairy-mound. A kneading-trough was in his hand with a pig upon it, and a cooked calf, and a bunch of wild garlic upon it. The time was Samain. The man came past Finn to reach the other fairy-mound. Finn made a cast with the spear of Fiacal mac Conchinn. He hurled it southward from him towards Sliab Mairge. Then said Finn: "If the spear should reach any one of us, may he escape alive from it! I think this a revenge for my comrade."

That passed, till forthwith he heard a lament, and a great wail, saying:

> On the Barrow, by a sharp-pointed spear,
> Aed, Fidga's son, has fallen:
> By the spear of Fiacal,
> Finn has slain him.

Then Fiacal came to Finn, and was at the two Paps of Anu. Fiacal asked him whom he had slain. "I know not," said Finn, "whether any good has come from the cast which I have thrown."

"'Tis likely, indeed," said Fiacal, "that some one has been slain. It seems to me if thou dost not do it to-night, thou wilt not do it to the end of another year." However, Finn said that he had sent a cast, and that it seemed likely to him that it had reached some one. And he heard a great wailing in the fairy-mound, saying:

> Venom is this spear,
> And venomous he whose it is,
> Venomous whoever threw it,
> Venom for him whom it laid low.

Outside the fairy-mound of Cruachan Bri Ele Finn seized a woman in pledge for his spear. The woman promised to send out the spear if he released her. Finn let the woman from him into the knoll. Then, as she went into the knoll the woman said:

> Venom the spear,
> And venom the hand that threw it!
> If it is not cast out of the knoll,
> A murrain will seize the land.

Thereupon the spear was thrown out, and Finn took it with him to where Fiacal was.

"Well," said Fiacal, "keep the spear with which thou hast done the famous deed." Then Fiacal said the occasion was fortunate, since the man had been slain who had killed Finn's comrade.

"He whom thou hast slain here," said he, "'tis he who used to kill every man that came to woo the maiden, because it is he who loved the maiden."

Thereupon Finn and Fiacal went onward. Now, Fiacal had a tryst with the fian at Inber Colptha. Then he said to Finn that they should go home . . . since their business was finished. Said Finn: "Let me go with thee," said he.

"I do not wish thee to go with me," says Fiacal, "lest thy strength should fail thee."

"I shall find out," said Finn.

Then they went forth. Twelve balls of lead were round the neck of Fiacal to restrain his vigor, such was his swiftness. He would throw one ball after another from him, and Finn took them with him, and yet Fiacal's running was no swifter than Finn's.

They reached Inber Colptha. Then Finn brought all the twelve balls of lead to him, and he was pleased. That night they slept there. They made Finn keep watch that night, and he was told to wake the warrior if he heard any cry of outrage. Now, one hour of the night, as Finn was watching, he heard a cry from the north, and did not wake the warrior. He went alone in the direction of the cry to Sliab Slanga. While Finn was there, among the men of Ulster, at the hour of midnight, he overtook three women before him, at a green mound, with cloaks of fairy-women. As they were wailing on that mound, they would all put their hands on the mound. Then the women fled into the fairy-mound before Finn. Finn caught one of the women as she was going into the fairy-mound of Slanga, and snatched her brooch out of her cloak. The woman went after him, and besought Finn to give her back the brooch of her cloak, and said it was not fit for her to go into the fairy-mound with a blemish, and she promised a reward for her release.[1]

[1] The story is unfinished.

THE PURSUIT OF DIARMUID AND GRAINNE

"The Pursuit of Diarmuid and Grainne" is the most striking and tragic tale of the Finn cycle. It relates the trials and sufferings of Diarmuid, one of Finn's warriors whom Grainne, Finn's affianced wife, forced to elope with her. The narrative is somewhat prolix, but because of its comparative inaccessibility, it is reproduced entire, except for one or two episodes not directly related to the main narrative. This story, which has often been compared with the tragic romance of "Tristan and Iseult," differs markedly in manner from the stories of the earlier tradition. It is more discursive, more delineative, and less restrained in style than the tales of the Ulster cycle or even than the earlier tales of Finn. And yet, its realistic treatment of human motive and its objective analysis of character, devoid of editorial comment, place it definitely in the most honorable line of Irish literary tradition. The episodic digressions contain a considerable amount of material that belongs to the fairy tradition of the folk in later generations rather than to the epic literature of earlier times, but they are none the less interesting and they illustrate the tendency, found even in the oldest recorded Irish literature, to combine such material with what we may call the "classical" tradition of the heroic age. The main plot of the story and the general conception of the characters are certainly ancient. The earliest reference to the love of Diarmuid and Grainne dates from the tenth century. The present version, however, represents accretions through many generations.

On a certain day when Finn mac Cumaill rose at early morn in Almu, in Leinster, and sat upon the grass-green plain, having neither servant nor attendant with him, there followed him two of his people; that is, Oisin the son of Finn, and Diorruing the son of Dobar O'Baoiscne. Oisin spoke, and what he said was:

"What is the cause of this early rising of thine, O Finn?" said he.

"Not without cause have I made this early rising," said Finn; "for I am without a wife since Maignes the daughter of Garad Glundub mac Moirne died; for he is not wont to have slumber nor sweet sleep who happens to be without a fitting wife, and that is the cause of my early rising, O Oisin."

"What forceth thee to be thus?" said Oisin; "for there is not a wife nor a mate in the green-landed island of Erin upon whom thou mightest turn the light of thine eyes or of thy sight, whom we would not bring by fair means or by foul to thee."

And then spoke Diorruing, and what he said was: "I myself could discover for thee a wife and a mate befitting thee."

"Who is she?" said Finn.

"She is Grainne the daughter of Cormac the son of Art the son of Conn the Hundred-Fighter," said Diorruing, "that is, the woman that is fairest of feature and form and speech of the women of the world together."

"By my hand, O Diorruing," said Finn, "there has been strife and variance between Cormac and myself for a long time, and I think it not good nor seemly that he should give me a refusal of marriage; and I had rather that ye should both go to ask the marriage of his daughter for me of Cormac, for I could better endure a refusal of marriage to be given to you than to myself."

"We will go there," said Oisin, "though there be no profit for us there, and let no man know of our journey until we come back again."

After that, those two good warriors went their way, and they took farewell of Finn, and it is not told how they fared until they reached Tara. The king of Erin chanced to be holding a gathering and a muster before them upon the plain of Tara, and the chiefs and the great nobles of his people were with him. A friendly welcome was given to Oisin and Diorruing, and the gathering was then put off until another day, for the king was certain that it was upon some pressing matter that those two had come to him. Afterwards Oisin called the king of Erin to one side, and told him that it was to ask of him the marriage of his daughter for Finn mac Cumaill that they themselves were then come. Cormac spoke, and what he said was:

"There is not a son of a king or of a great prince, a hero or a battle-champion in Erin, to whom my daughter has not given refusal of marriage, and it is on me that all and every one lays the blame for that; so I will not give you any formal decision until ye betake yourselves before my daughter, for it is better that ye hear her own words than that ye be displeased with me."

After that they went their way to the dwelling of the women, and Cormac sat him upon the side of the couch and of the high bed by Grainne; and he said: "Here, O Grainne," said he, "are two of the people of Finn mac Cumaill coming to ask thee as wife and as mate for him, and what answer wouldst thou give them?"

Grainne answered, and what she said was: "If he be a fitting son-in-law for thee, why should he not be a fitting husband and mate for me?"

Then they were satisfied; and after that a feast and banquet was made for them in the bower with Grainne and the women, so that they became exhilirated and mirthful; and Cormac made a tryst with them and with Finn a fortnight from that night at Tara.

Thereafter Oisin and Diorruing arrived again at Almu, where they found Finn and the fian, and they told them their news from beginning to end. Now as every thing wears away, so also did that space of time; and then Finn collected and assembled the seven battalions of the standing fian from every quarter where they were, and they came where Finn was, in Almu the great and broad of Leinster; and on the last day of that period of time they went forth in great bands, in troops, and in impetuous fierce impenetrable companies, and we are not told how they fared until they reached Tara. Cormac was before them upon the plain with the chiefs and the great nobles of the men of Erin about him, and they made a gentle welcome for Finn and all the fian, and after that they went to the king's mirthful house called Midcuart. The king of Erin sat down to enjoy drinking and pleasure, with his wife at his left shoulder, that is, Eitche, the daughter of Atan of Corcaig, and Grainne at her shoulder, and Finn mac Cumaill at the king's right hand; and Cairbre Liffecair the son of Cormac sat at one side of the same royal house, and Oisin the son of Finn at the other side, and each one of them sat according to his rank and to his patrimony from that down.

There sat there a druid and a skilful man of knowledge of the people of Finn before Grainne the daughter of Cormac; that is, Daire Duanach mac Morna; and it was not long before there arose gentle talking and mutual discourse between himself and Grainne. Then Daire Duanach mac Morna arose and stood before Grainne, and sang her the songs and the verses and the sweet poems of her fathers and of her ancestors; and then Grainne spoke and asked the druid,

"What is the reason wherefore Finn is come to this place tonight?"

"If thou knowest not that," said the druid, "it is no wonder that I know it not."

"I desire to learn it of thee," said Grainne.

"Well then," said the druid, "it is to ask thee as wife and as mate that Finn is come to this place to-night."

"It is a great marvel to me," said Grainne, "that it is not for Oisin that Finn asks me, for it were fitter to give me such as he, than a man that is older than my father."

"Say not that," said the druid, "for were Finn to hear thee he himself would not have thee, neither would Oisin dare to take thee."

"Tell me now," said Grainne, "who is that warrior at the right shoulder of Oisin the son of Finn?"

"Yonder," said the druid, "is Goll mac Morna, the active, the warlike."

"Who is that warrior at the shoulder of Goll?" said Grainne.

"Oscar the son of Oisin," said the druid.

"Who is that graceful-legged man at the shoulder of Oscar?" said Grainne.

"Cailte mac Ronain," said the druid.

"What haughty impetuous warrior is that yonder at the shoulder of Cailte?" said Grainne.

"The son of Lugaid of the mighty hand, and that man is sister's son to Finn mac Cumaill," said the druid.

"Who is that freckled sweet-worded man, upon whom is the curling dusky-black hair and the two red ruddy cheeks, upon the left hand of Oisin the son of Finn?"

"That man is Diarmuid the grandson of Dubne, the white-toothed, of the light-some countenance; that is, the best lover of women and of maidens that is in the whole world."

"Who is that at the shoulder of Diarmuid?" said Grainne.

"Diorruing the son of Dobar Damad O'Baoiscne, and that man is a druid and a skilful man of science," said Daire Duanach.

"That is a goodly company," said Grainne; and she called her attendant handmaid to her, and told her to bring to her the jewelled golden-chased goblet which was in the bower behind her. The handmaid brought the goblet, and Grainne filled the goblet forthwith, and it contained the drink of nine times nine men. Grainne said,

"Take the goblet to Finn first, and bid him drink a draught out of it, and disclose to him that it is I that sent it to him."

The handmaid took the goblet to Finn, and told him everything that Grainne had bidden her say to him. Finn took the goblet, and no sooner had he drunk a draught out of it than there fell upon him a stupor of sleep and of deep slumber. Cormac took the draught and the same sleep fell upon him, and Eitche, the wife of Cormac, took the goblet and drank a draught out of it, and the same sleep fell upon her as upon all the others. Then Grainne called the attendant handmaid to her, and said to her:

"Take this goblet to Cairbre Liffecair and tell him to drink a draught out of it, and give the goblet to those sons of kings by him."

The handmaid took the goblet to Cairbre, and he was not well able to give it to him that was next to him, before a stupor of sleep and of deep slumber fell upon him too, and each one that took the goblet, one after another, fell into a stupor of sleep and of deep slumber.

When Grainne saw that they were in a state of drunkenness and of trance, she rose fairly and softly from the seat on which she was, and spoke to Oisin, and what she said was:

"I marvel at Finn mac Cumaill that he should seek such a wife as I, for it were fitter for him to give me my own equal to marry than a man older than my father."

"Say not that, O Grainne," said Oisin, "for if Finn were to hear thee he would not have thee, neither would I dare to take thee."

"Wilt thou receive courtship from me, O Oisin?" said Grainne.

"I will not," said Oisin, "for whatsoever woman is betrothed to Finn, I would not meddle with her."

Then Grainne turned her face to Diarmuid O'Duibne, and what she said to him was: "Wilt thou receive courtship from me, O O'Duibne, since Oisin received it not from me?"

"I will not," said Diarmuid, "for whatever woman is betrothed to Oisin I may not take her, even were she not betrothed to Finn."

"Then," said Grainne, "I put thee under taboos of danger and of destruction, O Diarmuid, that is, under the taboos of mighty druidism, if thou take me not with thee out of this household to-night, ere Finn and the king of Erin arise out of that sleep."

"Evil bonds are those under which thou hast laid me, O woman," said Diarmuid; "and wherefore hast thou laid those taboos upon me before all the sons of kings and of high princes in the king's mirthful house called Midcuart this night, seeing that there is not of all those one less worthy to be loved by a woman than myself?"

"By thy hand, O O'Duibne, it is not without cause that I have laid those taboos on thee, as I will tell thee now.

"One day when the king of Erin was presiding over a gathering and muster on the plain of Tara, Finn and the seven battalions of the standing fian chanced to be there that day; and there arose a great goaling match between Cairbre Liffecair the son of Cormac, and the son of Lugaid, and the men of Mag Breg, and of Cerna, and the stout champions of Tara arose on the side of Cairbre, and the fian of Erin on the side of the son of Lugaid; and there were none sitting in the gathering that day but the king, and Finn, and thyself, O Diarmuid. It happened that the game was going against the son of Lugaid, and thou didst rise and stand, and tookest his hurly-stick from the next man to thee, and didst throw him to the ground and to the earth, and thou wentest into the game, and didst win the goal three times upon Cairbre and upon the warriors of Tara. I was at that time in my bower of the clear view, of the blue windows of glass, gazing upon thee; and I turned the light of mine eyes and of my sight upon thee that day, and I never gave that love to any other man from that time to this, and will not for ever."

"It is a wonder that thou shouldest give me that love instead of Finn," said Diarmuid, "seeing that there is not in Erin a man that is fonder of a woman than he; and knowest thou, O Grainne, on the night that Finn is in Tara that he it is that has the keys of Tara, and that so we cannot leave the stronghold?"

"There is a wicket-gate to my bower," said Grainne, "and we will pass out through it."

"It is a prohibited thing for me to pass through any wicket-gate whatsoever," said Diarmuid.

"Howbeit, I hear," said Grainne, "that every warrior and battle-champion can pass by the shafts of his javelins and by the staves of his spears, in or out over the rampart of every fort and of every stronghold, and I will pass out by the wicket-gate, and do thou follow me so."

Grainne went her way out, and Diarmuid spoke to his people, and what he said was: "O Oisin, son of Finn, what shall I do with this taboo that has been laid on me?"

"Thou art not guilty of the taboo which has been laid upon thee," said Oisin, "and I tell thee to follow Grainne, and keep thyself well against the wiles of Finn."

"O Oscar, son of Oisin, what is good for me to do as to those bonds which have been laid upon me?"

"I tell thee to follow Grainne," said Oscar, "for he is a sorry wretch that fails to keep his taboos."

"What counsel dost thou give me, O Cailte?" said Diarmuid.

"I say," said Cailte, "that I have a fitting wife, and yet I had rather than the wealth of the world that it had been to me that Grainne gave that love."

"What counsel givest thou me, O Diorruing?"

"I tell thee to follow Grainne, though thy death will come of it, and I grieve for it."

"Is that the counsel of you all to me?" said Diarmuid.

"It is," said Oisin, and said all the others together.

After that Diarmuid arose and stood, and stretched forth his active warrior hand over his broad weapons, and took leave and farewell of Oisin and of the chiefs of the fian; and not bigger is a smooth-crimson whortleberry than was each tear that Diarmuid shed from his eyes at parting with his people. Diarmuid went to the top of the stronghold, and put the shafts of his two javelins under him, and rose with an airy, very light, exceeding high, bird-like leap, until he attained the breadth of his two soles of the beautiful grass-green earth on the plain without, and Grainne met him. Then Diarmuid spoke, and what he said was: "I believe, O Grainne, that this is an evil course upon which thou art come; for it were better for thee have Finn mac Cumaill for a lover than myself, seeing that I know not what nook or corner, or remote part of Erin I can take thee to now, and return again home, without Finn's learning what thou hast done."

"It is certain that I will not go back," said Grainne, "and that I will not part from thee until death part me from thee."

"Then go forward, O Grainne," said Diarmuid.

Diarmuid and Grainne went their way after that, and they had not gone beyond a mile from Tara when Grainne said, "I indeed am wearying, O O'Duibne."

"It is a good time to weary, O Grainne," said Diarmuid, "and return now to thine own household again, for I plight the word of a

true warrior that I will never carry thee, nor any other woman, to
all eternity."

"So needst thou not do," said Grainne, "for my father's horses
are in a fenced meadow by themselves, and they have chariots;
and return thou to them, and yoke two horses of them to a chariot,
and I will wait for thee on this spot till thou overtake me again."
Diarmuid returned to the horses, and he yoked two horses of them
to a chariot. It is not told how Diarmuid and Grainne fared until
they reached Beul Atha Luain.

And Diarmuid spoke to Grainne, and said: "It is all the easier
for Finn to follow our track, O Grainne, that we have the horses."

"Then," said Grainne, "leave the horses upon this spot, and I
will journey on foot by thee henceforth." Diarmuid got down at
the edge of the ford, and took a horse with him over across the ford,
and thus left one of them upon each side of the stream, and he and
Grainne went a mile with the stream westward, and reached land at
the side of the province of Connacht. It is not told how they fared
until they arrived at Doire Da Both, in the midst of Clan Ricard;
and Diarmuid cut down the grove around him, and made to it seven
doors of wattles, and he settled a bed of soft rushes and of the
tops of the birch under Grainne in the very midst of that wood.

As for Finn mac Cumaill, I will tell his tidings clearly. All that
were in Tara rose at early morn on the morrow, and they found
Diarmuid and Grainne wanting from among them, and a burning
jealousy and rage seized upon Finn. He found his trackers before
him on the plain, that is the Clan Neamuin, and he bade them
follow Diarmuid and Grainne. Then they carried the track as far
as Beul Atha Luain, and Finn and the fian of Erin followed them;
but they could not follow the track over across the ford, so that
Finn pledged his word that if they followed not the track out
speedily, he would hang them on either side of the ford.

Then the Clan Neamuin went up to the stream, and found a
horse on either side of the stream; and they went a mile with the
stream westward, and found the track by the side of the province
of Connacht, and Finn and the fian of Erin followed them. Then
spoke Finn, and what he said was: "Well I know where Diarmuid
and Grainne shall be found now, that is in Doire Da Both."
Oisin, and Oscar, and Cailte, and Diorruing son of Dobar Damad
O'Baoiscne, were listening to Finn speaking these words, and

Oisin spoke, and what he said was: "We are in danger lest Diarmuid and Grainne be yonder, and we must needs send him some warning. And look where Bran is, that is, the hound of Finn mac Cumaill, that we may send him to him, for Finn himself is not dearer to him than Diarmuid is; and, O Oscar, tell Bran to go with a warning to Diarmuid, who is in Doire Da Both"; and Oscar told that to Bran. Bran understood that with knowledge and wisdom, and went back to the hinder part of the host where Finn might not see him, and followed Diarmuid and Grainne by their track until he reached Doire Da Both, and thrust his head into Diarmuid's bosom, and he asleep.

Then Diarmuid sprang out of his sleep, and awoke Grainne also, and said to her: "There is Bran, the hound of Finn mac Cumaill, coming with a warning to us before Finn himself."

"Take that warning," said Grainne, "and fly."

"I will not take it," said Diarmuid, "for I would not that Finn caught me at any other time rather than now, since I cannot escape from him." When Grainne heard this, dread and great fear seized her; and Bran departed from them.

Then Oisin the son of Finn spoke and said: "We are in danger lest Bran have not gotten opportunity to go to Diarmuid, and we must needs give him some other warning; and look for Feargoir the henchman of Cailte."

"He is with me," said Cailte. Now Feargoir was so, that every shout he gave used to be heard in the three nearest districts to him. Then they made him give three shouts, in order that Diarmuid might hear him. Diarmuid heard Feargoir, and awoke Grainne out of her sleep, and what he said was: "I hear the henchman of Cailte mac Ronain, and it is with Cailte he is, and it is with Finn that Cailte is, and this is a warning they are sending me."

"Take that warning," said Grainne.

"I will not," said Diarmuid, "for we shall not leave this wood until Finn and the fian of Erin overtake us"; and fear and great dread seized Grainne when she heard that.

As for Finn, I will tell his tidings clearly. He did not abandon the chase until he reached Doire Da Both, and he sent the tribe of Emain to search out the wood, and they saw Diarmuid and a woman by him. They returned back again where were Finn and the fian of Erin, and Finn asked of them whether Diarmuid or Grainne were in the wood. "Diarmuid is there," they said, "and there is some woman by him; who she is we know not for we know Diarmuid's track, and we know not the track of Grainne."

"Foul fall the friends of Diarmuid O'Duibne for his sake," said Finn, "and he shall not leave the wood until he give me satisfaction for every thing he has done to me."

"It is a great token of jealousy in thee, O Finn," said Oisin, "to think that Diarmuid would stay upon the plain of Maenmag, seeing that there is there no stronghold but Doire Da Both, and thou too awaiting him."

"That shall profit thee nothing, O Oisin," said Finn, "and well I knew the three shouts that Cailte's servant gave, that it was ye that sent them as a warning to Diarmuid; and that it was ye that sent my own hound, that is, Bran, with another warning to him: but it shall profit you nothing to have sent him any of those warnings; for he shall not leave Doire Da Both until he give me compensation for everything that he hath done to me, and for every slight that he hath put on me."

"Great foolishness it is for thee, O Finn," said Oscar the son of Oisin, "to suppose that Diarmuid would stay in the midst of this plain, and thou waiting to take his head from him."

"Who else cut the wood thus, and made a close warm enclosure thereof, with seven tight slender-narrow doors to it? And with which of us, O Diarmuid, is the truth, with myself or with Oscar?" said Finn.

"Thou didst never err in thy good judgment, O Finn," said Diarmuid, "and I indeed and Grainne are here." Then Finn bade the fian of Erin come round Diarmuid and take him for himself. Thereupon Diarmuid rose up and gave Grainne three kisses in the presence of Finn and of the fian, so that a burning of jealousy and rage seized Finn upon seeing that, and he said that Diarmuid should give his head for those kisses.

As for Angus of the Brug,[1] that is, the tutor in learning of Diarmuid O'Duibne, who was in the Brug upon the Boyne, he saw the extremity in which his foster-son, Diarmuid, then was; and he proceeded accompanying the pure-cold wind, and he halted not till he reached Doire Da Both. Then he went unknown to Finn or

---

[1] Angus mac Oc, one of the most famous chiefs of the Tuatha De Danann, or fairy folk (see p. 2).

to the fian of Erin to the place wherein were Diarmuid and Grainne, and he greeted Diarmuid, and what he said was: "What is this thing that thou hast done, O O'Duibne?"

"This it is," said Diarmuid; "the daughter of the king of Erin has fled secretly with me from her father and from Finn, and it is not of my will that she has come with me."

"Then let one of you come under either border of my mantle," said Angus, "and I will take you out of the place where ye are without the knowledge of Finn or of the fian of Erin."

"Take thou Grainne with thee," said Diarmuid, "but as for me, I will never go with thee; howbeit, if I be alive presently I will follow thee, and if I do not, do thou send Grainne to her father, and let him treat her well or ill."

After that Angus put Grainne under the border of his mantle, and went his way without knowledge of Finn or of the fian of Erin, and no tale is told of them until they reached Ros Da Soileach which is now called Luimneach.

After Angus and Grainne had departed from Diarmuid, he arose as a straight pillar and stood upright, and girded his arms and his armor and his various sharp weapons about him. After that he drew near to one of the seven wattled doors that there were in the enclosure, and asked who was at it. "No foe to thee is any man who is at it," said they who were without, "for here are Oisin the son of Finn, and Oscar the son of Oisin, and the chieftains of the Clan Baoiscne together with us; and come out to us, and none will dare to do thee harm, hurt, or damage."

"I will not go to you," said Diarmuid, "until I see at which door Finn himself is." He drew near to another wattled door, and asked who was at it.

"Cailte the son of Crannacar mac Ronain, and the Clan Ronain together with him; and come out to us and we will fight and die for thy sake."

"I will not go to you," said Diarmuid, "for I will not cause Finn to be angry with you for welldoing to myself." He drew near to another wattled door, and asked who was at it.

"Here are Conan the son of Finn of Liathluacra, and the Clan Morna together with him; and we are enemies to Finn, and thou art far dearer to us than he, and for that reason come out to us, and none will dare meddle with thee."

"Surely I will not go," said Diarmuid, "for Finn had rather the death of every man of you should come to pass, than that I should be let out." He drew near to another wattled door, and asked who was there.

"A friend and a dear comrade of thine is here, that is, Finn the son of Cuadan mac Murchada, the royal chief of the fian of Munster, and the Munster fian together with him; and we are of one land and one country with thee, O Diarmuid, and we will give our bodies and our lives for thee and for thy sake."

"I will not go out to you," said Diarmuid, "for I will not cause Finn to be displeased with you for welldoing to myself." He drew near to another wattled door and asked who was at it.

"It is Finn the son of Glor, the royal chief of the fian of Ulster, and the Ulster fian along with him; and come out to us, and none will dare cut or wound thee."

"I will not go out to you," said Diarmuid, "for thou art a friend to me, and thy father; and I would not that he should bear the enmity of Finn for my sake." He drew near to another wattled door, and asked who was at it.

"No friend to thee is any that is here," said they, "for here are Aed Beg of Emain, and Aed Fada of Emain, and Caol Croda of Emain, and Goineach of Emain, and Gothan Gilmeurach of Emain, and Aife the daughter of Gothan Gilmeurach of Emain, and Cuadan Lorgaire of Emain; and we bear thee no love, and if thou wouldst come out to us we would wound thee till thou shouldst be like a stone, without respite."

"Evil the company that is there," said Diarmuid, "O ye of the lie, and of the tracking, and of the one brogue; and it is not the fear of your hand that is upon me, but from enmity to you I will not go out to you." He drew near to another wattled door, and asked who was at it.

"Here are Finn mac Cumaill, the son of Art, the son of Trenmor O'Baoiscne, and four hundred hirelings with him; and we bear thee no love, and if thou shouldst come out to us we would cleave thy bones asunder."

"I pledge my word," said Diarmuid, "that the door at which thou art, O Finn, is the very door by which I will pass of all the doors."

Having heard that, Finn charged his battalions on pain of death and instant destruction not to let Diarmuid pass them without their knowledge. Diarmuid having heard that arose with an airy, high, exceeding light bound, by the shafts of his javelins and by the staves of his spears, and went a great way out beyond Finn and beyond his people without their knowledge or perception. He looked back upon them and proclaimed to them that he had passed them, and slung his shield upon the broad arched expanse of his back, and so went straight westward; and he was not long in going out of sight of Finn and of the fian. Then when he saw that they followed him not, he turned back where he had seen Angus and Grainne departing out of the wood, and he followed them by their track, holding a straight course, until he reached Ros Da Soileach.

He found Angus and Grainne there in a warm well-lighted hut, and a great wide-flaming fire kindled before them, with half a wild boar upon spits. Diarmuid greeted them, and the very life of Grainne all but fled out through her mouth with joy at meeting Diarmuid. Diarmuid told them his tidings from beginning to end; and they ate their meal that night, and Diarmuid and Grainne went to sleep together until the day came with its full light on the morrow. Angus arose early, and what he said to Diarmuid was: "I will now depart, O O'Duibne, and this counsel I leave thee; not to go into a tree having but one trunk in flying before Finn; and not to go into a cave of the earth to which there shall be but the one door; and not to go on to an island of the sea with but one channel between it and the land. And in whatever place thou shalt cook thy meal, there eat it not; and in whatever place thou shalt eat, there sleep not; and in whatever place thou shalt sleep, there rise not on the morrow."

He took leave and farewell of them, and went his way after that. Then Diarmuid and Grainne journeyed with the Shannon on their right hand westward until they reached Garb Aba of the Fian, which is now called Leaman; and Diarmuid killed a salmon on the bank of the Leaman, and put it on a spit to broil. Then he himself and Grainne went over across the stream to eat it, as Angus had told them; and they went thence westward to sleep. Diarmuid and Grainne rose early on the morrow, and journeyed straight westward until they reached the marshy moor of Finn-liath, and they met a youth upon the moor, and the feature and form of that youth were good, but he had not fitting arms nor armor. Then Diarmuid greeted that youth, and asked tidings of him. "I am a young warrior seeking a lord," said he, "and Muadan is my name."

"What wilt thou do for me, O youth?" said Diarmuid.

"I will do thee service by day, and I will watch thee by night," said Muadan.

"I tell thee to retain that youth," said Grainne, "for thou canst not always remain without followers." Then they made bonds of compact and agreement one with the other, and journeyed forth westward until they reached the Carrthach; and when they had reached the stream, Muadan asked Diarmuid and Grainne to go upon his back so that he might bear them across over the stream. "That were a great burden for thee," said Grainne. Then he nevertheless took Diarmuid and Grainne upon his back and bore them over across the stream. They journeyed forth westward until they reached the Beith, and when they had reached the stream Muadan did likewise with them, and they went into a cave of the earth at the side of Currach Cinn Admuid, over Tonn Toime; and Muadan dressed a bed of soft rushes and of birch-tops for Diarmuid and Grainne in the further part of that cave. He himself went into the next wood to him, and plucked in it a straight long rod of a quicken tree; and he put a hair and a hook upon the rod, and put a holly berry upon the hook, and went and stood over the stream, and caught a fish that cast. He put on a second berry, and caught a second fish; and he put up a third berry, and caught a third fish. He then put the hook and the hair under his girdle, and the rod into the earth, and took his three fish with him to where Diarmuid and Grainne were, and put the fish upon spits. When they were broiled Muadan said: "I give the dividing of these fish to thee, Diarmuid."

"I had rather that thou shouldst divide them thyself," said Diarmuid.

"Then," said Muadan, "I give the dividing of these fish to thee, O Grainne."

"It suffices me that thou divide them," said Grainne.

"Now hadst thou divided the fish, O Diarmuid," said Muadan, "thou wouldst have given the largest share to Grainne; and had it been Grainne that divided them, it is to thee she would have given the largest share; and since it is I that am dividing it, have thou the largest fish, O Diarmuid, and let Grainne have the second largest fish, and let me have the smallest fish." Know, O reader, that Diarmuid kept himself from Grainne, and that he left a spit of flesh uncooked in Doire Da Both as a token to Finn and to the fian that he had not sinned with Grainne, and know also that he left the second time seven salmon uncooked upon the bank of the Leaman, wherefore it was that Finn hastened eagerly after him. They ate their meal that night, and Diarmuid and Grainne went to sleep in the further part of the cave, and Muadan kept watch and ward for them until the day arose with its full light on the morrow.

Diarmuid arose early, and made Grainne sit up; and told her to keep watch for Muadan, and that he himself would go to walk the country. Diarmuid went his way, and went upon the top of the nearest hill to him, and he stood gazing upon the four quarters around him; that is, eastward and westward, southward and northward. He had not been a long time there before he saw a great swift fleet, and a fearful company of ships, coming towards the land straight from the west; and the course that the people of the fleet took in coming to land was to the foot of the hill upon which was Diarmuid. Nine times nine of the chieftains of that fleet came ashore, and Diarmuid went to ask tidings of them; and he greeted them and inquired of them news, of what land or what country they were.

"We are the three royal chiefs of the Sea of Wight," said they, "and Finn mac Cumaill hath sent for us because of a forest marauder, and a rebellious enemy of his that he has outlawed, who is called Diarmuid O'Duibne; and to curb him are we now come. Also we have three savage hounds, and we will loose them upon his track, and it will be but a short time before we get tidings of him; fire burns them not, water drowns them not, and weapons do not wound them; and we ourselves number twenty hundreds of stout stalwart men, and each man of us is a man commanding a hundred. Moreover, tell us who thou thyself art, or hast thou any word of the tidings of O'Duibne?"

"I saw him yesterday," said Diarmuid, "and I myself am but a warrior who am walking the world by the strength of my hand and the temper of my sword; and I vow that ye will have to deal with no ordinary man if Diarmuid meets you."

"Well, no one has been found yet," said they.

"What are ye called yourselves?" said Diarmuid.

"Dub-cosach, Finn-cosach, and Tren-cosach are our names," said they.

"Is there wine in your ships?" asked Diarmuid.

"There is," they said.

"If ye were pleased to bring out a tun of wine," said Diarmuid, "I would perform a feat for you." Certain men were sent to seek the tun, and when it was come Diarmuid raised it between his two arms and drank a draught out of it, and the others drank the rest of it. After that Diarmuid lifted the tun and took it to the top of the hill, and he himself mounted upon it, and rolled it down the steep of the hill until it reached the lower part of it, and he rolled the tun up the hill again, and he did that feat three times in the presence of the strangers, and remained himself upon the tun as it both came and went. They said that he was one that had never seen a good feat, seeing that he called that a feat; and with that one of them got upon the tun. Diarmuid gave the tun a kick, and the stranger fell to the ground before ever the tun began to roll; and the tun rolled over that young warrior, so that it caused his bowels and his entrails to come out about his feet. Thereupon Diarmuid followed the tun and brought it up again, and a second man mounted upon it. When Diarmuid saw that, he gave it a kick, and the first man had not been more speedily slain than was the second. Diarmuid urged the tun up again, and the third man mounted upon it; and he too was slain like the others. Thus were slain fifty of their people by Diarmuid's trick that day, and as many as were not slain of them went to their ships that night. Diarmuid went to his own people, and Muadan put his hair and his hook upon his rod, and caught three salmon. He stuck the rod into the ground, and the hair under his girdle, and took the fish to Diarmuid and Grainne, and they ate their meal that night; and Muadan dressed a bed under Diarmuid and under Grainne in the further part of the cave, and he went himself to the door of the cave to keep watch and ward for them until the clear bright day arose on the morrow.

Diarmuid arose at early day and beaming dawn on the morrow, and roused Grainne, and told her to watch while Muadan slept. He went himself to the top of the same hill, and he had not been

there long before the three chiefs came towards him, and he enquired of them whether they would like to perform any more
feats. They said that they had rather find tidings of Diarmuid
O'Duibne. "I have seen a man who saw him to-day," said Diarmuid; and thereupon Diarmuid put from him his weapons and his
armor upon the hill, every thing but the shirt that was next his
skin, and he stuck his javelin, the Crann Buide of Manannan
mac Lir, upright with its point uppermost. Then Diarmuid rose
with a light, bird-like bound, so that he descended from above
upon the javelin, and came down fairly and cunningly off it,
having neither wound nor cut upon him.

A young warrior of the people of the foreigners said, "Thou art
one that never hast seen a good feat since thou wouldst call that
a feat"; and with that he put his weapons and his armor from
him, and he rose in like manner lightly over the javelin, and descended upon it full heavily and helplessly, so that the point of
the javelin went up through his heart and he fell down dead to
the earth. Diarmuid drew the javelin out and placed it standing
the second time; and the second man of them arose to do the feat,
and he too was slain like the other. Likewise, fifty of the people
of the foreigners fell by Diarmuid's feat on that day; and they
bade him take away the javelin, saying that he should slay no
more of their people with that feat. And they went to their ships.

And Diarmuid went to Muadan and Grainne, and Muadan
brought them the fish of that night, and Diarmuid and Grainne
slept by each other that night, and Muadan kept watch and ward
for them until morning.

Diarmuid rose on the morrow, and took with him to the aforesaid hill two forked poles out of the next wood, and placed them
upright; and the Moralltach, that is, the sword of Angus of the
Brug, between the two forked poles upon its edge. Then he himself rose exceeding lightly over it, and thrice measured the sword
by paces from the hilt to its point, and he came down and asked
if there was a man of them who could perform that feat.

"That is a bad question," said a man of them, "for there never
was done in Erin any feat which some one of us would not do."
He then rose and went over the sword, and as he was descending
from above it happened to him one of his legs slipped down on
either side of the sword, so that there was made of him two halves

to the crown of his head. Then a second man rose, and as he descended from above he chanced to fall crossways upon the sword, so that there were two portions made of him. In like manner, there had not fallen more of the people of the foreigners of the Sea of Wight on the two days before that, than there fell upon that day. Then they told him to take away his sword, saying that already too many of their people had fallen by him; and they asked him whether he had gotten any word of the tidings of Diarmuid O'Duibne. "I have seen him that saw him to-day," said Diarmuid, "and I will go to seek tidings to-night."

Diarmuid went where were Grainne and Muadan, and Muadan caught three fish for them that night; so they ate their meal, and Diarmuid and Grainne went to sleep in the hinder part of the cave, and Muadan kept watch and ward for them.

Diarmuid rose at early dawn of the morning, and girt about him his suit of battle and of conflict; under which, through which, or over which, it was not possible to wound him; and he took the Moralltach, that is, the sword of Angus of the Brug, at his left side; which sword left no stroke nor blow unfinished at the first trial. He took likewise his two thick-shafted javelins of battle, that is, the Gae Buide ("Yellow Javelin"), and the Gae Derg ("Red Javelin"), from which none recovered, or man or woman, that had ever been wounded by them. After that Diarmuid roused Grainne, and bade her keep watch and ward for Muadan, saying that he himself would go to view the four quarters around him. When Grainne beheld Diarmuid, brave and daring, clothed in his suit of anger and of battle, fear and great dread seized her, for she knew that it was for a combat and an encounter that he was so equipped; and she asked of him what he intended to do. "Thou seest me thus for fear lest my foes should meet me." That soothed Grainne, and then Diarmuid went in that array to meet the foreigners.

They came to land forthwith, and enquired of him tidings of O'Duibne.

"I saw him not long ago," said Diarmuid.

"Then show us where he is," said they, "that we may take his head before Finn mac Cumaill."

"I should be keeping him but ill," said Diarmuid, "if I did as ye say; for the body and the life of Diarmuid are under the protection of my prowess and of my valor, and therefore I will do him no treachery."

"Is that true?" said they.

"It is true, indeed," said Diarmuid.

"Then shalt thou thyself not quit this spot," said they, "and we will take thy head before Finn, since thou art a foe to him."

"I should doubtless be bound," said Diarmuid, "should I let my head go with you"; and as he thus spoke, he drew the sword Moralltach from its sheath, and dealt a furious stroke of destruction at the head of him that was next to him, so that he made two halves of it. Then he drew near to the host of the foreigners, and began to slaughter and to attack them heroically and with swift valor. He rushed under them, through them, and over them, as a hawk would go through small birds, or a wolf through a large flock of small sheep; even thus it was that Diarmuid hewed crossways the glittering very beautiful mail of his opponents, so that there went not from that spot a man to tell tidings or to boast of great deeds, without having the grievousness of death and the final end of life executed upon him, except the three chiefs and a small number of their people that fled to their ship.

Diarmuid returned back having no cut nor wound, and went his way till he reached Muadan and Grainne. They gave him welcome, and Grainne asked him whether he had received any word of the tidings of Finn mac Cumaill and of the fian of Erin. He said that he had not, and they ate their food and their meat that night.

Diarmuid rose at early day and beaming dawn on the morrow, and halted not until he had reached the aforesaid hill, and having gotten there he struck his shield mightily and soundingly, so that he caused the shore to tremble with the noise around him. Then said the foreign chief Dub-cosach that he would himself go to fight with Diarmuid, and straightway went ashore. Then he and Diarmuid rushed upon one another like wrestlers, making mighty and ferocious efforts, straining their arms and their swollen sinews, as it were two savage oxen, or two frenzied bulls, or two raging lions, or two fearless hawks on the edge of a cliff. And this is the form and fashion of the hot, sore, fearful strife that took place betwixt them.

They both threw their weapons out of their hands, and ran to encounter each other, and locked their knotty hands across one another's graceful backs. Then each gave the other a violent mighty twist; but Diarmuid hove Dub-cosach upon his shoulder, and hurled his body to the earth, and bound him firm and fast upon the spot. Afterwards came Finn-cosach and Tren-cosach to combat with him, one after the other; and he bound them with the same binding, and said that he would take their heads from them, were it not that he had rather leave them in those bonds to increase their torments: "for none can loosen you," said he; and he left them there weary and in heavy grief.

As for Diarmuid, he went to look for Muadan and for Grainne; and they ate their meal and their meat that night, and Diarmuid and Grainne went to sleep, and Muadan kept watch and ward for them until morning.

Diarmuid rose and told Grainne that their enemies were near them; and he told her the tale of the strangers from beginning to end, how three fifties of their people had fallen three days one after the other by his feats, and how fifteen hundred of their host had fallen on the fourth day by the fury of his hand, and how he had bound the three chiefs on the fifth day. "And they have three deadly hounds by a chain to do me evil," said he, "and no weapon can wound them."

"Hast thou taken their heads from those three chiefs?" said Grainne.

"I have not," said Diarmuid, "for I had rather give them long torment than short; for it is not in the power of any warrior nor hero in Erin to loose the binding with which they are bound, but only four; that is, Oisin the son of Finn, and Oscar the son of Oisin, and Lugaid of the Mighty Hand, and Conan mac Morna; and I know that none of those four will loose them. Nevertheless Finn will shortly get tidings of them, and that will sting his heart in his bosom; and we must depart out of this cave lest Finn and the deadly hounds overtake us."

After this, Diarmuid and Grainne and Muadan came forth out of the cave, and went their way westward until they reached the moor of Finnliath. Grainne began to weary then, and Muadan took her upon his back until they reached the great Sliab Luachra. Then Diarmuid sat him down on the brink of the stream which wound through the heart of the mountain; and Grainne was washing her hands, and she asked Diarmuid for his dagger to cut her nails.

As for the strangers, as many of them as were alive, they came upon the hill where the three chiefs were bound and thought to loose them speedily, but those bonds were such that they only drew the tighter upon them.

They had not been long thus before they saw the woman messenger of Finn mac Cumaill coming with the speed of a swallow, or weasel, or like a blast of a sharp pure-swift wind, over the top of every high hill and bare mountain towards them; and she inquired of them who it was that had made that great, fearful, destroying slaughter of them.

"Who art thou that askest?" said they.

"I am the female messenger of Finn mac Cumaill," said she; "and Deirdiu of Dub Sliab ('Black Mountain') is my name, and it is to look for you that Finn has sent me."

"Well then, we know not who he was," said they, "but we will inform thee of his appearance; that is, he was a warrior having curling dusky-black hair, and two red ruddy cheeks, and he it is that hath made this great slaughter of us; and we are yet more sorely grieved that our three chiefs are bound, and that we cannot loose them; he was likewise three days one after the other fighting with us."

"Which way went that man from you?" said Deirdriu.

"He parted from us late last night," said they; "therefore we cannot tell."

"I swear," said Deirdriu, "that it was Diarmuid O'Duibne himself that was there, and do ye bring your hounds with you and loose them on his track, and I will send Finn and the fian of Erin to you."

Then they brought their hounds with them out of their ship, and loosed them upon the track of Diarmuid; but they left a druid attending upon the three chiefs that were bound. As for them, they followed the hounds upon the track of Diarmuid until they reached the door of the cave, and they went into the hinder part of the cave, and found the bed of Diarmuid and Grainne there. Afterwards they went their way towards the west till they reached the Carrthach, and thence to the moor of Finnliath, and to Garb Aba of the Fian, which is called Leaman now, and to the fair plain of Concon, and to the vast and high Sliab Luachra.

Howbeit, Diarmuid did not perceive them coming after him in that pursuit until he beheld the banners of soft silk, and the threatening standards, and three mighty warriors in the forefront of the hosts, full fierce, and bold, and dauntless, having their three deadly hounds by three chains in their hands. When Diarmuid saw them coming towards him in that manner, he became filled with hatred and great abhorrence of them. And there was a green well-dyed mantle upon him that was in the forefront of the company, and he was out far beyond the others: then Grainne reached the dagger to Diarmuid, and Diarmuid thrust it upon his thigh, and said: "I suspect thou bearest the youth of the green mantle no love, Grainne."

"Truly I do not," quoth Grainne, "and I would I never to this day had borne love to any." Diarmuid drew his dagger and thrust it into its sheath and went his way after that, and then Muadan put Grainne upon his back and carried her a mile up the length of the mountain.

It was not long before one of the three deadly hounds was loosed after Diarmuid, and Muadan told Diarmuid to follow Grainne, saying that he would ward off the hound from him. Then Muadan went back and took a hound's whelp from beneath his girdle, and set him upon his palm. When the whelp saw the hound rushing towards him, having his jaws and throat open, he rose from Muadan's palm and sprang into the gullet of the hound, so that he reached the heart and rent it out through his side; and then he sprang back again upon Muadan's palm, leaving the hound dead after him.

Muadan departed after Diarmuid and Grainne, and took up Grainne again, and bore her another mile up the mountain. Then was loosed the second hound after them, and Diarmuid spoke to Muadan, and what he said was: "I indeed hear that there can no spells be laid upon weapons that wound by magic, nor upon the throat of any beast whatever, and will ye stand until I put the Gae Derg through the body, the chest, and the heart of yonder hound?" and Muadan and Grainne stood to see that cast. Then Diarmuid aimed a cast at the hound, and put the javelin through his navel, so that he let out his bowels and his entrails, and having drawn out the javelin he followed his own companions.

They had not been long after that before the third hound was loosed upon them; Grainne spoke, and what she said was: "That is the fiercest of them, and I greatly fear him, and keep thyself well against him, O Diarmuid." It was not long before the hound reached them, and the place where he overtook them was Lic Dubain on Sliab Luachra. He rose with an airy light bound over Diarmuid, and would fain have seized Grainne, but Diarmuid caught his two hind legs, and struck a blow of his carcass against the nearest rock, so that he let out his brains through the openings of his head and of his ears. Thereupon Diarmuid took his arms and his armor, and put his tapering finger into the silken string of the Gae Derg, and aimed a triumphant cast at the youth of the green mantle that was in the forefront of the host, so that he slew him with that cast; he made also a second cast at the second man, and slew him; and the third man he slew likewise. Then, since it is not usual for defence to be made after the fall of lords, when the strangers saw that their chiefs and their lords were fallen, they suffered defeat, and betook themselves to utter flight; and Diarmuid pursued them, violently scattering them and slaughtering them, so that unless some one fled over the tops of the forests, or under the green earth, or under the water, there escaped not even a messenger nor a man to tell tidings. The gloom of death and of instant destruction was executed upon every one of them except Deirdriu of Dub Sliab, that is, the woman messenger of Finn mac Cumaill, who went wheeling and hovering around whilst Diarmuid was making slaughter of the strangers.

As for Finn, when he heard the tidings of the foreigners being bound by Diarmuid, he loudly summoned the fian of Erin; and they went forth by the shortest ways and by the straightest paths until they reached the hill where the three chiefs were bound, and that was torment of heart to Finn when he saw them. Then Finn spoke and what he said was: "O Oisin, loose the three chiefs for me."

"I will not," said Oisin, "for Diarmuid bound me not to loose any warrior whom he should bind."

"O Oscar, loose them," said Finn.

"Nay," said Oscar, "I vow that I would fain put more bonds upon them." Then Lugaid and Conan refused likewise to loose them. Howbeit, they had not been long at this discourse before the three chiefs died of the hard bonds that were on them. Then Finn caused to be dug three wide-sodded graves for them; and a tombstone was put over their graves, and their names were written in ogam, and their burial ceremony was performed, and weary and heavy in heart was Finn after that.

At that very time and hour Finn saw coming towards him Deirdriu of Dub Sliab, with her legs failing, and her tongue raving, and her eyes dropping in her head; and when Finn saw her come towards him in that plight he asked tidings of her. "I have great and evil tidings to tell thee, and methinks I am one without a lord"; and she told him the tale from first to last of all the slaughter that Diarmuid O'Duibne had made, and how the three deadly hounds had fallen by him; "and hardly I have escaped myself," said she. "Whither went Diarmuid O'Duibne?" said Finn. "That I know not," said she. And then Finn and the fian of Erin departed, and no tidings are told of them until they reached Almu in Leinster.

Touching Diarmuid and Grainne, a further tale is told. They went their way eastward to Sliab Luachra, and through the territory of the Ui Conaill Gabra, and thence with their left hand to the Shannon eastward to Ros Da Soileach, which is called Limerick now, and Diarmuid killed for them that night a wild deer; then they ate and drank their fill of flesh and pure water, and slept till the morn on the morrow. Muadan rose early and spoke to Diarmuid, and said that he would now depart. "Thou shouldst not do so," said Diarmuid, "for all that I promised thee has been fulfilled without dispute." Muadan did not suffer Diarmuid to hinder him, and took leave and farewell of them, and left them on the spot, and gloomy and grieved were Diarmuid and Grainne after Muadan.

After that they journeyed on straight northward towards Sliab Echtge, and thence to the district of Ui Fiachrach, and as they passed through that district Grainne wearied; and when she considered that she had no man to carry her but Diarmuid, seeing that Muadan had departed, she took heart and began to walk by Diarmuid's side boldly. When they were come into the forest, Diarmuid made a hunting booth in the very midst of the forest, and slew a wild deer that night; so that he and Grainne ate and drank their fill of flesh and pure water. Diarmuid rose early and went to the Searban Lochlannach, and made bonds of covenant and compact with him, and got from him license to hunt and to chase provided that he would never meddle with his berries.

As for Finn and the fian, having reached Almu, they were not long there before they saw fifty warriors coming toward them, and two that were tall, heroic, valiant, and that exceeded the others for bulk and beauty in the very front of that company and troop; and Finn inquired of the fian whether they knew them.

"We know them not," they said, "and canst thou tell who they are, O Finn?"

"I cannot," said Finn; "but I think they are enemies to me."

That company of warriors came before Finn during this discourse, and they greeted him. Finn answered them and asked tidings of them, from what land or region they were. They told him that they were indeed enemies to him, that their fathers had been at the slaying of Cumall the son of Trenmor O'Baoiscne at the battle of Cnucha, "and our fathers themselves died for that deed; and it is to ask peace of thee we are now come."

"Where were ye yourselves when your fathers were slain?" sa'd Finn.

"In our mothers' wombs," said they, "and our mothers were two women of the Tuatha De Danann, and we think it time to get our fathers' place and station among the fian."

"I will grant you that," said Finn, "but ye must give me a recompense for my father."

"We have no gold, nor silver, nor riches, nor various wealth, kine nor cattle-herds, which we might give thee, O Finn."

"Ask of them no fine, O Finn," said Oisin, "beyond the fall of their fathers as a recompense for thy father."

"Methinks," said Finn, "were one to kil! me that it would be an easy matter to satisfy thee in my recompense, O Oisin; and none shall come among the fian but he that shall give me a fine for my father."

"What fine askest thou?" said Angus the son of Art Oc mac Morna.

"I ask but the head of a warrior, or a fistful of the berries of the quicken tree of Dubros."

"I will give you good counsel, O children of Morna," said Oisin: " return to where ye were reared, and do not ask peace of Finn as long as ye shall live. It is no light matter for you to bring to Finn anything he asks of you, for know ye what head that is which Finn asks you to bring him as a fine?"

"We know not," said they.

"The head of Diarmuid O'Duibne is the head that Finn asks of you, and were ye as many in number as twenty hundred men of full strength, Diarmuid O'Duibne would not let that head go with you, that is, his own head."

"What berries are they that Finn asks of us?" said they.

"Nothing is more difficult for you to get than that," said Oisin, "as I will tell you now. There arose a dispute between two women of the Tuatha De Danann, that is, Aife the daughter of Manannan, and Aine the other daughter of Manannan the son of Lir. Aife had become enamored of the son of Lugaid, that is, sister's son to Finn mac Cumaill, and Aine had become enamored of Lin of the fairy-mound of Finnchad, so that each woman of them said that her own man was a better hurler than the other; and the fruit of that dispute was that a great goaling match was arranged between the Tuatha De Danann and the fian of Erin, and the place where that goal was played was upon a fair plain by Loch Lein of the rough pools.

"The fian of Erin and the Tuatha De Danann came to that tryst, and these are the noblest and proudest of the Tuatha De Danann that came there; namely, the three Garbs of Sliab Mis, and the three Mases of Sliab Luachra, and the three yellow-haired Murcads, and the three Eochaids of Aine, and the three heroic Loegaires, and the three Conalls of Collaman, and the three Finns of Finnmur, and the three Sgals of Brug, and the three Ronans of Ath na Rig, and the three Eogans from Es Ruad mac Badairn, and the Cathbuilleach, and the three Ferguses, and the Glas of Mag Breg, and the Suirgeach Suairc from Lionan, and the Meidir from Benn Liath, and Donn from the fairy-mound of Breg, and the Man of Sweet Speech from the Boyne, and Colla Crincosach from Bernan Eile, and Donn Dumach, and Donn of the Island, and Donn of Cnoc na n-Os, and Donn of Leincnoc, and Bruitha Abac, and Dolb the Bright-Toothed, and the five sons of Finn of the fairy-mound of Cairn Cain, and Ilbreac son of Manannan, and Neamanach the son of Angus, and Bodb Derg the son of the Dagda, and Manannan the son of Lir, and Abortach the son of Ildathach, and Figmuin of Finnmur, and many others who are not enumerated here.

"We, the fian of Erin, and they were for the space of three days and three nights playing hurly from Garbaba of the fian, which is

called Leaman, to Cromglenn of the fian, which is called Glenn
Fleisce now; and neither of us won a goal. Now the whole of the
Tuatha De Danann were all that time without our knowledge on
either side of Loch Lein, and they understood that if we, the fian,
were united, all the men of Erin could not win from us. And the
counsel which the Tuatha De Danann took, was to depart back
again and not to play out that goal with us. The provisions that
the Tuatha De Danann had brought with them from Tir Tairngire
(fairyland) were these: crimson nuts, catkin apples, and fragrant
berries; and as they passed through the district of Ui Fiacrach by
the Muaid, one of the berries fell from them, and a quicken tree
grew out of that berry, and that quicken tree and its berries have
many virtues; for no disease or sickness seizes any one that eats
three berries of them, and they who eat feel the exhilaration of wine
and the satisfying of old mead; and were it at the age of a century,
he that tasted them would return again to be thirty years old.

"When the Tuatha De Danann heard that those virtues belonged to the quicken tree, they sent from them a guard over it,
that is, the Searban Lochlannach, a youth of their own people,
that is, a thick-boned, large-nosed, crooked-tusked, red-eyed,
swart-bodied giant of the children of wicked Cam the son of Noa;
whom neither weapon wounds, nor fire burns, nor water drowns,
so great is his magic. He has but one eye only in the fair middle of
his black forehead, and there is a thick collar of iron round that
giant's body, and he is fated not to die until there be struck upon
him three strokes of the iron club that he has. He sleeps in the top
of that quicken tree by night, and he remains at its foot by day to
watch it; and those, O children of Morna, are the berries which
Finn asks of you," said Oisin. "Howbeit, it is not easy for you to
meddle with them by any means; for that Searban Lochlannach
has made a wilderness of the districts around him, so that Finn
and the fian dare not chase or hunt there for the dread of that
terrible one."

Aod the son of Andala mac Morna spoke, and what he said was,
that he had rather perish in seeking those berries than go back
again to his mother's country; and he bade Oisin keep his people
until they returned again; and should he and his brother fall in
that adventure, to restore his people to Tir Tairngire. And the
two good warriors took leave and farewell of Oisin and of the

chiefs of the fian, and went their way; nor is it told how they fared until they reached Ros Da Soileach, which is called Luimneach now, and it is not told how they were entertained that night. They rose early on the morrow, nor halted until they reached Dubros of Ui Fiacrach, and as they went towards the forest they found the track of Diarmuid and Grainne there, and they followed the track to the door of the hunting booth in which were Diarmuid and Grainne. Diarmuid heard them coming to the hunting booth, and stretched an active warrior hand over his broad weapons, and asked who they were that were at the door. "We are of the Clan Morna," said they.

"Which of the Clan Morna are ye?" said Diarmuid.

"Aod the son of Andala mac Morna, and Angus the son of Art Oc mac Morna," said they.

"Wherefore are ye come to this forest?" said Diarmuid.

"Finn mac Cumaill has sent us to seek thy head, if thou be Diarmuid O'Duibne."

"I am he, indeed," said Diarmuid.

"Well then," said they, "Finn will not choose but get thy head, or the full of his fist of the berries of the quicken of Dubros from us as a fine for his father."

"It is no easy matter for you to get either of those things," said Diarmuid, "and woe to him that may fall under the power of that man. I also know that he it was that slew your fathers, and surely that should suffice him as recompense from you."

.   .   .   .

"What berries are those that Finn requires," asked Grainne, "that they cannot be got for him?"

"They are these," said Diarmuid: "the Tuatha De Danann left a quicken tree in the district of Ui Fiachrach, and in all berries that grow upon that tree there are many virtues, that is, there is in every berry of them the exhilaration of wine and the satisfying of old mead; and whoever should eat three berries of that tree, had he completed a hundred years he would return to the age of thirty years. Nevertheless there is a giant, hideous and foul to behold, keeping that quicken tree; every day he is at the foot of it, and every night he sleeps at the top. Moreover, he has made a desert of the district round about him, and he cannot be slain until three terrible strokes be struck upon him with an iron club that he has, and that club is thus; it has a thick ring of iron through its end, and the ring around the giant's body; he has moreover forced an agreement with Finn and with the fian of Erin not to hunt in that district, and when Finn outlawed me and became my enemy, I got of him leave to hunt, provided that I should never meddle with the berries. And, O children of Morna," said Diarmuid, "choose ye between combat with me for my head, and going to seek the berries from the giant."

"I swear by the rank of my tribe among the fian," said each of the children of Morna, "that I will rather do battle with thee."

Thereupon those good warriors, that is, the children of Morna and Diarmuid, harnessed their comely bodies in their array of weapons of valor and battle, and the combat that they resolved upon was to fight by the strength of their hands.

The outcome of the contest was that Diarmuid vanquished and bound them both upon that spot. "Thou hast fought that strife well," said Grainne, "and I vow that even if the children of Morna go not to seek those berries, I will never lie in thy bed unless I get a portion of them, although that is no fit thing for a woman to do being pregnant; and I indeed am now heavy and pregnant, and I shall not live if I taste not those berries."

"Force me not to break peace with the Searban Lochlannach," said Diarmuid, "for he would not the more readily let me take them."

"Loose these bonds from us," said the children of Morna, "and we will go with thee, and we will give ourselves for thy sake."

"Ye shall not come with me," said Diarmuid, "for were ye to see one glimpse of the giant, ye would more likely die than live after it."

"Then do us the grace," said they, "to slacken the bonds on us, and to let us go with thee privately that we may see thy battle with the giant before thou hew the heads from our bodies"; and D armuid did so.

Then Diarmuid went his way to the Searban Lochlannach, and the giant chanced to be asleep before him. He dealt him a stroke of his foot, so that the giant raised his head and gazed up at Diarmuid, and what he said was, "Dost thou wish to break peace, O O'Duibne?"

"It is not that," said Diarmuid, "but that Grainne the daughter of Cormac is heavy and pregnant, and she has conceived a desire for those berries which thou hast, and it is to ask the full of a fist of those berries from thee that I am now come."

"I swear," said the giant, "were it even that thou shouldst have no children except that birth now in her womb, and were there but Grainne of the race of Cormac the son of Art, and were I sure that she should perish in bearing that child, that she should never taste one berry of those berries."

"I may not deceive thee," said Diarmuid; "therefore I now tell thee it is to seek them by fair means or foul that I am come."

The giant, having heard that, rose up and stood, and put his club over his shoulder, and dealt Diarmuid three mighty strokes, so that he wrought him some little hurt in spite of the shelter of his shield. And when Diarmuid marked the giant off his guard he cast his weapons upon the ground, and made an eager exceeding strong spring upon the giant, so that he was able with his two hands to grasp the club. Then he hove the giant from the earth and hurled him round him, and the iron ring that was about the giant's body and through the end of the club stretched, and when the club reached Diarmuid he struck three mighty strokes upon the giant, so that he dashed his brains out through the openings of his head and of his ears, and left him dead without life; and those two of the Clan Morna were looking at Diarmuid as he fought that strife.

When they saw the giant fall they too came forth, and Diarmuid sat him down weary and spent after that combat, and bade the children of Morna bury the giant under the brushwood of the forest, so that Grainne might not see him, "and after that go ye to seek her also, and bring her." The children of Morna drew the giant forth into the wood, and put him underground, and went after Grainne and brought her to Diarmuid. "There, O Grainne," said Diarmuid, "are the berries thou didst ask for, and do thou thyself pluck of them whatever pleases thee."

"I swear," said Grainne, "that I will not taste a single berry of them but the berry that thy hand shall pluck, O Diarmuid." Thereupon Diarmuid rose and stood, and plucked the berries for Grainne and for the children of Morna, so that they ate their fill of them.

When they were filled Diarmuid spoke, and said: "O children of Morna, take as many as ye can of these berries, and tell Finn that it was ye yourselves that slew the Searban Lochlannach."

"We swear," said they, "that we grudge what we shall take to Finn of them"; and Diarmuid plucked them a load of the berries. Then the children of Morna spoke their gratitude and thanks to Diarmuid after the gifts they had received from him, and went their way to where Finn and the fian of Erin were. Now Diarmuid and Grainne went into the top of the quicken tree, and laid them in the bed of the Searban Lochlannach, and the berries below were but bitter berries compared to the berries that were upon the top of the tree.

The children of Morna reached Finn, and Finn asked their news of them from first to last. "We have slain the Searban Lochlannach," said they, "and have brought the berries of Dubros as a fine for thy father's death, if perchance we may get peace for them."

Then they gave the berries into the hand of Finn, and he knew the berries, and put them under his nose, and said to the children of Morna, "I swear," said Finn, "that it was Diarmuid O'Duibne that gathered these berries, for I know the smell of O'Duibne's skin on them, and full sure I am that he it was that slew the Searban Lochlannach; and I will go to learn whether he is alive at the quicken tree. But it shall profit you nothing to have brought the berries to me, and ye shall not get your fathers' place among the fian until ye give me the recompense for my father."

After that he caused the seven battalions of the standing fian to assemble in one place, and he went his way to Dubros of Ui Fiachrach; and followed Diarmuid's track to the foot of the quicken tree, and found the berries without any watch upon them, so that they all ate their fill of them. The great heat of the noon day then overtook them, and Finn said that he would stay at the foot of the quicken tree till that heat should be past: "for I know that Diarmuid is in the top of the tree."

"It is a great sign of envy in thee, O Finn, to suppose that Diarmuid would abide in the top of the quicken tree, and he knowing that thou art intent on slaying him," said Oisin.

After this Finn asked for a chessboard to play, and he said to Oisin, "I would play a game with thee upon this chessboard." They sat down at either side of the board; namely, Oisin and

Oscar and the son of Lugaid and Diorruing the son of Dobar O'Baoiscne on one side, and Finn upon the other side.

Thus they were playing that game of chess with skill and exceeding cunning, and Finn so played the game against Oisin that he had but one move alone to make, and Finn said: "One move there is to win thee the game, O Oisin, but I am not there to teach thee that move."

"It is worse for thee that thou art thyself," said Grainne, "in the bed of the Searban Lochlannach, in the top of the quicken tree, with the seven battalions of the standing fian round about thee intent upon thy destruction, than that Oisin should lack that move." Then Diarmuid plucked one of the berries, and aimed at the man that should be moved; and Oisin moved that man and thus turned the game against Finn. They began to play again and Oisin was again worsted. When Diarmuid beheld that, he cast a second berry upon the man that should be moved; and Oisin moved that man and turned the game against Finn as before. Finn was about to win the game against Oisin the third time, Diarmuid struck a third berry upon the man that would give Oisin the game, and the fian raised a mighty shout at that game. Finn spoke, and what he said was: "I marvel not at thy winning that game, O Oisin, seeing that Oscar is doing his best for thee, and that thou hast with thee the zeal of Diorruing, the skilled knowledge of the son of Lugaid, and the prompting of Diarmuid."

"It shows great envy in thee, O Finn," said Oscar, "to think that Diarmuid O'Duibne would stay in the top of this tree with thee in wait for him."

"With which of us is the truth, O O'Duibne," said Finn, "with me or with Oscar?"

"Thou didst never err in thy good judgment, O Finn," said Diarmuid, "and I indeed and Grainne are here in the bed of the Searban Lochlannach." Then Diarmuid caught Grainne, and gave her three kisses in the presence of Finn and the fian.

"It grieves me more that the seven battalions of the standing fian and all the men of Erin should have witnessed thee the night thou didst take Grainne from Tara, seeing that thou wast my guard that night, than that these that are here should witness thee; and thou shalt give thy head for those kisses," said Finn.

Thereupon Finn arose with the four hundred hirelings that he had on wages and on stipend, with intent to kill Diarmuid; and Finn put their hands into each others' hands round about that quicken tree, and warned them on pain of losing their heads, and as they would preserve their life, not to let Diarmuid pass out by them. Moreover, he promised them that to whatever man of the fian of Erin should go up and bring him the head of Diarmuid, he would give his arms and his armor, with his father's and his grandfather's rank among the fian freely. Garb of Sliab Cua answered, and what he said was, that it was Diarmuid's father, Donn O'Donncuda, who had slain his father; and to requite that he would go to avenge him upon Diarmuid, and he went his way up. Now it was shown to Angus of the Brug, Diarmuid's foster-father, what a strait Diarmuid was in, and he came to succor him without knowledge of the fian; and when Garb of Sliab Cua had got up into the top of the quicken tree, Diarmuid gave him a stroke of his foot and flung him down into the midst of the fian, so that Finn's hirelings took off his head, for Angus had put the form of Diarmuid upon him. After he was slain his own shape came upon him again, and Finn and the fian of Erin knew him and they said that it was Garb that was fallen.

Then said Garb of Sliab Crot that he would go to avenge his father also upon Diarmuid, and he went up, and Angus gave him a kick, so that he flung him down in the midst of the fian with the form of Diarmuid upon him, and Finn's people took off his head; and Finn said that that was not Diarmuid but Garb, for Garb assumed his own form again.

Garb of Sliab Guaire said that he too would go, and that it was Donn O'Donncuda that had slain his father, and that therefore he would go to avenge him upon O'Duibne, and he climbed into the top of the quicken tree. Diarmuid gave him also a kick, so that he flung him down, and Angus put the form of Diarmuid upon him, so that the fian slew him.

Now the nine Garbs of the fian were thus slain under a false appearance by the people of Finn. As for Finn, after the fall of the nine Garbs of the fian, he was full of anguish and of faint-heartedness and of grief.

Angus of the Brug then said that he would take Grainne with him. "Take her," said Diarmuid, "and if I be alive at evening

I will follow you; and if Finn kills me, whatever children Grainne may have rear and bring them up well, and send Grainne to her own father to Tara." Angus took leave and farewell of Diarmuid, and flung his magic mantle about Grainne and about himself, and they departed, without knowledge of the fian, and no tidings are told of them until they reached the Brug upon the Boyne.

Then Diarmuid spoke, and what he said was: "I will go down to thee, O Finn, and to the fian; and I will deal slaughter and discomfiture upon thee and upon thy people, seeing that I am certain thy wish is to allow me no deliverance, but to work my death in some place; and moreover, it is not mine to escape from this danger which is before me, since I have no friend nor companion in the far regions of the great world under whose safeguard or protection I may go, because full often have I wrought the warriors of the world death and desolation for love of thee. For there never came upon thee battle nor combat, strait nor extremity in my time, but I would adventure myself into it for thy sake and for the sake of the fian, and moreover I used to do battle before thee and after thee. And I swear, O Finn, that I will well avenge myself, and that thou shalt not get me for nothing."

"Therein Diarmuid speaks truth," said Oscar, "and give him mercy and forgiveness."

"I will not," said Finn, "to all eternity; and he shall not get peace nor rest for ever till he give me satisfaction for every slight that he has put upon me."

"It is a foul shame and sign of jealousy in thee to say that," said Oscar; "and I pledge the word of a true warrior," said he, "that unless the firmament fall down upon me, or the earth open beneath my feet, I will not suffer thee nor the fian of Erin to give him cut nor wound; and I take his body and his life under the protection of my bravery and my valor, vowing that I will save him in spite of the men of Erin. And, O Diarmuid, come down out of the tree, since Finn will not grant thee mercy; and I take thee, pledging my body and my life that no evil shall be done thee today."

Then Diarmuid rose and stood upon a high bough of the tree, and rose up with an airy bound, light, bird-like, by the shafts of his spears, so that he got the breadth of his two soles of the grass-green earth, and he passed out far beyond Finn and the fian of Erin.

.   .   .   .

After that Oscar and Diarmuid proceeded onwards, neither one or other of them being cut nor wounded, and no tidings are told of them until they reached the Brug upon the Boyne, and Grainne and Angus met them with joy and good courage. Then Diarmuid told them his tidings from first to last, and it lacked but little of Grainne's falling into the numb stupor of instant death through the fear and the horror of that story.

After the departure of Diarmuid and of Oscar, Finn found nine chieftains and ten hundred warriors in a mangled bloody mass, and he sent every one that was curable where he might be healed, and caused to be dug a broad-sodded grave, and put into it every one that was dead. Heavy, weary, and mournful was Finn after that time, and he swore and vowed that he would take no rest until he should have avenged upon Diarmuid all that he had done to him. Then he told his trusty people to equip his ship, and to put a store of meat and drink into her. Thus did they and, the ship being ready, he himself and a thousand warriors of his people together with him went on board. They weighed her anchors forthwith, and urged the ship forward with exceeding strong rowing, so that they launched her forth the space of nine waves into the blue-streamed ocean, and they caught the wind in the bosom of the sails of the mast, and it is not told how they fared until they took haven and harbor in the north of Alba. They made fast the ship to the mooring posts of the harbor, and Finn with five of his people went to the stronghold of the king of Alba, and Finn struck the knocker upon the door. The doorkeeper asked who was there; and it was told him that Finn mac Cumaill was there. "Let him be admitted," said the king. Finn was thereupon admitted, and he himself and his people went before the king. A kindly welcome was given to Finn by the king, and he caused Finn to sit down in his own seat. Thereafter were given to them mead mild and pleasant to drink, and strong fermented liquors, and the king sent to fetch the rest of the people of Finn, and he made them welcome in the stronghold. Then Finn told the king the cause and matter for which he was come from beginning to end, and that it was to seek counsel and aid against Diarmuid O'Duibne that he was then come. "And truly thou oughtest to give me an army, for Diarmuid it was that slew thy father and thy two brothers and many of thy chiefs likewise."

"That is true," said the king, "and I will give thee my own two
sons and a host of a thousand about each man of them." Joyful
was Finn at the soldiers that the king of Alba had given him, and
Finn with his people took leave and farewell of the king and of his
household, and left them good wishes for life and health, and the
king sent the same with the fian. Finn and his company went
their way, and no tidings are told of them until they reached the
Brug upon the Boyne, and he and his people went ashore. After
that Finn sent messengers to the house of Angus of the Brug to
proclaim battle against Diarmuid.

"What shall I do about this, O Oscar?" said Diarmuid.

"We will both of us give them battle, and destroy them, and
rend their flesh, and not suffer a servant to escape alive of them,
but we will slay them all," said Oscar.

The next morning Diarmuid and Oscar rose, and harnessed
their fair bodies in their suits of arms of valor and battle, and
those two mighty heroes went their way to the place of that
combat, and woe to those, either many or few, who might meet
those two good warriors when in anger. Then Diarmuid and Oscar
bound the rims of their shields together that they might not
separate from one another in the fight. After that they proclaimed
battle against Finn, and then the soldiers of the king of Alba said
that they and their people would go to strive with them first.
They came ashore forthwith, and rushed to meet and to encounter
them, and Diarmuid passed under them, through them, and over
them, as a hawk would go through small birds, or a whale through
small fish, or a wolf through a large flock of sheep; and such was
the dispersion and terror and scattering that those good warriors
wrought upon the strangers, that not a man to tell tidings or to
boast of great deeds escaped of them, but all of them fell by
Diarmuid and by Oscar before the night came, and they themselves
were smooth and free from hurt, having neither cut nor wound.
When Finn saw that great slaughter, he and his people returned
out to sea, and no tidings are told of them until they reached
Tir Tairngire (fairyland), where Finn's nurse was. Finn came to
her, and she received him joyfully. Finn told the cause of his
travel and of his journey to the hag from first to last, and the
reason of his strife with Diarmuid, and he told her that it was to
seek counsel from her that he was then come; also that no strength

of a host or of a multitude could conquer Diarmuid, if perchance
magic alone might not conquer him. "I will go with thee," said
the hag, "and I will practise magic against him." Finn was joyful
thereat, and he remained with the hag that night; and they resolved
to depart on the morrow.

Now it is not told how they fared until they reached the Brug
upon the Boyne, and the hag threw a spell of magic about Finn
and the fian, so that the men of Erin knew not that they were
there. It was the day before that Oscar had parted from Diarmuid, and Diarmuid chanced to be hunting and chasing on the
day that the hag concealed the fian. This was revealed to the
hag, and she caused herself to fly by magic upon the leaf of a
water lily, having a hole in the middle of it, in the fashion of the
quern-stone of a mill, so that she rose with the blast of the pure-
cold wind and came over Diarmuid, and began to aim at and
strike him through the hole with deadly darts, so that she wrought
the hero great hurt in the midst of his weapons and armor, and
that he was unable to escape, so greatly was he oppressed; and
every evil that had ever come upon him was little compared to
that evil. What he thought in his own mind was, that unless he
might strike the hag through the hole that was in the leaf she
would cause his death upon the spot; and Diarmuid laid him upon
his back having the Gae Derg in his hand, and made a triumphant
cast of exceeding courage with the javelin, so that he reached the
hag through the hole, and she fell dead upon the spot. Diarmuid
beheaded her there and then and took her head with him to
Angus of the Brug.

Diarmuid rose early on the morrow, and Angus rose and went
where Finn was, and asked him whether he would make peace
with Diarmuid. Finn said that he would, in whatever way Diarmuid would make peace. Then Angus went where the king of
Erin was to ask peace for Diarmuid, and Cormac said that he
would grant him that. Again Angus went where Diarmuid and
Grainne were, and asked Diarmuid whether he would make peace
with Cormac and with Finn. Diarmuid said that he would if he
obtained the conditions which he should ask of them. "What are
those conditions?" said Angus.

"The district," said Diarmuid, "which my father had, that is,
the district of O'Duibne, Finn shall not hunt nor chase therein,

and it must be free of rent or tribute to the king of Erin; also the district of Benn Damuis, that is, Dubcarn in Leinster as a gift for myself from Finn, for it is the best district in Erin: and the district of Ces Corann from the king of Erin as dowry with his daughter; and those are the conditions upon which I would make peace with them."

"Wouldst thou make peace on those conditions if thou wert to get them?" asked Angus.

"I could better bear to make peace by getting those conditions," said Diarmuid. Then Angus went with those tidings to where the king of Erin and Finn were, and he got those conditions from him every one, and they forgave Diarmuid all he had done as long as he had been outlawed, namely for the space of sixteen years; and Cormac gave his other daughter for wife and mate to Finn, that he might let Diarmuid be, and so they made peace with each other; and the place that Diarmuid and Grainne settled in was Rath Grainne in the district of Ces Corann, far from Finn and from Cormac. Then Grainne bore Diarmuid four sons and one daughter; namely, Donncad, Eochaid, Connla, Selbsercach, and Druime; and he gave the district of Benn Damuis, that is, Dubcarn in Leinster, to the daughter, and he sent attendants to serve her there. They abode a long time fulfilling the terms of the peace with each other, and people used to say that there was not living at the same time with him a man richer in gold and silver, in kine and cattle-herds and sheep, and who made more successful raids, than Diarmuid.

Then Grainne spoke to Diarmuid upon a certain day, and what she said was, that it was a shame for them, seeing the number of their people and the greatness of their household, and that their expenditure was untold, that the two best men in Erin had never been in their house, that is, Cormac the High-King of Erin, and Finn mac Cumaill. "Wherefore sayest thou so, O Grainne," said Diarmuid, "when they are enemies to me?"

"I would fain," said Grainne, "give them a feast, that so thou mightest win their love."

"I permit that," said Diarmuid.

"Then," said Grainne, "send word and messengers to thy daughter to bid her to prepare another feast, so that we may take the king of Erin and Finn mac Cumaill to her house; and how do we

know but that there she might get a fitting husband?" Thereupon two great feasts were prepared by Grainne and by her daughter for the length of a year, and at the end of that space and season word and messengers were sent for the king of Erin, and for
Finn mac Cumaill, and for the seven battalions of the standing
fian, and for the chiefs of Erin likewise, and they were for a year
and a day enjoying that feast.

Now on the last day of the year Diarmuid was in Rath Grainne
asleep; and Diarmuid heard the voice of a hound in his sleep in
the night, and that caused Diarmuid to start out of his sleep, so
that Grainne caught him and threw her two arms about him, and
asked him what he had seen. "It is the voice of a hound I have
heard," said Diarmuid, "and I marvel to hear it in the night."

"Mayest thou be kept safely," said Grainne, "for it is the
Tuatha De Danann that are doing that to thee to spite Angus of
the Brug, and lay thee down on thy bed again." Nevertheless
no slumber or sleep fell upon Diarmuid then, but again the voice
of the hound roused him, and he was fain to go to seek the hound.
Grainne caught him and laid him down the second time, and told
him it was not meet for him to go look for a hound because of
hearing its voice in the night. Diarmuid laid him upon his couch,
and a heaviness of slumber and of sweet sleep fell upon him, and
the third time the voice of the hound awoke him.

The day came then with its full light, and he said, "I will go
to seek the hound whose voice I have heard, since it is day."

"Well then," said Grainne, "take with thee the Moralltach,
that is, the sword of Manannan, and the Gae Derg."

"I will not," said Diarmuid, "but I will take the Begalltach
and the Gae Buide with me in my hand, and my hound Mac an
Cuill by a chain in my other hand."

Then Diarmuid went forth from Rath Grainne, and made no
halt nor stopping until he reached the summit of Benn Gulban,
and he found Finn before him there without any one with him or
in his company. Diarmuid gave him no greeting, but asked him
whether it was he that was holding that chase. Finn said that it
was not he, but that a company of the fian had risen out after
midnight, "and one of our hounds, being loose by our side, came
across the track of a wild pig, but they have not hitherto been
able to overtake him. Now it is the wild boar of Benn Gulban

that the hound has met, and the fian do but foolishly in following him; for oftentimes ere now he has escaped them, and thirty warriors of the fian were slain by him this morning. He is even now coming up against the mountain towards us, with the fian fleeing before him, and let us leave this hill to him." Diarmuid said that he would not leave the hill through fear of him.

"It is not meet for thee to do thus," said Finn, "for thou art under taboos never to hunt a pig."

"Wherefore were those taboos laid upon me?" said Diarmuid.

"That I will tell thee," said Finn.

"On a certain day I chanced to be in Almu in Leinster, with the seven battalions of the standing fian about me, Bran Beg O'Buidcain came in and asked me whether I remembered not that it was one of my taboos not to be ten nights one after the other in Almu without being out of it for a single night; now those taboos had not been laid upon any man of the fian but upon myself alone. The fian went into the great hall that night, and no man staid by me but thy father and a small number of the bards and learned men of the fian, with our staghounds and our other dogs. Then I asked of them that were with me where we should go to be entertained that night. Thy father, that is, Donn O'Donncuda, said that he would give me entertainment for that night, 'for if thou remember, O Finn,' said Donn, 'when I was outlawed and banished by thee and from the fian, Crocnuit the daughter of Currac of Liffe became pregnant by me, and bore a smooth beautiful man-child of that heavy pregnancy, and Angus of the Brug took that son from me to foster him. Crocnuit bore another son after that to Roc mac Dicain, and Roc asked me to take that son to foster him, seeing that Angus had my son, and he said that he would provide a sufficient meal for nine men at the house of Angus every evening. I said that I thought it not fitting to take the commoner's son, and I sent to Angus praying him to receive that son to foster him. Angus received the commoner's son, and there was not a time thenceforth that Roc did not send a nine men's meal to the house of Angus for me. Howbeit, I have not seen him for a year, and we shall, as many as there are here of us, get entertainment for this night there.'

"I and Donn went our way after that," said Finn, "to the house of Angus of the Brug, and thou wast there that night, O

Diarmuid, and Angus showed thee great fondness. The son of
the steward was thy companion that night, and not greater was
the fondness that Angus showed thee than the fondness that
the people of Angus showed the son of the steward, and thy father
suffered great derision for that. It was no long time after that
that there arose a quarrel between two of my staghounds about
some broken meat that was thrown them, and the women and
the lesser people of the place fled before them, and the others
rose to separate them. The son of the steward went between thy
father's knees, flying before the staghounds, and he gave the child
a mighty, powerful, strong squeeze of his two knees, so that he
slew him upon the spot, and he cast him under the feet of the
staghounds. The steward came and found his son dead, and he
uttered a long very pitiful cry. Then he came before me, and what
he said was: 'There is not in this house to-night a man that hath
got out of this uproar worse than myself, for I had no children
but one son only, and he has been slain; and how shall I get a
recompense from thee, O Finn?' I told him to examine his son,
and if he found the trace of a staghound's tooth or nail upon him
that I would myself give him a fine for him. The child was examined, and no trace of a staghound's tooth or nail was found on
him. Then the steward laid me under the fearful perilous taboos
of Drum Druidecta that I should show him who had slain his son.
I asked for a chessboard and water to be brought to me, and I
washed my hands and put my thumb under my tooth of divination, so that true and exact divination was shown me, namely,
that thy father had slain the son of the steward between his two
knees. I offered a fine myself when that was shown me, but the
steward refused that; so that I was forced to tell him that it was
thy father that had slain his son. The steward said that there
was not in the house a man for whom it was more easy to give a
fine than thy father, for that he himself had a son therein, and
that he would not take any fine whatever except that thou shouldst
be placed between his two legs and his two knees, and that he
would forgive the death of his son if he let thee from him safe.
Angus became angry with the steward at that speech, and thy
father thought to take off his head, until I separated them. Then
came the steward again with a magic wand of sorcery, and struck
his son with that wand so that he made of him a cropped green

pig, having neither ears or tail, and he said, 'I conjure thee that thou have the same length of life as Diarmuid O'Duibne, and that it be by thee that he shall fall at last.' Then the wild boar rose and stood, and rushed out by the open door. When Angus heard those spells laid upon thee, he conjured thee never to hunt a swine; and that wild boar is the wild boar of Benn Gulban, and it is not meet for thee to await him upon this hill."

"I knew not of those conjurations hitherto," said Diarmuid, "now will I leave this hill through fear of him before he comes to me, and do thou leave me thy hound Bran beside Mac an Cuill."

"I will not," said Finn, "for oftentimes this wild boar has escaped him before." Finn went his way after that, and left Diarmuid alone and solitary upon the summit of the hill.

"By my word," said Diarmuid, "it is to slay me that thou hast made this hunt, O Finn; and if it be here I am fated to die I have no power now to shun it."

The wild boar then came up the face of the mountain with the fian after him. Diarmuid slipped Mac an Cuill from his leash against him, and that profited him nothing, for he did not await the wild boar but fled before him. Diarmuid said, "Woe to him that heeds not the counsel of a good wife, for Grainne bade me at early morn to-day take with me the Moralltach and the Gae Derg." Then Diarmuid put his small white-colored ruddy-nailed finger into the silken string of the Gae Buide, and made a careful cast at the pig, so that he smote him in the fair middle of his face and of his forehead; nevertheless he cut not a single bristle upon him, nor did he give him wound or scratch. Diarmuid's courage was lessened at that, and thereupon he drew the Begalltach from the sheath in which it was kept, and struck a heavy stroke thereof upon the wild boar's back stoutly and bravely, yet he cut not a single bristle upon him, but made two pieces of his sword. Then the wild boar made a fearless spring upon Diarmuid, so that he tripped him and made him fall headlong, and when he rose up again it happened that one of his legs was on either side of the wild boar, and his face looking backward toward the hinder part of the wild boar. The wild boar fled down the fall of the hill and was unable to put off Diarmuid during that space. After that he fled away until he reached Es Ruad (the Red Waterfall) of Mac Badairn, and having reached the red stream he gave three nimble leaps across the fall hither and thither, yet he could not put off Diarmuid during that space; and he came back by the same path until he reached up to the height of the mountain again. And when he had reached the top of the hill he put Diarmuid from his back; and when he was fallen to the earth the wild boar made an eager exceeding mighty spring upon him, and ripped out his bowels and his entrails so that they fell about his legs. Howbeit, as the boar was leaving the hill, Diarmuid made a triumphant cast of the hilt of the sword that chanced to be still in his hand, so that he dashed out the boar's brains and left him dead without life. Therefore Rath na h-Amrann ("Rath of the Marvel") is the name of the place that is on the top of the mountain from that time to this.

It was no long time after that when Finn and the fian of Erin came up, and the agonies of death and of instant dissolution were then coming upon Diarmuid. "It likes me well to see thee in that plight, O Diarmuid," said Finn; "and I grieve that all the women of Erin are not now gazing upon thee: for thy excellent beauty is turned to ugliness, and thy choice form to deformity."

"Nevertheless it is in thy power to heal me, O Finn," said Diarmuid, "if it were thy pleasure to do so."

"How should I heal thee?" said Finn.

"Easily," said Diarmuid; "for when thou didst get the noble precious gift of divining at the Boyne,[1] it was granted thee that to whomsoever thou should give a drink from the palms of thy hands he should after that be young, fresh, and sound from any sickness he might have at that time."

"Thou hast not deserved of me that I should give thee that drink," said Finn.

"That is not true," said Diarmuid, "well have I deserved it of thee; for when thou wentest to the house of Derc the son of Donnartad, and the chiefs and great nobles of Erin with thee, to enjoy a banquet and feast, Cairbre Liffecair son of Cormac son of Art, and the men of Mag Breg, and of Mide, and of Cerna, and the stout mighty pillars of Tara came around the stronghold against thee, and uttered three shouts loudly about thee, and threw fire and firebrands into it. Thereupon thou didst rise and stand, and wouldst fain have gone out; but I bade thee stay within enjoying drinking and pleasure, and that I would myself go out to avenge

[1] See p. 365.

it upon them. Then I went out and quenched the flames, and made three deadly courses about the stronghold, so that I slew fifty at each course, and came in having no cut nor wound after them. And thou wast cheerful, joyous, and of good courage before me that night, O Finn," said Diarmuid; "and had it been that night that I asked thee for a drink, thou wouldst have given it to me, and thou wouldst not have done so more justly that night than now."

"That is not true," said Finn; "thou hast ill deserved of me that I should give thee a drink or do thee any good thing; for the night that thou wentest with me to Tara thou didst bear away Grainne from me in the presence of all the men of Erin when thou wast thyself my guard over her in Tara that night."

"The guilt of that was not mine, O Finn," said Diarmuid, "but Grainne put a taboo upon me, and I would not have failed to keep my bonds for the gold of the world, and nothing, O Finn, is true of all that thou sayest, for thou wouldst own that I have well deserved of thee that thou shouldst give me a drink, if thou didst remember the night that Midach son of Colgan made thee the feast of Bruiden Chaorthainn ('the Hostel of the Quicken Tree').[1] He had a stronghold upon land, and a stronghold upon wave (i.e., upon an island), and he brought the king of the World and the three kings of Innis Tuile to the stronghold that he had upon the wave, with intent to take thy head from thee. The feast was being given in the stronghold that he had on land, and he sent and bade thee and the seven battalions of the standing fian to go and enjoy the feast in Bruiden Chaorthainn. Now thou wentest and certain of the chiefs of the fian together with thee, to enjoy that banquet in Bruiden Chaorthainn, and Midach caused some of the mould of Innis Tuile to be placed under thee, so that thy feet and thy hands clove to the ground; and when the king of the World heard that thou wast thus bound down, he sent a chief of an hundred to seek thy head. Then thou didst put thy thumb under thy tooth of divination, and knowledge and enlightenment was shewn thee. At that very time I came after thee to Bruiden Chaorthainn, and thou didst know me as I came to the stronghold, and didst make known to me that the king of the World and the three kings of Innis Tuile were in the stronghold

[1] The subject of a well-known tale of the Finn cycle.

of the island upon the Shannon, and that it would not be long ere some one would come from them to seek thy head and take it to the king of the World. When I heard that, I took the protection of thy body and of thy life upon me till the dawning of the day on the morrow, and I went to the ford which was by the stronghold to defend it.

"I had not been long by the ford before there came a chief of an hundred to me of the people of the king of the World, and we fought together; and I took his head from him, and made slaughter of his people, and brought the head even to the stronghold of the island where the king of the World was enjoying drinking and pleasure with the three kings of Innis Tuile by him. I took their heads from them, and put them in the hollow of my shield, and brought in my left hand the jewelled golden-chased goblet, full of old mead, pleasant to drink, which was before the king. Then I wrought sharply with my sword around me, and came by virtue of my fortune and of my valor to Bruiden Chaorthainn, and brought those heads with me. I gave thee the goblet in token of victory, and rubbed the blood of those three kings on thee and on the fian, as many of them as were bound, so that I restored to thee thy power over thy hands and the motion of thy feet; and had I asked a drink of thee that night, O Finn, I would have got it! Many is the strait, moreover, that hath overtaken thee and the fian of Erin from the first day that I came among you, in which I have perilled my body and my life for thy sake; and therefore thou shouldst not do me this foul treachery. Moreover, many a brave warrior and valiant hero of great prowess hath fallen by thee, nor is there an end of them yet; and shortly there will come a dire disaster upon the fian which will not leave them many descendants. Nor is it for thee that I grieve, O Finn; but for Oisin, and for Oscar, and for the rest of my faithful, fond comrades. And as for thee, O Oisin, thou shalt be left to lament after the fian, and thou shalt sorely lack me yet, O Finn."

Then said Oscar, "O Finn, though I am more nearly akin to thee than to Diarmuid O'Duibne, I will not allow thee to withhold the drink from Diarmuid; and I swear, moreover, that were any other prince in the world to do Diarmuid O'Duibne such treachery, there should only escape whichever of us should have the strongest hand, and bring him a drink without delay."

"I know no well whatever upon this mountain," said Finn.

"That is not true," said Diarmuid; "for but nine paces from thee is the best well of pure water in the world."

After that Finn went to the well, and raised the full of his two hands of the water; but he had not reached more than half way to Diarmuid when he let the water run down through his hands, and he said he could not bring the water. "I swear," said Diarmuid, "that of thine own will thou didst let it from thee." Finn went for the water the second time, and he had not come more than the same distance when he let it through his hands, having thought upon Grainne. Then Diarmuid hove a piteous sigh of anguish when he saw that. "I swear upon my arms," said Oscar, "that if thou bring not the water speedily, O Finn, there shall not leave this hill but either thou or I." Finn returned to the well the third time because of that speech which Oscar had made to him, and brought the water to Diarmuid, and as he came up the life parted from the body of Diarmuid.

Then that company of the fian of Erin that were present raised three great exceeding loud shouts, wailing for Diarmuid, and Oscar looked fiercely and wrathfully upon Finn and said, "that it was a greater pity that Diarmuid should be dead than it would have been had Finn perished, and that the fian had lost their mainstay in battle by means of him."

Finn then said, "Let us leave this hill, for fear that Angus of the Brug and the Tuatha De Danann might catch us; and though we have no part in the slaying of Diarmuid, he would none the more readily believe us."

"I swear," said Oscar, "had I known that it was with intent to kill Diarmuid that thou madest the hunt of Benn Gulban, that thou wouldst never have made it." Then Finn and the fian of Erin went their way from the hill, Finn holding Diarmuid's staghound, that is Mac an Cuill, but Oisin, and Oscar, and Cailte, and the son of Lugaid returned, and threw their four mantles about Diarmuid, and after that they went their way after Finn.

It is not told how they fared until they reached Rath Grainne. Grainne was before them out upon the ramparts of the stronghold, and she saw Finn and the fian of Erin coming to her. Then said Grainne, "that if Diarmuid were alive it was not by Finn that Mac an Cuill would be held coming to this place." Now Grainne was at that time heavy and pregnant, and she fell out over the ramparts of the stronghold, and brought forth three dead sons upon the spot. When Oisin saw Grainne in that plight he sent away Finn and the fian of Erin; and as Finn and the fian of Erin were leaving the place Grainne lifted up her head and asked Finn to leave her Mac an Cuill. He said that he would not give him to her, and that he thought it not too much that he himself should inherit so much of Diarmuid; but when Oisin heard that he took the staghound from the hand of Finn, gave him to Grainne, and then followed his people.

Then Grainne felt sure of the death of Diarmuid, and she uttered a long exceedingly piteous cry, so that it was heard in the distant parts of the stronghold; and her women and the rest of her people came to her, and asked her what had thrown her into that excessive grief. Grainne told them how Diarmuid had perished by the wild boar of Benn Gulban, by means of the hunt that Finn mac Cúmaill had made. "And truly my very heart is grieved," said Grainne, "that I am not myself able to fight with Finn, for were I so I would not have suffered him to leave this place in safety." Having heard of the death of Diarmuid, they too uttered three loud, fearful, vehement cries together with Grainne, so that those loud shouts were heard in the clouds of heaven, and in the wastes of the firmament; and then Grainne bade the five hundred that she had for household to go to Benn Gulban, and to bring her the body of Diarmuid.

At that very time and season it was shown to Angus that Diarmuid was dead upon Benn Gulban, for he had had no watch over him the night before, and he proceeded, on the wings of the pure-cold wind, so that he reached Benn Gulban at the same time with the people of Grainne; and when Grainne's household recognized Angus they held out the rough side of their shields in token of peace, and Angus knew them. Then when they were met together upon Benn Gulban, they and the people of Angus raised three exceeding great terrible cries over the body of Diarmuid, so that they were heard in the clouds of heaven, and in the wastes of the firmament of the air, and in the provinces of Erin likewise.

Then Angus spoke, and what he said was: "I have never been for one night, since I took thee with me to the Brug of the Boyne, at the age of nine months, that I did not watch thee and carefully

keep thee against thy foes, until last night, O Diarmuid! and alas
for the treachery that Finn hath done thee, for all that thou wast
at peace with him." And he sang the following lay:

> Alas, O Diarmuid O'Duibne,
>   O thou of the white teeth, thou bright and fair one;
>   Alas for thine own blood upon thy spear,
>   The blood of thy body hath been shed.
>
> Alas for the deadly flashing tusk of the boar,
>   Thou hast been sharply, sorely, violently lopped off;
>   Through the malicious, fickle, treacherous one.
>
>   .   .   .   .
>
> Numbing venom hath entered his wounds,
>   At Rath Finn he met his death;
>   The Boar of Benn Gulban with fierceness,
>   Hath laid low Diarmuid the bright-faced.
>
> Raise ye fairy shouts without gainsaying,
>   Let Diarmuid of the bright weapons be lifted by you;
>   To the smooth Brug of the everlasting rocks—
>   Surely it is we that feel great pity.

After that lay Angus asked the household of Grainne wherefore
they were come to that spot. They said Grainne had sent them
for the body of Diarmuid to bring it to her to Rath Grainne.
Angus said that he would not let them take Diarmuid's body,
but that he would himself bear it to the Brug upon the Boyne;
"and since I cannot restore him to life I will send a soul into
him, so that he may talk to me each day." After that Angus
caused the body to be borne upon a gilded bier, with his (Diarmuid's) javelins over him pointed upwards, and he went to the
Brug of the Boyne.

As for Grainne's household, they returned back to Rath Grainne,
and they told how Angus would not let them bring the body of
Diarmuid, but that he himself had taken it to the Brug upon the
Boyne; and Grainne said that she had no power over him. Afterwards Grainne sent word and messengers for her children to the
district of Corca O'Duibne, where they were being reared and
protected; now those children of Diarmuid had sons of warriors
and of wealthy chieftains serving them, and each son of them
owned a district. Now Donnchad the son of Diarmuid O'Duibne
was the eldest son of them, and to him the other sons were subject;

that is, Eochaid, Connla, Selbsercach, and Ollann the long-bearded, the son of Diarmuid, that is, the son of the daughter of the king of Leinster; and Grainne bore greater love and affection to none of her own children than to Ollann. Those messengers thereupon went to the place where those youths were, and they told them the cause of their journey and of their coming from first to last; and as the youths were setting out with the full number of their household and of their gathering, their people of trust asked them what they should do since their lords were now going to encounter war and perilous adventure against Finn mac Cumaill and the fian of Erin. Donnchad the son of Diarmuid bade them abide in their own places, and that if they made peace with Finn their people need fear nothing; and if not, to choose which lord they would have, that is, to ride with Finn or to adhere to their own chiefs as they pleased.

And no tidings are told of them until they reached Rath Grainne, where Grainne gave them a gentle welcome, and gave a kiss and a welcome to the son of the daughter of the king of Leinster: and they entered together into Rath Grainne, and sat at the sides of the royal stronghold according to their rank, and their patrimony, and according to the age of each one of them. There were given them mead mild and pleasant to drink, and well-prepared sweet ale, and strong fermented draughts in fair chased drinking horns, so that they became exhilarated and mirthful. And then Grainne spoke with an exceeding loud and clear voice, and what she said was: "O dear children, your father has been slain by Finn mac Cumaill against his bonds and covenants of peace with him; now you are bound to avenge that upon him well; and there is your portion of the inheritance of your father," said she, "that is, his arms, and his armor, and his various sharp weapons, and his feats of valor and of bravery likewise. I will myself portion them out among you, and may the getting of them bring you success in battle. And I myself will have the goblets, and the drinking horns, and the beautiful golden-chased cups, and the kine and the cattle-herds undivided." And she sang this lay as follows:

> Arise ye, O children of Diarmuid,
>   Go forth and learn that I may see;
>   May your adventure be prosperous to you;
>   The tidings of a good man have come to you.

> The sword for Donnchad,
>> The best son that Diarmuid had;
>> And let Eochaid have the Gae Derg;
>> They lead to every advantage.
>
> Give his armor from me to Ollann,
>> Safe every body upon which it may be put;
>> And his shield to Connla,
>> To him that keeps the battalions firm.
>
> The goblets and the drinking horns,
>> The cups and the bowls;
>> They are a woman's treasure without thanks;
>> I alone shall have them all.
>
> Slay ye women and children,
>> Through hatred to your foes;
>> Do no guile nor treachery,
>> Hasten ye and depart.

After that lay Grainne bade them depart, and learn carefully all practice of bravery and of valor till they should have reached their full strength. And they were to spend a portion of their time with Bolcan, the smith of hell.

Then those good youths betook them to their journey, and they took farewell of Grainne and of her household, and left them wishes for life and health, and Grainne and her people sent the same with them: and they left not a warrior, a hero, nor a woman-warrior in the distant regions of the world, with whom they spent not a portion of their time, learning from them until they attained fullness of strength; and they were three years with Bolcan.

When Finn was informed that those children of Diarmuid had departed upon that journey, he was filled with hatred and great fear of them; and forthwith called a muster of the seven battalions of the standing fian from every quarter where they were, and when they were come to one place Finn told them in a loud, clear voice the story of that journey of the children of Diarmuid from first to last, and asked what he should do. "For it is with intent to rebel against me," said he, "that they are gone upon that journey."

Oisin spoke, and what he said was: "The guilt of that is no man's but thine, and we will not go to make up for the deed that we have not done. Foul is the treachery that thou didst show towards Diarmuid, though at peace with him, when Cormac also would have given thee his other daughter, in order that thou mightest bear Diarmuid no enmity nor malice. According as thou hast planted the oak so bend it thyself." Finn was grieved at those words of Oisin, nevertheless he could do nothing against him.

When Finn saw that Oisin, and Oscar, and all the Clan Baoiscne had abandoned him, he considered within his own mind that he would be unable to crush that danger if he did not win over Grainne; and he went therefore to Rath Grainne without the knowledge of the fian of Erin and without bidding them farewell, and greeted her craftily, and cunningly, and with sweet words. Grainne neither heeded nor hearkened to him, but told him to leave her sight, and straightway assailed him with her keen, sharp-pointed tongue. However, Finn left not plying her with sweet words and with gentle loving discourse, until he brought her to his own will; and he had the desire of his heart and soul of her. After that Finn and Grainne went their ways, and no tidings are told of them until they reached the fian of Erin; and when the fian saw Finn and Grainne coming towards them in that manner, they gave one shout of derision and mockery at her, so that Grainne bowed her head through shame. "We trow, O Finn," said Oisin, "that thou wilt keep Grainne well from henceforth."

As for the children of Diarmuid, after having spent seven years in learning all that beseems a warrior, they came out of the far regions of the great world, and it is not told how they fared until they reached Rath Grainne. When they had heard how Grainne had fled with Finn mac Cumaill without taking leave of them or of the king of Erin, they said that they could do nothing. After that they went to Almu of Leinster to seek Finn and the fian, and they proclaimed battle against Finn. "Rise, O Diorruing, and ask them how many they require," said Finn. Diorruing went and asked them. "We require a hundred men against each of us, or single combat," said they. Finn sent a hundred to fight with them, and when they had reached the battle field those youths rushed under them, through them, and over them, and made three heaps of them, namely, a heap of their heads, a heap of their bodies, and a heap of their arms and armor. "Our hosts will not last," said Finn, "if a hundred be slain each day. What shall we do concerning those youths, O Grainne?"

"I will go to them," said Grainne, "to try whether I may be able to make peace between you."

"I should be well pleased at that," said Finn, "and I would give them and their posterity freedom for ever, and their father's place among the fian, and bonds and securities for the fulfillment thereof to them for ever and ever."

Grainne went to meet them, gave them a welcome, and made them those offers. At last Grainne made peace between them, and the bonds and securities were given to them, and they got their father's place among the fian from Finn mac Cumaill. After that a banquet and feast was prepared for them, so that they became exhilarated and mirthful. And Finn and Grainne stayed by one another until they died.

Thus, then, the Pursuit of Diarmuid and Grainne.

THE HIDING OF THE HILL OF HOWTH

The following short piece is representative of a group of episodic narratives that arose out of the general tradition of the pursuit of Diarmuid and Grainne (see the full narrative, p. 370). The present selection is probably much older in date than the long narrative given above, but it was either unknown to the later redactor or was omitted purposely. As it stands it is an interesting example of the stories of trickery which delighted Irish audiences during the Middle Ages. The short poem, much as it inevitably suffers in translation, is one of the gems of early Irish lyric poetry.

Once Diarmuid son of Donn grandson of Duibne, was in the cave of the Hill of Howth (Ben Etair), after having carried off Grainne the daughter of Cormac in elopement from Finn. An old woman was with Diarmuid at that time, watching over him wherever he would be. The old woman went out of the cave, and when she was on the top of the Hill of Howth, she saw an armed man coming towards her alone. It was Finn, the warrior-king. The old woman asked tidings of him. "To woo thee I have come," said Finn, "and the cause I will tell thee afterwards, and what I desire is that thou shouldst live with me as my only wife."

The old woman believed the words of Finn, and promised him to do his will. But what Finn desired of her was to betray Diarmuid to him. The old hag consented to this. She dipped her cloak into the salt water and then went into the cave. Diarmuid asked why she was so wet. "I confess," said she, "I never saw or heard the like of it for cold and storms. For the frost has spread over the hillocks, and there is not a smooth plain in all Elga, in which there is not a long rushing river between every two ridges," said she. "And no deer or raven in Erin finds shelter in a cave or in any other place, or on an island, or in a bay of Falmag." Craftily she shook her raiment across the cave, and sang these staves:

> Cold, cold!
> Cold to-night is the broad plain of Lurg,
> Higher the snow than the mountain-range,
> The deer cannot get at their food.
>
> Cold till Doom!
> The storm has spread over all:
> A river is each furrow upon the slope,
> Each ford a full pool.

A great sea is each loch, which is full,
A full loch is each pool.
Horses do not get over Ross-ford,
No more do two feet get there.

The fishes of Inis Fail are a-roaming,
There is no marge nor well of waves,
In the lands there is no land,
Not a bell is heard, no crane talks.

The hounds of Cuan-wood find not
Rest nor sleep in the dwelling of hounds,
The little wren cannot find
Shelter in her nest on Lon-slope.

On the little company of the birds has broken forth
Keen wind and cold ice,
The blackbird cannot get a lee to her liking,
Shelter at the side in Cuan-woods.

Cozy our pot on the hook,
Crazy the hut on Lon-slope:
The snow has smoothed the wood here,
Toilsome to climb by kine-horned staves.

Glenn Rigi's ancient bird
From the bitter wind gets grief,
Great her misery and her pain,
The ice will get into her mouth.

From flock and from down to rise
—Take it to heart!—were folly for thee:
Ice in heaps on every ford,
That is why I keep saying "cold"!

Then the old woman went out. As for Grainne, when she noticed
that the old woman had gone, she put out her hand on the garment
that was about her, and put it on her tongue, and found the taste
of salt on her cloak. "Woe, oh Diarmuid!" she cried, "the old
woman has betrayed thee. And arise quickly and take thy warrior's
dress about thee!" Diarmuid did so, and went out, and Grainne
with him. Then they beheld the warrior-king with the fian around
him coming towards them. Diarmuid glanced across at the sea
around Erin, and saw a skiff in the shelter of the harbor near him.
He and Grainne entered it. A man was awaiting them in the little
boat with a beautiful raiment about him, with a broad-braided
golden-yellow mantle over his shoulder behind. That was Angus
of the Brug, the foster-father of Diarmuid, who had come to rescue
him from the danger he was in from Finn and the fian of Erin.

THE DEATH OF FINN

No cycle of heroic tales in any country is regarded as complete without the story of the death of the central hero. All readers of epic literature recall the death of Beowulf, of Sigfried, and of Roland. In medieval Ireland the desire for harmony and system called into existence the death tales of not only the central heroes Cu Chulainn (p. 333) and Finn, but also of other famous warriors and kings. The story of Finn's death no doubt belongs to an early and authentically Irish tradition. The date of composition of the piece in its present form has not been established, but it is comparatively late, probably of about the same period as "The Colloquy of the Old Men" (p. 457). The rhetoric is flamboyant and, at times, over-conventionalized, yet the narrative is direct, and proceeds inevitably to its conclusion without interruption. The final scene in which the fierce old warrior faces his life-long enemies in his last battle is one of memorable tragic dignity.

The story begins with a great boar-hunt held by Finn and his companions. During a pause in the activities there is told the story of the origin of Finn's magic horn, which bears a mysterious curse. Then the boar-hunt itself is resumed. Oscar kills a terrible boar that has long been feared by the people of Erin. The following selection begins immediately after the killing of the boar. The actual death of Finn is not included, since the end of the story is lacking in the manuscript.

Finn meditated upon a decision to leave Ireland for fear of the prophecy [1] which the Cronanach had made to him; for dread and fear had seized upon him that the fian would be slaughtered and he himself would meet with death that year. And this is the decision that he made, to leave Ireland and go across the sea eastward to Britain, there to conclude his fian-ship, for his power was no less in Britain than here, so that the issue of that year and of the prophecy which had been made of him might be the further off. And he communicated that decision about going eastward across the sea to Angus of the Brug and to the nobles of his people and to all the fian, and he uttered the lay:

Let us go across the murmuring placid sea, oh fian of Finn from great Tara; unless I find speedy help I shall part from ever-fair Ireland.

To the Luagne the battle is destined, not a deed of wailing, but a cause of tears; unless I find proper help I shall part from my own fian here.

Angus mac Oc will come to our help for the sake of kinship; it is easy to go to the Brug before going on the journey.

[1] The prophecy of destruction made in connection with the horn.

Then the nobles of the fian went to hold counsel, and they came to the decision not to let Finn cross the sea that year. "Do not go across the sea, O royal leader of the fian," said they, "for if chase and spoil fail us in Ireland, there are enough of us here, leaders of the fian, and landowners, to support you to the end of the year; and we shall make a fresh feast for you every night until the year is ended." And upon this decision they fixed, and the fian dispersed to their strongholds and homesteads to prepare for Finn, so that he might find a banquet in the house of every one of them. And the one to whom it fell to attend and serve Finn on that night was Fer-tai son of Uaithne Irgalach the fian-chief of Conall Muirthemne and the Luagne of Tara. And the wife of Fer-tai was Iuchna Ardmor daughter of Goll mac Morna; and he had a notable, distinguished son, valorous, wise, and clever, whose mother was Iuchna, and who was called Fer-li. He resembled his grandfather Goll in size and stateliness and soldiership, in virulence and strength and championship, in liberality and prowess and might, in vigor and dexterity and abundance, in hardness and boldness, in knightliness, recklessness, and intrepidity, in magnanimity, in beauty of form, in valor and dauntlessness.

Now when Fer-li saw the small number of the host that Finn had with him, he meditated to practice treachery and deceit and guile upon him with his people; for there were of his people with him only Cedach Cithach the son of the King of Norway, and Loegaire of the Swift Blows son of Dub son of Salmor son of the King of the Men of Fannal, and five hundred warriors with each of them. They had just come across the sea to meet Finn, who had taken them with him that night as an honor to them, having left behind all his own clan and his usual company except Aed Ballderg son of Faelan son of Finn, and the three Cu's from Moenmuig and five hundred other warriors, together with these four, so that the whole company of Finn numbered five thousand. And Fer-li communicated his treacherous design to Emer Glunglas son of Aed son of Garad son of Morna. "That is a fitting, forcible design," said Emer; "for Finn is our hereditary enemy, since Goll the Great son of Morna has fallen by him, and all the Clan Morna and our fathers and grandfathers."

And they determined to slay Finn, with his people, by treachery. And those who came to that decision were·Fer-li son of Fer-tai, and Emer Glunglas son of Aed son of Garad, and the five sons of Urgriu of the Luagne of Meath, and the three Taiblinnachs from the stable plain of Fermoy. And these all vowed to slay Finn with his people, and thus they arranged and shaped the treachery; that is, to disperse and hold up the small company that was with Finn; for there were with him only five thousand, not counting the hounds and gillies. And this is the device they shaped: that fierce, stark-naked men should come to the household of Fer-tai to where Finn was billeting his people, and they should say that slaughter and loss were being inflicted by Finn's people on those of Fer-tai, so that the story might be the beginning of a conspiracy, and of a general onslaught to kill Finn.

When Finn had billeted his people, a splendid wide-doored hostel was arranged for him in the stronghold of Fer-tai, with choice drapery and fresh rushes, and a great pile of fire was kindled before Finn and Fer-tai and the few sons of kings and princes that were with them. When Finn sat down with his people to enjoy the feast, they saw the conspirators and traitors coming toward them into the hostel equipped with edge-speckled shields on the back of each champion. When Finn saw the bloody aspect of assassins upon those men, he knew what they were, and did not allow the entertainment to proceed, but kept watching the crew of veritable enemies that had come into the hostel to him. And Finn was arrayed thus: he had a broad-chested, wadded corslet about him, in which were twenty-seven board-like, compact, waxed shirts protecting his body against fights and the hazards of battle.

It was but a short time after that when they heard the loud angry hue and cry, and fierce, stark-naked men clamoring and vociferating coming toward the stronghold where those nobles were. And this is what they said, that the fian and Finn's people were slaughtering and attacking the cows and the farmers of the land.

"We do not like these sudden raids," said Fer-li.

"It shall be well, however," said Finn; "for any damages shall be suitably made good, for two cows shall be given for each single cow, and two sheep for one."

"It is not for that purpose thou hast come," said Fer-li, "but to slay us as thou hast slain our father and our grandfathers before us." And as he said that he attacked Finn suddenly, furiously, like one out of his senses. But that was not an attack unawares,

for Finn and his people responded to it stoutly, martially, wrathfully, and the battle was fought between them manfully, bravely,
fiercely, upon the central floor of the hostel. And Fer-tai was
intervening and was protecting Finn. However, the champions
did not deign to look at each other until thrice nine brave warriors
had fallen between them upon the floor of the hostel.

It was then that Iuchna Ardmor, wife of Fer-tai and mother of
Fer-li, heard the turmoil of the multitude and the fierce shouts of
the warriors as they were hacking each other, and she came to the
hostel, tore her checkered coif from her head, loosed her fair yellow
hair, bared her breasts, and said, "My son, it is the ruin of honor
and disgrace to a soldier and a reproach to tell and dispelling of
luck to betray the princely Finn of the fian; and now quickly leave
the hostel, my son," said she.

And Fer-li left the hostel to his mother. And as he went forth
he said, "I announce battle to thee to-morrow, Finn."

"That battle will be responded to," said Finn, "for we should
be in no strait, if we were an equal number to give battle to thee."
And that night Finn was served until he was satiated, invigorated,
and cheerful, both he and his fian. And Finn said, "It ill suits my
honor that Fer-li should importune me to-night nor grant me fair
play. A time will come," said he, "when no one will grant fair
play to another," and then he made this lay:

O Fer-li, whether it will be long or short till it come, the time when the
keen man will come he will not submit to the like of thee.

He will be put down in the time of the blue-weaponed foreigners, nor
will he get Ireland from me, but a rout in the north and a rout in
the south.

The time will come when the foreigners will be slaughtered. Whether
it be long or short till it come, it is senseless for anyone to overthrow his
children.

I am Finn; good is your ale: so drink and drink! Since thou dost not
grant justice or fair play, thy grave will be on the Boyne, O man.

When he had finished that song Finn said: "Warriors, I fear the
words which Fer-li speaks to us, remembering his feud against us.
It is true indeed," said he, "that I have seen Garad son of Morna
in the battle of Cruinmoinn cutting down the fian so that they did
not dare to face him for the boiling wrath of the champion. And
indeed I have also seen the veteran in sore plight by the fian," said
Finn, and then he spoke the lay:

Iuchna Ardmor daughter of Goll, mother of Fer-li of slender hand; many are they whose head he has bowed; the son resembles Goll.

Fer-li son of Fer-tai without fault, Emer who is accustomed to many a fight, my two foster-sons will fall with me; to me they grant no justice, meseems.

I saw Garad early; he would drain a lake as though it were a river; on the day he fell by the fian 'twas he that cried ah! and woe!

Goll was splitting shields; there was the lord that dealt out blood! in the battle of Cruinmoinn his hand and his wrath seethed.

Thereupon Fer-tai son of Uaithne Irgalach came into the house where Finn was and sat down by Finn's side and pressed drink and merriment upon him, and said, 'It is for this that the battle has been proclaimed against thee to-morrow, O royal fian-chief, because thou art without a host or multitude."

"I am by no means in that condition," said Finn. "For the son of the King of the Men of Fannal is by my side, that is Loegaire of the Swift Blows, and he will keep off three hundred warriors from me in this battle. And Cedach Citach son of the King of Norway is with me, who came to avenge his brothers upon me and the fian; and when he had seen the hounds and the men of the fian he fell greatly in love with them and abandoned his intent of plunder and spoliation and stayed with me. And he will keep off three hundred battle-armed warriors from me in the battle, O Fer-tai," said Finn. "And there are many other full-bold warriors of fierce deeds by my side who are eager for fight and agile in conflict and of unwearied powers and furious in the onset"; and then he spoke the lay:

Mac Duib son of Salmor of the cloaks, Loegaire of the Swift Blows, they will slay three hundred champions, the prophecy shall not be falsified.

There is here the son of Norway's king, Cedach Citach of the combats; by him three hundred of the host shall fall, of warriors fierce and sword-red.

Woe to him who will oppose the fian when all shall rise for combat! They do not refuse hard battle, reckless they rise all at once.

When the Luagne come to battle to-morrow in the morning, by dint of shields and blades and hands many a mother will be without a son.

That night they were discussing the appointed battle and conflict of the morrow. In the early-bright morning Finn arose and sent messengers for his people, who responded stoutly, bravely, and proudly from all directions; and Finn with his fifteen hundred

warriors went to Ath Brea on the southern Boyne, and they arrayed
themselves in battle-order upon the bottom of the ford in a mass
of shields and swords and helmets.

As for Fer-tai son of Uaithne Irgalach and Fer-li son of Fer-tai,
they gathered their host and multitude, and they came in fine,
huge, brave, companies to one place, so that they were three
thousand battle-armed warriors. And they came to Ath Brea and
when they saw the small number on the other side upon the bottom
of the ford, they grumbled at it. And this is the counsel they took:
they took their dresses of battle and combat about them and
advanced in their light dresses and in their ponderous armor.
And these are the nobles that were put in the front of the battalion
of the "pillars," that is, Fer-tai son of Uaithne Irgalach, and Fer-li
son of Fer-tai, and Emer Glunglas son of Aed son of Garad son of
Morna, and the five sons of Urgriu of the ancient tribes of Tara,
and the three Tablinnachs from the stable plain of Fermoy, and
the Luagne of Tara as well.

Now when the manful, puissant, powerful, terrible, fierce-
battling prince of the fian, and the valorous, fierce, combative
hero Finn mac Cumaill of many battalions beheld that battle-
phalanx arrayed against him, "It seems to me," said he, "those
men are giving us battle in earnest. And O my messenger Birgad,"
said Finn, "go and speak to those people and offer them terms."

"What terms?" said Birgad.

"I will tell you," said Finn. "It is I that gave them their wealth
and territory and their landed estates, and I will give them as much
again if they will not at this time come against me. And remind
them that they are foster-sons of mine," said Finn.

Then Birgad the female messenger came to where those nobles
were and told them that. "It is just to accept the terms," said
Fer-tai, "for Finn loves thee dearly, Fer-li," he said. "For thou
wast one of the twelve men that used to be with Finn in his house;
and thou always hadst the first of counsel from him and the last
of drink. And thou art a foster-son of his," said he.

"I pledge my word," said Fer-li, "that I and Finn shall never
again drink together in friendship, nor will I ever enter his house
again."

"That is ill advice," said Fer-tai, "because Finn is a noble,
puissant, excellent prince," said he, "for he with his fian is valiant

and ready for fight and attack. And I have seen Finn in battles and combats, and I never saw his equal for swiftness, for vigor, for fury, for hardness, for boldness, for fierceness, for heroism in slaying hosts and multitudes"; and then he spoke this lay and Fer-li replied:

Fer-tai. Woe to him who would give battle to the fian if he were in his senses,—their deeds are fierce. It were better to stay by Finn himself and to go submissive to his house.

Fer-li. I shall not go to Finn, I shall meet him in the round of battle, and I shall not stay by him, nor shall I go submissive to his house.

Fer-tai. Finn is good at cutting down the battalions; his is the vanquishing hand in every direction; whoever fights with the brilliant king, it is woe to himself, it seems to me.

"It is ill advice," said Fer-tai, "to give battle to Finn, on account of his nobility and fierceness and valor."

"Not so at all," said Fer-li; "we shall accept nothing at all from him but battle. For yon decrepit old warrior will not stand up against us," said he, "for readiness and bravery in the up-rising of battle"; and the messenger turned back and reported these words to Finn.

"I pledge my word," said Finn, "if our army would come to us, we should not propose those terms to them. Go thou again, my messenger," said Finn, "and offer them further terms."

"What further terms?" said the messenger.

"The award of judges, and in addition to it their own award to them."

And again the messenger came and offered those terms. "It is just to accept the terms," said Fer-tai; "and whoever has given battle to Finn unjustly has always been routed by Finn"; and Fer-tai spoke a lay thus and Fer-li replied:

Fer-tai. I have seen Finn cutting down hosts on which he broke the battle; to fight with him is an unequal contest, woe to him who goes to meet him!

Fer-li. Finn will not go without fighting him though fierce be his prowess, until he be as I wish, without sense, without reason.

Fer-tai. The men of Moinmuig will be there with mighty blades; from your conflict, O fearless fian, oxen will be without a yoke.

"It is time for me to depart now," said the messenger.

"No other substance or terms will be accepted from you except battle," said Emer Glunglas son of Aed son of Garad; and so said the sons of Urgriu son of Lugaid Corr, and so said the Luagne of Tara.

The messenger went and gave a true account to Finn; "and they say that you are a worn-out, feeble-handed old man, Finn," said the messenger.

"I pledge my word," said Finn, "that I will fight them like a youngster," and then he spoke this lay:

The ancient Luagne of Tara with false words, if they come to Brea, I shall give vigorous battle.

The son of Aed son of Garad, Emer Glunglas, this is the end of his sway to be in this battle.

The sons of Urgriu will fall in witness of it; every wrong which I recount, to them it shall be destruction.

Foes will deem it sport when they scatter spears; they will carry with them on their lips the ancient stories.

Thereupon Finn said, "Go, my messenger, and offer them further terms on account of the pride of their host and the excellence of their prowess and the boldness of their noblemen and the daring of their counsel; for every enemy is unforgiving, my messenger," said he; "and offer them their own award, for a battle without terms is not good."

So Birgad the messenger came to where those chieftains were and offered them their own award. "We shall not accept substance nor terms nor territory nor land, but battle, so that we may avenge our ancient wrongs," said the old warrior. And Fer-li attempted to kill the messenger but he was prevented. "I pledge my word for it," said Fer-li, "O Birgad, if thou art seen again, that I will shorten thy life."

And Birgad returned upon the road and lifted up her dress to the rounds of her legs, her tongue quivering with the great danger in which she was, and so she came to where Finn was.

.   .   .   .

"O royal chief of the fian," said Birgad, "those yonder have with one accord taken their counsel against you," said she, "and act bravely against those warriors and the Luagne of Tara."

"It shall be done, then," said Finn; "for the debtor's speech which I shall hold with them will be bloody and crushing, wrathful and relentless."

Then rose the royal chief of the fian of Erin and Scotland and of the Saxons and Britons, of Lewis and Norway, and of the hither islands, and put on his battle-dress of combat and conflict, a thin, silken shirt of wonderful, choice satin of the fair-cultivated Land of Promise over the face of his white skin: and outside over that he put his twenty-four waxed, stout shirts of cotton, firm as a board, about him, and on the top of these he put his beautiful plaited, three-meshed coat of mail of cold, refined iron, and around his neck his graven gold-bordered breastplate, and about his waist he put a stout corslet with a decorated firm belt with gruesome images of dragons, so that it reached from the thick of his thighs to his arm-pit, whence spears and blades would rebound. And his stout-shafted martial, five-edged spears were placed over against the king, and he put his gold-hafted sword in readiness on his left, and he grasped his broad-blue, well-ground Norse lance, and upon the arched expanse of his back he placed his emerald-tinted shield with flowery designs and with variegated, beautiful bosses of pale gold, and with delightful studs of bronze, and with twisted stout chains of old silver; and to protect the hero's head in battle he seized his crested, plated, four-edged helmet of beautiful, refined gold with bright, magnificent, crystal gems and with flashing, full-beautiful, precious stones which had been set in it by the hands of master-smiths and great artists.

And in that way he went forth, a famous tree of upholding battle, and a bush of shelter for brave warriors, and a stable stake for hosts and multitudes, and a protecting door-valve for warriors and battle-soldiers of the western world; nor did he stop in his course until he reached the brink of the ford. Truly it was no wonder that the kingship of Erin and Scotland and the headship of the fian of the whole world would be in the hands of Finn mac Cumaill at that time; for he was one of the five masters in every great art, and one of the three sons of comfort to Erin, along with Lug Lamfada son of Cian, who ousted the race of Fomorians from Ireland; and Brian Boruma (Boru) son of Cennedig, who brought Ireland out of bondage and oppression so that there was not a winnowing-sheet of any kiln without a Norse slave to work it until Brian cast them out; and Finn mac Cumaill, the third son of comfort to Ireland, who expelled from Ireland marauders and reavers and monsters and many beasts and full many a fleet of exiles and every other pest. And there came a plague to Ireland from one corner to another; and for a whole year Finn fed the men of Ireland and put seven cows and a bull in every single farmstead in Ireland.

Now, however, that illustrious puissant chieftain came and pledged the small host that was with him to behave bravely against the army before them. And the fifteen hundred fian-warriors that were with Finn rose at the powerful urging of the voice of their lord; and each warrior leaped into his coat of mail and grasped his sword and seized his lance, so that they were a mass of shield and sword and helmet around Finn mac Cumaill and Cedach Citach son of the King of Norway, and around Loegaire of the Swift Blows the son of Dub son of Salmor son of the King of the Men of Fannall, and around Aed Ballderg son of Faelan son of Finn, and the three Cus of Moinmuige. And they lifted up a dense, vast, huge, dark-red, and flaming forest of stout-shafted, martial, fire-edged spears and of broad-blue lances and of bloody, red-edged javelins, and made a triumphant, angry, fierce fold, and a firm, compact, indestructible, inseparable platform of beautiful, bulging shields, and of delightful, all-white shields, and of graven, emerald shields, and of crimson, blood-red shields, and of shining, variegated shields, and of crimson, spiky shields, and of yellow-speckled, buffalo-horn shields. It was enough of horror and heart-trembling to their enemies to see them in that wise, for the venomousness of their weapons and the warlike array of their equipment and the stoutness of their hearts and the ferocity of their intent. And they made a fierce, swift, light-winged, intrepid rush in their well-arranged phalanx and in their destructive mass and in their furious band to the center of the ford.

Then from the other side came to the ford the three thousand battle-equipped warriors that the "pillars" of Tara numbered, and put their attire of battle and contest about them, and their trumpets were sounded before them, and their war-cries were raised defiantly, and their battle was put in order, and their impetuous, bold soldiers and their fierce warriors and their valiant heroes were arrayed in the forefront of the mutual smiting, that is, Fer-tai son of Uaithne Irgalach, and Fer-li son of Fer-tai, and Emer Glunglas son of Aed son of Garad, and the five sons of Urgriu, and Aithlech Mor son of Dubriu, and Urgriu himself, and the three Tablinnachs from the stable plain of Fermoy. And they made a swarming, swift, torrential rush to the center of the ford from the other side against Finn and his people.

And they did not long rest content with looking at each other, before the two armies flung themselves against one another. And they uttered loud, mighty shouts so that their echo rang in woods and rocks, in cliffs and river-mouths and the caves of the earth and in the cold outer zones of the firmament. And there were hurled between them showers of bloody, sharp-edged javelins, and of broad half-spears for throwing, and of hard, mighty stones. And the battle became closer and the conflict intense, and the slaughter grew vast, and the combat became embittered, and each warrior attacked another vehemently, fiercely, impatiently, furiously, madly, and they made an angry, wrathful, crushing, masterful, brisk, bitter, earnest fight, and they flung huge stones to break each other's heads and skulls and helmets, and the fringes of the two armies became mingled in confusion. Then indeed many a stout spear was broken, and many a hard-ground sword bent, and many a shield shattered, and helmets and head-pieces broken to pieces, while soldiers and champions were inflicting wounds. Then there were many bodies maimed and skins lacerated, and sides pierced, and bold warriors mangled, and champions cut down, and bodies of heroes in their litter of blood. It was enough to kill half-hearted warriors and cowards merely to behold the transverse smiting of the crooked blades upon the shoulders of men, and to hear the roar of the champions as they fell, and the clangor of the shields as they were split, and the crack of the lined corslets as they were broken, and the ringing of the swords upon the crests of helmets, and the outcry of the hosts as they were defending themselves against the champions.

And the warriors did not cease from the deadly conflict until from one end to the other the ford was crimson and turbid, and until with the mass of blood that flowed out of the warriors' wounds the heavy troubled waters of the Boyne from the ford downward were a blood-red foaming cauldron. Then came a couple of Finn's people into the battalion of the "pillars," that is Tnuthach son of Dubtach, and Tuaran son of Tomar, and these two brought disaster upon the troops, so that nine warriors fell by each of them, until two of the sons of Urgriu came against them in the battle, so that the four fought together. And that couple of Finn's people fell by the sons of Urgriu in the confines of the combat.

Thereupon a fierce, implacable warrior of Finn's people came into the battalion of the "pillars," namely, Loegaire of the Swift Blows son of Dub son of Salmor son of the King of the Men of Fannall, and he made a breach of a hundred in the battle right in front of him, and he plied his wrath upon the Luagne of Tara, so that one hundred warriors of the people of Fer-li fell by it. However, when Fer-li saw the spreading of the slaughter and that great royal clearance and the battle-breaking which Loegaire wrought on his people, he came to meet him. "Furious are these onslaughts, O Loegaire," said Fer-li.

"It is true, indeed," said Loegaire, "and no thanks to thee. 'Tis not a friendly discourse which you have held with our people."

Then came a hundred flaming full-keen warriors of Fer-li's people against Loegaire in battle, and they all fell by Loegaire's hand before the eyes of their lord. And Loegaire wounded Fer-li, and in return for his wound Fer-li wounded him. And just then there came another hundred angry implacable warriors of Fer-li's people, and those hundred also fell by Loegaire's hand in the confines of the battle. And he wounded Fer-li and Fer-li wounded him. However, these two pledged each other to encounter and combat, so that they planted stout-shafted martial hard-socketed spears into each other's sides and ribs. It was confusion to the companies and trembling to the battalions to be looking on at the encounter of these two, until Loegaire fell by Fer-li in the confines of combat, and Fer-li boasted of the triumph.

That did not intimidate or frighten Finn or his people, but they pressed the battle and urged the attack. After the fall of Loegaire came Cedach Citach son of the King of Norway, into the battalion of the "pillars," and terrible were the slaughters which he wrought among the battalions round about him, so that sole would touch sole, and arm arm, and neck neck, wherever he went among the enemy. When Emer Glunglas beheld the slaughter of the warriors and that onset of the royal hero, he came himself to meet Cedach like an angry combative bull to a trial of strength. When they saw one another they rushed at each other stoutly for the contest, so that everyone who was looking on was confounded. However,

three hundred valiant, fierce warriors fell between them, and their
household guard fell, nor was there any help found against the
men, and to come near them was certain end of life. They never
spared one another's body until they both fell at each other's
hands in the presence of the battalions.

Then came Aed Ballderg son of Faelan Finn among the hosts
of the "pillars," and a wide passage was made for him in the battle,
so that he was terrible to see wherever he went. And Aitlech Mor
son of Dubriu, and Aed met in battle, so that thrice nine warriors
of the flower of Urgriu's people fell by Aed Ballderg, and they
made a valiant bloody heroic combat against one another. Those
were terrible wounds and perilous maimings, and intersecting
were the injuries which they inflicted on each other's bodies, until
Aed Ballderg fell in the confines of the combat.

Now when the prince of the fian, Finn, saw that the champions
of the fian were laid low and that their strong men had fallen and
men of rank had been slain, the perfect, wise chieftain understood
that fame was more lasting than life for him and that it was better
for him to die than to flinch before the enemy. 'Twas then the
royal fian-chief came to the hosts of the "pillars," and his spirits
grew high and his courage rose and he quickened his hands and
he plied his blows, so that his bird of valor arose over the breath
of the royal warrior, so that crowds of warriors were unable to
stand against his prowess, so that men fell round his knee and a
heap of them was piled up in their maimed-bodied and bloody-
truncated necks and litter of gore wherever he would go into the
battle. And he went among them and through them and over
them like a fierce, furious bull that has been badly beaten, or like
a lion whose young have been wounded, or like a turbulent wave
of deluge that in the time of flood spouts from the breast of a
high mountain, breaking and crushing everything that it reaches.
And three times he went round the battalion of the "pillars," as
the woodbine hugs a tree, or as a fond woman clasps her son, and
the crushing of thighs and shin-bones and halves of heads under
the edge of his sword in the battle was like the smiting of a smith
in the forge, or like the uproar of withered trees cracking, or like
sheets of ice under the feet of a cavalcade. And pale-faced and
buck-shaped sprites and red-mouthed battle-demons and the
specters of the glen and the fiends of the air and the giddy phan-

toms of the firmament shrieked as they waged warfare and strife above the head of the fian-chief wherever he went in the battle. And the royal warrior never ceased from that onset until the battalion of the "pillars" was annihilated both by slaughter and flight, all save Fer-li, Fer-tai, and the five sons of Urgriu.

When Fer-li saw Finn by himself without any troops to protect him and without a friend to guard his back, he came to meet him and rehearsed his enmity against the royal fian-chief. Finn answered Fer-li and said, "Thou wilt thyself fall because of these feuds." And these two began a long combat on the spot. The encounter of these two was impetuous, vengeful, stern, and of fierce strokes. The harsh clashing of the swords and of the tusk-hilted blades against the helmets of each other was horrible, parlous. When Fer-li had worn out his sword against the head and body of the royal fian-chief, he seized his stout-shafted, five-edged spear and made a stout, valiant, justly-poised warrior-like cast at Finn, so that he sent the spear through the ample dress which was about the royal warrior, so that the spear pierced him through and through after mangling his body. Angrily and destructively did the royal fian-chief answer that murderous wound which Fer-li had inflicted upon him, so that he gave him a fierce, hard, bone-crushing blow with his sword, and struck his head off his body. And Finn boasted of that veteran warrior and that prop of battle having fallen by him.

However, when Fer-tai beheld his son falling he came vehemently, sullenly, impatiently towards Finn, and said, "Those in sooth are great deeds, Finn."

"That is true," said Finn, "and why hast thou not come until now?"

"I had hoped thou wouldst have fallen by Fer-li, and I should have liked thee to fall by him rather than by me."

"Hast thou come to commiserate me," said Finn, "or to attack me?"

"To attack thee indeed," said Fer-tai; "for nought of lordship nor of wealth has been appointed for which I should forgive the slaying of my son."

And he attacked Finn without sense, without reflection, and without sparing. Finn met that truly bold champion. Those two performed many heroic feats to destroy and annihilate each other;

but it were difficult and impossible to give a description of that fight, for the charges were bull-like, headlong, and fierce, parlous, and dangerous were the wounds and cruel and terrible the injuries which they inflicted on each other. And Fer-tai seized an opportunity of wounding the royal fian-chief, and gave him such a thrust with his spear that the wound yawned no less on the other side than on the side on which he had struck. And in revenge for his wound Finn dealt Fer-tai such a fierce blow with his sword that neither the long corslet nor the compact wadding nor the hard foreign armor was any protection to Fer-tai, so that the champion fell to the ground in two heavy pieces. And Finn boasted of having achieved that great deed.

This was the hour in which the five sons of Urgriu came upon the scene and turned their faces toward Finn. When Finn beheld these inveterate enemies making for him, he avoided them not. And each of them planted a spear in the royal fian-chief. And he replied to the five champions with equal force and gave them wound for wound. When the sons of Urgriu saw that the hero had been wounded in the earlier combats which he had fought with Fer-tai and his son Fer-li, and that he was feeble from loss of blood. . . .

(The rest is lacking in the manuscript.)

OISIN IN THE LAND OF YOUTH

The story of the visit of Oisin son of Finn to fairyland, the Happy Otherworld of the ancient Irish, belongs less definitely to the heroic tradition than the other Finn tales printed in this group. The central motif, of course, belongs to the oldest period (*cf.* "The Adventures of Connla the Fair," p. 488, and "Cormac's Adventures in the Land of Promise," p. 503), but the present form dates only from the eighteenth century, when it was written by the poet Michael Comyn. The dialogue form in which Patrick acts as interlocutor shows the influence of "The Colloquy of the Old Men" (p. 457). The translation, which is very free, aims to reproduce the complicated system of alliteration and internal rhyme used in Irish bardic poetry.

The events of the story are supposed to have taken place just after the celebrated battle of Gabra, in which Finn's band met its final defeat, but the introduction of the Rip Van Winkle motif carries the action through many years to a period long after the decline and ruin of the celebrated fian. The story furnishes an explanation of the tradition that Oisin survived Finn and the rest of the fian long enough to converse with St. Patrick, as in "The Colloquy of the Old Men." The fact that the return of Oisin is used as a basis for parts of the "Colloquy of the Old Men" is an indication of the antiquity of the theme.

Patrick.   O noble Oisin, son of the king,
               Whose deeds men sing this day in song!
               Thy grief abate and to us relate
               By what strange fate thou hast lived so long!

Oisin.   O Patrick, here's the tale for thee,
               Tho' sad to me its memories old—
               'Twas after Gabra—I mind me well,
               The field where fell my Oscar bold!

        One day the generous Finn my sire
               With olden fire led forth the chase—
               But our band was small when gather'd all,
               For past recall were the hosts of our race.

        'Twas a summer's morn and a mist hung o'er
               The winding shore of sweet Loch Lein,
               Where fragrant trees perfume the breeze
               And birds e'er please with a joyous strain.

We soon awoke the woodland deer
   That forced by fear fled far away—
   Keenly our hounds with strenuous bounds
   O'er moors and mounds pursued their prey.

When lo! into sight came a figure bright,
   In a blaze of light from the west it rushed—
   A lady fair of radiance rare
   Whom a white steed bore to our band, now hush'd!

Amazed we halt, though hot the chase,
   To gaze on the face of the fair young queen—
   A marvel to Finn and his fian band,
   Who ne'er in the land such beauty had seen!

A golden crown on her brow she bore,
   A mantle she wore of silken sheen
   All studded with stars of bright red gold—
   Ample each fold fell on herbage green.

Her golden hair all fair to view
   In golden curls on her shoulders fell—
   Bright and pure were her eyes of blue
   As drops of the dew in a blue harebell.

Ruddier far her cheek than the rose,
   Her bosom more white than the swan's so free,
   Sweeter the breath of her balmy mouth
   Than spice of the south from over the sea.

Her milk-white steed was of worth untold
   Nor bridle of gold did the charger lack—
   A saddle all covered with purple and gold
   Lay bright to behold on the steed's proud back.

Four shoes of gold his hoofs did guard,
   Of gold unmarred by mixture base,
   A silver wreath on his crest was shown—
   Such steed was unknown on the earth's fair face.

To Finn's great presence drew the maid
   Thus bright array'd and softly spake—
   "O King of the fian host," she cried
   "Far have I hied for sweet love's sake!"

"Who art thou, pray, O princess rare,
    Of form most fair, of face divine?
    Gently thy errand to us make known—
    What land's thine own, what name is thine?"

"Niam the Golden-haired I'm named,
    —O Finn far-famed for wisdom and truth!—
    My praise harps ring, and bards e'er sing,
    And my sire's the King of the Land of Youth!"

"Then tell us, most lovely lady now,
    Why comest thou o'er seas so far?
    Has heartless husband left thee to weep
    With grief most deep, thy mind to mar!"

"No husband has left me, O lordly Finn,
    —My heart within ne'er man did gain,
    Till hero of Erin, thy famous son,
    Its young love won, for aye to reign!"

"On which of my gallant sons, O maid,
    Is thy heart's love laid, so frankly free?
    Now hide not from us, O princess dear,
    The causes clear of thy visit to me!"

"His name, O Finn, then I'll declare—
    'Tis thy famed son, so fair, so brave,
    Oisin the warrior, Erin's bard,
    My fair reward for crossing the wave!"

"Then why hast thou hastened to give thy love,
    O maiden above all maids most fair—
    To Oisin my own beyond all known
    Of princes high both rich and rare?"

"Good cause I ween for my course shall be seen,
    O king of the Fian, when I tell thee truth:
    Oisin's high deeds and noble name
    Have won him fame in the Land of Youth.

"Full many a prince of high degree
    Hath offered me both heart and hand;
    But whoso appealed, I ne'er did yield
    But my heart kept sealed for my hero grand!"

Oisin.   O Patrick stern, how my soul did yearn
    And with ardor burn for the peerless maid—
    No shame to tell—each word was a spell,
    That bound me well past mortal aid.

    I took her gentle hand in mine
        And with every sign of love I said,
        "Welcome a hundred thousand times,
        From fairy climes, O royal maid!

    "Of women the rarest, fairest seen,
        Thou art O queen, without compeer!
        My soul, my life, my chosen wife,
        Star of my way of ray most clear!"

    "Request refused by no true knight
        Who knoweth aright the knightly vogue,
        I make of thee now—'tis hence to speed
        With me on my steed to *Tír na n-Óg!* [1]

    "Delightful land beyond all dreams!
        Beyond what seems to thee most fair—
        Rich fruits abound the bright year round
        And flowers are found of hues most rare.

    "Unfailing there the honey and wine
        And draughts divine of mead there be,
        No ache nor ailing night or day—
        Death or decay thou ne'er shalt see!

    "The mirthful feast and joyous play
        And music's sway all blest, benign—
        Silver untold and store of gold
        Undreamt by the old shall all be thine!

    "A hundred swords of steel refined,
        A hundred cloaks of kind full rare,
        A hundred steeds of proudest breed,
        A hundred hounds—thy meed when there!

    "A hundred coats of mail shall be thine,
        A hundred kine of sleekest skin,
        A hundred sheep with fleece of gold,
        And gems none hold these shores within.

[1] The fairy otherworld, literally, "The Land of the Young."

"A hundred maidens young and fair
  Of blithesome air shall tend on thee,
  Of form most meet, as fairies fleet
  And of song more sweet than the wild thrush free!

"A hundred knights in fights most bold
  Of skill untold in all chivalrie,
  Full-armed, bedight in mail of gold
  Shall in *Tír na n-Óg* thy comrades be.

"A corslet charmed for thee shall be made
  And a matchless blade of magic power,
  Worth a hundred blades in a hero's hands,
  Most blest of brands in battle's hour!

"The royal crown of the King of Youth
  Shall shine in sooth on thy brow most fair,
  All brilliant with gems of luster bright
  Whose worth aright none might declare.

"All things I've named thou shalt enjoy
  And none shall cloy—to endless life—
  Beauty and strength and power thou'lt see
  And I'll e'er be thy own true wife!"

"Refusal of mine thou ne'er shalt hear,
  O maid without peer, of the locks of gold!
  My chosen wife for life I know
  And gladly I'll go to *Tír na n-Óg!*"

Forthwith the steed I then bestrode;
  Before me rode my royal queen,
  Who said, "O Oisin with caution ride
  Till side of dividing sea we've seen!"

Then up rose that steed with a mighty bound,
  Gave forth three sounding startling neighs,
  His mane he shook, then with fiery look
  His riders he took to the sea's known ways.

Now when from Finn and the fian host
  The steed to the coast was coursing so,
  There burst from the chief a cry of grief,
  A wail of grief not brief nor low.

"Oh Oisin," cried Finn with faltering voice—
  "My son most choice must I then lose,
  With never a hope to see thee again?
  —My heart in twain 'twill break and bruise!"

His noble features now clouded o'er
  And tears did pour in showers free
  Till breast and beard in tears were drowned—
  "My grief! he e'er found this maid from the Sea!"

Oh Patrick, I grieve to tell thee the tale,
  My words now fail to find their way—
  How the father did part from the son of his heart,
  My tears e'er start when I think of the day.

I drew up the steed for a moment's rest
  And tenderly pressed on my sire a kiss,
  Then bade farewell to the fian band,
  Tho' the tears did stand in my eyes, I wis.

Full many a day great Finn and I
  And our host all nigh in gay array
  Held glorious feast where harps ne'er ceased
  And highest and least had their choice alway.

Full oft our race held a royal chase
  While at boldest pace ran our sweet-voiced hounds—
  Anon in battle our javelins rattle
  And men like cattle fall in heaps and mounds!

Patrick. O vain old Oisin, dwell no more
  On thy deeds of yore in the fian ranks,
  How didst thou go to *Tír na n-Óg?*
  Come let me know and I'll owe much thanks.

Oisin. We turned away as I truly said
  And our horse's head we gave to the west,
  When lo! the deep sea opened before
  While behind us bore the billows that pressed.

Anon we saw in our path strange sights,
  Cities on heights and castles fair,
  Palaces brilliant with lights and flowers—
  The brightest of bowers were gleaming there.

And then we saw a yellow young fawn
    Leap over a lawn of softest green,
    Chased by a graceful, snow-white hound
    That with airy bound pressed on most keen.

We next beheld—I tell thee true,
    A maid in view on a bright bay steed,
    An apple of gold in her hand did she hold,
    O'er the waves most bold she hied with speed.

And soon we saw another sight,
    A youthful knight who a white steed rode,
    The rider in purple and crimson array'd
    Whilst a glittering blade in his hand he showed.

"Yon youthful pair both knight and maid—
    Pray tell," I said, "who they may be—
    The lady mild as a summer's morn
    And knight high-born that fares so free."

"In all thy sight may light on here,
    O Oisin dear, I say with truth,
    There's nought of beauty, nought of strength,
    Till we reach at length the Land of Youth!"

And now as we rode we came in sight
    Of a palace bright, high-placed, and strong,
    Shapely its hall and lofty its wall
    Far beyond all e'er famed in song.

"What royal fort is yon, O queen,
    That stands serene on yon hill-side,
    Whose towers and columns so stately spring—
    What prince or king doth there abide?"

"In yonder fort a sad queen dwells
    Whom force compels her life to mourn—
    Whom Fomor fierce of the Mighty Blows
    Doth there enclose from friends' arms torn.

"But captive though to that pirate proud,
    She yet hath vowed by taboos grave,
    Never for life to be his wife
    Till won in strife 'gainst champion brave!"

'Blessing and bliss be thine," I cried
  "O maid bright eyed, for thy welcome word,
    Tho' grieved that woman such fate should meet,
    Music more sweet I ne'er have heard!

'For now we'll go to that high-placed fort
  And help full soon that maid distressed;
    A champion's steel shall Fomor feel
    And 'neath my heel shall his neck be pressed!"

To Fomor's stronghold then we rode—
  Unblest abode for a captive sweet!
    At once the queen with joyous mien,
    Came forth on the green with welcome meet.

In robe of rich-hued silk arrayed
  Was this queenly maid with the brow of snow,
    Her neck all fair could with swan's compare
    Her cheeks did wear the rose's glow.

Of golden hue was her hair, 'tis true,
  Of heavenly blue her bright eyes clear,
    Her lips were red as berries on bough,
    Shapely each brow with rare compeer!

To seat ourselves we then were told—
  In a chair of gold each one sat down,
    Most royal fare was set forth there
    In royal ware of great renown.

Now when of food we had had our fill
  And of wine as will might fancy e'en,
    Thus spoke the queen, her face now pale,
    "Now list my tale, with ears all keen!"

From first to last she told her tale
  Her cheek all pale and wet with tears—
    How kith and kin ne'er more she'd see
    Whilst Fomor free provoked her fears.

"Then weep no more, O fair young queen,
  Henceforth, I ween, thou needst not mourn,
    Fomor shall pay with his life this day
    In mortal fray for the wrongs thou'st borne!"

"Alas! no champion can be found
    On earth's great round, I fear me much,
    Could hand to hand such foe withstand
    Or free me from this tyrant's clutch."

"I tell thee truly, lady fair,
    I'll boldly dare him to the field,
    Resolved to save thee or in strife
    Never while life doth last to yield!"

Ere cease my words, in savage trim
    The giant grim against us hies—
    In skins of beasts uncouthly clad,
    Whilst a club he had of monstrous size.

No salutation from him came,
    But his eyes aflame glared all around;
    Forthwith he challenged me to fight
    And I with delight took up my ground.

For full three nights and eke three days
    Our deadly fray's end seemed in doubt,
    Till at length his head with my sword I sped
    O'er the plain now red with the blood pour'd out!

Now when the two young maids beheld
    Fierce Fomor felled by my good sword,
    They gave three shouts of joy and glee
    Of joy for freedom now restored.

We then returned to the giant's fort,
    Where faint in swoon at last I fell,
    Faint from wounds and loss of blood
    That still in flood gushed like a well.

But now the maid from Fomor freed
    Ran up with speed, to help me fain—
    My wounds she washed, and bathed with balm,
    And health and calm I found again.

The giant grim we buried him
    Deep down in earth in widest grave—
    We raised a stone his grave to note
    And his name we wrote in Ogam-craev.

A merry feast we then did hold
   And stories told of olden days—
   And when night fell we rested well
   On couches such as poets praise.

When morning fair the sun did greet,
   From slumbers sweet we fresh awoke—
   "Dear friend, to my land now depart—"
   'Twas thus my lovely princess spoke.

We soon equipped us for our way,
   For longer stay was needed not,
   Sad, sorrowful the leave we took,
   And sad the maiden's look, I wot.

The further fate of that sweet maid,
   O Patrick staid, I could not tell,
   No word of her I've heard one say
   E'er since the day we said farewell.

We turned once more upon our course,
   And fleetly sped our horse along—
   No wind that sweeps the mountain drift
   Was half so swift or half so strong.

But now the sky began to lower,
   The wind in power increased full fast—
   Red lightning lights the mad sea-waves,
   And madly raves the thunder past!

A while we cowered 'neath the storm,
   —All nature's form in darkness dread—
   When lo! the winds' fierce course was run,
   And bright the sun appear'd o'erhead!

And now there spread before our sight
   A land most bright, most rich, and fair,
   With hill and plain and shady bower
   And a royal tower of splendor rare.

And in this royal mansion fair
   All colors were that eye hath seen—
   The blue most bright, the purest white
   With purple and yellow and softest green.

To left and right of this palace bright
    Rose many a hall and sun-lit tower,
    All built of brilliant gems and stones
    By hands, one owns, of wondrous power.

"What lovely land is that we see?
    Pray answer me with maiden's truth—
    Is't penned in page that man may read,
    Or is it indeed the Land of Youth?"

"It is indeed the Land of Youth—
    And maiden's truth I've ever told—
    No joy or bliss I've promised thee
    But thou shalt see this land doth hold!"

And now there rode from the king's abode
    To meet us on the lawn of green
    Thrice fifty champions of might,
    In armor bright, of noble mien.

And then there came in hues arrayed
    A hundred maids in maiden vogue—
    In silken garments bright and brave
    Who welcome gave to *Tír na n-Óg.*

And next marched forth a chosen band
    Of the troops of that land, a lovely sight—
    A king at their head of kingly tread
    Of mighty name and fame in fight.

A yellow shirt of silken weft,
    A cloak most deftly broidered o'er
    On the king in folds hung freely down
    Whilst a glittering crown on his head he wore.

And close behind him there was seen
    His youthful queen—a consort meet—
    With fifty maidens in her train
    Who sang a strain divinely sweet.

Then spoke the king in kindly voice,
    "O friends, rejoice, for here you see
    Oisin the famous son of Finn,
    Who spouse of our Niam shall be!"

He takes me warmly by the hand,
    Then as we stand he speaks anew—
    "Welcome," he cries, "I give thee now,
    A hundred thousand welcomes true!

"This kingdom which o'er seas and lands
    Thou'st sought, now stands reveal'd to thee;
    Long shalt thou live our race among
    And ever young as thou shalt see.

"No pleasure e'er that entered mind
    But here thou'lt find without alloy,
    This is the land thy bards e'er sing,
    And I am the King of this Land of Joy.

"Here is our gentle, fair young queen,
    Mother of Niam the Golden-haired,
    Who crossed for thee the stormy sea
    And thine to be all dangers dared!"

I thanked the king with grateful heart,
    To the queen apart I bowed me low—
    We tarried no longer without the walls
    But entered the halls of *Rí na n-Óg*.[1]

There came the nobles of all that land,
    The great and grand to sing our praise—
    And feast was held with all delights
    For ten long nights and ten long days.

I then was wedded to Gold-haired Niam—
    And there to leave the tale were well—
    Thus did I go to *Tír na n-Óg*,
    Though grief and woe 'tis now to tell.

Patrick. Come, finish the charming tale thou'st told,
    O Oisin of gold, of the weapons of war—
    Why from such land didst thou e'er return?
    I fain would learn what the causes are.

And say whilst there thou didst abide
    If thee thy bride any children bore,
    Or wast thou for long in the Land of Youth?
    —I long in truth to list such lore!

[1] "King of [the Land of] the Young."

Oisin.   I had by Niam of the Golden Hair
      Three children fair as ever smiled,
      Whose sweetness gave us daily joys—
      Two gallant boys and a maiden mild.

Patrick. O sweet-voiced Oisin, do not grieve,—
      Where didst thou leave those children sweet?
      Tell me the names of thy offspring fair,
      And tell me where they mirthful meet.

Oisin.   Those children three rich heirs would be
      To kingdoms free and fair and great,
      To royal scepter, crown of gold
      And wealth untold, no tongue could state.

My gentle Niam on her boys bestowed
      The names I owed most honor to—
      Finn the bright of the hosts of might,
      And Oscar who'd fight for the right and true.

And I my daughter fair did call
      By a name which all fair names o'ershades—
      In beauty's virtue and sweetness' power
      By rightful dower—the Flower-of-Maids!

Long lived I there as now appears,
      Tho' short the years seemed e'er to me,
      Till a strong desire of my heart took hold
      Finn and my friends of old to see.

One day of the king I asked for leave
      And of loving Niam who grieved the while,
      To visit dear Erin once again
      My native plain, my native isle.

"I will not hinder thee," she cried,
      "From crossing the tide for duty dear,
      Tho' it bodes me ill and my heart doth fill
      With doubts that chill and deadly fear!"

"Why shouldst thou fear, O queen my own,
      When the way shall be shown by the magic steed—
      The steed that bore us o'er the sea—
      And home to thee I'll safely speed?"

"Remember then what now I say—
  If thou shouldst lay a foot to ground,
  There's no return for thee e'ermore
  To this fair shore where home thou'st found!

"I tell thee truly, vain's thy might
  Shouldst thou alight from thy white steed,
  For never again shouldst thou in truth
  See Land of Youth or hither speed.

"A third time now I thee implore
  And beg thee sore thy seat to hold,
  Or else at once thy strength shall go,
  And thou shalt grow both blind and old!

"'Tis woe to me, Oisin, to see
  How thou canst be so anxious-soul'd
  About green Erin, changed for aye—
  For past's the day of the fian bold.

"In Erin green there's now nought seen
  But priests full lean and troops of saints—
  Then Oisin, here's my kiss to thee,
  Our last, may be—my heart now faints!"

  I gazed into her soft sad eyes
  Whilst the tears did rise and well in my own—
  O saint severe, thou'dst weep a tear
  To hear that dear wife's hopeless moan!

By solemn vow I then was bound,
  To Erin's ground ne'er to descend,
  And if to keep this vow I failed
  No power availed or could befriend.

I pledged to keep my solemn vow
  And do all now enjoined had been,
  I mounted then my magic steed
  And said farewell to king and queen.

I kissed once more my Gold-haired Niam,
  —My heart doth grieve as I tell the tale—
  I kissed my sons and daughter young,
  Whose hearts were wrung and cheeks were pale.

I turned my steed at last to the strand
  And passed from the Land of Lasting Youth—
  Boldly my horse pursued his course
  And the billows' force was nought in sooth.

O Patrick of the orders pure,
  No lie, full sure, I've told but truth,
  Thus have I tried my tale to weave
  And thus did I leave the Land of Youth.

If of good bread I could get my fill
  As Finn at will gave to each guest,
  Each day I'd pray to the King of Grace
  That Heaven might be thy place of rest.

Patrick. Thou shalt of bread have quite thy fill
  And drink at will, O ancient bard!
  Dear to me thy pleasant tale!
  It ne'er can fail to win regard.

Oisin. I need not tell each thing befell
  Me and my spell-borne steed each day,
  But at length green Erin's isle we reach,
  And up the beach we bend our way.

When once I found my steed trod ground,
  I looked around on every side,
  Anxious for tidings small or great
  Of Finn and his state, once Erin's pride.

Not long in doubt had I thus stayed
  When a cavalcade came up the way—
  Strange crowd, I thought, of women and men,
  And past my ken their strange array.

Right gently they saluted me
  But marvell'd much to see my size,
  They marvell'd at my wondrous steed,
  For on such breed they'd ne'er set eyes.

I asked—with fear my heart within—
  If the noble Finn were yet alive,
  Or if his hosts that kept the coasts
  Of Erin safe, did yet survive.

"Of Finn," they said, "we oft have heard—
  His name and fame are now world-wide,
  But full three hundred years have passed
  Since Finn and the last of the fian died.

"Many a book and many a tale
  Have bards of the Gael that treat of Finn—
  Of his strength and valor and wisdom bright,
  Of his race of might and mighty kin.

"We've also heard of Finn's great son—
  A youth of wondrous mien and mould,
  That a lady came hither from over the sea
  And with her went he to *Tír na n-Óg!*"

Now when those words fell on mine ear—
  That Finn and his heroes were no more—
  My heart was chilled—my soul was filled
  With woe unwilled ne'er felt before.

I stopped no longer upon my course
  But swift my horse urged onward flew,
  Till Almu's hill o'er Leinster's plain
  Rose once again before my view.

What shock I felt none could report,
  To see the court of Finn of the steeds
  A ruin lone, all overgrown
  With nettles and thorns and rankest weeds!

I found alas, 'twas a vain pursuit,
  A bootless, fruitless, visit mine!
  Great Finn was dead and the hosts he led—
  For this I'd sped thro' ocean's brine!

But let me tell my story all—
  Tho' Almu's roofless hall I'd seen,
  I still would see spots dear to me
  Where the fian free and Finn had been.

In passing through the Thrushes' Glen
  A crowd of men in straits I see;
  Full thrice five score and haply more
  At toil full sore awaited me.

Then forth there spoke a man of that herd,
  With suppliant word to me address'd—
  "Come to our help, O champion brave,
  Come quick to save us thus distress'd!"

I rode up briskly to the crowd
  And found them bow'd beneath a weight—
  A flag of marble great and long
  Bore down the throng who moaned their fate.

Now all who tried to lift that stone
  Did pant and groan most piteously—
  Till some its crushing weight drove mad
  And some fell dead, most sad to see!

Then cried a steward of that crowd,
  And said aloud, "O haste and hie,
  O gallant chief to our relief,
  Or else 'tis brief ere all shall die!

"A shameful thing it is to say
  —For such array of men these days—
  They're powerless of blood and bone
  Full easily that stone to raise!

"If Oscar, Oisin's valiant son
  Laid hold upon that marble stone,
  With right hand bare he'd hurl't in air,
  Flinging it fair, with ne'er a groan!"

Asked thus for help, I did not lag
  But 'neath the flag I placed one hand—
  Full perches seven that stone I hurl
  And scare each churl in all that band!

But scarce alas! that stone had passed
  With that fair cast when ah! the strain—
  The strain it broke the white steed's girth,—
  I fell to earth, doomed now to pain!

No sooner had I touched the ground
  Than with a bound my steed took fright—
  Away, away, to the west he rushed!
  Whilst all stood hush'd at such strange sight!

At once I lost the sight of my eyes,
　My youth's bloom died, lean age began,
　And I was left of strength bereft,
　A helpless, hopeless, blind old man!

O Patrick, now the tale thou hast,
　As each thing passed, indeed, in truth,
　My going away, my lengthened stay,
　And return for aye from the Land of Youth!

THE COLLOQUY OF THE OLD MEN

Chief among the earlier tales dealing with Finn and his companions is the famous "Colloquy of the Old Men." This long and elaborate piece, composed not far from A. D. 1200, is a framework story in which are embedded a large number of heroic tales and place-name legends. At the beginning of the narrative Oisin (Ossian) son of Finn, and Cailte son of Crunnchu mac Ronain, accompanied by a small band, are represented as the only survivors of Finn mac Cumaill's great fian. A century and a half have elapsed since the death of Finn and the battles in which the fian met with destruction. After visiting Finn's old nurse, Oisin and Cailte separate, one going north to seek Oisin's mother, who is one of the Tuatha De Danann; the other moving south toward Tara. On the way Cailte and his companions meet with St. Patrick and accept Christianity. St. Patrick's interest in the traditions of Ireland elicits from Cailte many stories of the pagan heroic age. On arriving at Tara, Cailte and St. Patrick find Oisin installed in the court of King Diarmuid mac Cerbaill. There the ancient heroes entertain the guests with tales of pagan Ireland. Whether the piece as a whole emanates from ecclesiastical or secular sources, it is both surprising and pleasant to find at such an early period a representation of friendly and sympathetic relations between pagan and Christian.

When the Battle of Comar, the Battle of Gabra, and the Battle of Ollarba had been fought, and after the fian were for the most part extinguished, the residue of them had dispersed in small bands and in companies throughout all Ireland, until at the time which concerns us there remained of them two good warriors only: Oisin son of Finn, and Cailte son of Crunnchu son of Ronan (whose lusty vigor and power of spear-throwing were now dwindled down), and so many fighting men as with themselves made twice nine. These twice nine came out of the flowery-soiled and well-wooded borders of Sliab Fuait and into the Lugbarta Bana, at the present day called Lugmad, where at the falling of the evening clouds that night they were melancholy, dispirited.

Cailte said to Oisin then, "Good now, Oisin, before the day's end what path shall we take in quest of entertainment for the night?"

Oisin answered, "I know not, seeing that of the ancients of the fian, and of Finn's former people but three survive: I and thyself, Cailte, with Cama, the female-chief and female-custodian who,

457

from the time he was a boy until the day he died, kept Finn mac Cumaill safe."

Cailte said, "We are entitled to this night's lodging and provision from her; for it is not possible to rehearse nor to show the quantity which Finn, captain of the fian, bestowed on her of precious things and of treasures, including the third best thing of price that Finn ever acquired, namely, the Angalach or drinking horn which Moriath daughter of the king of Greece gave to Finn, and Finn to Cama."

With Cama, therefore, they got hospitality for the night; their names she inquired of them and at their sound wept vehement showers of tears; then she and they, each of the other, sought to have tidings. Next they entered into the bed-house disposed for them, and Cama the female chief prescribed their repast: that the freshest of all kinds of meats and the oldest of all sorts of drink be given them, for she knew in what fashion they used to be fed. She knew also how much it was that many a time before the present had constituted a sufficiency for Oisin and Cailte. Languidly and feebly she arose and held forth on the fian and on Finn mac Cumaill; of Oisin's son Oscar too she spoke, of Mac Lugach, of the Battle of Gabra with other matters; and by reason of this in the end a great silence settled on them all.

Then Cailte said, "Such matters we hold to be not more painful than the way in which the twice nine that we are of the remnant of that great and goodly fellowship must perforce part, and separate from each other."

Oisin answered, "Since they have departed, in me, by my word, there is no more fight and pith."

Valiant as were these warrior-men, here nevertheless with Cama they wept, in gloom, in sadness, and in dejection. Their adequate allowance of meat and drink was given them; they tarried there for three days and three nights, then bade Cama farewell, and Oisin said:

Cama to-day is sorrowful: she is come to the point where she must swim; Cama without either son or grandson: it has befallen her to be old and blighted.

Forth from the enclosure they came now, and out upon the green; there they took a resolve, which was this: to separate, and this parting of theirs was a sundering of soul and body. Even so they did: for Oisin went to the fairy-mound of Uch Cletigh, where was his mother, Blai daughter of Derc Dianscothach; while Cailte took his way to Inber Bic Loingsigh which at present is called Mainister Droichid Atha (the monastery of Drogheda) from Beg Loigsech son of Arist that was drowned in it, that is, the king of the Romans' son, who came to invade Ireland; but a tidal wave drowned him there in his *inber* (river-mouth). He went on to Linn Feic (Fiacc's Pool), on the bright-streaming Boyne; southwards over the Old Mag Breg, and to the rath (stronghold) of Drum Derg, where Patrick mac Calpuirn was.

Just then Patrick was chanting the Lord's order of the canon (*i.e.*, Mass), and lauded the Creator, and pronounced a benediction on the rath where Finn mac Cumaill had been, the rath of Drum Derg. The clerics saw Cailte and his band draw near them; and fear fell upon them before the tall men with their huge wolf-dogs that accompanied them, for they were not people of one epoch or of one time with the clergy.

Then Heaven's distinguished one, that pillar of dignity and angel on earth, Calpurn's son Patrick, apostle of the Gael, rose and took the sprinkler to sprinkle holy water on the great men; floating over whom until that day there had been and were now a thousand legions of demons. Into the hills and brush wood, into the outer borders of the region and of the country, the demons departed forthwith in all directions; after which the enormous men sat down.

"Good now," said Patrick to Cailte, "what name hast thou?"

"I am Cailte son of Crunnchu son of Ronan."

For a long while the clergy marvelled greatly as they gazed upon them; for the largest man of them reached but to the waist, or else to the shoulder of any given one of the others, and they sitting.

Patrick said again, "Cailte, I wish to beg a favor of thee."

He answered, "If I have but that much strength or power, it shall be had; at all events, tell me what it is."

"To have in our vicinity here a well of pure water, from which we might baptize the tribes of Breg, of Meath, and of Usnech."

"Noble and righteous one," said Cailte, "that have I for thee," and they, crossing the rath's wall, came out; in his hand Cailte took Patrick's staff and in a little while right in front of them they saw a loch-well, sparkling and very clear. The size and thickness

of the cress and of the brooklime that grew on it was a wonderment
to them; then Cailte began to tell its fame and qualities, in doing
of which he said:

O Well of Traig Da Ban (Strand of the Two Women), beautiful thy
cresses, luxurious-branching. Since thy produce is neglected on thee
thy brooklime is not suffered to grow. Forth from thy banks thy trout
are to be seen, thy wild swine in the neighboring wilderness; the deer of
thy fair hunting cragland, thy dappled and red-chested fawns! Thy mast
all hanging on the branches of thy trees; thy fish in estuaries of thy rivers;
lovely the color of thy purling streams, O thou that thyself art azure-hued,
and again green with reflection of surrounding copsewood! . . .

" 'Tis well," Patrick said; "hath our dinner and our provisions
reached us yet?"

"It has so," answered the bishop Sechnall.

"Distribute it," said Patrick, "and one half give to yon nine
tall warriors of the survivors of the fian." Then his bishops and his
priests and his psalmodists arose and blessed the meat; and of both
meat and liquor they consumed their full sufficiency, yet so as to
serve their soul's welfare.

Patrick said then, "Was he not a good lord with whom ye were,
that is, Finn mac Cumaill?"

Upon which Cailte uttered this little tribute of praise:

Were but the brown leaf which the wood sheds from it gold—were but
the white billows silver—Finn would have given it all away.

"Who or what was it that maintained you so in your life?"
Patrick inquired; and Cailte answered, "Truth that was in our
hearts, and strength in our arms, and fulfilment in our tongues."

"Good, Cailte," Patrick went on; "in the houses which before
our time thou didst frequent were there drinking-horns, or cups,
or goblets of crystal and of pale gold?"

And Cailte answered, "The number of the horns that were in
my lord's house was as follows:

Twelve drinking-horns and three hundred made of gold Finn had;
whenever they came to the pouring out, the quantity of liquor they held
was immense.

"Were it not for us an impairing of the devout life, an occasion
of neglecting prayer, and of deserting converse with God, we, as
we talked with thee, would feel the time pass quickly, O warrior."

Then Cailte began to rehearse the drinking-horns, with the chiefs and lords whose they had been:

Horns that were in Finn's house, their names I bear in mind.

.   .   .   .

"Success and benediction attend thee, Cailte," Patrick said; "this is to me a lightening of spirit and of mind; and now tell us another tale."

"I will indeed; but say what story thou wouldst be pleased to have."

"In the fian had ye horses or cavalry?"

Cailte answered, "We had so; thrice fifty foals from one mare and a single sire."

"Whence were they procured?"

"I will tell thee the truth of the matter:

"A young man that served with Finn, Arthur son of Beine Brit, his company being thrice nine men. Finn set on foot the hunting of Benn Etair (which indeed turned out to be a bountiful and fruitful hunt). They slipped their hounds accordingly, while Finn took his seat on Carn an Feinneda (Cairn of the Fian) between Etar's top and the sea; there his spirit was gay within him when he listened to the maddened stags' bellowing as by the hounds of the fian they were rapidly killed.

"Where Arthur son of Beine Brit was stationed was between the main body of the hunt and the sea in order that the deer should not take to the sea and elude them by swimming. But Arthur, being thus on the outside and close against the shore, marked three of Finn's hounds, Bran, Sceolaing, and Adnuall, and he resolved on a plan, which was: himself and his three nines to depart away across the sea, he carrying off with him into his own land those same three hounds. This plot was put into action then; for well I know that they, having with them those three hounds, crossed the sea's surface and at Inber Mara Gaimiach in Britainland took harbor and haven. They landed there, proceeded to the mountain of Lodan son of Lir, and hunted it.

"After this occurrence the fian made an end of their hunting and of their woodland slaughter, and camped on the eminence of Etgaeth's son Etar (Benn Etair), and, as the custom was then, Finn's hounds were counted. Now his hounds were many in number, as the poet said:

An enumerating of branches on the tree was that of Finn's full-grown hounds with his sleek melodious pack of youngsters; three hundred of the first there were, and puppy-hounds two hundred.

"Many men they must have been who owned those," said Patrick.

"True for you indeed," Cailte answered, "for the tale that used to be in Finn's house was this:

They that dwelt in the house of Finn were three times fifty of joyous leaders of the fian; three hundred confidential servitors as well, and two hundred fosterlings that were worthy of their chiefs.

"But when the hounds were counted, a great shortcoming was discovered in them: Bran, Sceolaing, Adnuall were missing, and it was told to Finn. 'Have all three battalions of the fian searched out,' he said; yet though the search was made the hounds were not found.

" To Finn then was brought a long basin of pale gold; he washed his kingly face, put his thumb under his tooth of knowledge, truth was revealed to him, and he said, ' The king of the Britons' son has deprived you of your hounds; pick ye therefore nine men to go in quest of them!' They were chosen, their names being these: Diarmuid O'Duibne, of the Erna of Munster in the south; Goll mac Morna—"

"Was Goll a chief's son, or a simple warrior's?" Patrick inquired.

"A chief's," answered Cailte:

He was son of Teigue son of Morna of the Mag, that was son of Feradach son of Fiacha son of Art of the Mag son of Muiredach son of Eochaid.

"There was Cael Croda the hundred-slayer, grandson of Nem-nann, a champion that Finn had, and endowed with a deadly property, that his arm never delivered a cast that missed its mark, and that never was his hand bloodied on a man but that the same would before a nine days' term were out be dead; there was Finn's son Oisin—he that, if only a man had a head to eat with and legs to go upon and carry off his largess, never refused any."

" Cailte," said Patrick, " that is a great character."

"And though it be so is it a true one," Cailte answered, and said:

In the matter of gold, of silver, or concerning meat, Oisin never denied any man; nor, though another's generosity were such as might fit a chief, did Oisin ever seek ought of him.

"There was Oisin's son Oscar, the chief's son that in all Ireland was best for spear-throwing and for vigorous activity; also Ferdo-man son of Bodb Derg son of the Dagda; Finn's son Raigne Wide-eye; his son Caince the Crimson-red; Glas son of Enchard Bera mac Lugach; and myself. Now, saintly Patrick, we the aforesaid within ourselves were confident that from Taprobane in the east to the garden of the Hesperides in the world's westernmost part were no four hundred warriors but, on the battle-field and hand-to-hand, we were a match for them. We had not a head without a helmet, nor a shoulder without a whitened shield, nor a right fist that grasped not two great and lengthy spears. On this expedition we went our way then until we reached Lodan mac Lir's mountain in Britain, where we had been no long time before we heard talk of men that hunted in the field.

"As regards Beine Brit's son Arthur, he just then, with his people, sat on his hunting ground. Them we charged in lively fashion, and killed all Arthur's people; but round him Oscar knit both his arms, gave him quarter, and we brought off our three hounds. Here Goll mac Morna chancing to look about him saw an iron-grey horse, flecked with spots, and wearing a bridle fitted with wrought ornaments of gold. At another glance that he threw to his left he discerned a bay horse, one not easy to lay hold of, having a wrought bridle of twice-refined silver fitted with a golden bit. This second horse Goll also seized and put into the hand of Oisin, who passed him on to Diarmuid. After successful execution and due celebration of our slaughter we came away, bringing with us the heads of those thrice nine, our hounds, and the horses, too, with Arthur himself a prisoner, and so back to where Finn was on Benn Etair. We reached his tent, and Cailte said, 'We have brought Arthur.' This latter entered into bonds with Finn, and thereafter, up to the day on which he died, was Finn's follower. The two horses we gave to Finn, horse and mare, of whose seed were all the horses of the fian, who hitherto had not used any such. The mare bred eight times, at every birth eight foals, which were made over to the various detachments and notables of the fian, and these afterwards had chariots made." . . .

"Success and benediction be thine, Cailte. All this is to us a recreation of spirit and of mind, were it only not a destruction of devotion and a dereliction of prayer."

There they were until the morrow's morning came, when Patrick robed himself and emerged upon the green; together with his three score priests, three score psalmodists, and holy bishops three score as well, that with him spread faith and piety throughout Ireland. Patrick's two guardian angels came to him now—Aibellan and Solusbretach, of whom he inquired whether in God's sight it were convenient for him to be listening to stories of the fian. With equal emphasis, and concordantly, the angels answered him, "Holy cleric, no more than a third part of their stories do those ancient warriors tell, by reason of forgetfulness and lack of memory; but by thee be it written on tables of poets, and in learned men's words; for to the companies and nobles of the later time to give ear to these stories will be a pastime." Which said, the angels departed.

From Patrick messengers were accordingly dispatched to fetch Cailte, and he, along with the nine that were in his company, were brought to the saint; whose names were Failbe son of Flann, Eogan the Red-weaponed the King of Ulster's son, Flann son of Fergus king of Kinelconnell, Conall the Slaughterer son of Angus king of Connacht, Scannlan son of Ailill king of Ossory, Baedan son of Garb king of Corkaguiney, Luamnech Linn son of the king of Dalaradia's sons out of the north, with Fulartach son of Fingin king of the peoples of Breg and of Meath.

Patrick said, "Know ye why ye are brought to confer with me?"

"In truth we do not," they answered.

"To the end you should conform to the gospel of Heaven's and of Earth's king, the most glorious God." Then and there the water of Christ's baptism was by Patrick sprinkled on them preparatory to the baptism and conversion of all Ireland.

Then with his right hand Cailte reached across him to the rim of his shield, and gave to Patrick a ridgy mass of gold in which there were three times fifty ounces; this as a fee for the baptism of the nine with him. He said, "That was Finn's, the chief's, last wage to me and, Patrick, take it for my soul's and for my chief's soul's weal." The extent to which this mass reached on Patrick was from his middle finger's tip to his shoulder's highest point, while in width and in thickness it measured a man's cubit. Now this gold was bestowed upon the Tailchenn's [1] canonical hand-bells, on psalters, and on missals.

---

[1] The epithet *tailchenn*, "adze-head," suggested by the shape of the early Irish clerical tonsure, is often, as here, applied especially to St. Patrick.

Patrick said again, "It is well, Cailte. What was the best hunting that the fian ever had, whether in Ireland or in Scotland?"

"The hunting of Arran."

Patrick asked, "Where is that land?"

"Between Scotland and Pictland. On the first day of the Trogan-month (which is now called Lugnasad *i.e.*, Lammastide) we, to the number of the three battalions of the fian used to repair thither and there have our fill of hunting until such time as from the tree-tops the cuckoo would call in Ireland. More melodious than all music whatsoever it was to give ear to the voices of the birds as they rose from the billows and from the island's coast-line; thrice fifty separate flocks there were that encircled her, and they clad in gay brilliance of all colors, as blue and green and azure and yellow." Here Cailte uttered a lay:

Arran of the many stags—the sea impinges on her very shoulders! an island in which whole companies are fed—and with ridges among which blue spears are reddened! Skittish deer are on her pinnacles, soft black-berries on her waving heather; cool water there is in her rivers, and mast upon her russet oaks! Greyhounds there were in her, and beagles; berries and sloes of the dark blackthorn; dwellings with their backs set close against her woods, and the deer fed scattered by her oaken thickets! A crimson crop grew on her rocks, in all her glades a faultless grass; over her crags, affording friendly refuge, leaping went on and fawns were skipping! Smooth were her level spots—her wild swine, they were fat; cheerful her fields (this is a tale that may be credited), her nuts hung on her forest-hazels' boughs, and there was sailing of long galleys past her! Right pleasant their condition all when the fair weather sets in: under her rivers' brinks trout lie; the sea-gulls wheeling round her grand cliff answer one the other—at every fitting time delectable is Arran!

"Victory and blessing wait on thee, Cailte!" said Patrick; "for the future thy stories and thyself are dear to us."

Straightway now before him Patrick saw a stronghold, a fair dwelling, and, "Cailte," he said, "what is yon town?"

"That is the proudest place that ever I was in, in Ireland or in Scotland."

"Who lived there?"

"The three sons of Lugaid Menn son of Angus, that is, the king of Ireland's three sons: Ruide and Fiacha and Eochaid were their names."

"What procured them their great wealth?"

"It was once upon a time that they came to have speech of their father to Fert na Druad northwest of Tara. 'Whence come ye, young men?' he inquired. They made answer, 'From Echlais Banguba to the southward, out of our nurse's and our guardian's house.' 'My lads, what set you on your way?' 'To crave a heritage of you, a domain.' For a space the king was silent, and then said, 'No father it was that on me conferred either country or domain, but my own luck and bright achievement. Lands therefore I will not bestow on you, but win lands for yourselves.' Whereupon they, with the ready rising of one man, rose and took their way to the green of the Brug upon the Boyne where, none other in their company, they sat down. Ruide said, 'What is your plan to-night?' His brothers answered, 'Our project is to fast on the Tuatha De Danann, aiming thus to win from them good fortune in the shape of a country, of a domain, of lands, and to have vast riches.' Nor had they been long there when they marked a cheery-looking young man of a peaceful demeanor that came towards them. He saluted the king of Ireland's sons, and they replied in like manner. 'Young man, whence art thou? Whence camest thou?' 'Out of yonder brug checkered with the many lights hard by you here.' 'What name wearest thou?' 'I am the Dagda's son Bodb Derg; and to the Tuatha De Danann it was revealed that you would come to fast here to-night for lands and for great fortune. But come with me.' Simultaneously they rose and entered into the brug; supper was served to them, but they ate it not. Bodb inquired of them why it was they took no meat. 'Because the king of Ireland, our father, denied us territory and lands. Now there are in Ireland but two tribes that are equal: the sons of Mil and the Tuatha De Danann; to the alternative one of which we have come now.'

"Then the Tuatha De Danann went into council, he that in such council was most noble in rank, and authoritative, being Mider Yellow-mane son of the Dagda, who said, 'Accommodate those yonder now with three wives, since it is from wives that either fortune or misfortune is derived.' Whereat were given to them Mider's three daughters, Doirenn and Aife and Ailbe. Said Mider, 'Tell us, Bodb, what gifts shall be given them?' Bodb said, 'I will tell you. Three times fifty sons of kings are in this

fairy-mound; every king's son shall give them thrice fifty ounces
of red gold, while from me they shall have in addition thrice fifty
suits of raiment various with all hues.' Aed son of Aeda Nabusach
from Cnoc Ardmulla out in the sea, which to-day is called Rach-
rainn, a youth of the Tuatha De Danann, said, 'From me too a gift
for them, viz. a horn and a vat; regarding which it needs but to
fill the vat with pure water, and of this it will make mead both
drinkable and having virtue to intoxicate; into the horn put bitter
brine out of the deep, and on the instant it shall turn into wine.'
'A gift for them from me,' said Lir of the fairy-mound of Finna-
chad; 'three times fifty swords, and thrice fifty well-riveted spears
of length.' 'A gift from me to them,' said the Dagda's son Angus
Oc; 'a fort and stronghold, and a most excellent spacious town
with lofty stockades, with light-admitting bowers, with houses of
clear outlook and very roomy; all this in whatsoever place it shall
please them between Rath Cobtaig and Tara.' 'A gift for them
from me,' said Aine daughter of Modarn; 'a she-cook that I have,
to whom it is taboo to refuse meat to any; but according as she
serves out, so too is her store replenished.' 'A gift from me to
them,' said Bodb Derg; 'a good minstrel that I have (Fertuinne
mac Trogain is his name), and though saws were being plied where
there were women in sharpest pains of childbirth, and brave men
that were wounded early in the day, nevertheless would they be
put to sleep by the wistful melody that he makes. Yet to the dwelling in which for the time being he actually is he is not minstrel
more effectively than to that whole country's inhabitants in general, for all they as well may hear him.' For three days and three
nights they abode in the fairy-mound.

"Angus told them to carry away out of Fid Omna three apple-
trees; one in full bloom, another shedding its blossoms, and another covered with ripe fruit. Then they repaired to the stronghold
given them by Angus, where they abode for three times fifty
years, and until those kings disappeared; for in virtue of marriage
alliance they returned again to the Tuatha De Danann and from
that time forth have remained there. And that, Patrick, is the
stronghold concerning which you inquired of me," said Cailte.
And he sang this lay:

Three things in great plenty, and O great plenty of three things, that
out of Ruide's high fort issued! a crowd of young men, a great troop of

horses, the numerous greyhounds of Lugaid's three sons. Three sorts of music and O music of three kinds, that comely kings enjoyed! music of harps, melody of sweet timpans, humming of Trogan's son Fertuinne. A triple stronghold and a stronghold of three fold! sound of tramping ascending from the green of that stronghold, uproar of racing, boom of lowing kine. Three noises, and O noises three! sound of its swine, span-thick in fat and excellent, buzz of the crowd upon the palace lawn, hilarity of revellers with mead-begotten clamor. Fruit-crops in three stages, and O crops in stages three, that used to be there hanging on its boughs! a tree shedding, a tree in bloom, and yet another laden ripe. Three sons it was that Lugaid left (though their great deeds are passed away): Ruide, spacious Lugaid's son, Eochaid, and manly Fiacha. I will testify to Eochaid that never took a step in flight: never was he without his customary music, nor ever for any time without quaffing of ale. I will testify to Fiacha, though the fame of his depredations be obscured: never he uttered an expression that was excessive, and in his time was none that excelled more in valor. I will testify to Ruide, to whom those aforesaid three things (young men, horses, hounds) in great plenty flowed in: that never a thing he denied to any man, nor of a man sought anything at all. Thirty chieftains, thirty leaders, thirty champions that might befit a king: while the strength of his hundredfold host was hundreds thirtyfold thrice told.

TALES OF THE TRADITIONAL KINGS

Many of the most interesting early Irish tales deal, not with Finn and his companions, the Ulster heroes, or Ireland's early settlers, but with traditional kings of Ireland or with persons connected with them. These kings are by no means all fictitious. The existence of many of them is duly attested by historical evidence. Upon their historical deeds there has, however, often been engrafted such a mass of legend that truth is hardly distinguishable from fiction. Though these stories do not fall into any one of the main cycles of early Irish literature, we should recall that some of them come from an authentically ancient period and may originally have formed parts of other cycles that have now all but disappeared. Certainly Irish literature would be much the poorer without the spirited accounts of the Lepracan king (p. 471) and of the king cured of his gluttony by the ruse of a wandering cleric (p. 551).

THE DEATH OF FERGUS MAC LEIDE

The title of this story, like many other titles in early Irish literature, is not precisely indicative of the main interest of the narrative. Though most of the tale is devoted to the visit of the king of the Lepracans to the court of Ulster, the story belongs essentially to the Tom Thumb tradition, and many of the amusing incidents remind us of the adventures, later recounted by Swift, of Gulliver in the country of the Brobdignagians. The setting is ostensibly that of the old Ulster cycle, for Fergus mac Leide was one of the Red Branch warriors, although he is seldom mentioned in the stories of the Ulster group. He gains a certain prestige in Irish narrative literature, perhaps, through being confused with the famous Fergus mac Roig. The strange narrative of his death as related here is not mentioned in the early stories dealing with the heroes of Emain Macha. The account given here is usually regarded as having been composed about 1100. The reader will recall that in modern Irish folk-lore the lepracans are diminutive fairy shoemakers.

A righteous king, a maintainer of truth and a giver of just judgments over the happy Clan Rudraige, or "Children of Rury," of Ulster, was Fergus son of Leide son of Rury; and these are they that were his heroes and men of war: Eirgenn, Amergin the Ravager, Conna Buie son of Iliach, and Dubtach son of Lugaid.

This king gave a great feast in Emain Macha, the capital of Ulster, and it was ready, fit to be consumed, and all set in order at the very season and hour at which the king of the Lepra and Lepracan [1] held a banquet: whose name was Iubdan son of Abdan.

These are the names of the men of war that were Iubdan's: Conan son of Ruiched, Gerrcu son of Cairid, and Rigbeg son of Robeg; Luigin son of Luiged, Glunan son of Gabarn, Febal son of Feornin, and Cinnbeg son of Gnuman; together with Buan's son Brigbeg, Liran son of Luan, and Mether son of Mintan. To them was brought the strong man of the region of the Lepra and Lepracan, whose prize feat that he used to perform was the hewing down of a thistle at a single stroke; whereas it was a twelve men's effort of the rest of them to give him singly a wrestling-fall. To them was brought the king's presumptive successor, Beg son of Beg ("Little son of Little"). So also was brought the king's poet

[1] *I.e.*, the midgets and tiny midgets.

471

and man of art likewise: Esirt son of Beg son of Buaidgen, and
the other notables of the land of the Lepra and Lepracan.

The guests were placed according to their qualities and to
precedence: at one side Iubdan was placed, having next to him
on either hand Bebo his wife, and his chief poet; at the other side
of the hall and facing Iubdan sat Beg son of Beg, with the notables
and chiefs; the king's strong man too, Glomar son of Glomrad's
son Glas, stood beside the doorpost of the house. Now were the
spigots drawn from the vats, the color of those vats being of a dusky
red like the tint of red yew. The carvers stood up to carve and
the cup-bearers to pour; and old ale, sleep-compelling, delicious,
was served out to the throng so that on one side as on the other
of the hall they were elated and made huge noise of mirth.

At last Iubdan, who was their king and the head of all their
counsel, having in his hand the *corn breac* or "variegated horn"
stood up, and on the other side, opposite to Iubdan and to do him
honor, arose Beg son of Beg. Then the king, by this time affably
inclining to converse, inquired of them, "Have you ever seen a
king that was better than myself?"

And they answered, "We have not."

"Have you ever seen a strong man better than my strong
man?"

"We have not."

"Horses or men of battle have you ever seen better than they
which to-night are in this house?"

"By our word," they made answer, "we never have."

"I, too," Iubdan went on, "give my word that it would be a
hard task forcibly to take out of this house to-night either captives
or hostages: so surpassing are its heroes and men of battle, so
many its lusty companions and men of might, so great the number
of its fierce and haughty ones, that are stuff out of which kings
might fittingly be made."

All which when he had heard, the king's chief poet Esirt burst
out laughing; whereupon Iubdan asked: "Esirt, what moved
thee to that laugh?" Said the poet: "I know of a province in
Ireland, one man of which could take hostages and captives from
all four battalions of the Lepracan."

"Lay the poet by the heels," cried the king, "that vengeance
be taken of him for his bragging speech!"

So it was done; but Esirt said, "Iubdan, this seizure of me will bear evil fruit; for in requital of the arrest thou shalt thyself be for five years captive in Emain Macha, whence thou shalt not escape without leaving behind thee the rarest thing of all thy wealth and treasures. By reason of this seizure Cobthach Cas also, son of Munster's king, shall fall, and the king of Leinster's son Eochaid; whilst I myself must go to the house of Fergus son of Leide and in his goblet be set floating till I be all but drowned. . . .

"An evil arrest is this thou hast made on me, O king," Esirt went on, "but grant me now a three-days' and three-nights' respite that I may travel to Emain Macha and to the house of Leide's son Fergus, to the end that if there I find some evident token by which thou shalt recognize truth to be in me, I may bring the same hither; or if not, then do to me what thou wilt."

Then Esirt, his bonds being loosed, rose and next to his white skin put on a smooth and glossy shirt of delicate silk. Over that he donned his gold-broidered tunic and his scarlet cloak, all fringed and beautiful, flowing in soft folds, the scarlet being of the land of the Finn, and the fringe of pale gold in varied pattern. Betwixt his feet and the earth he set his two dainty shoes of white bronze, overlaid with ornament of gold. Taking his white bronze poet's wand and his silken hood, he set out, choosing the shortest way and the straightest course, nor are we told how he fared until he came to Emain Macha and at the gate of the place shook his poet's rod.

When at the sound the gate-keeper came forth, he beheld there a man, comely and of a most gallant carriage, but so tiny that the close-cropped grass of the green reached to his knee, aye, and to the thick of his thigh. At sight of him wonder fell upon the gate-keeper; and he entered into the house to report the arrival to Fergus and to the company. All inquired whether he (Esirt) were smaller than Aed, this Aed being the poet of Ulster, and a dwarf that could stand on full-sized men's hands. And the gate-keeper said, "He would have room enough upon Aed's palm, by my word." Hereupon the guests with pealing laughter desired to see him, each one deeming the time to be all too long till he should view Esirt and, after seeing him, speak with him. Then upon all sides both men and women had free access to him, but Esirt cried, "Huge men that you are, let not your infected breaths so closely play upon me! but let yon small man that is the least of you approach me; who, little though he be among you, would yet in the land where I dwell be accounted of great stature." Into the great house therefore, and he standing upon his palm, the poet Aed bore him.

Fergus, when he had sought of him tidings who he might be, was answered: "I am Esirt son of Beg son of Buaidgen: chief poet, bard and rhymer, of the Lepra and Lepracan." The assembly were just then in actual enjoyment of the feast, and a cup-bearer came to Fergus. "Give to the little man that is come to me," said the king.

Esirt replied, "Neither of your meat will I eat, nor of your liquor will I drink."

"By our word," said Fergus, "seeing thou art a flippant and a mocking fellow, it were but right to drop thee into the beaker, where at all points round about thou shouldst then impartially quaff the liquor."

The cup-bearer closed his hand on Esirt and popped him into the goblet, in which upon the surface of the liquor that it contained he floated round. "You poets of Ulster," he vociferated, "much desirable knowledge and instruction there is which upon my conscience, ye sorely need to have of me, yet ye allow me to be drowned!"

With fair satin napkins of great virtue and with special silken fabrics he was plucked out and was cleaned spick and span, and Fergus inquired, "Of what impediment spakest thou a while ago as hindering thee from sharing our meat?"

"That will I tell thee," the little man replied: "but let me not incur thy displeasure."

"So be it," promised the king; "only explain to me the whole impediment " Then Esirt spoke and Fergus answered him.

Esirt. With poet's sharp-set words never be angered, Fergus; thy stern hard utterance restrain, nor against me take unjustifiable action.

Fergus. O wee man of the seizure, I will not.

Esirt. Judgments lucid and truthful, if they be those to which thou dost provoke me: then I pronounce that thou triflest with thy steward's wife, while thine own foster-son ogles thy queen. Women fair-haired and accomplished, rough kings of the ordinary kind (*i.e.*, mere chieftains):

how excellent soever be the form of these, 'tis not on them the former let their humor dwell (*i.e.*, when a genuine king comes in their way).

Fergus. Esirt, thou art in truth no child, but an approved man of veracity; O gentle one, devoid of reproach, no wrath of Fergus shalt thou know!

The king went on, "My share of the matter, by my word, is true; for the steward's wife is indeed my pastime, and all the rest as well therefore I the more readily take to be true."

Then said Esirt, "Now will I partake of thy meat, for thou hast confessed the evil; do it then no more." Here the poet, waxing cheerful and of good courage, went on, "Upon my own lord I have made a poem which, were it your pleasure, I would declaim to you." Fergus answered, "We would esteem it sweet to hear it," and Esirt began:

A king victorious, and renowned and pleasant, is Iubdan son of Abdan, king of Mag Life, king of Mag Faithlenn. His is a voice clear and sweet as copper's resonance, like the blood-colored rowan-berry is his cheek; his eye is bland as it were a stream of mead, his color that of the swan or of the river's foam. Strong he is in his yellow-haired host, in beauty and in cattle he is rich; and to brave men he brings death when he sets himself in motion. A man that loves the chase, active, a generous feast-giver; he is head of a bridle-wearing army, he is tall, proud and imperious. His is a solid squadron of grand headlong horses, of bridled horses rushing torrent-like; heads with smooth adornment of golden locks are on the warriors of the Lepra. All the men are comely, the women all light-haired; over that land's noble multitude Iubdan of truthful utterance presides. There the fingers grasp silver horns, deep notes of the timpan are heard; and however great be the love that women are reputed to bear thee, Fergus, 'tis surpassed by the desire that they feel for Iubdan.

The lay ended, the Ulstermen equipped the poet of the Lepracan with abundance of good things, until each heap of these as they lay there equalled their tall men's stature. "This, on my conscience," said Esirt, "is indeed a response that is worthy of good men; nevertheless take away those treasures, for I have no need of them, since in my lord's following is no man but possesses sufficient substance."

The Ulstermen said, however, "We pledge our words that we never would take back anything, though we had given thee our very wives and our cows. . . ."

"Then divide the gifts, bards and scholars of Ulster!" Esirt cried; "two thirds take for yourselves, and the other bestow on Ulster's horseboys and jesters."

So to the end of three days and three nights Esirt was in Emain, and he took his leave of Fergus and of the nobles of Ulster. "I will go with thee," said the Ulster poet and man of science, Aed, that dwarf who used to lie in their good warriors' bosoms, yet by Esirt's side was a giant. Esirt said, "'Tis not I that will bid thee come: for were I to invite thee, and kindness to be shown thee in consequence, thou wouldst say 'twas but what by implication had been promised thee; whereas if such be not held out to thee and thou yet receive it thou wilt be grateful."

Out of Emain the pair of poets now went their way and, Aed's step being the longer, he said, "Esirt thou art a poor walker." Esirt then took such a fit of running that he was an arrow's flight in front of Aed, who said again, "Between those two extremes lies the golden mean."

"On my word," retorted Esirt, "that is the one category in which since I have been among you I have heard mention made of the golden mean!"

On they went then till they gained Traig na Trenfer, or "Strand of the Strong Men," in Ulster. "And what must we do now?" Aed asked here.

"Travel the sea over her depths," said the other.

Aed objected, "Never shall I come safe out of that trial."

Esirt made answer: "Seeing that I accomplished the task, it would be strange that thou shouldst fail." Then Aed uttered a strain and Esirt answered him:

Aed. In the vast sea what shall I do? O generous Esirt, the wind will bear me down to the merciless wave on which, though I mount upwards, yet none the less shall I perish in the end.
Esirt. To fetch thee, fair Iubdan's horse will come. Get thee upon him and cross the stammering sea: an excellent horse truly and of passing color, a king's valued treasure, good on sea as upon land. A beautiful horse that will carry thee away. Sit on him and be not troubled; go, trust thyself to him.

They had been no long time there when they marked something which, swiftly careering, came towards them over the billows' crests. "Upon itself be the evil that it brings," Aed cried.

"What seest thou?" Esirt asked.

"A russet-clad hare I see," answered Aed.

But Esirt said, "Not so—rather is it Iubdan's horse that comes to fetch thee." Of which horse the fashion was this: two fierce flashing eyes he had, an exquisite pure crimson mane, with four green legs and a long tail that floated in wavy curls. His general color was that of prime artificers' gold-work, and a gold-encrusted bridle he bore withal. Esirt bestriding him said, "Come up beside me, Aed."

But again Aed objected, "Nay, poet, to serve even thee alone as a conveyance is beyond his powers."

"Aed, cease from fault-finding, for ponderous as may be the wisdom that is in thee, yet will he carry us both."

They both being now mounted on the horse traversed the combing seas, the mighty main's expanse and ocean's great profound, until in the end they, undrowned and without mishap, reached Mag Faithlenn, and there the Lepracan were before them in assembly. "Esirt approaches," they cried, "and a giant bears him company!"

Then Iubdan went to meet Esirt, and gave him a kiss. "But, poet," said he, "wherefore bringest thou this giant to destroy us?"

"No giant is he, but Ulster's poet and man of science, and the king's dwarf. In the land whence he comes he is the least, so that in their great men's bosoms he lies down and, as it were an infant, stands on the flat of their hands. Yet he is such that before him you would do well to be careful of yourselves."

"What is his name?" they asked.

"Poet Aed."

"Alack, man," they cried to Esirt, "thy giant is huge indeed!"

Next, Esirt addressing Iubdan said, "On thee, Iubdan, I lay taboos which true warriors may not break that in thine own person thou go to view the region out of which we come, and that of the 'lord's porridge' which for the king of Ulster is made to-night thou be the first man to make trial."

Then Iubdan, grieving and faint of spirit, proceeded to confer with Bebo his wife. He told her how that by Esirt he was laid under taboos, and bade her bear him company. "That will I," she said; "but by laying Esirt in bonds thou didst unjustly." So they mounted Iubdan's golden horse and that same night made good their way to Emain, where they entered unperceived into the place. "Iubdan," said Bebo, "search the town for the porridge spoken of by Esirt, and let us depart again before the people of the place shall rise."

They gained the inside of the palace and there found Emain's great cauldron, having in it the remnant of the "people's porridge." Iubdan drew near, but could by no means reach it from the ground. "Get upon thy horse," said Bebo, "and from the horse upon the cauldron's rim." This he did, but, the porridge being too far down and his arm too short, he could not touch the shank of the silver ladle that was in the cauldron; whereupon, as he made a downward effort, his foot slipped, and up to his very navel he fell into the cauldron; in which as though all existing iron gyves had been upon him he now found himself fettered and tethered both hand and foot. "Long thou tarriest, dark man!" Bebo cried to him (for Iubdan was thus: hair he had that was jet-black and curled, his skin being whiter than foam of wave and his cheeks redder than the forest's scarlet berry: whereas—saving him only— all the Lepra people had hair that was ringleted indeed, but of a fair and yellow hue; hence then he was styled "dark man"). Bebo spoke now, Iubdan answering her:

She. O dark man, and O dark man! dire is the strait in which thou art: to-day it is that the white horse must be saddled, for the sea is angry and the tide at flood.

He. O fair-haired woman, and O woman with fair hair! gyves hold me captive in a viscous mass nor, until gold be given for my ransom, shall I ever be dismissed. O Bebo, and O Bebo! morn is at hand; therefore flee away; fast in the doughy remnant sticks my leg, if here thou stay thou art but foolish, O Bebo!

She. Rash word it was, 'twas a rash word, that in thy house thou utteredst: that but by thine own good pleasure none under the sun might hold thee fast, O man!

He. Rash was the word, the word was rash, that in my house I uttered: a year and a day I must be now, and neither man nor woman of my people see!

"Bebo," cried Iubdan, "flee away now, and to the Lepraland take back that horse."

"Never say it," she answered; "I will surely not depart until I see what turn things shall take for thee."

The dwellers in Emain, when they were now risen, found Iubdan in the porridge cauldron, out of which he could not contrive to escape; in which plight when they saw him the people sent up a mighty roar of laughter, then picked Iubdan out of the cauldron and carried him off to Fergus. "My conscience," said the king, "this is not the tiny man that was here before: seeing that, whereas the former little fellow had fair hair, this one has a black thatch. What art thou at all, mannikin, and out of what region dost thou come?"

Iubdan made answer: "I am of the Lepra-folk, over whom I am king; this woman that you see by me is my wife, and queen over the Lepra: her name is Bebo, and I have never told a lie."

"Let him be taken out," cried Fergus, "and put with the common rabble of the household—guard him well!" Iubdan was led out accordingly. . . .

Said Iubdan, "But if it may please thee to show me some favor, suffer me no longer to be among yonder loons, for the great men's breaths do all infect me; and my word I pledge that till by Ulster and by thee it be permitted, I will never leave you."

Fergus said, "Could I but believe that pledge, thou shouldst no more be with the common varlets."

Iubdan's reply was, "Never have I overstepped, nor ever will transgress, my plighted word."

Then he was conducted into a fair and private chamber that Fergus had, where a trusty servant of the king of Ulster was set apart to minister to him. "An excellent retreat indeed is this," he said, "yet is my own retreat more excellent than it"; and he made a lay:

In the land that lies away north I have a retreat, the ceiling of which is of the red gold, and the floor all of silver. Of the white bronze its lintel is, and its threshold of copper; of light-yellow bird-plumage is the thatch on it indeed. Golden are its candelabra, holding candles of rich light and gemmed over with rare stones, in the fair midst of the house. Save myself only and my queen, none that belongs to it feels sorrow now; a retinue is there that ages not, that wears wavy yellow tresses. There every man is a chess-player, good company is there that knows no stint: against man or woman that seeks to enter it the retreat is never closed.

Ferdiad, or "man of smoke," Fergus's fire-servant, as in Iubdan's presence he kindled a fire, threw upon it a woodbine that twined round a tree, together with somewhat of all other kinds of timber, and this led Iubdan to say, "Burn not the king of trees, for he ought not to be burnt; and wouldst thou, Ferdiad, but act by my counsel, then neither by sea nor by land shouldst thou ever be in danger." Here he sang a lay:

O man that for Fergus of the feasts dost kindle fire, whether afloat or ashore never burn the king of woods. Monarch of Inis Fail's forests the woodbine is, whom none may hold captive; no feeble sovereign's effort is it to hug all tough trees in his embrace. The pliant woodbine if thou burn, wailings for misfortune will abound; dire extremity at weapons' points or drowning in great waves will come after. Burn not the precious apple-tree of spreading and low-sweeping bough: tree ever decked in bloom of white, against whose fair head all men put forth the hand. The surly blackthorn is a wanderer, and a wood that the artificer burns not; throughout his body, though it be scanty, birds in their flocks warble. The noble willow burn not, a tree sacred to poems; within his bloom bees are a-sucking, all love the little cage. The graceful tree with the berries, the wizards' tree, the rowan, burn; but spare the limber tree: burn not the slender hazel. Dark is the color of the ash: timber that makes the wheels to go; rods he furnishes for horsemen's hands, and his form turns battle into flight. Tenterhook among woods the spiteful briar is, by all means burn him that is so keen and green; he cuts, he flays the foot, and him that would advance he forcibly drags backward. Fiercest heat-giver of all timber is green oak, from him none may escape unhurt; by partiality for him the head is set on aching and by his acrid embers the eye is made sore. Alder, very battle-witch of all woods, tree that is hottest in the fight —undoubtingly burn at thy discretion both the alder and the whitethorn. Holly, burn it green; holly, burn it dry; of all trees whatsoever the best is holly. Elder that hath tough bark, tree that in truth hurts sore: him that furnishes horses to the armies from the fairy-mound burn so that he be charred. The birch as well, if he be laid low, promises abiding fortune. Burn up most surely and certainly the stalks that bear the constant pods. Suffer, if it so please thee, the russet aspen to come headlong down: burn, be it late or early, the tree with the trembling branch. Patriarch of long-lasting woods is the yew, sacred to feasts as is well known: of him now build dark-red vats of goodly size. Ferdiad, thou faithful one, wouldst thou but do my behest, to thy soul as to thy body, O man, 'twould work advantage!

After this manner then, and free of all supervision, Iubdan abode in the town; while to them of Ulster it was recreation of mind and body to look at him and to listen to his words. . . .

One day Iubdan went to the house of a certain soldier of the king's soldiers who chanced to fit on himself new brogues that he had: discoursing as he did so, and complaining, of their soles that were too thin. Iubdan laughed. The king asked: "Iubdan, why laughest thou thus?"

"Yon fellow it is that provokes my laughter, complaining of his brogues while for his own life he makes no moan. Yet, thin as be those brogues, he never will wear them out." Which was true for Iubdan, seeing that before night that man and another one of the king's people fought and killed each other. . . .

Yet another day the household disputed of all manner of things, how they would do this or that, but never said: "if it so please God." Then Iubdan laughed and uttered a lay:

Man talks but God sheweth the outcome; to men all things are but confusion, they must leave them as God knoweth them to be. All that which Thou, Monarch of the elements, hast ordained must be right; He, the King of kings, knows all that I crave of thee, Fergus. No man's life, however bold he be, is more than the twinkling of an eye; were he a king's son he knoweth not whether it be truth that he utters of the future.

Iubdan now tarried in Emain until the Lepracan folk, being seven battalions strong, came to Emain in quest of him; and of these no single one did, whether in height or in bulk, exceed another. Then to Fergus and to Ulster's nobles that came out to confer with them they said, "Bring us our king that we may redeem him, and we will pay for him a good ransom."

Fergus asked, "What ransom?"

"Every year, and that without ploughing, without sowing, we will cover this vast plain with a mass of corn."

"I will not give up Iubdan," said the king.

"To-night we will do thee a mischief."

"What mischief?" asked the king.

"All Ulster's calves we will admit to their dams, so that by morning time there shall not in the whole province be found the measure of one babe's allowance of milk."

"So much ye will have gained," said Fergus, "but not Iubdan."

This damage accordingly they wrought that night; then at morn returned to the green of Emain Macha and, with promise of making good all that they had spoiled, again asked for Iubdan. Fergus refusing them, however, they said, "This night we will do another deed of vengeance: we will defile the wells, the rapids, and the river-mouths of the whole province."

But the king answered, "That is but a puny mischief " (whence the old saying " dirt in a well "), " and ye shall not have Iubdan."

They, having done this, came again to Emain on the third day and demanded Iubdan. Fergus said, "I will not give him."

"A further vengeance we will execute upon thee."

"What vengeance is that?"

"To-night we will burn the millbeams and the kilns of the province."

"But you will not get Iubdan," said the king.

Away they went and did as they had threatened, then on the fourth day repaired to Emain and clamored for Iubdan. Said Fergus, "I will not deliver him."

"We will execute vengeance on thee."

"What vengeance?"

"We will snip the ears off all the corn that is in the province."

"Neither so shall you have Iubdan."

This they did, then returned to Emain Macha on the fifth day and asked for Iubdan. Fergus said, "I will not give him up."

"Yet another vengeance we will take on thee."

"What vengeance?"

"Your women's hair and your men's we will shave so that they shall for ever be covered with reproach and shame."

Then Fergus cried, "If you do that, by my word I will slay Iubdan!"

But here Iubdan said, "That is not the right thing at all; rather let me be freed, that in person I may speak with them and bid them first of all to repair such mischief as they have done, and then depart."

At sight of Iubdan they then, taking for granted that the license accorded him must needs be in order to let him depart with them, sent up a mighty shout of triumph. Iubdan said, however, "My trusty people, depart now, for I am not permitted to go with you; all that which you have spoiled make good also, neither spoil anything more for, if you do so, I must die." They thereupon, all gloomy and dejected, went away; a man of them making this lay:

A raid upon thee we proclaim this night, O Fergus, owner of many strong places! from thy standing corn we will snip the ears, whereby thy tables will not benefit. In this matter we have already burnt thy kilns, thy millbeams too we have all consumed; thy calves we have most accurately and universally admitted to their dams. Thy men's hair we will crop, and all locks of thy young women: to thy land it shall be a disfigurement, and such shall be our mischief's consummation. White be thy horse till time of war, thou king of Ulster and of warriors stout! but crimsoned be his trappings when he is in the battle's press. May no heat inordinate assail thee, nor inward flux e'er seize thee, nor eye-distemper reach thee during all thy life: but Fergus, not for love of thee! Were it not for Iubdan here, whom Fergus holds at his discretion, the manner of our effecting our depredations would have been such that the disgrace incurred by Fergus would have shown his refusal to be an evil one.

"And now go," said Iubdan; "for Esirt has prophesied of me that before I shall have left here the choicest one of all my precious things I may not retain."

So till a year's end all but a little he dwelt in Emain, and then said to Fergus: "Of all my treasures choose thee now a single one, for so thou mayest. My precious things are good too"; and in a lay he proceeded to enumerate them:

Take my spear, O take my spear, thou, Fergus, that hast enemies in number! in battle 'tis a match for a hundred, and a king that holds it will have fortune among hostile spear-points. Take my shield, O take my shield, a good price it is for me, Fergus! be it stripling or be it grey-beard, behind his shelter none may wounded be. My sword, and O my sword! in respect of a battle-sword there is not in a prince's hand throughout all Inis Fail a more excellent thing of price. Take my cloak, O take my cloak, the which if thou take it will be ever new! my mantle is good, Fergus, and for thy son and grandson will endure. My shirt, and O my shirt! whoe'er he be that in time to come may be within its weft—my grand-sire's father's wife, her hands they were that spun it. Take my belt, O take my belt! gold and silver appertain to a knowledge of it; sickness will not lay hold on him that is encircled by it, nor on skin encompassed by my girdle. My helmet, O my helmet, no prize there is more admirable! no man that on his scalp shall assume it will ever suffer from the reproach of baldness. Take my tunic, O my tunic take, well-fitting silken garment! the which though for an hundred years it were on one, yet were its crimson none the worse. My cauldron, O my cauldron, a special rare thing for its handy use! though they were stones that should go into my cauldron, yet would it turn them out meat befitting princes. My vat, and O my vat! as compared with other vats of the best, by any that shall bathe in it life's stage is traversed thrice. Take my mace, O take my mace, no better treasure canst thou choose! in time of war, in sharp encounter, nine heads besides thine own it will protect. Take my horse-rod, O my horse-rod take—rod of the yellow horse so fair to see! let but the whole world's women look at thee with that rod in thy hand, and in thee will center all their hottest love. My timpan, O my timpan endowed with string-sweet-ness, from the Red Sea's borders! within its wires resides minstrelsy suffic-ing to delight all women of the universe. Whosoe'er should in the matter of tuning up my timpan be suddenly put to the test, if never hitherto he had been a man of art, yet would the instrument of itself perform the minstrel's function. Ah, how melodious is its martial strain, and its low cadence, ah, how sweet! all of itself too how it plays, without a finger on a single string of all its strings. My shears, and O my shears, that Barran's smith did make! of them that take it into their hands every man will secure a sweetheart. My needle, O my needle, that is made of the finest gold! . . . Of my swine two porkers take! they will last thee till thy dying day; every night they may be killed, yet within the watch will live again. My halter, O my halter! whoe'er should be on booty bent, though 'twere a black cow he put into it, incontinently she would become a white one. Take my shoes, my shoes, O take, brogues of the white bronze, of virtue marvellous! alike they travel land and sea, happy the king whose choice shall fall on these!

"Fergus," said Iubdan, "from among them all choose thee now one precious thing, and let me go."

But this was now the season and the hour when from his adventure the Ulster poet Aed returned; and him the sages examined concerning Iubdan's house, his household, and the region of the Lepra. Concerning all which Aed forthwith began to tell them, inditing a lay:

A wondrous enterprise it was that took me away from you, our poets, to a populous fairy palace with a great company of princes and with little men. Twelve doors there are to that house of roomy beds and window-lighted sides; 'tis of vast marble blocks, and in every doorway doors of gold. Of red, of yellow and green, of azure and of blue its bedclothes are; its authority is of ancient date: warriors' cooking-places it includes, and baths. Smooth are its terraces of the egg-shells of Iruath; pillars there are of crystal, columns of silver and of copper too. . . . Reciting of tales, of the fian-lore, was there every day; singing of poems, instrumental music, the mellow blast of horns, and concerted minstrelsy. A noble king he is: Iubdan son of Abdan, of the yellow horse; he is one whose form undergoes no change, and who needs not to strive after wisdom. Women are there, that in a pure clear lake disport themselves: satin their raiment is, and with each one of them a chain of gold. As for the king's men-at-arms, that wear long tresses, hair ringleted and glossy: men of the mould ordinary with the Lepra can stand upon those soldiers' palms. Bebo—Iubdan's blooming queen—an object of desire—never is the white-skinned beauty without three hundred women in her train. Bebo's women—'tis little they chatter of evil or of arrogance; their bodies are pure white, and their locks reach to their ankles. The king's chief poet, Esirt son of Beg son of Buaidgen: his eye is blue and gentle, and less than a doubled fist that man of poems is. The poet's wife—to all things good she was inclined; a lovely woman and a wonderful: she could sleep in my rounded glove. The king's cup-bearer—in the banquet-hall a trusty man and true: well I loved Feror that could lie within my sleeve. The king's strong man—Glomar son of Glomrad's son Glas, stern doer of doughty deeds: he could fell a thistle at a blow. Of those the king's confidentials, seventeen "swans" (*i.e.*, pretty girls) lay in my bosom; four men of them in my belt and, all unknown to me, among my beard would be another. They (both fighting men and scholars of that fairy-mound) would say to me, and the public acclamation ever was: "Enormous Aed, O very giant!" Such, O Fergus mac Leide of forests vast, such is my adventure: of a verity there is a wondrous thing befallen me.

Of all Iubdan's treasures then Fergus made choice, and his choice was Iubdan's shoes. This latter therefore, leaving them his blessing and taking theirs, bade Fergus and the nobles of Ulster farewell, Ulster grieving for his departure, and with him the story henceforth has no more to do.

As regards Fergus, however, this is why he picked out Iubdan's shoes: he with a young man of his people walking one day hard by Loch Rudraige, they entered into the loch to bathe; and the monster that dwelt in the loch—the *sinech* ("Stormy One") of Loch Rudraige—was aware of them. Then she, shaking herself till the whole loch was in great and tempestuous commotion, reared herself on high as if it had been a solid arc hideous to behold, so that in extent she equalled a rainbow of the air. They both, marking her coming towards them, swam for the shore, she in pursuit with mighty strokes that in bursting deluge sent the water spouting from her sides. Fergus allowed his attendant to gain the land before himself, whereby the monster's breath reaching the king turned him into a crooked and distorted squint-eyed being, with his mouth twisted round to the back of his head. But he knew not that he was so; neither dared any enquire of him what it might be that had wrought this change in him, nor venture to leave a mirror in the same house with him.

The servant, however, told all the matter to his wife and the woman showed it to Fergus's wife, the queen. Later, therefore, when there was a falling-out between the king and queen over precedence in use of the bath-stone, the king gave her a blow with his fist which broke a tooth in her head; whereupon anger seized the queen, and she said, "To avenge thyself on the *sinech* of Loch Rudraige that dragged thy mouth round to thy poll would become thee better than to win bloodless victories over women." Then to Fergus she brought a mirror, and he looking upon his image said, "The woman's words are true, and to this appearance it is indeed the *sinech* of Loch Rudraige that hath brought me." And hence it was that before all Iubdan's other precious wares Fergus had taken his shoes.

In their ships and in their galleys the whole province of Ulster, accompanying Fergus, now gathered together to Loch Rudraige. They entering the loch gained its center; the monster rose and shook herself in such fashion that of all the vessels she made little bits and, as are the withered twigs beneath horses' feet, so were they severally crushed, and all swamped before they could reach the strand.

Fergus said to the men of Ulster: "Bide here and sit you all down, that ye may witness how I and the monster shall deal together." Then he, be'ng shod with Iubdan's shoes, leaped into the loch, erect and brilliant and brave, making for the monster. At sound of the hero's approach she bared her teeth as does a wolf-dog threatened with a club; her eyes blazed like two great torches kindled, suddenly she put forth her sharp claws' jagged array, bent her neck with the curve of an arch and clenched her glittering tusks, throwing back her ears hideously, till her whole semblance was one of gloomy cruel fury. Alas, for any in this world that should be fated to do battle with that monster: huge-headed long-fanged dragon that she was! The fearsome and colossal creature's form was this: a crest and mane she had of coarse hair, a mouth that yawned, deep-sunken eyes; on either side thrice fifty flippers, each armed with as many claws recurved; a body impregnable. Thrice fifty feet her extended altitude; round as an apple she was in contraction, but in bulk equalled some great hill in its rough garb of furze.

When the king sighted her he charged, instant, impetuous, and as he went he made this rhapsody:

> The evil is upon me that was presaged, . . . etc.

Then both of them came to the loch's middle part and so flogged it that the salmon of varied hue leaped and flung themselves out upon the shore because they found no resting-place in the water, for the white bottom-sand was churned up to the surface. Now was the loch whiter than new milk, at once all turned to crimson froth of blood. At last the beast, like some vast royal oak, rose on the loch and before Fergus fled. The hero-king, pressing her, plied her with blows so stalwart and so deadly that she died; and with the sword that was in his hand, with the *caladcolg*,[1] best blade that

---

[1] *Caladbolg*, the original of King Arthur's famous sword Excalibur.

was then in Ireland, he hewed her all in pieces. To the loch's port where the Ulstermen were he brought her heart; but though he did, his own wounds were as many as hers, and than his skin no sieve could be more full of holes. To such effect truly the beast had given him the tooth, that he brought up his very heart's red blood and hardly might make utterance, but groaned aloud.

As for the Ulstermen, they took no pleasure in viewing the fight, but said that were it upon land the king and the beast had striven they would have helped him, and that right valiantly. Then Fergus made a lay:

My soul this night is full of sadness, my body mangled cruelly; red Loch Rudraige's beast has pushed sore through my heart. Iubdan's shoes have brought me through undrowned; with sheeny spear and with the famous sword I have fought a hardy fight. Upon the monster I have avenged my deformity—a signal victory this. Man! I had rather death should snatch me than to live misshapen. Great Eochaid's daughter Ailinn it is that to mortal combat's lists compelled me; and 'tis I assuredly that have good cause to sorrow for the shape imposed on me by the beast.

He went on: "Ulstermen, I have gotten my death; but lay ye by and preserve this sword, until out of Ulster there come after me one that shall be a fitting lord; whose name also shall be Fergus; namely, Fergus mac Roig." [1]

Then lamentably and in tears the Ulstermen stood over Fergus. The poet Aed also, the king's bard, came and standing over him mourned for Fergus with this quatrain:

By you now be dug Fergus's grave, the great monarch's, grave of Leide's son; calamity most dire it is that by a foolish petty woman's words he is done to death!

Answering whom Fergus said:

By you be laid up this sword wherewith "the iron-death" is wrought; here after me shall arise one with the name of Fergus. By you be this sword treasured, that none other take it from you; my share of the matter for all time shall be this: that men shall rehearse the story of the sword.

So Fergus's soul parted from his body: his grave was dug, his name written in the ogam, his lamentation-ceremony all performed; and from the monumental stones (*ulad*) piled by the men of Ulster this name of *Ulad* (Ulster) had its origin.

Thus far the Death of Fergus and the Lepra-people's doings.

[1] The famous Fergus mac Roig of the Ulster cycle (p. 127).

THE ADVENTURES OF CONNLA THE FAIR

The following story is one of the most ancient in our collection, dating probably from the eighth century. Its directness and restraint are in distinct contrast to the more florid narrative method of "The Death of Finn" (p. 424) and "The Second Battle of Moytura" (p. 28). The observant reader is in no danger of mistaking the economy and terseness of this story for barrenness of imagination. The struggle of the father for possession of his son is told in almost as few words as Goethe's famous "Erl-King," and although artistic comparison between the Old Irish tale and the great modern ballad would be unprofitable, we cannot fail to recognize a strong emotional kinship between them.

It will be noted that the story is thrown into the form of the "Dinnsenchas" (p. 596). Of course this is only a mechanical trick. The widespread theme of the mortal who follows a supernatural woman to fairyland is here artificially linked to the explanation of the name. Having the prediction of St. Patrick come from the lips of one of the pagan fairy folk is an engaging touch. Conn the Hundred-Fighter, the father of Art and Connla, was one of the earliest high-kings of Ireland. According to the annals he flourished during the first half of the second century after Christ.

Why was Art the Lone One so called? Not hard to say.

One day as Connla the Bold, son of Conn the Hundred-Fighter, was with his father on the Hill of Usnech he saw a woman in unfamiliar dress. Said Connla, "Where do you come from, O woman?"

The woman answered, "I come from the Lands of the Living, where there is neither death nor want nor sin. We keep perpetual feast without need for service. Peace reigns among us without strife. A great fairy-mound (*sid*) it is, in which we live; wherefore we are called 'folk of the fairy-mound' (*aes side*)."

"Who is it you are speaking to?" Conn asked his son; for none could see the woman save Connla alone.

The woman answered, "He is speaking to a young and beautiful woman of noble descent, who will know neither death nor old age. Long have I loved Connla, and I summon him to Mag Mell, where Boadach the Eternal is king, a king in whose realm there has been no weeping and no sorrow since he began his rule.

"Come with me, O bold Connla, with rosy neck, gleaming like a candle. The fair crown that sits above thy ruddy countenance is a token of thy royalty. If thou wilt follow me thy form shall never decrease in youth or beauty, even to the marvellous Day of Judgment."

Then Conn spoke to his druid (Corann was his name), for they had all heard everything the woman had said, although they did not see her:

> I appeal to you, Corann,
> Skilled in song, skilled in arts!
> A power has come over me
> Too great for my skill,
> Too great for my strength;
> A battle has come upon me
> Such as I have not met since I took the sovereignty.
> By a treacherous attack the unseen shape overpowers me,
> To rob me of my fair son,
> With heathen words of magic.
> He is snatched from my royal side
> By women's words of magic.

Whereupon the druid sang a magic incantation against the voice of the woman, so that no one could hear her voice, and Connla saw no more of her at that time. But as the woman departed before the potent chanting of the druid, she threw Connla an apple.

Connla remained to the end of a month without food or drink, for no nourishment seemed to him worthy to be consumed save only the apple. What he ate of the apple never diminished it, but it remained always unconsumed.

Longing seized upon Connla for the woman he had seen. On the day when the month was completed Connla was seated with his father in Mag Archommin, and he saw the same woman coming toward him. She spoke to him thus:

> A woeful seat where Connla sits!
> Among short-lived mortals,
> Awaiting only dreadful death.
> The living, the immortal call to you;
> They summon you to the people of Tethra
> Who behold you every day
> In the assemblies of your native land,
> Among your beloved kinsmen.

When Conn heard the voice of the woman, he called to his attendants, "Summon me the druid. I see that her tongue is loosed to-day."

Then said the woman:

> O Conn the Hundred-Fighter,
> Thou shouldst not cling to druidry!
> It will not be long before there will come
> To give judgments on our broad strand
> A righteous one,[1] with many wonderful companies.
> Soon his law will reach you.
> He will annihilate the false law of the druids
> In the sight of the black magic demon.

Then Conn wondered why Connla made no answer except when the woman came. "Has it touched your heart, what the woman says, O Connla?" asked Conn.

Then said Connla, "It is not easy for me. Although I love my people, longing for the woman has seized me."

The woman said:

> Thou strivest—most difficult of wishes to fulfill—
> Against the wave of longing which drives thee hence.
> That land we may reach in my crystal boat,
> The fairy-mound of Boadach.
>
> There is yet another land
> That is no worse to reach;
> I see it, now the sun sinks.
> Although it is far, we may reach it before night.
>
> That is the land which rejoices
> The heart of everyone who wanders therein;
> No other sex lives there
> Save women and maidens.

Then Connla gave a leap into the woman's crystal boat. The people saw him going away. Hardly could their eyes follow Connla and the maiden as they fared forth over the sea. From that day forward they were never seen again. And then said Conn as he gazed upon his other son Art, "To-day is Art left the lone one." Hence he came to be called "Art the Lone One" (*Art Óenfer*).

[1] St. Patrick.

THE ADVENTURES OF ART SON OF CONN

Art son of Conn the Hundred-Fighter, referred in the preceding tale, was one of the early traditional kings of Ireland, his reign extending from A.D. 220 to 254. As a usual thing the material regarding traditional kings is later in time of composition than the material of the Ulster cycle. This story, however, although it appears in a late manuscript, has all the appearance of belonging to the Old-Irish tradition. In this, as in several other stories dealing with the early kings, there is a rather strong emphasis on the legal and governmental system of ancient Ireland. Superstitions regarding the kingship, curious ideas about the influence of the moral and physical state of the monarch upon that of his people, the custom of human sacrifice for the good of the country—all these make the material of this selection especially interesting to the student of early Irish social history. Here, as in numerous other romantic tales included in the present volume, we encounter the motif of a visit to the fairy world, the Land of Promise, the Land of Youth. As appears from the context, Conn and Art are regarded as contemporaries of Finn mac Cumaill (p. 355).

Conn the Hundred-Fighter son of Fedlimid Rechtmar son of Tuathal Techtmar son of Feradach Findfechtnach son of Crimthann Nia Nair son of Lugaid Riab Derg son of the three white triplets, Bres and Nar and Lothar, the names of the sons of Eochaid Find,[1] was once at Tara of the kings, the noble conspicuous dwelling of Ireland, for a period of nine years, and there was nothing lacking to the men of Ireland during the time of this king, for, indeed, they used to reap the corn three times in the year. And his wife was Ethne Taebfada (Long-Side) daughter of Brislinn Binn the king of Norway. He loved her dearly.

After their living a long time together Ethne died, and was buried with honor in Tailltiu; for Tailltiu was one of the three chief burial-places of Ireland, which were the Fair of Tailltiu, and the Brug beside the Boyne, and the cemetery of Cruachan. And he was dejected on account of his wife Ethne's death, and it weighed so heavily on him, that he was unable any longer to rule or govern the kingdom. And there was lacking to Ireland at that time one thing only, that the king of Ireland should find a helpmate worthy of him in her stead.

[1] The father of the triplets is usually Eochaid Fedlech, the brother of the king here referred to.

One day, however, he was all alone; and he went straight out of Tara to Benn Etair maic Etgaith. There he bewailed and lamented his wife and helpmate. It was on that very day the Tuatha De Danann happened to be gathered in council in the Land of Promise, because of a woman who had committed transgression, and whose name was Becuma Cneisgel daughter of Eogan Inbir, that is, the wife of Labraid Luathlam-ar-Claideb (Swift-Hand-on-Sword); and Gaidiar, Manannan's son, it was that had committed transgression with her. And this was the sentence passed on her: to be driven forth from the Land of Promise, or to be burned according to the counsel of Manannan, and Fergus Findliath, and Eogan Inbir, and Lodan son of Lir, and Gaidiar, and Gaei Gormsuilech, and Ilbrec son of Manannan. And their counsel was to banish her from the Land of Promise. And Manannan said not to burn her lest her guilt should cleave to the land or to themselves.

Messengers came from Labraid to the house of Angus of the Brug, his own son-in-law; for a daughter of Labraid's was the wife of Angus of the Brug, and her name was Nuamaisi. It was for this reason messengers were despatched: in order that Becuma Cneisgel should not find a place for her head in any of the fairy-mounds of Ireland. Accordingly she was banished beyond the expanse of the sea and the great deep; and it was into Ireland in particular she was sent, for the Tuatha De Danann hated the sons of Mil after they had been driven out of Ireland by them.

The girl had a lover in Ireland, Art son of Conn the Hundred-Fighter, but Art did not know that he was her lover. As for the girl, she found a coracle (boat) which had no need of rowing, but leaving it to the harmony of the wind over sea she came to Ben Etair maic Etgaith. Thus was the girl. She had a green cloak of one color about her, with a fringe of red thread of red gold, and a red satin smock against her white skin, and sandals of white bronze on her, and soft yellow hair, and a gray eye in her head, and lovely-colored teeth, and thin red lips, black eyebrows, arms straight and fair of hue, a snowy white body, small round knees, and slender choice feet, with excellence of shape, and form, and complexion, and accomplishments. Fair was the attire of that maiden, even Eogan Inbir's daughter. One thing only, however,—a woman was not worthy of the high-king of Ireland who was banished for her own misdeed.

When she arrived, Conn was on Ben Etair, sorrowful, restless, and lamentful, bewailing his wife. The maiden recognized him as the high-king of Ireland, and she brought her coracle to land and sat down beside Conn. Conn asked tidings of her. The maiden answered, and said that she was come from the Land of Promise in quest of Art, whom she had loved from afar, because of the tales about him. And she said that she was Delbchaem daughter of Morgan. "I would not come between thee and thy choice of courtship," said Conn, "though I have no wife."

"Why hast thou no wife?" said the maiden.

"My helpmate died," replied Conn.

"What then shall I do?" said the maiden; "is it with thee or with Art that I shall sleep?"

"Make thine own choice," replied Conn.

"This is my choice," said the maiden, "since thou dost not accept me: let me have my choice of courtship in Ireland."

"I see no defects in thee for which it were right to refuse thee, unless they are concealed in thee."

Then the maiden asked her own judgment of Conn, and it was granted her. And they made a union, Conn and the maiden, and she bound him to do her will. And her judgment was that Art should not come to Tara until a year was past. Conn's mind was vexed because of the banishing of his son from Ireland without cause. After that they both set out for Tara; and the maiden left her coracle in the clefts of the rocks in shelter and concealment, for she knew not when she might need that coracle again.

Art was at Tara then playing chess, and Cromdes, Conn's druid, along with him. And the druid said, "A move of banishment of thine, my son, and because of the woman thy father marries thou art being banished." The king and his wife arrived at the place, and his son was brought to him straightway. And Conn said to Art, "Leave Tara and Ireland for a year, and make thy preparation at once, for I have pledged myself to this." And the men of Ireland deemed it a great wrong that Art should be banished for the sake of a woman. Nevertheless, Art left Tara that night, and Conn and Becuma were a year together in Tara, and there was neither corn nor milk in Ireland during that time. And the men of Ireland were in the greatest difficulty about that matter; and the druids of all Ireland were sent with the help of their science and their true wisdom to show what had brought that dreadful evil into Ireland. The question was put to them, and the druids related to the king of Tara and the nobles of Ireland the cause of the evil: because of the depravity of Conn's wife and her unbelief it was sent. And it was declared, through whom their deliverance would be possible, namely, that the son of a sinless couple should be brought to Ireland and slain before Tara, and his blood mingled with the soil of Tara. This was told to Conn, but he knew not where there was such a boy. And he assembled the men of Ireland in one place, and said to them, "I will go in quest of that sinless boy; and do you give the kingdom of Ireland to Art yonder so long as I am away, and, moreover, let him not leave Tara while I am absent until I come again."

Then Conn proceeded straight to Ben Etair, and he found a coracle there. And he was a fortnight and a month on the sea wandering from one isle to another without knowledge or guidance save that of trusting to the course of the stars and the luminaries. And seals and leviathans, and adzeheads and porpoises, and many strange beasts of the sea rose up around the coracle, and swiftly uprose the waves, and the firmament trembled. And the hero all alone navigated the coracle until he came to a strange isle. He landed and left his coracle in a secret lonely place. And it is thus the island was: having fair fragrant apple-trees, and many wells of wine most beautiful, and a fair bright wood adorned with clustering hazel-trees surrounding those wells, with lovely golden-yellow nuts, and little bees ever beautiful humming over the fruits, which were dropping their blossoms and their leaves into the wells. Then he saw near-by a shapely hostel thatched with birds' wings, white, and yellow, and blue. And he went up to the hostel. 'Tis thus it was: with doorposts of bronze and doors of crystal, and a few generous inhabitants within. He saw the queen with her large eyes, whose name was Rigru Rosclethan daughter of Lodan from the Land of Promise, that is, the wife of Daire Degamra son of Fergus Fialbrethach from the Land of Wonders. Conn saw there in the midst of the hostel a little boy with excellence of shape and form, in a chair of crystal, and his name was Segda Saerlabraid son of Daire Degamra.

Conn sat down on the bedside of the hostel, and was attended upon, and his feet washed. And he knew not who had washed his feet. Before long he saw a flame arising from the hearth, and the hero was taken by an invisible hand which guided him to the fire, and he went towards the fire. Then food-laden boards of the house with varied meats rose up before him, and he knew not who had given them to him. After a short space he saw a drinking-horn there, and he knew not who had fetched the horn. Then the dishes were removed from him. He saw before him a vat excellent and finely wrought of blue crystal, with three golden hoops about it. And Daire Degamra bade Conn go into the vat and bathe, so that he might put his weariness from him. And Conn did so. . . . A fair cloak was thrown over the king, and he awoke refreshed. Food and nourishment was set before him. He said that it was taboo for him to eat by himself. And they answered that there was no taboo at all among them, save that none of them ever ate with the other. "Though no one has eaten," said the little boy Segda Saerlabraid, "I will eat along with the king of Ireland, so that he may not violate his taboo." And they lay in the same bed that night.

Conn arose on the morrow, and laid before the household his need and his trouble. "What is thy need?" said they.

"That Ireland is without corn and milk for a year now."

"Why hast thou come hither?"

"In quest of your son," replied Conn, "if you are willing; for it has been told us that it is through him our deliverance will come; namely, that the son of a sinless couple should be invited to Tara, and afterwards bathed in the water of Ireland; and it is you that possess the same, so let this young person, even Segda Saerlabraid, be given up."

"Alas," said Daire son of Fergus Fialbrethach, "we would not lend our son for the kingship of the world; for never did his father and mother come together except when yonder little boy was made; and moreover our own fathers and mothers never came together save at our making."

"Evil is the thing you say," said the boy, "not to respond to the king of Ireland; I will go myself with him."

"Do not say that, son," said the household.

"I say that the king of Ireland should not be refused."

"If that is so," said the household, "it is thus we shall let thee go from us, under protection of the kings of all Ireland, and Art son of Conn, and Finn son of Cumall, and the men of art, so that thou shalt come back safe to us again."

"All that shall be given," said Conn, "if I can."

As for Conn and his coracle, after having had this adventure, it was only a sail of three days and three nights for them to Ireland. The men of all Ireland were then gathered in assembly awaiting Conn at Tara. And when the druids saw the boy with Conn, this is the counsel they gave: to slay him and mingle his blood with the blighted earth and the withered trees, so that its due mast and fruit, its fish, and its produce might be in them. And Conn placed the boy he had brought with him under the protection of Art and Finn, and the men of art, and the men of Ireland. The latter, however, did not accept that responsibility, but the kings accepted it at once, that is Conn, and Finn, and Art Oenfer, and they were all outraged as regards the boy.

As soon as they had finished this council, the boy cried out with a loud voice: "O men of Ireland, leave me alone in peace, since you have agreed to slay me. Let me be put to death, as I shall say myself," said the boy. Just then they heard the lowing of a cow, and a woman wailing continually behind it. And they saw the cow and the woman making towards the assembly. The woman sat down between Finn and Conn the Hundred-Fighter. She asked tidings of the attempt of the men of Ireland, that the innocent boy should be put to death in despite of Finn, and Art, and Conn. "Where are those druids?"

"Here," said they.

"Find out for me what those two bags are at the cow's sides, that is, the bag at each side of her."

"By our conscience," said they, "we know not indeed."

"I know," said she; "a single cow that has come here to save that innocent youth. And it is thus it will be done to her: let the cow be slaughtered, and her blood mixed with the soil of Ireland, and save the boy. And moreover, there is something which it were more fitting for you to take heed to, that is, when the cow is cut up, let the two bags be opened, and there are two birds inside, a bird with one leg, and a bird with twelve legs."

And the cow was slaughtered and the birds taken out of her. And as they were beating their wings in the presence of the host, the woman said, "It is thus we shall discover which is the stronger if they encounter." Then the one-legged bird prevailed over the bird with twelve legs. The men of Ireland marvelled at that. Said the woman, "You are the bird with the twelve legs, and the little boy the bird with one leg, for it is he who is in the right. Take those druids there," said the woman, "for it were better for them to die, and let them be hanged." And the young man was not put to death. Then the woman rose up and called Conn aside, and spoke as follows: "Put this sinful woman away, this Becuma Cneisgel, daughter of Eogan Inbir, and wife of Labraid Luathlam-ar-Claideb, for it is through transgression she has been driven out of the Land of Promise."

"That is good counsel," said Conn, "if I could put her away; but since I cannot, give us good advice."

"I will," said the woman, "for it is worse it will be; a third of its corn, and its milk, and its mast will be lacking to Ireland so long as she is with you." And she took leave of them then and went off with her son, Segda. Jewels and treasures were offered to them, but they refused them.

Becuma chanced to be out on the green then, and she saw Conn's son Art playing chess there. It was not pleasant for Art to see his enemy. "Is that Conn's son Art?" said she.

"It is indeed," said they.

"I lay a taboo upon him," said she, "unless he play chess with me for stakes."

This was told to Art son of Conn. A chess-board was brought to them then, and they played, and Art won the first game. "This is a game on thee, girl," said Art.

"That is so," said she.

"And I lay a taboo on thee," said he, "if thou eat food in Ireland until thou procure the warrior's wand which Cu Roi mac Dairi had in his hand when taking possession of Ireland and the great world, and fetch it to me here."

Then the girl proceeded to the dewy light-flecked brug, wherein was Angus, with his dear wife at his side, even Nuamaisi daughter of Labraid. However, she searched most of the fairy-mounds of Ireland, and found no tidings of the wand until she came to the fairy-mound of Eogabal, and a welcome was given her here by Aine daughter of Eogabal, for they were two foster-sisters. "Thou wilt get thy quest here," said she; "and take yonder thrice fifty youths with thee until thou come to the stronghold of Cu Roi on the top of Sliab Mis." And they found it there, and she rejoiced.

Thereupon she set out for Tara, and she brought the wand to Art, and laid it upon his knees. The chess-board was brought to them, and they played. And the men of the fairy-mound began to steal the pieces. Art saw that, and said, "The men of the fairy-mound are stealing the pieces from us, girl; and it is not thou that art winning the game, but they."

"This is a game on thee," said the girl.

"It is so indeed," said the young man; "and give thy judgment."

"I will this," said she; "thou shalt not eat food in Ireland until thou bring with thee Delbchaem the daughter of Morgan."

"Where is she?" said Art.

"In an isle amid the sea, and that is all the information thou wilt get."

Art set out for Inber Colptha; and he found a coracle with choice equipment on the shore before him. And he put forth the coracle, and travelled the sea from one isle to another until he came to a fair, strange island; and lovely was the character of that island, full of wild apples and lovely birds, with little bees ever beautiful on the tops of the flowers. A house, hospitable and noble, in the midst of the island, thatched with birds' wings, white and purple, and within it a company of blooming women, ever beautiful, among them Creide Firalainn daughter of Fidech Foltlebor.

A hearty welcome was then given to him, and food set before him, and tidings are asked of him. And he said that he was come from Ireland, and that he was the King of Ireland's son, and his name was Art. "That is true," said Creide. After that she put out her hand, and gave him a variegated mantle with adornments of burnished gold from Arabia, and he put it on him, and it was right for him. "'Tis true," said she, "that thou art Conn's son Art, and it is long since thy coming here has been decreed." And she gave him three kisses, dearly and fervently. And she said, "Look at the crystal bower." And fair was the site of that bower, with its doors of crystal and its inexhaustible vats, for, though everything be emptied out of them, they were ever full again.

He remained a fortnight and a month in that island, after which he took leave of the girl, and related his errand. "'Tis true," said she, "that is thine errand; and it will be no little time until the maiden will be found, for the way is bad thither, and there is sea and land between thee and her, and, even if thou dost reach it, thou wilt not go past it. There is a great ocean and dark between; and deadly and hostile is the way there, for there is a wood that is traversed as though there were spear-points of battle under one's feet, like leaves of the forest under the feet of men. There is a luckless gulf of the sea full of dumb-mouthed beasts on this side of that wood, even an immense oak forest, dense and thorny before a mountain, and a narrow path through it, and a dark house in the mysterious wood at the head of the same path, with seven hags and a bath of molten lead awaiting thee, for thy coming there has been fated. And there is somewhat more grievous still, even Ailill Black-tooth son of Mongan Minscothach. And weapon cannot harm him. And there are two sisters of mine there, daughters of Fidech Foltlebor, Finscoth and Aeb their names. There are two cups in their hands—a cup filled with poison, and one filled with wine. And the cup which is on thy right hand, drink therefrom when thou hast need. And near at hand is the stronghold of the maiden. Thus it is, with a palisade of bronze round about it, and a man's head on every stake of it, after being slain by Coinchenn Cennfada (Dog-Head Long-Head), save on one stake alone. And Coinchenn daughter of the king of the Coinchinn the mother of the girl, even Delbchaem daughter of Morgan."

Art then set out after he had been instructed by the girl, until he came to the crest of that hapless sea full of strange beasts. And on all sides the beasts and great sea-monsters rose up around the coracle. And Art son of Conn donned his battle attire, and engaged them warily and circumspectly. And he began to slaughter them and maim them until they fell by him.

After that he came to the forest wild where the Coinchenn and the wicked, perverse hags were, and Art and the hags encountered. It was not a fair encounter for him, the hags piercing and hacking at him until morning. Nevertheless the armed youth prevailed over that hapless folk. And Art went on his way using his own judgment until he came to the venomous icy mountain; and the forked glen was there full of poisonous toads, which were lying in wait for whoever came there. And he passed thence to Saeb Mountain beyond, wherein were full many lions with long manes lying in wait for the beasts of the whole world.

After that he came to the icy river, with its slender narrow bridge, and a warrior giant with a pillar-stone, and he grinding his teeth on it, namely, Curnan Cliabsalach. Nevertheless they encountered, and Art overcame the giant, so that Curnan Cliabsalach fell by him. And he went thence to where Ailill Dubdedach son of Mongan was. And 'tis thus that man was: a fierce champion was he; no weapon could harm him, or fire burn him, or water drown him. Then Art and he took to wrestling, and they made a manly combat, a stern, heroic, equally-sharp fight. And Ailill Dubdedach began abusing Art, and they were haranguing one another. But Art overcame the giant, so that his head came off the back of his neck. After that Art wrecked the stronghold; and he seized Ailill's wife, and he threatened to do her injury until she told him the way to Morgan's stronghold, and the Land of Wonders.

It was there Coinchenn Cennfada, Morgan's wife, was; and she had the strength of a hundred in battle or conflict. She was the daughter of Conchruth king of the Coinchinn. And the druids had foretold her that if ever her daughter should be wooed, in that same hour she would die. Therefore, she put to death everyone that came to woo her daughter. And it was she that had organized the hags with the bath of lead to meet him, and Curnan Cliabsalach son of Duscad, the door-keeper of Morgan's house. And it was she that had put Ailill Dubdedach in the way of Art son of Conn, because Art would come on that expedition to woo her daughter, as it had been foretold her. And it was she that had contrived the venomous toads, and the icy bridge, and the dark forest, and the mountain full of lions, and the hapless sea-gulf.

Thus came Art to the stronghold which he was in quest of, that is, Morgan's stronghold, and pleasant it was. A fair palisade of bronze was round about it, and houses hospitable and extensive, and a stately palace . . . in the midst of the enclosure. An ingenious, bright, shining bower set on one pillar over the enclosure, on the very top, where that maiden was. She had a green cloak of one hue about her, with a gold pin in it over her breast, and long, fair, very golden hair. She had dark-black eyebrows, and flashing grey eyes in her head, and a snowy-white body. Fair was the maiden both in shape and intelligence, in wisdom and embroidery, in chastity and nobility. And the maiden said: "A warrior has come to this place to-day, and there is not in the world a warrior fairer in form, or of better repute. It is true," said she, "he is Art; and it is long since we have been preparing for him. And I will go into a house apart," said she, "and do thou bring Art into the bower; for I fear lest the Coinchenn may put him to death, and have his head placed on the vacant stake before the stronghold."

With that Art went into the bower, and when the women-folk saw him they made him welcome, and his feet were bathed. After that came the Coinchenn, and the two daughters of Fidech along with her, Aeb and Finscoth, to pour out the poison and the wine for Art.

Then the Coinchenn arose and put on her fighting apparel, and challenged Art to combat. And it was not Art who refused a fight ever. So he donned his fighting gear, and before long the armed youth prevailed over the Coinchenn; and her head came off from the back of her neck, and he placed it on the vacant stake in front of the fortress.

Now concerning Art son of Conn and Delbchaem daughter of Morgan. That night they lay down merry, and in good spirits, the whole stronghold in their power, from small to great, until Morgan king of the Land of Wonders arrived; for indeed he was not there at the time. Then, however, Morgan arrived, full of wrath, to avenge his fortress and his good wife on Art son of Conn. He challenged Art to combat. And the young man arose, and put on his battle-harness, his pleasant, satin mantle, and the white light-speckled apron of burnished gold about his middle. And he put his fine dark helmet of red gold on his head. And he took his fair, purple, embossed shield on the arched expanse of his back. And he took his wide-grooved sword with its blue hilt, and his two thick-shafted, red-yellow spears, and they attacked each other, Art and Morgan, like two enormous stags, or two lions, or two waves of destruction. And Art overcame Morgan, and he did not part from him until his head had come off his neck. After which Art took hostages of Morgan's people, and also possession of the Land of Wonders. And he collected the gold and silver of the land also, and gave it all to the maiden, even Delbchaem daughter of Morgan.

The stewards and overseers followed him from the land, and he brought the maiden with him to Ireland. And they landed at Benn Etair. When they came into port, the maiden said: "Hasten to Tara, and tell to Becuma daughter of Eogan that she abide not there, but to depart at once, for it is a bad hap if she be not commanded to leave Tara."

And Art went forward to Tara, and was made welcome. And there was none to whom his coming was not pleasing, but the wanton and sorrowful Becuma. But Art ordered the sinful woman to leave Tara. And she rose up straightway lamenting in the presence of the men of Ireland, without a word of leave-taking, until she came to Benn Etair.

As for the maiden Delbchaem, the seers, and the wise men, and the chiefs were sent to welcome her, and she and Art came to Tara luckily and auspiciously. And the nobles of Ireland asked tidings of his adventures from Art; and he answered them, and made a lay.

Thus far the Adventures of Art son of Conn, and the Courtship of Delbchaem daughter of Morgan.

CORMAC'S ADVENTURES IN THE LAND OF PROMISE

King Cormac, the hero of the present narrative, was the son of Art, who figures in the preceding selection. The piece is not a single unified story; it is a collection of narratives based on an ancient account of various legal ordeals, and later expanded into a story of a visit to the fairy world. Here, as in the preceding story, we see illustrated the strong tendency toward moralizing and social criticism exhibited by Irish literature of the middle period. These stories, of course, are not told entirely for the purpose of expounding the legal or social ideas to which they refer; they merely capitalize upon an already established interest and follow the usual Irish literary habit of furnishing a narrative to explain every well-known fact.

Cormac's Cup was a cup of gold which he had. The way in which it was found was thus:

One day, at dawn in Maytime, Cormac son of Art son of Conn the Hundred-Fighter was alone on Mur Tea in Tara. He saw coming towards him a calm, greyhaired warrior, with a purple, fringed mantle around him, a ribbed, goldthreaded shirt next his skin, and two blunt shoes of white bronze between his feet and the earth. A branch of silver with three golden apples was on his shoulder. Delight and amusement enough it was to listen to the music made by the branch, for men sore-wounded, or women in child-bed, or folk in sickness would fall asleep at the melody which was made when that branch was shaken. The warrior saluted Cormac. Cormac saluted him. "Whence hast thou come, O warrior?" said Cormac.

"From a land," he replied, "wherein there is nought save truth, and there is neither age nor decay nor gloom nor sadness nor envy nor jealousy nor hatred nor haughtiness."

"It is not so with us," said Cormac. "A question, O warrior: shall we make an alliance?"

"I am well pleased to make it." So they became allies.

"Give me the branch!" said Cormac.

"I will give it," said the warrior, "provided the three boons which I shall ask in Tara be granted to me in return."

"They shall be granted," said Cormac.

Then the warrior bound Cormac to his promise, and left the branch and went away; and Cormac knew not whither he had gone. Cormac returned to the palace, and the household marvelled at the branch. Cormac shook it at them, and cast them into slumber from that hour to the same time on the following day.

At the end of a year the warrior came and asked of Cormac the consideration agreed upon for his branch. "It shall be given," said Cormac.

"I will take thy daughter Ailbe today," said the warrior. So he took the girl with him. The women of Tara uttered three loud cries after the daughter of the king of Erin. But Cormac shook the branch at them, so that he banished grief from them all and cast them into sleep.

A month later the warrior returned and took with him Cairbre Liffecair the son of Cormac. Weeping and sorrow ceased not in Tara at the loss of the boy, and that night no one ate or slept, and they were in grief and exceeding gloom. But Cormac shook 'the branch at them, and their sorrow left them.

The same warrior came a third time.

"What askest thou today?" said Cormac.

"Thy wife," said he, "even Ethne Taebfada daughter of Dunlang king of Leinster." Then he took the woman away with him.

That thing Cormac could not endure. He went after them, and every one followed him. A great mist was brought upon them in the midst of the plain, and Cormac found himself alone. There was a large fortress in the midst of the plain with a wall of bronze around it. In the fortress was a house of white silver, and it was half-thatched with the wings of white birds. A fairy host of horsemen were at the house, with lapfuls of the wings of white birds in their bosoms to thatch the house. A gust of wind would blow and would carry away all of it that had been thatched. Cormac saw a man kindling a fire, and the thick-boled oak was cast upon it, top and butt. When the man came again with another oak, the burning of the first oak had ended. Then he saw another royal stronghold, and another wall of bronze around it. There were four palaces therein. He entered the fortress and saw the vast palace with its beams of bronze, its wattling of silver, and its thatch of the wings of white birds. Then he saw in the enclosure a shining fountain, with five streams flowing out of it, and the hosts in turn drinking its water. Nine hazels of Buan grew over the well. The purple hazels dropped their nuts into the fountain, and the five salmon which were in the fountain severed them and sent their husks floating down the streams. Now the sound of the falling of those streams was more melodious than any music that men sing.

He entered the palace. There was one couple inside awaiting him. The warrior's figure was distinguished owing to the beauty of his shape, the comeliness of his form, and the wonder of his countenance. The girl along with him, mature, yellow-haired, with a golden head-dress, was the loveliest of the world's women. Cormac's feet were washed by invisible hands. There was bathing in a pool without the need of attendance. The heated stones of themselves went into and came out of the water.

As they were there after the hour of nine they saw a man coming into the house. A wood-axe was in his right hand, and a log in his left hand, and a pig behind him. "'Tis time to make ready within," said the warrior; "because a noble guest is here."

The man struck the pig and killed it. And he cleft his log so that he had three sets of part-cleavings. The pig was cast into the cauldron.

"It is time for you to turn it," said the warrior.

"That would be useless," said the kitchener; "for never, never will the pig be boiled until a truth is told for each quarter of it."

"Then," said the warrior, "do thou tell us the first truth."

"One day," said he, "when I was going round the land, I found another man's cows on my property, and I brought them with me into a cattle-pound. The owner of the cows followed me and said that he would give me a reward for letting his cows go free. I gave him his cows. He gave me a pig and an axe and a log, the pig to be killed with the axe every night, and the log to be cleft by it, and there would then be enough firewood to boil the pig, and enough for the palace besides. And, moreover, the pig would be alive the next morning and the log be whole. And from then till today they have been like that."

"True, indeed, is that tale," said the warrior.

The pig was turned in the cauldron and only one quarter of it was found boiled.

"Let us have another tale of truth," said they.

"I will tell one," said the warrior. "Ploughing-time had come. When we desired to plough that field outside, it was found ploughed, harrowed and sown with wheat. When we desired to reap it, the crop was found stacked in the field. When we desired to draw it into that side out there, it was found in the enclosure all in one thatched rick. We have been eating it from then till today; but it is no whit greater nor less."

Then the pig was turned in the cauldron, and another quarter was found to be cooked.

"It is now my turn," said the woman. "I have seven cows and seven sheep. The milk of the seven cows is enough for the people of the Land of Promise. From the wool of the seven sheep comes all the clothing they require."

At this story the third quarter of the pig was boiled.

"It is now thy turn," they said to Cormac.

So Cormac related how his wife and his son and his daughter had been taken from him, and how he himself had pursued them until he arrived at that house.

So with that the whole pig was boiled.

Then they carved the pig, and his portion was placed before Cormac. "I never eat a meal," said Cormac, "without fifty in my company." The warrior sang a song to him and put him asleep. After this he awoke and saw fifty warriors, and his son and his wife and his daughter, along with him. Thereupon his spirit was strengthened. Then ale and food were dealt out to them, and they became happy and joyous. A cup of gold was placed in the warrior's hand. Cormac was marvelling at the cup, for the number of the forms upon it and the strangeness of its workmanship. "There is something about it still more strange," said the warrior. "Let three falsehoods be spoken under it, and it will break into three. Then let three true declarations be made under it, and it will unite again as it was before." The warrior spoke under it three falsehoods, and it broke into three parts. "It would be well to utter truth," said the warrior, "for the sake of restoring the cup. I declare, O Cormac," said he, "that until today neither thy wife nor thy daughter has seen the face of a man since they were taken from thee out of Tara, and that thy son has not seen a woman's face." The cup thereupon became whole.

"Take thy family now," said the warrior, "and take the cup that thou mayst have it for discerning between truth and falsehood. And thou shalt have the branch for music and delight. And on the day that thou shalt die they all will be taken from thee. I am Manannan son of Lir," said he, "king of the Land of Promise; and to see the Land of Promise was the reason I brought thee hither. The host of horsemen which thou beheldest thatching the house are the men of art in Ireland, collecting cattle and wealth which passes away into nothing. The man whom thou sawest kindling the fire is a thriftless young chief, and out of his housekeeping he pays for everything he consumes. The fountain which thou sawest, with the five streams out of it, is the Fountain of Knowledge, and the streams are the five senses through which knowledge is obtained. And no one will have knowledge who drinks not a draught out of the fountain itself and out of the streams. The folk of many arts are those who drink of them both."

Now on the morrow morning, when Cormac arose, he found himself on the green of Tara, with his wife and his son and daughter, and having his Branch and Cup.

THE ADVENTURES OF THE SONS OF EOCHAID MUGMEDON

Here, as in the succeeding tale, the hero is Niall of the Nine Hostages, who, according to the annals, was high-king of Ireland from A.D. 379 to 405. Niall, the eponymous ancestor of the O'Neills, is reputed to have been one of the most powerful kings of ancient Ireland. The tale is not an especially good example of the Irish story-teller's art, but it is full of interest for the student of ancient Irish beliefs. It is still more noteworthy as an early example of a theme dear to the Irish people, the personification of Ireland in the form of a beautiful woman. The plot itself is of a type widely circulated in medieval Europe and perhaps best known to the general reader in the form given to it by the Wife of Bath in Chaucer's *Canterbury Tales*. The story in its present form is not older than the eleventh century.

There was a wondrous and noble king over Erin, namely, Eochaid Mugmedon. Five sons he had: Brian, Ailill, Fiachra, Fergus, and Niall. The mother of Brian, Fiachra, Fergus and Ailill was Mongfinn, daughter of Fidach. The mother of Niall was Cairenn the curly-black, daughter of Sachell Balb, king of the Saxons. Niall was hated by Queen Mongfinn, for Eochaid had begotten him on Cairenn instead of on her. Great then was the hardship which Cairenn suffered from the queen: so great was the hardship that she was compelled to draw the water of Tara, apart, and every handmaid in turn in sight of her; and even when she was with child with Niall, she was forced to do all that in order that the babe might die in her womb.

The time of her lying-in arrived, and yet she ceased not from the service. Then on the green of Tara, beside the pail, she brought forth a man-child, and she durst not take up the boy from the ground, but she left him there exposed to the birds. And not one of the men of Erin dared carry him away, for dread of Mongfinn; since great was her magical power, and all were in fear of her. Then Torna the poet came across the green, and beheld the babe left alone, with the birds attacking it. So Torna took the boy into his bosom, and to him was revealed all that would be thereafter. And he said:

Welcome, little guest; he will be Niall of the Nine Hostages.

In his time he will redden a multitude.

Plains will be greatened, hostages will be overthrown, battles will be fought.

Longside of Tara, host-leader of Mag Femin, custodian of Maen-mag.

Revered one of Almain, veteran of Liffey, white-knee of Codal.

Seven-and-twenty years he will rule Erin, and Erin will be inherited from him for ever.

Good indeed was Niall's beginning and his success, manly, rough-haired, till he died in the afternoon on a Saturday by the sea of Wight,[1] slain by Eochaid son of Enna Cennselach.

Torna took the boy with him, and fostered him; and after that neither Torna nor his fosterling came to Tara until the boy was fit to be king. Then Torna and Niall came to Tara. 'Twas then that Cairenn, Niall's mother, as she was bringing water to Tara, chanced to meet them. Said Niall to her: "Let this work alone."

"I dare not," she answered, "because of the queen."

"My mother," said he, "shall not be serving, and I the son of the king of Erin." Then he took her with him to Tara, and clad her in purple raiment.

Anger seized Mongfinn, for that seemed evil to her. But this was the will of the men of Erin, that Niall should be king after his father. Wherefore Mongfinn said to Eochaid: "Pass judgment among thy sons, as to which of them shall receive thy heritage."

"I will not pass judgment," he answered; "but Sithchenn the wizard will do so." Then they sent to Sithchenn the smith, who dwelt in Tara, for he was a wise man and a wondrous prophet.

The smith set fire to his forge in which the four sons were placed. Niall came out carrying the anvil and its block. "Niall vanquishes," said the wizard, "and he will be a solid anvil forever." Brian came next, bringing the sledgehammers. "Brian to be your fighters," said the wizard. Then came Fiachra, bringing a pail of beer and the bellows. "Your beauty and your science with Fiachra," said the wizard. Then came Ailill with the chest in which were the weapons. "Ailill to avenge you!" said the wizard. Last came Fergus with the bundle of withered wood and a bar of yew therein. "Fergus the withered!" said the wizard. That was true,

[1] The "sea of Wight" is the English Channel. The tradition that Niall was slain here is not incorporated among the traditions given on p. 516.

for the seed of Fergus was no good, excepting one, Cairech Dergain of Cloonburren.   And hence is the saying "a stick of yew in a bundle of firewood."

To bear witness of that the shanachie sang:

> Eochaid's five sons, Niall the great anvil,
> Brian the sledge-hammer for true striking,
> Ailill the chest of spears against a tribe,
> Fiachra the blast, Fergus the withered.
>
> Fiachra has the drink of ale,
> Ailill has the warlike spears,
> Brian has the entrance to battle,
> But Niall has the prize.

Now this was grievous to Mongfinn, and she said to her sons, "Do you four sons quarrel, so that Niall may come to separate you, and then kill him."

Then they quarrelled.   "I wish to separate them," said Niall.

"Nay," said Torna, "let the sons of Mongfinn be peaceful." Hence is the proverb.

Then Mongfinn said that she would not abide by Sithchenn's judgment.   So she sent her sons to the same Sithchenn to ask for arms.   They went to the smith, and he made arms for them; the weapon that was finest he put into Niall's hand, and the rest of the arms he gave to the other sons.   "Now go to hunt and try your arms," said the smith.   So the sons went and hunted, and it happened that they went far astray.

When they ceased from straying they kindled a fire, broiled some of their quarry, and ate it until they were satisfied.   Then they were thirsty and in great drouth from the cooked food.   "Let one of us go and seek for water," they said.   "I will go," said Fergus.   The lad went seeking water, till he chanced on a well and saw an old woman guarding it.

Thus was the hag: every joint and limb of her, from the top of her head to the earth, was as black as coal.   Like the tail of a wild horse was the gray bristly mane that came through the upper part of her head-crown.   The green branch of an oak in bearing would be severed by the sickle of green teeth that lay in her head and reached to her ears.   Dark smoky eyes she had: a nose crooked and hollow.   She had a middle fibrous, spotted with pustules, diseased, and shins distorted and awry.   Her ankles were thick, her shoulder-blades were broad, her knees were big, and her nails were green. Loathsome in sooth was the hag's appearance.

"That is so," said the youth.

" 'Tis so indeed," said she.

"Art thou guarding the well?" asked the youth.

"Yea truly," she answered.

"Dost thou permit me to take away some of the water?" said the youth.

"I will permit," she answered, "provided there come from thee one kiss on my cheek."

"By no means!" said he.

"Then no water shalt thou get from me," said she.

"I give my word," he answered, "that I would rather perish of thirst than give thee a kiss."

The lad then went back to the place where his brothers were biding, and told them that he had not found water. So Ailill went to look for water, and chanced on the same well. He too refused to kiss the hag, returned without water, and did not confess that he had found the well. Then Brian, the eldest of the sons, went to seek water, chanced on the same well, refused to kiss the old woman, and returned waterless. Fiachra then went, found the well and the hag, and asked her for water. "I will grant it," said she; "but give me a kiss."

"I would give few kisses for it."

"Thou shalt visit Tara," said she. That fell true, for two of his race took the kingship of Erin, namely Dathi and Ailill Wether, and no one of the race of the other sons, Brian, Ailill, Fergus, took it. So Fiachra returned without water.

So then Niall went seeking water and happened on the same well. "Give me water, O woman," said Niall.

"I will give it," she answered, "but first give me a kiss."

"Besides giving thee a kiss, I will lie with thee!" Then he threw himself down upon her and gave her a kiss. But then, when he looked at her, there was not in the world a damsel whose figure or appearance was more loveable than hers! Like the snow in trenches was every bit of her from head to sole. Plump and queenly forearms she had: fingers long and slender: calves straight and beautifully colored. Two blunt shoes of white bronze between her little, soft-white feet and the ground. A costly full-purple mantle she wore, with a brooch of bright silver in the clothing of the mantle. Shining pearly teeth she had, an eye large and queenly, and lips red as rowanberries.

"That is many-shaped, O lady!" said the youth.

"True," said she.

"Who art thou?" said the youth.

"I am the Sovereignty of Erin," she answered; and then she said:

O king of Tara, I am the Sovereignty:
I will tell thee its great goodness, etc.

"Go now to thy brothers," she said, "and take water with thee, and the kingship and the domination will for ever abide with thee and thy children, save only with twain of the seed of Fiachra, namely, Dathi and Ailill Wether, and one king out of Munster, namely Brian Boru ("of the Tribute")—and all these will be kings without opposition. And as thou hast seen me loathsome, bestial, horrible at first and beautiful at last, so is the sovereignty; for seldom it is gained without battles and conflicts; but at last to anyone it is beautiful and goodly. Howbeit, give not the water to thy brothers until they have granted thee seniority over them, and that thou mayst raise thy weapon a hand's-breadth above their weapons."

"So shall it be done," said the youth. Then he bade her farewell, and took water to his brothers; but did not give it to them until they had granted to him every boon that he asked of them, as the damsel had taught him. He also bound them by oaths never to oppose himself or his children.

Then they went to Tara. There they raised their weapons, and Niall raised his the breadth of a hero's hand above them. They sat down in their seats with Niall among them in the midst. Then the king asked tidings of them. Niall made answer and related the adventure, and how they went seeking water, and how they chanced on the well and came to the woman, and what she had prophesied to them. "What is the cause," said Mongfinn, "that it is not the senior, Brian, that tells these tales?"

They answered, "We granted our seniority and our kingship to Niall for the first time in exchange for the water."

"You have granted it permanently," said Sithchenn, "for henceforward he and his children will always have the domination and kingship of Erin."

Now that was true, for from Niall onward no one, except with opposition, took the kingship of Erin save one of his children or descendants, until the Strong-Striker of Usnech, Maelsechlann son of Domnall. For it was taken by six and twenty of the O'Neills of the North or of the South, that is, ten kings of the kindred of Conall and sixteen of the kindred of Eogan; as said the poet:

> I know the number that took
> Erin after Niall of the lofty valor,
> From Loegaire's reign, if it be a fault,
> To the Strong-Striker of Usnech.
>
> Loegaire and his sons, I will not conceal,
> Diarmaid and mighty Tuathal,
> Nine of sound Aed Slane,
> And seven of the clans of Colman.
>
> Sixteen kings of lofty Eogan,
> Ten of cruel-savage Conall:
> Niall got with speedy course
> The kingship always for his race.

THE DEATH OF NIALL OF THE NINE HOSTAGES

Though the following story in its present form can hardly be older than the eleventh century, it doubtless contains reminiscences of Irish invasions of Great Britain during the late fourth and early fifth centuries, when, as we know from British records and other evidence, the inhabitants of Britain were suffering from the inroads of the Scots (Irish).

Once Eochaid the son of Enna Cennselach went from the house of Niall of the Nine Hostages, son of Eochaid Mugmedon, southward to his own land, that is, Leinster. Then it befell that in order to ask for food he went to the house of Niall's poet. That was Laidcenn, son of Bairchid, the chief-poet of Niall. The young man was refused hospitality by the poet.

The same Eochaid came again from the south, destroyed the stronghold of the poet, and killed his only son, Leat son of Laidcenn. Thereupon for a whole year the poet kept satirizing and lampooning the men of Leinster and cursing them, so that neither grass nor corn grew with them, nor a leaf, to the end of a year.

Then Niall went to Leinster on a raid, and he said that he would not go from them so long as he was alive, or until Eochaid were given him as a pledge and hostage. And this had to be done. So Eochaid was taken to Ath Fadat in Gothart Fea on the bank of the Slaney, and was left there before Niall, with a chain around his neck, and the end of the chain through the hole of a stone pillar. Nine champions advanced towards him to slay him. "Woe!" said Eochaid, "this is bad indeed!" With that he gave himself a twist, so that the chain broke in two. He seized the iron bolt that was through the chain, and advanced to meet them. He plied the bolt on them so that the nine fell. The other men turned before him down the hill. Those of Leinster pursued them and slaughtered them, so that they fell.

Thereupon Niall came southward once more and reached Inis Fail. "A guarantee shall be given from the men of Leinster," said Laidcenn, "and let Eochaid come that he may be seen by us at this river for so long as a cow is being milked."

"Let it be done!" said Eochaid.

Then his arms were taken away from him. The poet began to revile the men of Leinster and Eochaid, so that they melted away before him. As he was reviling them, Eochaid let fly at him a champion's stone which he had in his belt, so that it hit the crown of his forehead and lodged in his skull. Thus it was that Laidcenn was killed. Whence the quatrain was sung:

> A champion's handstone—'tis well known—was hurled . . .
> Eochaid son of Enna threw it at Laidcenn the son of Bairchid.

After having raided Leinster, Niall went home, and Eochaid was exiled from Ireland so long as Niall reigned. He wandered until he came to the house of Erc the son of Eochaid Munremur, king of Scotland.

Niall, however, went to obtain kingship as far as Gaul and Italy, and he was called "of the Nine Hostages" because he had five hostages from Ireland, and one hostage each from Scotland and from the Saxons, the Britons and the Franks, whence it is said:

> Eochaid's son of high dignity, noble Niall fiercest shout,
> Seized the sway of kingship of Erin and of Alba.
> He had a hostage from each province throughout the land of Erin,
> He brought to his will without severance four hostages out of Alba.
> Hence he was called among the hosts of battlesome warriors,
> In the row of bountiful kings, combative Niall of the Nine Hostages.

Now, when they came to the Alps, there was a great river before them, to wit, the Loire of the Alps. They were unable to cross it, and sat down on its banks. As they were there, they saw a single warrior coming towards them. A crimson five-folded cloak was about him. In his hands he held two five-pronged spears. A bent-rimmed shield with a boss of gold was on him. On his belt hung an ivory-hilted sword. His hair was in plaits over his back. "Welcome to the hero whom we do not know!" said Niall.

"It is for this we have come," said he.

"What is it for which thou hast come?" said Niall.

"I have come from the Romans to have speech with thee," said he, "and this day fortnight their hostages will come to thee. Until they come, here am I as a preliminary hostage for thee."

Others say that their hostages were trysted to the house of Erc son of Eochaid Munremur, the king of Scotland, and that it is there Niall was killed among the bards of the Picts as he was exhibiting his shape to them.   Or that it may have been the maidens of the Franks who desired him to exhibit his shape.

Then Erc went towards the assembly.   "I shall go with thee," said Eochaid, "to see my brother in his royal seat before the men of the world."   When they had arrived, Erc said: "That is he yonder!"   There was a glen between them.   Without the knowledge of Erc, Eochaid shot an arrow from the bow, so that the king fell dead from that single shot.   Thereupon the Franks attacked the Gaels, and the men of Scotland stood by the latter for the sake of their kinship.   So they came to Ireland, carrying the body of their king with them.   And seven battles were fought in the presence of the dead king.

It was Torna the poet, of Carrac Luachra, who had fostered Niall.[1]   Now, when he heard the report that his foster-son had been slain, his foster-brother Tuirn son of Torna said:

When we used to go to the gathering with the son of Eochaid Mugmedon,
As yellow as the primrose was the hair upon the head of Cairenn's son.

Cairenn the curly-black, daughter of Sachell Balb, king of the Saxons, was the mother of Niall.

Said his foster-mother:

His white teeth, his red lips, . . . under anger,
His shape like a fiery blaze surmounting warlike Erin.
The hue of his cheeks at all times, even and symmetrical as they were,
Like the foxglove, like a calf's blood—a feast without a flaw! like the top-branches of a forest in May.
Like the moon, like the sun, like a firebrand was the splendor of Niall,
Like a dragon-ship from the wave without a fault was Niall the son of Eochaid Mugmedon.
This is a yearnful music, the wail of every mouth in Kerry:
It brings grief upon us in our house for the death of Niall grandson of Muircertach.
'Twas great delight, 'twas great ease to be in the company of my dear foster-son,
When with the son of Eochaid—'twas no small thing! we used to go to the gathering.

They say, however, that grief for Niall carried off Torna.

By a man of Leinster, then, Niall was killed.   Whence is said:

[1] See p. 509.

Niall, Eochaid's son, great in fight—Erin and Scotland are in affliction:
He through whom a swift Saxon arrow was put by Eochaid, son of
glorious Enna.

That is the Death of Niall son of Eochaid, and of Laidcenn
son of Bairchid, by the hand of Eochaid son of Enna Cennselach.

THE DEATH OF MUIRCERTACH MAC ERCA

Muircertach mac Erca, according to the Irish annals, was high-king of Ireland during the first half of the sixth century. The story here related is rich in details that throw light on the early social history of Ireland. Notice, for example, Muircertach's prophetic dream, the fear of having one's name uttered, the account of the standards of Tyrconnel and Tyrone, the blood-covenant, the magic powers of the enchantress Sin, the practice of beheading foes and placing their heads on stakes, the washing of corpses in a river, and women going to battle. Like "The Adventures of Art Son of Conn" (p. 491), the story tells of the machinations of a supernatural woman who fascinates a mortal and involves him in difficulties. It also illustrates the introduction of ecclesiastical elements into pagan heroic tales, and a special point is made of the conflict between pagan and Christian ideals. The writer shows considerable skill in building up the climax which leads to the death of the unfortunate king. Though relatively late, the story is certainly older than the twelfth century.

When Muircertach son of Muiredach [1] King of Ireland, was in the palace of Cletech, on the bank of Boyne of the Brug—and he had a wife, Duaibsech daughter of Duach Brazentongue King of Connacht —that king came forth one day to hunt on the border of the Brug, and his hunting companions left him alone on his hunting mound.

He had not been there long when he saw a solitary damsel beautifully formed, fair-headed, bright-skinned, with a green mantle about her, sitting near him on the turf mound; and it seemed to him that of womankind he had never beheld her equal in beauty and refinement; and all his body and his nature filled with love for her, for gazing at her it seemed to him that he would give the whole of Ireland for one night's loan of her, so utterly did he love her at first sight. And he welcomed her as if she were known to him, and he asked tidings of her.

"I will tell thee," she said. "I am the darling of Muircertach mac Erca, King of Erin, and to seek him I came here."

That seemed good to Muircertach, and he said to her, "Dost thou know me, O damsel?"

[1] Muircertach, like Conchobar of Ulster (p. 132) and other early Irish kings, was named, not for his father, but for his mother. His mother's name was Erc.

"I do," she answered; "for skilled am I in places more secret than this, and known to me art thou and the other men of Erin."

"Wilt thou come with me, O damsel?" said Muircertach.

"I would go," she answered, "provided my reward be good."

"I will give thee power over me, O damsel," said Muircertach.

"Thy word for this!" rejoined the damsel.

And he gave it at once and she sang this song:

> This is power that is opportune,
> But for the teachings of the clerics, etc.

"I will give thee a hundred of every herd, and a hundred drinking-horns, and a hundred cups, and a hundred rings of gold, and a feast every other night in the house of Cletech."

"Nay," said the damsel; "not so shall it be. But my name must never be uttered by thee, and Duaibsech, the mother of thy children, must not be in my sight, and clerics must never enter the house that I am in."

"All this shalt thou have," said the king, "for I pledged thee my word; but it would be easier for me to give you half of Ireland. And tell me truly," said the king, "what name is thine, so that we may avoid it by not uttering it."

And she said, "Sigh, Sough, *Sin* (Storm), Rough Wind, Winter-Night, Cry, Wail, Groan."

So then he uttered this lay:

> Tell me thy name, O damsel,
> Thou most beloved, starbright lady, etc.

Each of these things was promised to her, and thus he pledged himself. Then they went together to the house of Cletech. Good was the arrangement of that house, and good were its household and staff, and all the nobles of the Clan of Niall, cheerfully and spiritedly, gaily and gladly consuming the tribute and wealth of every province in the trophy-decorated house of Cletech above the brink of the salmon-filled, ever-beautiful Boyne, and over the border of the green-topped Brug.

Now when Sin saw the house with its household she said, "Good is the house we have come to!"

"Good it is," said the king; "and never has there been built for Tara or for Naas or for the Craeb Ruad or for Emain Macha or for

Ailech Neit or for Cletech a house the like of it. And give thou testimony as to this house," said the king.

So she said:

> Never has been built by a king over flood
> A house like thy home above the Boyne, etc.

"What shall be done here now?" demanded the damsel.

"That which thou desirest," replied Muircertach.

"If so," said Sin, "let Duaibsech and her children leave the house, and let a man of every craft and art in Ireland come with his wife into the drinking-hall."

Thus it was done, and each began praising his own craft and art, and a stave was made by every craftsman and artist who was therein:

> Delightful, delightful the noble realm
> Of Erin's land, great is its rank, etc.

When the drinking was ended Sin said to Muircertach, "It is ˙ime now to leave the house to me, as hath been promised." Then she put the Clan of Niall, and Duaibsech with her children, forth out of Cletech; and this is their number, both men and women, two equally great and gallant battalions.

Duaibsech went with her children from Cletech to Tuilen, to seek her confessor the holy bishop Cairnech. When she got to Cairnech she uttered these words:

> O cleric, bless my body,
> I am afraid of death to-night, etc.

> Go thou thyself, O cleric, there
> To the children of Eogan and Conall, etc.

Thereafter Cairnech came to the Children of Eogan and Conall, and they went back together to Cletech, but Sin would not let them near the fortress. At this act the Clan of Niall were distressed and mournful. Then Cairnech was greatly angered, and he cursed the house, and made a grave for the king, and said, "He whose grave this is hath finished; and truly it is an end to his realm and his princedom!" And he went to the top of the grave, and said:

> The mound of these bells forever
> Henceforward everyone will know,
> The grave of the champion Mac Erca:
> Not slack have been his journeyings.
>
> A curse upon this hill,
> On Cletech with hundreds of troops!
> May neither its corn nor its milk be good,
> May it be full of hatred and evil plight!
>
> May neither king nor prince be in it,
> May no one come out of it victoriously!
> During my day I shall remember
> The King of Erin's grave in the mound.

So then Cairnech cursed the fortress and blessed a place therein, and then he came forth in grief and sorrow. And the Clan of Niall said to him, "Bless us now, O cleric, that we may go to our own country, for we are not guilty as regards thee."

Cairnech blessed them and left a grant to them, namely, to the Clan Conall and the Clan Eogan, that whenever they had not the leadership or the kingship of Ireland, their power should be over every province around them; and that they should have the succession of Ailech and Tara and Ulster; and that they should take no wage from any one, for this was their own inherent right, the kingship of Ireland; and that they should be without fetter or hostage, and that there should be decay upon the hostages if they absconded; and that they should gain victory in battle provided it was delivered for a just cause, and that they should have three standards, namely, the Cathach and the Bell of Patrick (*i.e.*, of the Bequest), and the Misach of Cairnech, and that the grace of these reliquaries should be on any one of them against battle, as Cairnech left to them, saying:

> My blessing on you till doomsday,
> O Clan of Niall wontedly, etc.

Each of them went into his own stronghold and his own good place.

Cairnech came on towards his monastery, and there met him great hosts, namely the descendants of Tadg son of Cian son of Ailill Olom. And they brought Cairnech with them to make their arrangement and their treaty with Muircertach mac Erca; and when the king was told of this, he came forth from his stronghold and bade them welcome.

But when Muircertach espied the cleric with them, there came a great blush upon him, and he exclaimed, "Why hast thou come to us, O cleric, after cursing us?"

"I have come," he answered, "to make peace between the descendants of Tadg son of Cian and the descendants of Eogan mac Neill."

Then a treaty was made between them, and Cairnech mingled the blood of both of them in one vessel, and wrote how they had made the treaty then. And Muircertach said to Cairnech:

> Go, thou cleric, afar,
> Be not near, against our will, etc.

Then when the treaty had been made, and when Cairnech had blessed them all, and left shortness of life and hell to him who should knowingly infringe the treaty, he quitted them and returned to his monastery. And the king went to his stronghold, and those hosts with him, to guard against the Clan of Niall. The king sat on his throne, and Sin sat on his right, and never on earth had there come a woman better than she in shape and appearance. The king looked on her, and sought knowledge and asked questions of her, for it seemed to him that she was a goddess of great power; and he asked her what was the power that she had. Thus he spoke and she answered:

Muircertach. Tell me, thou ready damsel,
             Believest thou in the God of the clerics?
             Or from whom hast thou sprung in this world?
             Tell us thy origin.

Sin.   I believe in the same true God
             Helper of my body against death's attack;
             Ye cannot work in this world a miracle
             Of which I could not work its like.
             I am the daughter of a man and a woman
             Of the race of Adam and Eve;
             I am fit for thee here,
             Let no regret seize thee.
             I could create a sun and a moon,
             And radiant stars:
             I could create men fiercely
             Fighting in conflict.
             I could make wine—no falsehood—
             Of the Boyne, as I can obtain it,

> And sheep of stones,
> And swine of ferns.
> I could make silver and gold
> In the presence of the great hosts:
> I could make famous men
> Now for thee.

"Work for us," said the king, "some of these great miracles." Then Sin went forth and arrayed two battalions equally great, equally strong, equally gallant; and it seemed to them that never came on earth two battalions that were bolder and more heroic than they, slaughtering and maiming and swiftly killing each other in the presence of every one.

"Seest thou that?" said the damsel; "indeed my power is in no wise a fraud."

"I see," said Muircertach, and he said:

> I see two battalions bold and fair
> On the plain in strife, etc.

Then the king with his household came into the fortress. When they had been a while seeing the fighting, some of the water of the Boyne was brought to them, and the king told the damsel to make wine of it. The damsel then filled three casks with water, and cast a spell upon them; and it seemed to the king and his household that never came on earth wine of better taste or strength. So of the fern she made fictitious swine of enchantment, and then she gave the wine and the swine to the host, and they partook of them until, as they supposed, they were sated. Furthermore she promised that she would give them forever and forever the same amount; whereupon Muircertach said:

> Hitherto never has come here
> Food like the food ye see, etc.

So the descendants of Tadg son of Cian, when the partaking of the magical feast was ended, kept watch over the king that night. When he rose on the morrow he was as if he were in a decline, and so was every one else who had partaken of the wine and the fictitious magical flesh which Sin had arranged for that feast. And the king said:

> O damsel, my strength has departed,
> My final burial has almost come, etc.

Then the king said to her, "Show us something of thy art, O damsel!"

"I will do so indeed," said she.

They fared forth, that is, Muircertach and all the hosts that were with him. Then Sin made of the stones blue men, and others with heads of goats; so that there were four great battalions under arms before him on the green of the Brug. Muircertach then seized his arms and his battle-dress and went among them like a swift, angry, mad bull, and forthwith took to slaughtering them and wounding them, and every man of them that he killed used to rise up after him at once. And thus he was killing them through the fair day till night. Though great were the rage and the wrath of the king, he was wearied thus, and he said:

> I see a marvel on that side,
> On the bushy pools of the river, etc.

So when the king was weary from fighting and smiting the hosts, he came sadly into the fortress, and Sin gave him magical wine and magical pig's flesh. And he and his household partook of them, and at the end he slept heavily until morning, and when rising on the morrow he had neither strength nor vigor. And he said:

> I am without strength, thou gentle lady, etc.
> Give, says the chaste cleric, etc.

As they were saying this, they heard the heavy shout of the hosts and the multitudes, calling Muircertach forth and challenging him to battle. Then in his presence in the Brug were two battalions equally great, to wit, blue men in one of the two and headless men in the other. Muircertach was enraged at the challenge of the hosts, and he rose up suddenly, but fell exhausted on the floor, and uttered the lay:

> A heavy shout, a noise which hosts make,
> A battalion of blue men to the north of us,
> Headless men who begin battle
> In the glen to the south of us.
> Weak is my strength: unto a host,
> 'Twas many times that I have brought victory;
> Great was the host, stark their division,
> Rude their name, rough their shout.

Then he went into the Brug and charged through the hosts, and took to slaughtering and maiming them long through the day. There came Sin to them and gave Muircertach kingship over them, and he rested from battling. And then the king fared forth to Cletech, and Sin formed two great battalions between him and the fortress. When he saw them he charged through them and began to do battle against them.

Now when he was delivering that battle, then Cairnech sent Masan and Casan and Cridan to seek him, so that he might have God's assistance, for the high saint knew of the oppression he suffered at that time. The clerics met him in the Brug, while he was hacking the stones and the sods and the stalks; and one of the clerics spoke and Muircertach answered:

Cleric.   Wherefore dost thou fell the stones,
             O Muircertach, without reason?
             We are sad that thou art strengthless
             According to the will of an idolater working magic.

Muircertach. The cleric who attacked me,
             I came into conflict with him:
             I know not furthermore
             That the stones are not alive.

Cleric.   Put Christ's mysterious cross
             Now over thine eyes:
             Abate for a time thy furies:
             Wherefore dost thou fell the stones?

Then the soldier's royal wrath ceased, and his senses came to him, and he put the sign of the Cross over his face, and then he saw nothing there save the stones and sods of the earth. Then he asked tidings of the clerics, and said, "Why do you come?"

"We came," they answered, "to meet thy corpse, for death is near thee."

And he said:

> Why came ye from the church,
> O sons of full-melodious study? etc.

The clerics marked out a church there in the Brug, and told him to dig its trench in honor of the great Lord of the Elements. "It shall be done," said he. Then he began digging the trench, so that it was then for the first time that the green of the Brug was injured. And he was telling the clerics his own tidings, and making God a fervent repentance. He said:

> I give thanks to Mary's son,
> My wrath has ended here, etc.

> Since I came over sea to Erin,
> I remember the number of years,
> I have never been a day—lasting the fame—
> Without a hero's head and a triumph over him, etc.

> Two years I was east in Alba:
> I have killed my grandsire:
> I have brought a host there into troubles:
> By my deeds Lorn fell.

> Two years I was afterwards
> In kingship over Danes:
> There has been no night thereat
> Without the heads of two on stakes, etc.

Now after this confession the clerics blessed water for him, and he partook of the Body of Christ, and made to God a fervent repentance. And he told them to relate to Cairnech how he had made his confession and repentance. So then he said:

> Faithful, faithful, a poor body of clay,
> Remember, remember the form of the stag-beetles.

The clerics remained for that night in the church of the Brug, and the king went to Cletech and sat there at his lady's right hand. Sin asked him what had interrupted his combat on that day. "The clerics came to me," he answered, "and they put the sign of the Cross of Christ over my face, and then I saw nothing save fern and stone and puff-balls. And since there was no one there to fight me, I came away."

Then Sin spoke and Muircertach answered her:

Sin. Never believe the clerics,
For they chant nothing save unreason:
Follow not their unmelodious verses,
For they do not reverence righteousness.

Cleave not to the clerics of churches,
If thou desirest life without treachery:
Better am I as a friend here:
Let not repentance come to thee.

Muircertach.   I will be always along with thee,
               O fair damsel without evil plight;
               Likelier to me is thy countenance
               Than the churches of the clerics.

Then Sin beguiled his mind and came between him and the teachings of the clerics, and on that night she made a magical wine for the king and his troops. The seventh night she was at her magic, on the eve of Wednesday after Samain (Hallowe'en) precisely. When the hosts were intoxicated there came the sigh of a great wind. "This is 'the sigh of a winter-night,'" said the king.

And Sin said:

> 'Tis I am Rough-Wind, Sin, a daughter of fair nobles:
> Winter-night is my name, for every place together.

> Sigh and Wind: Winter-Night so, etc.

And then she caused a great snow-storm there; and never had come a noise of battle that was greater than the shower of thick snow that poured there at that time, and from the northwest precisely it came. Then the king came forth and went into the house again, and began reproaching the storm; and he said:

> Evil is the night tonight,
> Never came one equally bad, etc.

When the feasting ended, then the hosts lay down, and in no one of them was the strength of a woman in childbed. Then the king lay down on his couch, and a heavy sleep fell upon him. Then he made a great screaming out of his slumber and awoke from his sleep.

"What is that?" said the damsel.

"A great host of demons has appeared to me," he answered; whereupon he said:

> A Form of red fire has appeared to me, etc.

> The house of Cletech as a fatal fire,
> Round my head blazing forever,
> The Clan of Niall in wrongful suffering
> Through the spells of witches, etc.

> The cry of a mighty host under red fire;
> This is what has appeared to me.

The king rose up, for the vision which he beheld did not let him sleep, and he came forth out of the house, and in the little church of the Brug he saw a little fire by the clerics. He came to them and said, "There is neither strength nor vigor in me tonight." And he related his vision and his dream. "And it is hard," said he, "to show prowess tonight even though hosts of foreign enemies should attack me, because of the weakness in which we are and the badness of the night."

So then the clerics began instructing him. He came in at once and there he said:

> Full evil is this storm (*sin*) tonight
> To the clerics in their camp;
> They dare not ever sleep
> From the roughness of the night's storms.

Sin. Why sayest thou my name, O man,
> O son of Erc and Muiredach?
> Thou wilt find death—feast without disgrace—
> Sleep not in the House of Cletech.

Muircertach. Tell me, thou griefless lady,
> What number of the hosts shall fall by me?
> Hide it not from me, tell without commandment,
> What number will fall by my right hand?

Sin. No one will fall by thee on the floor,
> O son of Erc of the high rank:
> Thou, O king, hast surely ended:
> Thy strength has gone to naught.

Muircertach. A great defect is my being without strength,
> O noble Sin of many forms,
> Often have I killed a fierce warrior,
> Though tonight I am under oppression.

Sin. Many have fallen by thy effort,
> O son of Lorn's daughter!
> Thou hast brought a multitude of hosts to silence;
> Alas, that thou art in evil case!

"That is true, O damsel," said he; "death is nigh me; for it was foretold that my death and the death of Lorn my grandsire would be alike; for he did not fall in battle, but was burnt alive."

"Sleep then tonight," said the damsel, "and leave to me to watch thee and to guard thee from the hosts; and, if it is thy fate, the house will not be burnt over thee tonight."

"Truly there is coming with designs upon us Tuathal Maelgarb son of Cormac Caich son of Cairbre son of Niall of the Nine Hostages."

"Though Tuathal with all his hosts be coming with designs upon thee, have thou no fear of him tonight," said the damsel, "and sleep now."

Then he went into his bed and asked the damsel for a drink, and she cast a sleeping charm upon that deceptive wine, so that when he drank a draught of it, it made him drunk and feeble, without sap or strength. Then he slept heavily and he saw a vision, to wit, that he went in a ship to sea, and his ship foundered, and a taloned griffin came to him and carried him into her nest, and then he and the nest were burnt, and the griffin fell with him.

The king awoke and ordered his vision to be taken to his foster-brother Dub Da Rinn son of the druid Saignen, and Dub Da Rinn gave him the meaning of it thus: "This is the ship wherein thou hast been, to wit, the ship of thy princedom on the sea of life, and thou steering it. This is the ship that foundered, and thy life is to come to an end. This is the taloned griffin that has carried thee into her nest, to wit, the woman that is in thy company, to make thee intoxicated, and to bring thee with her into her bed, and to detain thee in the house of Cletech so that it will burn over thee. Now the griffin that fell with thee is the woman who will die by reason of thee. This then is the significance of that vision."

The king then slept heavily after Sin had cast the sleep-charm upon him. Now while he was in that sleep Sin arose and arranged the spears and the javelins of the hosts in readiness in the doors and then turned all their points toward the house. She formed by magic many crowds and multitudes throughout the house and the sidewalls, and then she entered the bed.

It was then that the king awoke from his sleep.

"What is it?" asked the damsel.

"A host of demons has appeared to me, burning the house upon me and slaughtering my people at the door."

"Thou hast no hurt from that," said the damsel; "it only seemed so."

Now when they were thus in converse, they heard the crash of the burning house, and the shout of the host of demons and wizardry around it.

"Who is around the house?" asked the king.

Said Sin, "Tuathal Maelgarb son of Cormac Caich son of Niall of the Nine Hostages, with his armies. He is here taking vengeance on thee for the battle of Granard."

And the king knew not that this was untrue, and that no human host was surrounding the house. He arose swiftly and came to seek his arms, and found no one to answer him. The damsel went forth from the house, and he followed her at once, and he met a host in front of him, so that he went heavily through them. From the door he returned to his bed. The hosts thereupon went forth, and no one of them escaped without wounding or burning.

Then the king came again towards the door, and between him and it were the embers and hails of fire. When the fire had filled the doorway and all the house around and he found no shelter for himself, he got into a cask of wine, and therein he was drowned, as he went under it every second time for fear of the fire. Then the fire fell on his head, and five feet of his length was burnt; but the wine kept the rest of his body from burning.

The day after, when the morning came, the clerics Masan and Casan and Cridan came to the king and carried his body to the Boyne and washed it. Cairnech also came to him and made great grief in bewailing him, and said, "A great loss to Ireland today is Mac Erca, one of the four best men that have gained possession of Erin without trickery and without force, namely, Muircertach mac Erca, Niall of the Nine Hostages, Conn the Hundred-Fighter, and Ugaine Mor." And the body was lifted up by Cairnech, to be carried to Tuilen and there interred.

Then Duaibsech, the wife of Muircertach, met the clerics while the corpse was among them, and she made a great, mournful lamentation, and struck her palms together, and leaned her back against the ancient tree in Anach Reil; and a burst of gore broke from her heart in her breast, and straightway she died of grief for her husband. Then the clerics put the queen's corpse along with the corpse of the king. And then said Cairnech:

> Duaibsech, Mac Erca's noble wife,
> Let her grave be dug by you here, etc.

And then the queen was buried and her grave was made. The king was buried near the church on the north side, and Cairnech declared the king's character and uttered this lay:

> The grave of the King of Ailech will abide forever,
> In Tuilen, every pine will hear it, etc.

When the clerics had finished the burial they saw coming toward them a solitary woman, beautiful and shining, robed in a green mantle with its fringe of golden thread. A smock·of priceless silk was about her. She reached the place where the clerics were and saluted them, and so the clerics saluted her. And they perceived upon her an appearance of sadness and sorrow and they recognized that she it was that had ruined the king. Cairnech asked tidings of her and said:

> Tell us thy origin,
> O damsel, without darkening;
> Thou hast wrought our shame,
> Though beauteous is thy body:
> Thou hast killed the King of Tara,
> With many of his households,
> By an awful, evil deed, etc.

Then the clerics asked her who she herself was, or who was her father or her mother, and what cause she had from the king that she should ruin him.

"Sin," she replied, "is my name, and Sige son of Dian son of Tren is my father. Muircertach mac Erca killed my father, my mother, and my sister in the Battle of Cerb on the Boyne, and also destroyed in that battle all the Old-Tribes of Tara and my fatherland." So then Cairnech said and Sin replied:

Cairnech. Say, oh Sin, a statement without question,
     Tell truly who was thy father, etc.

Sin.   Not dearer to thee was thy own father
     Than Muircertach descendant of Niall was to me, etc.

     Myself will die of grief for him,
     The high-king of the western world,
     And for the guilt of the sore tribulations
     That I brought on the sovereign of Erin.

     I made poison for him, alas!
     Which overpowered the king of the noble hosts, etc.

Then she confessed to Cairnech, and to God she made fervent repentance, as was taught her, and she went in obedience to Cairnech, and straightway died of grief for the king. So Cairnech said that a grave should be made for her, and that she should be put under the sward of the earth. It was done as the cleric ordered, and he said·

> Sin: not dear were her doings
> Until this day in which we are, etc.

As for Cairnech, he showed great care for Muircertach's soul, but he did not bring it out of hell. Howbeit he composed a prayer which from its beginning is called *Parce mihi Domine* ("Spare me, O Lord"), etc., and he repeated it continually for the sake of the soul of the king. Whereupon an angel came to Cairnech and told him that whoever would sing that prayer continually would without doubt be a dweller in Heaven. So then said the angel:

> Whoever should sing strongly
> The prayer of Cairnech of the mysteries,
> 'Twould be enough to succor
> Judas, who was the worst ever born, etc.

So far the Death of Muircertach, as Cairnech related it, and Tigernach and Ciaran and Mochta and Tuathal Maelgarb; and it was written and revised by those holy clerics, commemorating it for every one from that time to this.

THE WOOING OF BECFOLA

"The Wooing of Becfola" is connected with Diarmuid, son of the well-known high-king Aed Slane, who flourished during the first half of the seventh century after Christ. In its present form the story appears to consist of confused reminiscences of humanly possible events colored by Irish fairy lore. The allusion to "bearded heroes" is to be explained by the fact that Dam Inis ("Ox Island"), in Loch Erne, associated with the famous Saint Molassa, was regarded as a sanctuary for women.

Diarmuid son of Aed Slane was in the sovereignty of Tara; Crimthann son of Aed was in fosterage with him, and in hostage-ship as a pledge from the Leinstermen. He and his pupil, *i.e.*, Crimthann, went one day to the Ford of Truim, of Ui Loegaire, and one servant with them. They saw a woman coming eastward over the ford in a chariot; she wore two blunt shoes of white bronze, two gems of precious stones in them, a tunic interwoven with red gold upon her, a crimson robe, a brooch of gold fully chased and set with gems of various colors in the robe over her bosom, a necklace of burnished gold around her neck, a diadem of gold upon her head, two black-grey steeds to her chariot, a yoke with trappings of silver upon them.

"Whence have you come, O woman?" said Diarmuid.

"Not very far," said she.

"Whither do you go?" said Diarmuid. "To seek seed-wheat," said she; "I have good soil and I require suitable seed."

"If it be the seed of this country you desire," said Diarmuid, "you shall not pass me."

"I do not object," said she, "if I get a reward."

"I will give you this little brooch," said Diarmuid.

"I will accept it," said she.

He brought her with him to Tara. "Who is this woman, O Diarmuid?" said they.

"She has not given me her name," said Diarmuid.

"What did you give as her bride-price?"

"My little brooch," said Diarmuid. "That is a *bec fola* ('small dowry')," said they. "Let Bec Fola be her name then," said the druid.

533

She, however, fixed her mind on Diarmuid's fosterling, *i.e.*, on Crimthann son of Aed, whom she continued to seduce and solicit for a long time. She at length prevailed upon the youth to come to meet her at Cluain Da Caileach at sunrise on Sunday in order to elope with her. When he told this to his people, they forbade him to run away with the wife of the high-king of Erin.

She rose early on Sunday morning from Diarmuid's side. "What is the matter, O woman?" said he.

"Not a good thing," said she; "some things of mine that are at Cluain Da Caileach, the servants have left and have fled away."

"What are the things?" said Diarmuid.

"Seven tunics with their garniture, and seven brooches of gold, and three diadems of gold, and it is a pity to let them be lost."

"Do not go," said Diarmuid, "on Sunday; a Sunday journey is not good." "Some one will go with me from this place," said she. "Not one of my servants," said Diarmuid.

She and her handmaid went then from Tara southward till they reached Dubthor in Leinster; she wandered about there for part of the night till wild dogs came and killed the handmaid, and she fled into a tree to avoid them.

When she was in the tree she saw a fire in the middle of the wood. She went to the fire, and saw a young warrior at the fire cooking a pig. He wore a garment of bright purple silk, with circlets of gold and silver, a diadem of gold and silver and crystal upon his head, bunches and weavings of gold around every lock of his hair reaching down to the tips of his two shoulders, two balls of gold upon the two plaits of his hair, each of them as large as a man's fist; his gold-hilted sword upon his girdle, and his two flesh-mangling spears in the leather of his shield, with bosses of white bronze upon it; he wore a many-colored cloak. His two arms were covered with bracelets of gold and silver up to his two elbows.

She went and sat with him at the fire. He looked at her, but paid no further attention to her until he had finished the cooking of the pig. He then made a pork roast, ate it, washed his hands, and went away from the fire; she followed him till they reached a lake.

A boat of bronze was in the middle of the lake. A cable of bronze was from the middle of the boat to the land, and another cable from it to the island which was in the middle of the lake. The warrior hauled in the boat; she entered it ahead of him; they left the boat in a boathouse of bronze on the island; and they went to a house with admirable carvings and beds. He sat down; she sat near him; and then he drew forth a dish with food for them. They both ate and drank, but so that neither of them became intoxicated. There was no other person in the house, and they were not interrupted. He went into his bed, and she lay under his garment, between him and the wall; he did not turn towards her. In the early morning they heard a call from the boathouse: "Come out, Flann, the men are here." He rose instantly, put on his armor, and went out; she followed him to the door of the house, and saw the three men at the boathouse. In features, age, and form, the three were like him. She then saw four other men moving along the island holding their shields down in their hands; the two groups then advanced against each other and fought until all the men were gory. When the fight was over, Flann came back again.

"The triumph of your valor to you," said she; "that was a heroic fight."

"It would be good, truly, if it were against enemies," said he.

"Who are the warriors?" said she. "One of them is my brother's son," said he; "the other three are my three brothers."

"What did you fight for?" said the woman.

"This island," said he.

"What is the name of the island?" said she.

"Inis Fedach Maic in Daill (*i.e.*, Dam Inis, 'Ox Island,' in Loch Erne)."

"And what is your name?" said she.

"Flann O' Fedach," said he; "it is the Ui Fedach who are fighting for it. The island is good; the dinner of one hundred men is supplied every evening. Since there were only two persons on it last night, there came but their supply."

"I ask," said she, "why should I not remain with you?"

"It would be a bad arrangement for you, indeed," said he, "to remain with me and to abandon the king of Erin, with the blame to be upon me and the vengeance to follow me."

"Why should we not dwell together?" said she.

"Let us not now," said he, "but if the island become mine, and

I alive, I will seek you, and you shall be my constant wife residing with me. But depart now for the present."

"I am grieved to leave my handmaid," said she.

"She is alive at the foot of the same tree," said he; "the calves of the island surrounded her and detained her to screen us." This was true.

She returned home and found Diarmuid there rising on the same Sunday. "It is well, O woman," said he, "that you have not journeyed on a Sunday against our command."

"I should not have dared to disobey your order," said she, just as if she had not gone at all. Her only word from that time forth was:

> I was a night in the wood
> In the house of Inis Maic in Daill:
> Though it was with a man, there was no sin,
> When we parted it was not early.

> Inis Fedach Maic in Daill,
> In the land of Leinster in Dubthor,
> Though it is near unto the road,
> Bearded heroes do not find it.

Every person wondered at these words. At the end of a year from that day, however, Diarmuid was upon his bed with his wife, Bec Fola, and they saw a wounded man passing the door of the house. It was then Bec Fola said:

> Superior in valor of fierce men, I ween,
> In the battle of Dam Inis,
> The four men who conquered
> The other four men in Dam Inis.

The wounded man, who was Flann, replied:

> O woman, cast not thy reproach
> Upon the heroes to disparage them;
> It was not manly valor that vanquished them,
> But men with charms on their spears.

Said she, "I cannot help disparaging the valor of the men, because it was Flann that was wounded in the conflict of the eight," and so she went away out of the house after Flann to his own abode.

"Let her depart," said Diarmuid, "the evil one; for we know not whither she goes or whence she comes."

While they were conversing, they saw four ecclesiastical students coming into the house. "What is this?" said Diarmuid, "the clerics travelling on Sunday!" Thus saying, he drew his cloak over his head so that he might not see them at all.

"It is by order of our superior we travel," said the ecclesiastical students, "not for our pleasure. Molassa of Dam Inis sent us to confer with you. A farmer of the people of Dam Inis, while herding his cows this morning, saw four armed men with their shields slung down traversing the island; he then saw four other men coming against them: they struck each other so that the clashing of the shields was heard all over the island during the conflict, till they all fell but one wounded man who alone escaped.

"Molassa buried the other seven; they left, moreover, all that two of us could carry of gold and silver, which was upon their garments, and upon their necks, and upon their shields, and upon their spears, and upon their swords, and upon their hands, and upon their tunics. We have come to ascertain thy share of that gold."

"Not so," said Diarmuid; "what God has sent to him, I will not participate in. Let him take possession of it." This was true.

It was with this silver now, and with this gold, Molassa's treasures were ornamented, namely, his shrine and his minster and his crozier. Bec Fola, however, went off with Flann O'Fedach, and she has not since returned. That is the courtship of Bec Fola.

HOW RONAN SLEW HIS SON

The following tale is older than the twelfth-century manuscript in which it first appears; yet it is clearly not as ancient as the historical period in which the scene is laid. The Ronan of our story is evidently identical with Ronan mac Colmain, king of Leinster, who, according to the annals, died about A.D. 610. According to the same authority, Eochaid king of Dunseverick, who figures in the story as the father-in-law of Ronan, did not die until half a century later. The suspicion that we are dealing here with romantic fiction rather than with historical facts is confirmed by the obvious similarity between our story and the Greek myth of Phaedra and Hyppolitus. Both the Irish tale and the Greek myth not only contain the theme of the young step-mother's love for her handsome step-son and the father's jealousy and revenge, but also correspond in matters of detail; Mael Fothartaig resembles Hyppolitus in being a mighty hunter who roams the forest and regards his hounds as his most precious possessions. It is by no means improbable that the Greek story found its way into Ireland and became attached to the royal family of Leinster.

A famous king was over Leinster, even Ronan son of Aed. And Ethne daughter of Cumascach son of Eogan of the Deisi of Munster was by his side. She bore a son to him, Mael Fothartaig son of Ronan, a son the most famous that ever came into Leinster. In his honor all would rise at gatherings and campings and games and fairs and fights and shooting contests. He was the desire of all their maidens and the darling of all their young women, Mael Fothartaig.

His mother died. For a long while Ronan was without a wife. "Why do you not take a wife?" said his son. "You were better with a wife by your side."

"I am told," said Ronan, "Eochaid, the king of Dunseverick in the north, has a fair daughter."

"Truly, you are not a mate for a girl," said the youth. "Will you not take a sedate woman? That would be more fitting than a little skittish thing of a girl."

It was impossible to hinder him. Ronan went and slept with her in the north, and brought her home with him. But Mael Fothartaig went on a journey in the south of Leinster.

She came down from the north. "Where is your son, Ronan?" said she; "I am told you have a good son."

"I have indeed," said Ronan, "a son the best there is in Leinster."

"Then let him be summoned to me that he may receive me and that he may receive my people and my treasures and my jewels."

"He shall come indeed," said Ronan.

Then Mael Fothartaig came and made great welcome to her. "You shall have love," said the youth. "Whatever we shall get of jewels and treasures for loving Ronan, it shall go to you."

"I am well pleased," said she, "that you should act for my advantage."

A fair young woman was in attendance on her. The queen sent her forthwith to Mael Fothartaig to solicit him, but the young woman dared not give the message lest Mael Fothartaig should kill her. Then the queen vowed to her that she would strike off her head unless she spoke. Mael Fothartaig was playing a game of chess with his two foster-brothers, Donn and Congal, the two sons of his foster-father. They were always about him. The young woman drew near them and began playing chess with them. Then she attempted to give the message but she dared not. She blushed, and the men noticed it. Mael Fothartaig went away.

"What is it that you want to say?" Congal said to the woman.

"It is not I that want it," said she, "but the daughter of Eochaid would like to have Mael Fothartaig as a lover."

"Do not say it, woman," said Congal. "You will be dead if Mael Fothartaig hears it. However, I will deal with Mael Fothartaig on your own behalf, if you wish it."

The young woman told the queen: "I am well pleased," said she, "for you will dare to say the message if you lie with him yourself. And you shall deal with him on my behalf thereafter."

It was done. The young woman slept with Mael Fothartaig.

"Well, now," said the queen, "you still do not plead for me with him. You would like better to have that man for yourself alone. You shall die then by my hand."

One day the young woman turned to Mael Fothartaig weeping. "What ails you, woman?" said he.

"The daughter of Eochaid is threatening to kill me," said she, "for my not pleading with you that she may meet with you."

"A likely story!" said he. "It was not bad of you that you have taken a safeguard. Woman," he said, "if I were thrust into a fiery

coal-pit that would make ashes and dust of me three times, I
would not meet with the wife of Ronan, though all should blame
me for it. I will go away, to avoid her." Thereupon he went with
fifty warriors into Scotland. He found great welcome with the
king of Scotland. He had hounds for hares, hounds for boars,
hounds for deer. Bur Doilin and Daithlenn, two hounds of Mael
Fothartaig, would kill every quarry in turn before them. Every
host that was routed before the king of Scotland, and every fight
that was won, it was the doing of Mael Fothartaig.

"What is this, O Ronan?" said the men of Leinster. "Did you
send Mael Fothartaig out of the land? You shall die by us unless
he return."

This news was brought to Mael Fothartaig, and he came back
from Scotland. This is where he chanced to come from the east,
to Dunseverick. Great welcome was made for him. "You do wrong,
Mael Fothartaig," said Eochaid, "that you do not go with our
daughter. To you we gave her, and not to yon old churl, Ronan."

"Bad is that indeed," said Mael Fothartaig. He went to Leinster and they gave him a great welcome. The same young woman
slept with him. "I must have that man from you," said the
daughter of Eochaid to her attendant, "or death upon your head!"

The queen's attendant told Mael Fothartaig. "What shall I do
in this matter, Congal?" said Mael Fothartaig.

"Give me a reward for it," said Congal, "and I will keep the
woman off you so that she shall no longer think of you."

"You shall have my horse with its bridle, and my clothing,"
said Mael Fothartaig.

"Nought will I take," said Congal, "save thy two hounds, so
that they shall be in my entire possession."

"You shall have them," said Mael-Fothartaig.

"Go then to-morrow," said Congal, "and hunt at the 'Cows of
Aife.'" The "Cows of Aife" are stones which are on the side of
the mountain. They are like white cows from afar. "Go and hunt
there. And the woman shall send her mistress to a tryst with us,
and I will put her from you."

"It shall be done," said her mistress to her.

It seemed long to her till morning. On the morrow they went to
the tryst, and saw Congal before them. "Whither away, harlot?"
he said. "You can be about no good walking about alone, or about

anything unless coming to a tryst with a man. Go home," he said, "and take a curse." Congal went with her to her house. And they saw her coming towards them once more. "Is it thus," said Congal, "you want to disgrace the king of Leinster, you vile woman! If I see you again, I shall take your head and put it on a stake before the face of Ronan. A bad woman to disgrace him in ditches and brakes going alone to meet a lad." He laid a horse-whip on her and left her in her house.

"I will spout a jet of blood in your face," said she.

Ronan came home. Mael Fothartaig's men came into the house before him. He stayed alone outside hunting. "Where is Mael Fothartaig to-night, Congal?" said Ronan.

"He is out doors," said Congal.

"Woe is me, my son to be abroad alone, and the number to whom he gives good things!"

"You have made us deaf with talking about your son," said his wife.

"It is right to talk of him," said Ronan. "For there is not in Ireland a son better according to the wish of his father. For his jealousy on my behalf is the same both with men and women at Ath Cliath and at Clar Daire Moir and at Drochet Cairbri as if it were for his own soul, so that there is ease for me and for you, woman," said Ronan.

"Truly," she said, "he shall not get from me the ease that he wishes, even to meet with me to your dishonor. I shall not be alive withstanding him any longer. Congal has taken me to him three times since morning, so that I with difficulty escaped from his hands."

"Malediction on your lips, you bad woman!" said Ronan. "It is false."

"You will see a proof of it now," said she. "I will sing half a quatrain to see whether it will fit with what Mael Fothartaig will sing." He used to do this every night to please her. He would sing one half quatrain, she would sing the other half.

He came in then and was drying his shins at the fire, and Congal by his side. His jester Mac Glass was at his games on the floor of the house. Then Mael Fothartaig said, for the day was cold:

> It is cold against the whirlwind
> For any one herding the cows of Aife.

"Hear this, Ronan," said she. "Sing that again," said she.

> It is cold against the whirlwind
> For any one herding the cows of Aife.

Said she:

> It is a vain herding,
> With no kine, with no lover to meet.

(That is, "neither did I come, nor did you take the cows with you.")

"It is true this time," said Ronan. There was a warrior by Ronan's side, Aedan son of Fiachna Lara. "O Aedan," said he, "a spear into Mael Fothartaig, and another into Congal!" When Mael Fothartaig had turned his back to them by the fire, Aedan planted the spear in him, so that he put its points through him, as he was on his seat. As Congal rose Aedan thrust a spear into him, so that it passed through his heart. The jester jumped up. Aedan sent a spear after him so that t brought his bowels out.

"You have wrought enough on the men, O Aedan!" said Mael Fothartaig from his seat.

"It was your luck," said Ronan, "that you found no woman to solicit but my wife."

"Wretched is that falsehood, O Ronan," said the youth, "which has been put on you to kill your only son without guilt. By your rank and by the tryst to which I go, the tryst with death, not greater is my guilt to think of meeting with her than that I should meet with my mother. But she has been soliciting me since she came into this land, and Congal has taken her back three times to-day that she might not meet me. There was no guilt in Congal that you should kill him." Then a raven carried the bowels of the jester on to the front-bridge . . . of the stronghold. The churls were laughing. Mael Fothartaig thought it a villainy. He said:

> O Mac Glass,
> Gather your bowels in,
> Though you know no shame,
> Churls are laughing at you.

Thereafter the three died. They were taken into a house apart. Ronan went and sat at the head of his son three days and three nights. But Donn, Mael-Fothartaig's foster-brother, Congal's brother, went with twenty horsemen to Dunseverick. They decoyed Eochaid to come to the border of the land, as it were to meet Mael Fothartaig that had eloped with his daughter. And they took his head and the heads of his son and of his wife.

Then said Ronan, sitting at the head of his son:

> It is cold against the whirlwind
> For any one herding the cows of Aife.
> That is a vain herding,
> With no cows, with no one to love.
>
> Cold is the wind
> In front of the warriors' house:
> They were dear warriors
> That were between me and the wind.
>
> Sleep, daughter of Eochaid,
> Great is the bitterness of the wind:
> Woe is me, Mael Fothartaig
> Is slain for the guilt of a lustful woman.
>
> Sleep, daughter of Eochaid,
> There is no rest for me though thou sleep not,
> To see Mael Fothartaig
> In his shirt full of blood.

The daughter of Eochaid said:

> Woe is me, O corpse in the corner,
> That wast the mark of many eyes,
> The sin that we committed,
> It was thy torment after thy banishment.

Ronan said:

> Sleep, daughter of Eochaid,
> Men are not mad:
> Though thou hast wetted thy mantle,
> It is not my son thou dost bewail.

Then came Donn and threw the head of Eochaid on his daughter's breast, and her mother's head and her brother's head.

Thereupon she arose and threw herself on to her knife, so that it came out through her back.

Then said Ronan:

> Eochaid has got but one shirt
> After having been in a mantle:
> The sorrow that is on Dun Ais
> Is on Dunseverick.

Give ye food, give drink
To the hound of Mael Fothartaig,
The hound of the man that would give food
To any one, whatever reward he might get.

Sad to me is the torture of the hound Dathlenn,
With rods of steel over her sides,
Our reproach is not on her,
It is not she who sold our dear ones.

. . . .

The men, the youths, the horses,
That were around Mael Fothartaig,
They would not envy any one's cheer,
While their chief was alive.

The men, the youths, the horses,
That were around Mael-Fothartaig,

. . . .

They would run a race of steeds.

The men, the youths, the horses,
That were around Mael Fothartaig,
Many a time they would set up
Triumphant shouts after lasting victories.

The men of Mael Fothartaig,
I allow that they were not insignificant;
Not well they stood by a man
Who would come when they needed him.

My son Mael Fothartaig,
Whose abode was the tall forest,
Kings and royal princes
Would not part from him without great respect.

My son Mael Fothartaig
Traversed Scotland of coasts:
He was a warrior among hosts of warriors,
When he would achieve his deeds on them.

My son Mael-Fothartaig,
He was the support of the host:
The white tall flashing salmon
Hath taken a cold dwelling.

Then the men of Leinster around Ronan began keening. Ronan
was thrown on his back. Mael Fothartaig's two sons, Aed and
Mael Tuile, set out after Aedan and seized him. Aed wounded

him and riddled him with a spear. "Let me get up, warriors," said
Ronan, "unless you wish to kill me. Is the man dead?" said he.

"Dead indeed," said the warriors.

"Who killed him?" said he.

"Aed slew him," said the warriors.

"Did Mael Tuile wound him?" said he.

"No," said the warriors.

"May he not wound a man till Doom!" said he. "But the palm
of prowess and of valor to the boy that slew him."

Then said Ronan:

> It is a great thing
> For the son of a churl to slay the son of a king;
> That was clear on his day of death
> To Aedan, son of Fiachna Lara.

Then the fight was carried near him up to the front of the house,
and he said:

> This battle on the plain
> I await without Mael Fothartaig:
> Awaiting the new fight,
> He does not support the old champion.

At that a spout of blood broke over his lips and he died forthwith.
That is how Ronan slew his son.

STORIES OF MONGAN

With the stories of Mongan we come upon an unusually puzzling phase of Irish literature. The characters of Mongan and Manannan mac Lir may have had a very early origin, but they appear to enjoy their greatest popularity in the later texts. They seem to belong to an age when people were more interested in getting the explanations of things than they were in simple narrative for its own sake. Little is definitely known about the original date of this material, but it seems certainly to be later than the beginning of the cycle of Finn. Its preoccupation with the bizarre and complicated is not necessarily an indication of a late date, but the fact may be significant that the demonstrably earlier texts seem to have no knowledge of the characters here involved. Mongan, as well as Mannanan, is regarded by many as a sort of Adonis-like divinity who has much in common with Angus of the Brug. In neither case, however, is the evidence for an originally divine character absolutely conclusive. That Mongan was looked upon as a reincarnation of the famous Finn mac Cumaill (p. 355) is clear enough from the texts preserved.

THE BIRTH OF MONGAN

Fiachna Lurga, the father of Mongan, was sole king of the province. He had a friend in Scotland, to wit, Aedan, the son of Gabran. A message went from him to Aedan. A message went from Aedan to him asking him to come to his aid. He was in warfare against the Saxons. A terrible warrior was brought by them to accomplish the death of Aedan in the battle. Then Fiachna went across, leaving his queen at home.

While the hosts were fighting in Scotland, a noble-looking man came to his wife in his stronghold in Rathmore of Moylinny. At the time he went, there were not many in the stronghold. The stranger asked the woman to arrange a place of meeting. The woman said there were not in the world possessions or treasures, for which she would do anything to disgrace her husband's honor. He asked her whether she would do it to save her husband's life. She said that if she were to see him in danger and difficulty, she would help him with all that lay in her might. He said she should do it then, "for thy husband is in great danger. A terrible man has been brought against him, and he will die by his hand. If we,

546

thou and I, make love, thou wilt bear a son thereof. That son will
be famous; he will be Mongan. I shall go to the battle which will
be fought to-morrow at the third hour, so that I shall save Fiachna,
and I shall vanquish the warrior before the eyes of the men of
Scotland. And I shall tell thy husband our adventures, and that
it is thou that hast sent me to his help."

It was done thus. When army was drawn up against army, the
hosts saw a noble-looking man before the army of Aedan and
Fiachna. He went towards Fiachna in particular, and told him the
conversation with his wife the day before, and that he had promised
to come to his help at that hour. Thereupon he went before the
army towards the other, and vanquished the warriors, so that
Aedan and Fiachna won the battle.

And Fiachna returned to his country, and the woman was
pregnant and bore a son, even Mongan son of Fiachna. And he
thanked his wife for what she had done for him, and she confessed
all her adventures. So that this Mongan is a son of Manannan
mac Lir, though he is called Mongan son of Fiachna. For when
the stranger went from her in the morning he left a quatrain with
Mongan's mother, saying:

> I go home,
> The pale pure morning draws near:
> Manannan son of Lir
> Is the name of him who came to thee.

A STORY OF MONGAN

Now once upon a time when Forgall the poet was with Mongan,
the latter at a certain hour of the day went before his stronghold,
where he found a bardic scholar learning his lesson. Said Mongan:

> All is lasting
> In a cloak of sackcloth;
> In due course thou shalt attain
> The end of thy studies.

Mongan then took pity on the scholar, who was in the cloak of
sackcloth. He had little of any substance. In order to know
whether he would be a truthful and good messenger, he said to
him: "Go now, until thou reach the fairy-mound of Lethet Oidni,
and bring a precious stone which I have there, and for thyself take

a pound of white silver, in which are twelve ounces. Thou shalt have help from them. This is thy journey from here, to Cnocc Bane. Thou wilt find welcome in the fairy-mound of Cnocc Bane for my sake. Thence to Duma Granerit. Thence to the fairy-mound of Lethet Oidni. Take the stone for me, and go to the stream of Lethet Oidni, where thou wilt find a pound of gold, in which are nine ounces. Take that with thee for me."

The scholar went on his journey. In the fairy-mound of Cnocc Bane he found a noble-looking couple to meet him. They gave great welcome to a messenger of Mongan's. It was his due. He went further. He found another couple in Duma Granerit, where he had the same welcome. He went to the fairy-mound of Lethet Oidni, where again he found another couple. They gave great welcome to a man of Mongan's. He was most hospitably entertained, as on the other nights. There was a marvellous chamber at the side of the couple's house. Mongan had told him that he should ask for its key. He did so. The key was brought to him. He opened it. He had been told to take nothing out of the house except what he had been sent for. He did so. The key he gave back to the couple; his stone, however, and his pound of silver he took with him. Thereupon he went to the stream of Lethet Oidni, out of which he took his pound of gold. He went back to Mongan, to whom he gave his stone and his gold. He himself took his silver. These were his wanderings.

A STORY FROM WHICH IT IS INFERRED THAT MONGAN WAS FINN MAC CUMAILL

Mongan was in Rathmore of Moylinny in his kingship. To him went Forgall the poet. Through him many a married couple complained to Mongan. Every night the poet would recite a story to Mongan. So great was his lore that they were thus from Hallowe'en to May-day. He received gifts and food from Mongan.

One day Mongan asked his poet what was the death of Fothad Airgdech. Forgall said he was slain at Duffry in Leinster. Mongan said it was false. The poet said he would satirize him with his lampoons, and he would satirize his father and his mother and his grandfather, and he would sing spells upon their waters, so that fish should not be caught in their river-mouths. He would sing upon their woods, so that they should not give fruit, upon their plains, so that they should be barren for ever of any produce. Mongan promised him his will of precious things as far as the value of seven bondmaids, or twice seven bondmaids, or three times seven. At last he offered him one-third, or one-half of his land, or his whole land; at last anything save only his own liberty with that of his wife Breothigernn, unless he were redeemed before the end of three days. The poet refused all except as regards the woman. For the sake of his honor Mongan consented. Thereat the woman was sorrowful. The tear was not taken from her cheek. Mongan told her not to be sorrowful, help would certainly come to them.

So it came to the third day. The poet began to enforce his bond. Mongan told him to wait till evening. He and his wife were in their bower. The woman wept as her surrender drew near and she saw no help. Mongan said: "Be not sorrowful, woman. He who is even now coming to our help, I hear his feet in the Labrinne."

They waited a while. Again the woman wept. "Weep not, woman! He who is now coming to our help, I hear his feet in the Main."

Thus they were waiting between every two watches of the day. She would weep, and he would still say: "Weep not, woman. He who is now coming to our help, I hear his feet in the Laune, in Loch Leane, in the Morning-star River between the Ui Fidgente and the Arada, in the Suir on Mag Femin in Munster, in the Echuir, in the Barrow, in the Liffey, in the Boyne, in the Dee, in the Tuarthesc, in Carlingford Loch, in the Nid, in the Newry river, in the Larne Water in front of Rathmore."

When night came to them, Mongan was on his couch in his palace, and his wife at his right hand, and she sorrowful. The poet was summoning them by their sureties and their bonds. While they were there, a man was announced approaching the enclosure from the south. His cloak was in a fold around him, and in his hand a headless spear-shaft that was not small. By that shaft he leapt across the three ramparts, so that he landed in the middle of the enclosure, thence into the middle of the palace, thence between Mongan and the wall at his pillow. The poet was in the back of the house behind the king. The question was argued in the house before the warrior that had come.

"What is the matter here?" said he.

"I and the poet yonder," said Mongan, "have made a wager about the death of Fothad Airgdech. He said it was at Duffry in Leinster; I said that was false." The warrior said the poet was wrong.

"It shall be proved. We were with thee, with Finn," said the warrior.

"Hush!" said Mongan, "that is not fair."

"We were with Finn, then," said he. "We came from Scotland. We met with Fothad Airgdech yonder on the Larne river. There we fought a battle. I made a cast at him, so that the spear passed through him and went into the earth beyond him and left its iron head in the earth. Here is the shaft that was in that spear. The bare stone from which I made that cast will be found, and the iron head will be found in the earth, and the tomb of Fothad Airgdech will be found a little to the east of it. A stone chest is about him there in the earth. There, upon the chest, are his two bracelets of silver, and his two arm-rings, and his neck-torque of silver. And by his tomb there is a stone pillar. And on the end of the pillar that is in the earth there is an inscription in ogam. This is what it says: 'This is Eochaid Airgdech. Cailte [1] slew me in an encounter against Finn.' "

They went with the warrior. Everything was found thus. It was Cailte, Finn's foster-son, that had come to them. Mongan, however, was Finn, though he would not let it be told.

[1] A well-known character in the tales of Finn mac Cumaill and his band of warriors (p. 457).

THE VISION OF MAC CONGLINNE

This story stands almost alone as perhaps the only extended piece of vernacular narrative from the earlier Middle Ages that was composed expressly for humorous purposes. It is one of the wildest extravaganzas of all literature; in fact we find nothing quite so preposterous again until we come to Rabelais. The writer adopts the conventional literary form of those who wrote for religious edification, and composes an uproarious satire on hagiography, ecclesiastical mendicancy, and royal gluttony. In his higher moments he throws overboard his satirical purpose for the sake of his gastronomical cadenzas. The piece is at least as old as the twelfth century and perhaps even more ancient. The vigor of the burlesque spirit is closely akin to that in the "Feast of Bricriu" (p. 254), one of the earlier tales of the Ulster cycle.

The four things to be asked of every composition must be asked of this composition: the place, the person, the time, and the cause of invention.

The place of this composition is Great Cork of Munster, and its author is Anier mac Conglinne of the Onacht Glenowra. In the time of Cathal mac Finguine son of Cucengairm or son of Cucenmathir it was made. The cause of its invention was to banish the demon of gluttony that was in the throat of Cathal mac Finguine.

Cathal mac Finguine was a good king, who governed Munster; a great warrior prince was he. A warrior of this sort: with the edge of a hound, he ate like a horse. A demon of gluttony that was in his throat, used to devour his rations with him. A pig and a cow and a bull-calf of three hands, with three score cakes of pure wheat, and a vat of new ale, and thirty heath-poults' eggs, that was his first portion, besides another snack, until his great feast was ready for him. As for the great feast, that passes account or reckoning.

The reason of the demon of gluttony being in the throat of Cathal mac Finguine was that he had, though he had never seen her, a first love for Ligach daughter of Maelduin king of Ailech; and she sister to Fergal son of Maelduin, also king of Ailech, who was then contending for the kingship of Ireland against Cathal mac Finguine, as is plain from the quarrel of the two hags, when they had a duel in quatrains at Freshford.

Said the northern hag:

> He comes from the North, comes from the North,
> The son of Maelduin, over the rocks,
> Over Barrow's brink, over Barrow's brink,
> Till cattle he take he will not stay.

Said the southern hag:

> He shall stay, shall stay;
> He will be thankful if he escapes.
> By my father's hand, by my father's hand,
> If Cathal meets him, he'll take no cattle.

Then kernels and apples and many sweets used to be brought from Ligach, Maelduin's daughter, to Cathal mac Finguine, for his love and affection. Fergal son of Maelduin heard this, and his sister was called unto him. And he gave her a blessing if she should tell him truth, and a curse if she should deny him it. The sister told him; for great as was her love and affection for Cathal mac Finguine, she feared her brother's curse reaching her. Then she told the true story.

The brother told her to send the apples to himself. And a scholar was summoned unto him, and he promised great rewards to the scholar for putting charms in those numerous sweets, to the destruction of Cathal mac Finguine. And the scholar put charms and heathen spells in those numerous sweets, and they were delivered to Fergal, who despatched messengers to convey them to Cathal. And they entreated him by each of the seven universal things,—sun and moon, dew and sea, heaven and earth, day and night—that he would eat those apples, since it was out of love and affection for him they were brought from Ligach daughter of Maelduin.

Cathal thereupon ate the apples, and little creatures through the poison spells were formed of them in his inside. And those little creatures gathered in the womb of one animal, so that there was formed the demon of gluttony. And this is the cause why the demon of gluttony abode in the throat of Cathal mac Finguine, to the ruin of the men of Munster during three half-years; and it is likely he would have ruined Ireland in another half-year.

There were eight persons in Armagh, the greatest of Ireland's seats of piety and learning at that time, of whom these lays were sung:

I have heard of eight to-night
In Armagh after midnight;
I proclaim them with hosts of deeds,
Their names are no sweet symphonies.

Comgan was the name of the Two Smiths' son;
Famous was he after the hunt.
Critan was Rustang's noble son,
It was a full fitting name.

The Two Tribes' Dark One, a shining cry,
That was the name of Stelene's son.
Dun Raven, a white nun, of Beare;
Rough Derry was the name of Saman's son.

Never-Refused was Mac Conglinne's name,
From the brink of the sweet-crested Bann.
Wee Man, Wee Wife, bag of carnage,
Were Dead Man's sire and dam.

My King, King of high Heaven,
That givest hosts victory over death,
Great son of Mary,—Thine the way—
A confluence of cries I heard.

One of these eight, then, was Anier mac Conglinne, a famous
scholar he, with abundance of knowledge. The reason why he was
called Anier was that he would satirize and praise all. No wonder,
indeed; for there had not come before him, and came not after
him, one whose satire or praise was harder to bear, wherefore he was
called Anera (*i.e.*, Non-refusal), because there was no refusing him.

A great longing seized the mind of the scholar, to follow poetry,
and to abandon his studies. For wretched to him was his life in
the shade of his studies. And he searched in his mind whither he
would make his first poetical journey. The result of his search was,
to go to Cathal mac Finguine, who was then on a royal progress in
Iveagh of Munster. The scholar had heard that he would get
plenty and enough of all kinds of whitemeats; for greedy and
hungry for whitemeats was the scholar.

This came into the mind of the scholar on a Saturday eve exactly, at Roscommon; for there he was pursuing his reading. Then
he sold the little stock he possessed for two wheaten cakes and a
slice of old bacon with a streak across its middle. These he put
in his book-satchel. And on that night two pointed shoes of hide,
of seven-folded dun leather, he shaped for himself.

He arose early on the morrow, and tucked up his shirt over the rounds of his fork, and wrapped himself in the folds of his white cloak, in the front of which was an iron brooch. He lifted his book-satchel on to the arched slope of his back. In his right hand he grasped his even-poised knotty staff, in which were five hands from one end to the other. Then, going right-hand-wise round the cemetery, he bade farewell to his tutor, who put charms about him to protect him.

He set out on his way and journey, across the lands of Connacht into Aughty, to Limerick, to Carnarry, to Barna-tri-Carbad, into Sliab Keen, into the country of the Fir Fene, which is this day called Fermoy, across Moinmore, until he rested a short time before vespers in the guest-house of Cork. On that Saturday he had gone from Roscommon to Cork.

This was the way in which he found the guest-house on his arrival; it was open. That was one of the days of the three things, wind and snow and rain about the door; so that the wind left not a wisp of thatch, nor a speck of ashes that it did not sweep with it through the other door, under the beds and couches and screens of the princely house.

The blanket of the guest-house was rolled, bundled, in the bed, and was full of lice and fleas. No wonder, truly, for it never got its sunning by day, nor its lifting at night; for it was not wont to be empty when it was lifted. The bath-tub of the guest-house, with the water of the night before in it, with its stones, was by the side of the door-post.

The scholar found no one who would wash his feet. So he himself took off his shoes and washed his feet in that bath-tub, in which he afterwards dipped his shoes. He hung his book-satchel on the peg in the wall, took up his shoes, and gathered his hands into the blanket, which he tucked about his legs. But, truly, as numerous as the sand of the sea, or sparks of fire, or dew on a May morning, or the stars of heaven, were the lice and fleas nibbling his legs, so that weariness seized him. And no one came to visit him or do reverence to him.

He took down his book-satchel, and brought out his psalter, and began singing his psalms. What the learned and the books of Cork relate is, that the sound of the scholar's voice was heard a mile beyond the city, as he sang his psalms, through spiritual mysteries, in lauds, and stories, and various kinds, in dia-psalms and syn-psalms and sets of ten, with paters and canticles and hymns at the conclusion of each fifty. Now, it seemed to every man in Cork that the sound of the voice was in the house next himself. This came of original sin, and Mac Conglinne's hereditary sin and his own plain-working bad luck; so that he was detained without drink, without food, without washing, until every man in Cork had gone to his bed.

Then it was that Manchin, abbot of Cork, said, after having gone to his bed: "Lad," he said, "are there guests with us to-night?"

"There are not," said the attendant.

However, the other attendant said: "I saw one going hastily, impatiently across the green a short time before vespers, a while ago."

"You had better visit him," said Manchin, "and take him his ration. For he has been too lazy to come back for his allowance, and moreover the night was very bad." His allowance was brought out, and these were the rations that were taken to him: a small cup of the church whey-water, and two sparks of fire in the middle of a wisp of oaten straw, and two sods of fresh peat.

The servants came to the door of the guest-house, and fear and terror seized them at the gaping open pitch-dark house. They knew not whether anybody was within, or not; whereupon one of the two asked, in putting his foot across the threshold: "Is there any one here?" says he.

"There is some one," answered Mac Conglinne.

"It is a breaking of the spells that are on this house to put it in order for one man."

"If ever the spells on it were broken," said Mac Conglinne, "they were to-night; for their breaking was fated, and it is I who break them."

"Rise," said the attendant, "and eat your meal."

"I pledge my God's doom," said he, "that since I have been kept waiting till now, until I know what you have there, I shall not rise."

The gillie put the two sparks of fire that were in the middle of the wisp of oaten straw, on the hearth, and pulled another wisp from the bed. He arranged the two sods of fresh peat round the wisps, blew the spark, lighted the wisp, and showed him his repast; whereupon Mac Conglinne said:

> My lad,
> Why should not we have a duel in quatrains?
> You compose a quatrain on the bread,
> I will make one on the relish.
>
> Cork, wherein are sweet bells,
> Sour is its sand,
> Its soil is sand,
> Food there is none in it.
>
> Unto Doom I would not eat,
> Unless famine befell them,
> The oaten ration of Cork,
> Cork's oaten ration.
>
> Along with thee carry the bread,
> For which thou hast made thy orison;
> Woe to him who eats this ration;
> That is my say, my lad.

The attendant remembered the quatrains, for his understanding was sharp. They took the food back to the place where Manchin was, and recited the quatrains to the abbot.

"Well," said Manchin, ". . . Little boys will sing those verses unless the words are avenged on him who made them."

"What do you mean to do, then?" said the gillie.

"This," said Manchin; "to go to the person who made them, to strip him of all his clothes, to lay scourges and horsewhips on him, until his flesh and skin break and sever from his bones, only let his bones not be broken; to put him in the Lee and give him his fill of the muddy water of the Lee. Then let him be put into the guest-house, without a stitch of clothing." (And there was no clothing in that house but the blanket, in which lice and fleas were as plentiful as May dew.) "There let him sleep that night, in the most wretched and darkest plight he ever was in. Let the house be closed on him from outside until morning, in order that he may not escape, until my counsel together with the counsel of the monks of Cork shall be held on him to-morrow, in the presence of the Creator and of St. Barre, whose servant I am. Our counsel shall be no other than his crucifixion to-morrow, for the honor of me and of St. Barre, and of the Church."

So it was done. And then it was that his hereditary transgression and his own plain-working sin rose against Mac Conglinne. The whole of his clothing was stripped off him, and scourges and horse-whips were laid on him. He was put into the Lee, and had his fill of its dead water. After which he lay in the guest-house until morning.

Early at morn Manchin arose on the morrow; and the monks of Cork were gathered by him, until they were in one place, at the guest-house. It was opened before them, and they sat down on the bed-rails and couches of the house. "Well, you wretch," said Manchin, "you did not do right in reviling the Church last night."

"The church-folk did no better," said Mac Conglinne, "to leave me without food, though I was only a party of one."

"You would not have gone without food, even though you had only got a little crumb, or a drink of whey-water in the church. There are three things, about which there should be no grumbling in the Church,—new fruit, new ale, and Sunday eve's portion. For however little is obtained on Sunday eve, what is nearest on the morrow is psalm-singing, then bell-ringing, Mass, with preaching and the Sacrament, and feeding the poor. What was wanting on the eve of Sunday will be got on Sunday or on the eve of Monday. You began grumbling early."

"And I profess," said Mac Conglinne, "that I acted in humility, and there was more than enough in requital."

"But I vow before the Creator and St. Barre," said Manchin, "you shall not revile again. Take him away with you, that he may be crucified on the green, for the honor of St. Barre and of the Church, and for my own honor."

"O cleric," said Mac Conglinne, "let me not be crucified, but let a righteous, just trial be given to me, which is better than to crucify me."

Then they proceeded to give him a trial. Manchin began to plead against him, and every man of the monks of Cork proceeded, according to rank, against Mac Conglinne. But, though a deal of wisdom and knowledge and learning had they, lawfully he was not convicted on a point of speech for which he could be crucified. Then was he taken without law to Rathin mac Aeda, a green in the southern quarter of Cork. He said: "A boon for me, O Manchin, and you monks of Cork!"

"Is it to spare you?" asked Manchin.

"That is not what I ask," said Mac Conglinne, "though I should be glad if that would come of it."

"Speak," said Manchin.

"I will not speak," said Mac Conglinne, "until I have pledges for it." Pledges and bonds stout and strong were imposed on the monks of Cork for its fulfilment, and he bound them upon his pledges.

"Say what it is you want," said Manchin.

"I wish," said Anier mac Conglinne: "to eat the viaticum that is in my book-satchel before going to death, for it is not right to go on a journey without being shriven. Let my satchel be given to me." His satchel was brought to him, and he opened it, and took out of it the two wheaten cakes and the slice of old bacon. And he took the tenth part of each of the cakes, and cut off the tenth of the bacon, decently and justly. "Here are tithes, you monks of Cork," said Mac Conglinne. "If we knew the man who has better right, or who is poorer than another, to him would we give our tithes."

All the paupers that were there rose up on seeing the tithes, and reached out their hands. And he began looking at them, and said: "Verily before God," said he, "it can never be known if any one of you stands in greater need of these tithes than I myself. The journey of none of you was greater yesterday than mine—from Roscommon to Cork. Not a morsel or drop tasted I after coming. I had eaten nothing on the road, I did not find a guest's welcome on my arrival, but I received insult, you curs and robbers and dung-hounds, you monks of Cork! The whole of my clothing was stripped off me, scourges and horsewhips were laid on me, l was plunged into the Lee, and obvious injustice was practised upon me. Fair play was not given me. In the presence of the Maker," said Mac Conglinne, "it shall not be the first thing the fiend shall lay to my charge after going yonder, that I gave to you these tithes, for you deserve them not."

So the first morsel that he ate was his tithes, and after that he ate his meal—his two cakes, with his slice of old bacon. Then, lifting up his hands, and giving thanks to his Maker, he said: "Now take me to the Lee!" On that he was taken, bonds and guards and all, towards the Lee.

When he reached the well, the name of which is "Ever-full," he doffed his white cloak, and laid it out to be under his side, his book-satchel under the slope of his back. He let himself down upon his cloak, supine, put his finger through the loop of his brooch, and dipped the point of the pin over his back in the well. And while the drop of water trickled down from the end of the brooch, the brooch was over his breath. The men that guarded him and held him in bonds grew tired. "Your own treachery has come about you, you curs and robbers, you monks of Cork! When I was in my cell, what I used to do was to hoard what bits might reach me during five or six days, and then eat them in one night, drinking my fill of water afterwards. This would sustain me to the end of three days and three nights without anything else, and it would not harm me. I shall be three days and nights subsisting on what I ate just now, three days and nights more doing penance, and another three days and nights drinking water, for I have pledges in my hands. I vow to God and St. Barre, whose I am here," said Mac Conglinne, "though neither high nor low of the monks of Cork should leave the place where they are, but should all go to death in one night, and Manchin before all or after all, to death and hell, —since I am sure of Heaven, and shall be in the Presence, to which there is neither end nor decay."

This story was told to the monks of Cork, who quickly held a meeting, and the upshot of the meeting was that Mac Conglinne should have a blessing on his going in humility to be crucified, or else that nine persons should surround him to guard him until he died where he was, that he might be crucified afterwards. That message was delivered to Mac Conglinne. "It is a sentence of curs," said he. "Nevertheless, whatever may come of it, we will go in humility, as our Master, Jesus Christ, went to His Passion." Thereupon he rose, and went to the place where were the monks of Cork. And by this time the close of vespers had come.

"A boon for us, O Manchin!" said the monks of Cork themselves.

"O my God, what boon?" cried Manchin.

"Respite for that poor devil until morning. We have not tolled bells, neither have we celebrated Mass, nor preached, nor made the Offering. The poor have not been satisfied by us with food against the Sunday, nor have we refreshed ourselves. Grant us a respite for him till morning."

"I pledge my word," said Manchin, "that respite shall not be given, but the day of his transgression shall be the day of his punishment."

Ochone! in that hour Mac Conglinne was taken to the Foxes' Wood, and an axe was put in his hand, his guard being about him. He himself cut his passion-tree, and bore it on his back to the green of Cork. He himself fixed the tree. And the time had outrun the close of vespers, and the one resolve they had was to crucify him there and then. "A boon for me, O Manchin, and you monks of Cork!" said Mac Conglinne.

"I pledge my word," said Manchin, "that no boon shall come from us."

"It is not to spare me I ask you, for, though it were asked, it would not be granted to me of your free will, you curs and you robbers and dung-hounds and unlettered brutes, you shifting, blundering, hang-head monks of Cork! But I want my fill of generous juicy food, and of tasty intoxicating sweet ale, and a fine light suit of thin dry clothing to cover me, that neither cold nor heat may strike me; a gorging feast of a fortnight for me before going to the meeting with death."

"I vow to you," said Manchin, "you shall not get that. But it is now the close of the day; it is Sunday. The convent, moreover, are entreating a respite for thee. But your scanty clothing shall be stripped off you, and you shall be tied to yonder pillar-stone, for a fore-torture before the great torture to-morrow."

So it was done. His scanty clothing was stripped off him, and ropes and cords were tied across him to the pillar-stone.

They turned away home, Manchin going to the abbot's house, that the poor and guests might be fed by them. They also ate something themselves. But they left that sage Mac Conglinne to fast, who came, having been sent by God and the Lord for the salvation of Cathal mac Finguine and the men of Munster, and the whole Southern Half of Ireland to boot. The justice of law was not granted him. He remained there until midnight. Then an angel of God came to him on the pillar-stone, and began to manifest a vision unto him. As long as the angel was on the pillar-stone it was too hot for Mac Conglinne, but when he moved on a ridge away from him, it was comfortable. (Hence the "Angel's Ridge" in the green of Cork, which was never a morning without dew.) At the end of the night the angel departed from him. Thereupon he shaped a little rhyme of his own, which would serve to relate what had been manifested to him, and there he remained until morning with the poetical account of his vision ready.

Early at morn the chapter-bell was tolled on the morrow by the monks of Cork, and all came to the pillar-stone. "Well, you miserable wretch," said Manchin, "how is it with you to-day?"

"It is well," said he, "if I am allowed to make known to you a few short words that I have, for a vision appeared to me last night," said Mac Conglinne, "and, if a respite is given me, I will relate the vision."

"By my word, I say," declared Manchin, "if the race of Adam were of my thinking, they would not give you respite even for a day or a night. As for myself, I will not give it."

"We pledge our word," said the monks, "though it be disagreeable to you, O Manchin, he shall have a respite, that he may relate his vision. Inflict on him afterwards whatever you wish."

Then it was that he traced Manchin back to Adam, according to the pedigree of food, saying:

Bless us, O cleric, famous pillar of learning,
Son of honey-bag, son of juice, son of lard,
  Son of stirabout, son of pottage, son of fair speckled fruit-clusters,
Son of smooth clustering cream, son of buttermilk, son of curds,
  Son of beer (glory of liquors!), son of pleasant bragget,
Son of twisted leek, son of bacon, son of butter,
  Son of full-fat sausage, son of pure new milk,
Son of nut-fruit, son of tree-fruit, son of gravy, son of drippings,
  Son of fat, son of kidney, son of rib, son of shoulder,
Son of well-filled gullet, son of leg, son of loin,
  Son of hip, son of flitch, son of striped breastbone,
Son of bit, son of sup, son of back, son of paunch,
  Son of slender tripe, son of cheese without decrease,
Son of fish of Inver Indsen, son of sweet whey, son of bastings,
  Son of mead, son of wine, son of flesh, son of ale,
Son of hard wheat, son of tripe, . . .
  Son of fair white porridge, made of pure sheep's milk,
Son of soft rich pottage, with its curls of steam,
  Son of rough curds, son of fair oatmeal gruel,
Son of sprouty meat-soup, with its purple berries,
  Son of the top of effeminate kale, son of soft white midriff,
Son of bone-nourishing nut-fruit, son of Abel, son of Adam.
  Fine is thy kindred of choice food, to the tongue it is sweet,
O thou of staid and steady step,—with the help of pointed staff.

"That hurts me not, Mac Conglinne," said Manchin. "Little did you care about slandering me and the Church when you composed a food-pedigree to commemorate me, such as has not been invented for any man before me, and will not be invented till Doom."

"It is no slander at all, O cleric," said Mac Conglinne, "but a vision that was manifested to me last night. That is its prelude. The vision is not out of place, and, if respite or leave be granted me, I will relate it."

And Manchin said, as before, that he would give no respite. But Mac Conglinne began to recount his vision, and it is said that from here onward is what the angel manifested to him, as he said:

> A vision that appeared to me,
> An apparition wonderful
>   I tell to all:
> A lardy coracle all of lard
> Within a port of New-milk Loch,
>   Up on the World's smooth sea.
>
> We went into the man-of-war,
> 'Twas warrior-like to take the road
>   O'er ocean's heaving waves.
> Our oar-strokes then we pulled
> Across the level sea,
> Throwing the sea's harvest up,
>   Like honey, the sea-soil.
>
> The fort we reached was beautiful,
> With outworks of custards thick,
>   Beyond the loch.
> New butter was the bridge in front,
> The rubble dyke was wheaten white,
>   Bacon the palisade.
>
> Stately, pleasantly it sat,
> A compact house and strong.
>   Then I went in:
> The door of it was dry meat,
> The threshold was bare bread,
>   Cheese-curds the sides.
>
> Smooth pillars of old cheese,
> And sappy bacon props
>   Alternate ranged;
> Fine beams of mellow cream,
> White rafters—real curds,
>   Kept up the house.

Behind was a wine well,
Beer and bragget in streams,
   Each full pool to the taste.
Malt in a smooth wavy sea,
Over a lard-spring's brink
   Flowed through the floor.

A loch of pottage fat
Under a cream of oozy lard
   Lay 'tween it and the sea.
Hedges of butter fenced it round,
Under a blossom of white-mantling lard,
   Around the wall outside.

A row of fragrant apple-trees,
An orchard in its pink-tipped bloom,
   Between it and the hill.
A forest tall of real leeks,
Of onions and of carrots, stood
   Behind the house.

Within, a household generous,
A welcome of red, firm-fed men,
   Around the fire.
Seven bead-strings and necklets seven,
Of cheeses and of bits of tripe,
   Hung from each neck.

The Chief in mantle of beefy fat
Beside his noble wife and fair
   I then beheld.
Below the lofty cauldron's spit
Then the Dispenser I beheld,
   His fleshfork on his back.

The good Cathal mac Finguine,
He is a good man to enjoy
   Tales tall and fine.
That is a business for an hour,
And full of delight 'tis to tell
The rowing of the man-of-war
   O'er Loch Milk's sea.

He then narrated his entire vision in the presence of the monks of Cork until he reached its close, and the virtues of the vision were manifested to Manchin. "Excellent, you wretch," said Manchin, "go straight to Cathal mac Finguine, and relate the vision to him; for it was revealed to me last night that this evil which afflicts Cathal would be cured through that vision."

"What reward shall I have for that?" asked Mac Conglinne.

"Is not the reward great," said Manchin, "to let you have your body and soul?"

"I care not for that, though it should be done. The windows of Heaven are open to receive me, and all the faithful from Adam and Abel, his son, even to the faithful one who went to Heaven in this very moment, are all chanting in expectation of my soul, that I may enter Heaven. The nine orders of Heaven, with Cherubim and Seraphim, are awaiting my soul. I care not, though Cathal mac Finguine and the men of Munster, along with all the Southern Half, and the people of Cork, and Manchin first or last, should go to death and hell in one night; while I myself shall be in the unity of the Father, and the Son, and the Holy Ghost."

"What reward do you require?" asked the monks of Cork.

"Not great indeed is what I ask," said Mac Conglinne, "merely the little cloak, which he refused to the clergy of the Southern Half, and for which they fasted on the same night, that is, Manchin's cloak!"

"Little is that thing in thy sight, but great in mine," said Manchin.

"Verily," he added, "I declare, in the presence of God and of St. Barre, that if the whole country between Cork and its boundary were mine, I would sooner resign it all than the cloak alone."

"Woe to him that gives not the cloak," cried all present, "for the salvation of Cathal and the Southern Half is better than the cloak."

"I will give it then," said Manchin, "but I never gave, nor shall I give, a boon more disagreeable to me; that is to say, I will give it into the hands of the bishop of Cork, to be delivered to the scholar if he helps Cathal mac Finguine."

It was then given into the hands of the bishop of Cork, and the monks of Cork were to deliver the cloak with him; but in the hands of the bishop it was left.

"Now go at once to Cathal!"

"Where is Cathal?" asked Mac Conglinne.

"Not hard to tell," answered Manchin. "In the house of Pichan son of Maelfinn King of Iveagh, at Dun Coba, on the borders of Iveagh and Corcalee, and you must journey thither this night."

Mac Conglinne thereupon went hastily, eagerly, impatiently; and he lifted his five-folded well-strapped cloak on to the slope of his two shoulders, and tied his shirt over the rounds of his fork, and strode thus across the green to the house of Pichan son of Maelfinn, to Dun Coba, on the confines of Iveagh and Corcalee. And at this pace he went quickly to the stronghold. And as he came to the very meeting house where the hosts were gathering, he put on a short cloak and short garments: each upper garment being shorter with him, and each lower one being longer. In this wise he began juggling for the host on the floor of the royal house, a thing not fit for an ecclesiastic, and practising satire and buffoonery and singing songs; and it has been said that there came not before his time, nor since, one more renowned in the arts of satire.

When he was engaged in his feats in the house of Pichan son of Maelfinn, then it was that Pichan said aside: "Though great your mirth, son of learning, it does not make me glad."

"What makes him sad?" asked Mac Conglinne.

"Know you not, O scholar," said Pichan, "that Cathal mac Finguine with the nobles of Munster is coming to-night; and though troublesome to me is the great host of Munster, more troublesome is Cathal alone; and though troublesome is he in his first meal, more troublesome is he in his primefeast; but most troublesome of all is his feast again. For at this feast three things are wanted, a bushel of oats, and a bushel of wild apples, and a bushel of flour-cakes."

"What reward would be given me," said Mac Conglinne, "if I shield you against him from this hour to the same hour to-morrow, and that he would not avenge it on your people or on yourself?"

"I would give you a golden ring and a Welsh steed," said Pichan.

"By my oath, you will add to it if it is to be accepted," said Mac Conglinne.

"I will give you besides," said Pichan, "a white sheep for every house and for every fold, from Carn to Cork."

"I will take that," said Mac Conglinne, "provided that kings and lords of land, poets and satirists are pledged to me for the delivery of my dues and for their fulfilment, so that they shall reach me in full, that is, kings to enforce the dues, lords of land to keep spending on the collectors while they are levying my dues, food and drink and necessaries; poets to scathe and revile, if I am cheated of my dues; and satirists to scatter the satires, and sing them against you and your children and your race, unless my dues reach me." And he bound Pichan then with this pledge.

Cathal mac Finguine came with the companies and hosts of horse of the Munstermen; and they sat themselves down on bed-rails and couches and beds. Gentle maidens began to serve and attend to the hosts and to the multitudes. But Cathal mac Finguine did not let the thong of his shoe be half-loosed, before he began supplying his mouth from both hands with the apples that were on the hides round about him. Mac Conglinne was there, and began smacking his lips at the other side of the house, but Cathal did not notice it. Mac Conglinne rose and went hastily, impatiently, like the fiend, in his furious rush and warlike bold pace across the royal house. And there was a huge block and warriors' stone of strength on which spears and rivets were wont to be fastened, and against which points and edges were wont to be ground; and a warrior's pillar-stone was that flag. And he lifted it on his back and bore it to the place where he had been before on the bed-rail, thrust the upper end of it in his mouth, rested the other end on his knee, and began grinding his teeth against the stone.

What the learned, and the elders, and the books of Cork relate is, that there was no one in the neighborhood of the stronghold, inside or outside, that did not hear the noise of his teeth against the stone, though it was of the smoothest. Thereat Cathal raised his head. "What makes you mad, son of learning?" asked Cathal.

"Two things," said Mac Conglinne; "Cathal, the right-beautiful son of Finguine, the high-king of the great Southern Half, the chief defender of Ireland against the children of Conn the Hundred-Fighter, a man ordained of God and the elements, the noble well-born hero of pleasant Onaght of Glenowra, according to the kindred of his paternity,—I grieve to see him eating anything alone; and if men from distant countries were within, soliciting request or gift, they will scoff if my beard wags not in mutual movement with yours."

"True," said Cathal, giving him an apple and jamming two or three into his own mouth. (During the space of three half-years that the fiend abode in the throat of Cathal mac Finguine, he had not performed such an act of humanity as the giving of that one wild apple to Mac Conglinne after it had been earnestly asked.)

"Better two things than one in learning," said Mac Conglinne. He flung him another.

"The number of the Trinity!" He gave him another.

"The four books of the Gospel, according to the Testament of Christ!" He threw him one.

"The five books of Moses, according to the Ten Commandments of the Law." He flung him one.

"The first numeral article which consists of its own parts and divisions, the number six; for its half is three, its third is two, and its sixth is one—give me the sixth." He cast him one apple.

"The seven things which were prophesied of God on earth, viz., His Conception, His Birth, His Baptism," etc. He gave him one.

"The eight Beatitudes of the Gospel, O Prince of kingly judgments." He threw him one.

"The nine orders of the kingdom of Heaven, O royal champion of the world!" He gave him one.

"The tenth is the order of Mankind, O defender of the province!" He cast him an apple.

"The imperfect number of the apostles after sin." He flung him one.

"The perfect number of the apostles after sin, even though they had committed transgression." He threw him one.

"The triumph beyond triumphs and the perfect number, Christ with his apostles."

"Verily, by St. Barre!" said Cathal, "You will devour me, if you pursue me any further." Cathal flung him hide, apples and all, so that there was neither corner, nor nook, nor floor, nor bed, that the apples did not reach. They were not nearer to Mac Conglinne than to all else; but they were the farther from Cathal. Fury seized Cathal. One of his eyes jumped so far back into his head that a pet crane could not have picked it out. The other eye started out until it was as large in his head as a heath-poult's egg. And he pressed his back against the side of the palace, so that he left neither rafter, nor pole, nor wattle, nor wisp of thatch, nor post, that was not displaced. And he sat down in his seat.

"Your foot and your cheek under you, O King!" said Mac Conglinne. "Curse me not, and cut me not off from Heaven!"

"What has caused you to act so, son of learning?" said Cathal.

"Good reason have I," said Mac Conglinne. "I had a quarrel last night with the monks of Cork, and they gave me their malediction. This is the cause of my behaving thus towards you."

"Come, Mac Conglinne," said Cathal. "By Emly Ivar, if it were my custom to kill students, either you would not have come, or you should not depart." (Now, the reason why Emly Ivar was an oath with him was, because it was there he used to get his fill of small bread; and he used to be there, dressed in a dun-colored soft cloak, his hard straight-bladed sword in his left hand, eating broken meats from one cell of the monastery to another. One day he went into the cell of a certain student, and got his fill of broken meats. He examined the bits. The student examined the page before him; and when he had finished studying the page, he thrust out his tongue to turn over the leaf.

"What caused you to do that, O student?" asked Cathal.

"Great cause have I," said he. "I have been pressed to go on military service with a host in arms to the world's borders, so that there is nothing that touches ashes and fire, that has not been dried up by smoke and wind during my absence, until there is neither sap nor strength in it, not so much as a biscuit-rim. I have not a morsel of bacon, nor of butter, nor of meat, no drink of any sort, except the dead water of the pool; so that I have been bereft of my strength and vigor. But first and last—the hosting!"

"Verily!" said Cathal mac Finguine, "By St. Barre, henceforth whilst I live, no cleric shall go a-soldiering with me." For up to that time the clerics of Ireland were forced to go a-soldiering with the king of Ireland; and he was therefore the first that ever exempted clerics from going on military service. He left his grace and blessings, moreover, to the pilgrims of Emly, and a profusion of small bread in Emly. And this is greatest in the southwestern part of it; for there he used to get his fill.)

But this is a digression.

"By your kingship, by your sovereignty, by the service to which you are entitled, grant me a little boon before I go," said Mac Conglinne.

Pichan was summoned into the house. "Yon student," said Cathal, "is asking a boon from me."

"Grant it," said Pichan.

"It shall be granted," said Cathal. "Tell me what it is you desire."

"I will not, until pledges are given for its fulfilment."

"They shall be given," said Cathal.

"Your princely word therein?" said Mac Conglinne.

"By my word," said he, "you shall have them, and now name the request."

"This is it," said Mac Conglinne. "I had a quarrel with the monks of Cork last night, when they all gave me their curse, and it was owing to you that that trouble was brought on me. And do you fast with me to-night on God, since you are an original brother, to save me from the malediction of the monks of Cork; that is what I ask."

"Say not that, son of learning," said Cathal. "You shall have a cow out of every enclosure in Munster, and an ounce from every house-owner, together with a cloak from every church, to be levied by a steward, and you yourself shall feast in my company as long as he is engaged in levying the dues. And by my God's doom," said Cathal, "I had rather you should have all there is from the west to the east, and from the south to the north of Munster, than that I should be one night without food."

"By my God's doom," said Mac Conglinne, "since your princely troth has passed in this, and since it is not lawful for a king of Cashel to transgress it, if all that there is in the Southern Half were given me, I would not accept it. Good reason have I, O arch-warrior and king-hero of Europe, why I should not accept conditions from you; for my own treasure is only in Heaven, or on earth, in wisdom, or in poetry. And not alone that—for the last thing is always the heaviest—but I shall go to endless, limitless perdition, unless you save me from the malediction of the monks of Cork."

"That shall be granted to you," said Cathal, "and there has not been given before, nor shall there be given hereafter to the brink of Doom, a thing more grievous to us than that."

Cathal fasted with him that night, and all that were there fasted also. And the student lay down on a couch by the side of a door-post, and closed the house.

As he lay there at the end of the night, up rose Pichan, the son of Maelfinn. "Why does Pichan rise at this hour?" said Mac Conglinne.

"To prepare food for these hosts," answered Pichan, "and 'twere better for us had it been ready since yesterday."

"Not so, indeed," said Mac Conglinne. "We fasted last night. The first thing we shall have to-morrow is preaching." And they waited until morning. Few or many as they were, not one of them went out thence until the time of rising on the morrow, when Mac Conglinne himself got up and opened the house. He washed his hands, took up his book-satchel, brought out his psalter, and began preaching to the hosts. And historians, and elders, and the books of Cork declare, that there was neither high nor low that did not shed three showers of tears while listening to the scholar's preaching.

When the sermon was ended, prayers were offered for the king, that he might have length of life, and that there might be prosperity in Munster during his reign. Prayers were also offered up for the lands, and for the tribes, and for the province as well, as is usual after a sermon. "Well," asked Mac Conglinne, "how are things over there to-day?"

"By my God's doom," answered Cathal, "it never was worse before, and never shall be until Doom."

"Very natural it is that you should be in evil case," said Mac Conglinne, "with a demon destroying and ravaging you now during the space of three half-years; and you did not fast a day or night on your own account, though you did so for the sake of a wretched, impetuous, insignificant person like me."

"What is the good of all this, son of learning?" asked Cathal Mac Finguine.

"This," said Mac Conglinne. "Since you alone did fast with me last night, let us all fast this night, as many of us as there are; and do you also fast, that you may obtain some succor from God."

"Say not that, son of learning," said Cathal. "For though the first trial was hard, seven times harder is the last."

"Do you not say that," said Mac Conglinne, "but act bravely in this."

Cathal fasted that night together with his host even until the end of the night. Then Mac Conglinne arose. "Is Pichan asleep?" he said.

"I will tell truth," answered Pichan. "If Cathal were to remain as he is to the brink of Doom, I should not sleep, I should not eat, nor smile, nor laugh."

"Get up," said Mac Conglinne. And he called for juicy old bacon, and tender corned-beef, and full-fleshed wether, and honey in the comb, and English salt on a beautiful polished dish of white silver, along with four perfectly straight white hazel spits to support the joints. The viands which he enumerated were procured for him, and he fixed unspeakable, huge pieces on the spits. Then putting a linen apron about him below, and placing a flat linen cap on the crown of his head, he lighted a fair four-ridged, four-apertured, four-cleft fire of ash-wood, without smoke, without fume, without sparks. He stuck a spit into each of the portions, and as quick was he about the spits and fire as a hind about her first fawn, or as a roe, or a swallow, or a bare spring wind in the flank of March. He rubbed the honey and the salt into one piece after another. And big as the pieces were that were before the fire, there dropped not to the ground out of these four pieces as much as would quench a spark of a candle; but what there was of relish in them went into their very center. It had been explained to Pichan that the very reason why the scholar had come was to save Cathal. Now, when the pieces were ready, Mac Conglinne cried out, "Ropes and cords here!"

"What is wanted with them?" asked Pichan. Now, that was a "question beyond discretion" for him, since it had been explained to him before; and hence is the old saying, "a question beyond discretion."

Ropes and cords were given to Mac Conglinne, and to those that were strongest of the warriors. They laid hands upon Cathal, who was tied in this manner to the side of the palace. Then Mac Conglinne came, and was a long time securing the ropes with hooks and staples. And when this was ended, he came into the house, with his four spits raised high on his back, and his white wide-spread cloak hanging behind, its two peaks round his neck, to the place where Cathal was. And he stuck the spits into the bed before Cathal's eyes, and sat himself down in his seat, with his two legs crossed. Then taking his knife out of his girdle, he cut a bit off the piece that was nearest to him, and dipped it in the honey that was on the aforesaid dish of white silver. "Here's the first for a male beast," said Mac Conglinne, putting the bit into his own mouth. And from that day to this the old saying has remained. He cut a morsel from the next piece, and dipping it in the honey, put it past Cathal's mouth into his own.

"Carve the food for us, son of learning!" exclaimed Cathal.

"I will do so," answered Mac Conglinne; and cutting another bit of the nearest piece, and dipping it as before, he put it past Cathal's mouth into his own.

"How long will you carry this on, student?" said Cathal.

"No more henceforth," answered Mac Conglinne, "for, indeed, you have hitherto consumed such a quantity and variety of agreeable morsels, that I shall eat the little that there is here myself, and this will be 'food from mouth' for thee." And that has been a proverb since.

Then Cathal roared and bellowed, and commanded the killing of the scholar. But that was not done for him.

"Well, Cathal," said Mac Conglinne, "a vision has appeared to me, and I have heard that you are good at interpreting a dream."

"By my God's doom!" exclaimed Cathal, "though I should interpret the dreams of the men of the world, I would not interpret yours."

"I vow," said Mac Conglinne, "even though you do not interpret it, it shall be related in your presence." He then began his vision, and the way he related it was, whilst putting two morsels or three at a time past Cathal's mouth into his own:

> A vision I beheld last night:
> I sallied forth with two or three,
> When I saw a fair and well-f lled house,
> In which there was great store of food.

> A lake of new milk I beheld
> In the midst of a fair plain.
> I saw a well-appointed house
> Thatched with butter.

> As I went all around it
> To view its arrangement,
> Puddings fresh-boiled
> They were its thatch-rods.

> Its two soft door-posts of custard,
> Its dais of curds and butter,
> Beds of glorious lard,
> Many shields of thin pressed cheese.

> Under the straps of those shields
> Were men of soft sweet smooth cheese,
> Men who knew not to wound a Gael,
> Spears of old butter had each of them.
>
> A huge cauldron full of meat
> (Methought I'd try to tackle it)
> Boiled, leafy kale, browny-white,
> A brimming vessel full of milk.
>
> A bacon house of two-score ribs,
> A wattling of tripe—support of clans—
> Of every food pleasant to man,
> Meseemed the whole was gathered there.

And he said further:

> A vision I beheld last night,
> 'Twas a fair spell,
> 'Twas a power of strength when to me appeared
> The kingship of Erin.
>
> I saw a court-yard topped with trees,
> A bacon palisade,
> A bristling rubble dyke of stone
> Of pregnant cheeses.
>
> Of chitterlings of pigs were made
> Its beautiful rafters,
> Splendid the beams and the pillars,
> Of marvellous pork.
>
> Marvellous the vision that appeared to me
> By my fireside:
> A butter draught-board with its men,
> Smooth, speckled, peaked.
>
> God bless the words I utter,
> A feast without fatigue!
> When I got to Butter-mount,
> A gillie would take off my shoes!

Though grievous to Cathal was the pain of being two days and a night without food, much greater was the agony of listening to the enumeration before him of the many various pleasant viands, and none of them for him! After this, Mac Conglinne began the fable.

"As I lay last night in my beautiful canopied bed, with its gilded posts, with its bronze rails, I heard something, viz., a voice coming towards me; but I answered it not. That was natural; such was the comfort of my bed, the ease of my body, and the soundness of my slumber. Whereupon it said again: 'Beware, beware, Mac Conglinne, lest the gravy drown you!' At early morn on the morrow I arose, and went to the well to wash my hands, when I saw a mighty phantom approaching me. 'Well, there,' said he to me. 'Well, indeed,' said I to him. 'Well, now, wretch,' said the phantom, 'it was I that gave you warning last night, lest the gravy should drown you. But, verily, 'twas

> Warning to one fey,
> Mocking a beggar,
> Dropping a stone on a tree,
> Whispering to the deaf,
> A legacy to a glum man,
> Putting a charm in a hurdle,
> A withe about sand or gravel,
> Striking an oak with fists,
> Sucking honey from roots of yew,
> Looking for butter in a dog's kennel,
> Dining on the husks of pepper,
> Seeking wool on a goat,
> An arrow at a pillar,
> Keeping a mare from breaking wind,
> Keeping a loose woman from lust,
> Water on the bottom of a sieve,
> Trusting a mad bitch,
> Salt on rushes,
> A settlement after marriage,
> A secret to a silly woman,
> Looking for sense in an oaf,
> Exalting slaves,
> Ale to infants,
> Competing with a king,
> A body without a head,
> A head without a body,
> A nun as bell-ringer,
> A veteran in a bishop's chair,
> A people without a king,
> Rowing a boat without a rudder,
> Corn in a basket full of holes,
> Milk on a hide,
> Housekeeping without a woman,
> Berries on a hide,
> Warning visions to sinners,
> Reproof to the face,
> Restoration without restitution,

> Putting seed in bad land,
> Property to a bad woman,
> Serving to a bad lord,
> An unequal contract,
> Uneven measure,
> Going against a verdict,
> To outrage the gospel,
> Instructing Antichrist, and

to instruct you, Mac Conglinne, regarding your appetite.'

" 'I declare by my God's doom,' said I, 'the reproof is hard and severe.'

" 'How is that?' asked the phantom.

" 'Not hard to say,' I answered. 'I know not whence you come, nor whither you go, nor whence you are yourself, to question you, or tell you again.'

" 'That is easily known,' said the phantom. 'I am Fluxy son of Elcab and Fearless, from the Fairy-mound of Eating.'

" 'If you are he,' I said, 'I fancy you have great news, and tidings of food and eating. Have you any?'

" 'I have indeed,' said the phantom; 'but though I have, 'twould be no luck for a friend who had no power of eating to come up with it.'

" 'How is that?' I asked.

" 'Indeed, it is not hard to tell,' said the phantom. 'Even so: unless he had a very broad-edged belly, five hands in diameter, in which could be fitted thrice nine eatings, and seven drinkings with the drink of nine in each of them, and of seven chewings, and nine digestions—a dinner of a hundred being in each of those eatings, drinkings, swallowings, and digestions respectively.'

" 'Since I have not that belly,' answered I, 'give me your counsel, for you have made me greedy.'

" 'I will indeed give you counsel,' said the phantom. 'Go to the hermitage from which I have come, even to the hermitage of the Wizard Doctor, where your appetite for all kinds of food, which your gullet and heart can desire, will find a cure; where your teeth will be polished by the many wonderful manifold viands of which we have spoken; where your melancholy will be attacked; where your senses will be startled; where your lips will be gratified with choice drink and choice morsels, with eating and putting away every sort of soft, savory, tender-sweet food acceptable to your body, and not injurious to your soul,—if only you get to the Wizard Doctor, and to sharp-lipped Becnat daughter of Baetan the monstrous Eater, the wife of the Wizard Doctor.

" 'The day you arrive at the fort will be the day on which his pavilion of fat will be raised about him, on its fair round wheat plains, with the two Loins, the Gullet, and the worthy Son of Fatkettle, with their mantles of . . . about them. It will be a happy day for you when you shall come unto the fort, O Mac Conglinne,' said the phantom; 'the more so as that will be the day on which the chieftains of the Tribe of Food will be summoned to the fort.'

" 'And what are their names?' I asked.

" 'Not hard to tell,' said the phantom; 'they are Little Sloey son of Smooth-juicy-bacon, Cakey son of Hung Beef, and Hollowsides son of Gullet, and Milkikin son of Lactulus, and Wristy-hand son of Leather-head, and young Mul-Lard son of Flitch of Old-Bacon.'

" 'And what is your own name, if we may ask?'

" 'Not hard to tell,' said the phantom:

> Wheatlet son of Milklet
> Son of juicy Bacon,
>   Is mine own name.
> Honeyed Butter-roll
> Is the man's name
>   That bears my bag.
>
> Haunch of Mutton
> Is my dog's name,
>   Of lovely leaps.
> Lard, my wife,
> Sweetly smiles
>   Across the kale-top.
>
> Cheese-curds, my daughter,
> Goes round the spit,
>   Fair is her fame.
> Corned Beef, my son,
> Whose mantle shines
>   Over a big tail.
>
> Savor of Savors
> Is the name of my wife's maid:
> Morning-early
> Across New-milk Lake she went.

Beef-lard, my steed,
An excellent stallion,
  That increases studs;
A guard against toil
Is the saddle of cheese
  On his back.

When a cheese-steed is sent after him,
  Rapid his course,
Fat . . . is on his ribs,
  Exceeding all shapes.

A large necklace of delicious cheese-curds
  Around his back,
His halter and his traces all
  Of fresh butter.

His bridle with its reins of fat
  In every place.
The horsecloth is of tripe with its . . .
  Tripes are his hoofs.

. . . .

" 'Off with you now to those delicious prodigious viands, O Mac Conglinne,' said the phantom,

> many wonderful provisions,
> pieces of every palatable food,
> brown red-yellow dishes,
> full without fault,
> perpetual joints of corned beef,
> smooth savory lard,
> and heavy flitches of boar.

" 'Off with you now to the suets and cheeses!' said the phantom.

" 'I will certainly go,' said I, 'and do you put a charm about me.'

" 'It shall be given,' said the phantom; 'even a gospel of four-cornered even dry cheese, and I will put my own paternoster around you, and neither greed nor hunger can visit him around whom it is put.' And he said:

" 'May smooth juicy bacon protect you, O Mac Conglinne!

" 'May hard yellow-skinned cream protect you, O Mac Conglinne!

" 'May the cauldron full of pottage protect you, O Mac Conglinne!'

" 'By my God's doom, in the presence of the Creator,' said I, 'I wish I could get to that fortress, that I might consume my fill of those old strained delicious liquors, and of those wonderful enormous viands.'

" 'If you really wish that,' said the phantom, 'you shall have them. Go as I tell you; but only, if you go, do not go astray.'

" 'How is that?' said I.

" 'You must place yourself under the protection and safeguard of the mighty peerless warriors, the chiefs of the Tribes of Food, lest the gravy destroy you.'

" 'How, then,' said I, 'which of the chiefs of the Tribes of Food are the most puissant safeguards against the heavy waves of gravy?'

" 'Not hard to tell,' said the phantom. 'The Suets and the Cheeses.'

"Thereupon I advanced," said Mac Conglinne, "erect, with exultant head, with stout steps. The wind that comes across that country—it is not by me I wished it to go, but into my mouth. And no wonder; so heavy was the disease, so scant the cure, so great the longing for the remedy. I advanced vehemently, furiously, impatiently, eagerly, greedily, softly, gliding, like a young fox approaching a shepherd, or as a clown to violate a queen, or a royston-crow to carrion, or a deer to the cropping of a field of winter-rye in the month of June. However, I lifted my shirt above my buttocks, and I thought that neither fly, nor gadfly, nor gnat could stick to my hinder part, in its speed and agility, as I went through plains and woods and wastes towards that lake and fort.

"Then in the harbor of the lake before me I saw a juicy little coracle of beef-fat, with its coating of tallow, with its thwarts of curds, with its prow of lard, with its stern of butter, with its thole-pins of marrow, with its oars of flitches of old boar in it.

"Indeed, she was a sound craft in which we embarked. Then we rowed across the wide expanse of New-milk Lake, through seas of broth, past river-mouths of mead, over swelling boisterous waves of butter-milk, by perpetual pools of gravy, past woods dewy with meat-juice, past springs of savory lard, by islands of cheeses, by hard rocks of rich tallow, by headlands of old curds, along strands of dry cheese; until we reached the firm, level beach between Butter-mount and Milk-lake and Curd-point at the mouth of the pass to the country of O'Early-eating, in front of the hermitage of the Wizard Doctor. Every oar we plied in New-milk Lake would send its sea-sand of cheese curds to the surface.

"It was then I said, at the top of my voice: 'Ha, ha, ha! these are not the seas that I would not take!'

"Then the Wizard Doctor spoke to his people: 'A troublesome party approaches you to-night, my friends, Anier mac Conglinne of the men of Munster, a youngster of deep lore, entertaining and delightful. And he must be well served; for he is melancholy, passionate, impetuous, violent, and impatient; and he is eager, fond of eating early; and he is voracious, niggardly, greedy; and yet he is mild, gentle, and easily moved to laughter. And he is a man great in thanks-givings and in upbraidings. And no wonder; for he has wit both to censure and to praise the hearth of a well-appointed, gentle, fine, mirthful house with a mead-hall.'

"Marvellous, indeed, was the hermitage at which I then found myself. Around it were seven score hundred smooth stakes of old bacon, and instead of the thorns above the top of every long stake was fried juicy lard of choice well-fed boar, in expectation of a battle against the tribes of Butter-pat and Cheese that were on New-milk Lake, warring against the Wizard Doctor. There was a gate of tallow to it, whereon was a bolt of sausage.

"I raised myself up then out of my boat," said Mac Conglinne, "and betook myself to the outer door of the entrance porch of the fortress, and seizing a branchy cudgel that lay directly on my right hand outside the porch of the fortress, I dealt a blow with it at the tallow door, on which was the sausage lock, and drove it before me along the outer porch of the fortress, until I reached the splendid inner chief residence of the enormous fort. And I fixed my ten pointed purple-bright nails in its smooth old-bacon door, which had a lock of cheese, flung it behind me, and passed through.

"Then I saw the doorkeeper. Fair was the shape of that man; and his name was Bacon-lad son of Butter-lad son of Lard; with his smooth sandals of old bacon on his soles, and leggings of pot-meat encircling his shins, with his tunic of corned beef, and his girdle of salmon skin around him, with his hood of flummery about him, with a seven-filleted crown of butter on his head, in each fillet of which was the produce of seven ridges of pure leeks; with his seven badges of tripe about his neck, and seven bosses of boiled lard on the point of every badge of them; his steed of bacon under him, with its four legs of custard, with its four hoofs of coarse oaten bread under it, with its ears of curds, with its two eyes of honey in its head, with its streams of old cream in its two nostrils, and a flux of bragget streaming down behind, with its tail of dulse, from which seven handfuls were pulled every ordinary day; with its smooth saddle of glorious choice lard upon it, with its faceband of the side of a heifer around its head, with its neck-band of old-wether spleen around its neck, with its little bell of cheese suspended from the neck-band, with its tongue of thick compact metal hanging down from the bell; and a whip in that rider's hand, the cords whereof were twenty-nine fair puddings of white-fat cows, and the substance of every juicy drop that fell to the ground from the end of each of these puddings would, with half a cake, be a surfeit for a priest; with his slender boiled stick of bundrish in his hand, and every juicy drop that trickled from the end of it, when he turned it downwards, would contain the full of seven vats.

" 'Open the hermitage to us,' said I.

" 'Come in, wretch!' answered the doorkeeper.

"On going in, then," said Mac Conglinne, "I saw on my left hand the servants of the Wizard Doctor with their hairy cloaks of . . ., with their hairy rags of soft custard, with their shovels of dry bread in their hands, carrying the tallowy offal that was on the lake-bridge of custard, from the porch of the great house to the outer porch of the fortress. On my right hand I then beheld the Wizard Doctor, with his two gloves of full-fat rump-steak on his hands, setting in order the house, which was hung all round with tripe from roof to floor. Then I went into the kitchen, and there I saw the Wizard Doctor's son, with his fishing-hook of lard in his hand, with its line made of fine brawn of a deer, viz., the marrow of its leg, with its thirty-hand rod of tripe attached to the line below, and he angling in a lake of lard. Now he would bring a flitch of old bacon, and now a weasand of corned beef from the lake of lard mixed with honey, on to a bank of curds that was near him in the kitchen. And in that lake it is that the Wizard Doctor's son was drowned.

"Afterwards I went into the great house. As I set my foot across the threshold into the house, I saw a pure white bed-tick of butter, on which I sat; but I sank in it to the tips of my two ears.

The eight strongest men that were in the king's house had hard work to pull me out by the top of the crown of my head. Then I was taken to the place where the Wizard Doctor himself was. 'Pray for me!' said I to him.

" 'In the name of cheese!' said he to me. 'Evil is the limp look of your face. Alas! it is the look of disease. Your hands are yellow, your lips are spotted, your eyes are gray. Your sinews have relaxed, they have risen over your brow and over your flesh, and over your joints and nails. The three hags have attacked you, even scarcity and death and famine, with sharp beaks of hunger. An eye that blesses not has regarded you. A plague of heavy disease has visited you. No wonder, truly; for yours is not the look of a full-suckled milk-fed calf, tended by the hands of a good cook. You have not the corslet look of well-nourished blood, but that of a youth badly reared under the vapors of bad feeding.'

" 'Very natural that,' said I. 'Such is the heaviness of my ailment, the scarcity of cure, the longing for the remedy.'

" 'Tell me your disease, my man,' said the Wizard Doctor.

" 'I will tell you,' said I, 'what it is that shrivels me up and makes me low-spirited, inactive,—even love of good cheer, hatred of bad cheer, desire of eating early, the gnawing of my many fancies, the gnawing of flesh, the consumption of whitemeats, greed and hunger; the thirst and voracity which I feel in consuming my food, so that what I eat gives neither satiety nor substance; inhospitality and niggardliness, refusal and uncharitableness regarding what is my own, so that I am a burden to myself, and dear to none; hunger, with its four-and-twenty subdivisions in addition thereto, sadness, niggardliness, anxiety to be welcomed before everybody to all kinds of food, and the injurious effect upon me of every food. My wish would be, that the various numerous wonderful viands of the world were before my gorge, that I might gratify my desires, and satisfy my greed. But alas! great is the misfortune to one like me, who cannot obtain any of these.'

" 'On my word,' said the Great Doctor, 'the disease is grievous. Woe to him on whom it has fallen, and not long will it be endured. But as you have come to me to my hermitage and to my fort at this time, you shall take home with you a medicine to cure your disease, and shall be forever healed therefrom.'

" 'What is that?' asked I.

" 'Not hard to tell,' answered the Great Doctor. 'If you go home to-night, go to the well to wash your hands, rub your teeth with your fists, and comb every straight rib of your hair in order. Warm yourself afterwards before a glowing red fire of straight red oak, or of octagonal ash that grows near a hill-side where little sparrows leave their droppings; on a dry hearth, very high, very low, that its embers may warm you, that its blaze may not touch you. Let a hairy calf-skin be placed under you to the north-east before the fire, your side resting exactly against a rail of alder. And let an active, white-handed, sensible, joyous woman wait upon you, who must be of good repute, of good discourse, red-lipped, womanly, eloquent, of a good kin, wearing a necklace, and a cloak, and a brooch, with a black edge between the two peaks of her cloak, that sorrow may not come upon her; with the three nurses of her dignity upon her, with three dimples of love and delight in her countenance, without an expression of harshness in her forehead, who shall have a joyous, comely appearance, a purple five-folded cloak about her, a red-gold brooch in her cloak, a fair broad face, a good blue eye in her head, two blue-black brows of the color of the black chafer over those eyes, ruddy even cheeks, red thin lips, white clear teeth in her head as though they were pearls, soft tender white fore-arms, two smooth snowy sides, beauteous shapely thighs, straight well-proportioned calves, thin white-skinned feet, long slender fingers, long pale-red nails. So that the gait and movements of the maiden may be graceful and quick, so that her gentle talk and address may be melodious as strings, soft and sweet; so that, from her crown to her sole, there may be neither fault, nor stain, nor blemish, on which a sharp watchful observer may hit.

" 'Let this maiden give you your thrice nine morsels, O Mac Conglinne, each morsel of which shall be as big as a heath-fowl's egg. These morsels you must put in your mouth with a swinging jerk, and your eyes must whirl about in your skull while you are eating them.'

" 'The eight kinds of grain you must not spare, O Mac Conglinne, wheresoever they are offered you, namely, rye, wild-oats, beare, buckwheat, wheat, barley, fidbach, oats. Take eight cakes of each fair grain of these, and eight condiments with every cake, and eight sauces with each condiment; and let each morsel you put in your mouth be as big as a heron's egg. Away now to the smooth panikins of cheese curds, O Mac Conglinne,

to fresh pigs,
to loins of fat,
to boiled mutton,
to the choice easily-discussed thing for which the hosts contend—the gullet of salted beef;
to the dainty of the nobles, to mead;
to the cure of chest-disease—old bacon;
to the appetite of pottage—stale curds;
to the fancy of an unmarried woman—new milk;
to a queen's mash—carrots;
to the danger awaiting a guest—ale;
to the sustenance of Lent—the cock of a hen;
to a broken head—butter-roll;
to hand-upon-all—dry bread;
to the pregnant thing of a hearth—cheese;
to the bubble-burster—new ale;
to the priests' fancy—juicy kale;
to the treasure that is smoothest and sweetest of all food—white porridge; . . .
to the double-looped twins—sheep's tripe;
to the dues of a wall—sides of bacon;
to the bird of a cross—salt;
to the entry of a gathering—sweet apples;
to the pearls of a household—hens' eggs;
to the glance of nakedness—kernels.

"When he had reckoned me up those many viands, he ordered me my drop of drink. 'A tiny little measure for you, Mac Conglinne, not too large, only as much as twenty men will drink, on the top of those viands: of very thick milk, of milk not too thick, of milk of long thickness, of milk of medium thickness, of yellow bubbling milk, the swallowing of which needs chewing, of the milk that makes the snoring bleat of a ram as it rushes down the gorge, so that the first draught says to the last draught: "I vow, you mangy cur, before the Creator, if you come down, I'll go up, for there is no room for the doghood of the pair of us in this treasure-house." Whatever disease may seize you from it, Mac Conglinne, 'tis I that will cure you, excepting one disease, I mean the disease of sages and of gentlemen, the best of all diseases, the disease that is worth perpetual health—loose bowels.' "

Thus far the vision.

At the pleasure of the recital and the recounting of those many various pleasant viands in the king's presence, the lawless beast that abode in the inner bowels of Cathal mac Finguine came forth, until it was licking its lips outside his head. The scholar had a large fire beside him in the house. Each of the pieces was put in order to the fire, and then one after the other to the lips of the king. One time when one of the pieces was put to the king's mouth, the son of malediction darted forth, fixed his two claws in the piece that was in the student's hand, and taking it with him across the hearth to the other side, bore it below the cauldron that was on the other side of the fire. And the cauldron was overturned upon him. (Hence is said "*lonchoire*," from the demon (*lon*) of gluttony that was in Cathal's throat, being under the cauldron (*coire*).) This is not what some story-tellers relate, who say that it was down the throat of the priest's gillie he went, and that the gillie was drowned in the millpond of Dun Cain opposite the fortress of Pichan son of Maelfinn, in the land of the men of Fene. But it is not so in the books of Cork, which state that he was put under the cauldron, and was burned under it.

"To God and Brigit we give thanks," said Mac Conglinne, clapping his right palm over his own mouth, and his left palm over the mouth of Cathal. And linen sheets were put round Cathal's head and he was carried out.

"What is most necessary for us to do now?" asked Pichan.

"The easiest thing in the world," said Mac Conglinne. "Let the hosts and multitudes, the kings and queens and people, the herds, flocks and cattle, and the entire gold and silver treasure of the fortress be taken out beyond the fortress."

And the learned say, that the price of a chafer's leg of any kind of property was not left in the large central royal pavilion of the fort, except the cauldron that was about the demon's head. And the house was then shut on him from the outside, and four huge fires were kindled here and there in the house. When the house was a tower of red flame and a huge blaze, the demon sprang to the rooftree of the palace above, and the fire was powerless to do anything to him, and he sat on the house that was next to it.

"Well, now you men of Munster," said Mac Conglinne, "yonder is your friend. Shut your mouths that I may speak with that un-worshipful monk. Now, wretch," he shouted, "do obeisance unto us."

"And indeed I will," said the devil, "since I cannot help it. For you are a man with the grace of God, with abundance of wisdom, with acuteness of intellect, with intensive humility, with the desire of every goodness, with the grace of the seven-fold Spirit. I am a demon by nature, of infrangible substance, and I shall tell you my story. I have been three half-years in Cathal's mouth, to the ruin of Munster and the Southern Half of Ireland besides, and if I were to continue three half-years more, I should ruin all Ireland. Were it not for the nobleness of the monks of great Cork of Munster, and for their wisdom, for their purity and for their honesty, and for the multitude of their bishops and their confessors, from whom you have come against me; and were it not for the worth of the voice and the word, honor and soul of the noble venerable king, whom you have come to save; and again, were it not for your own nobility and worth, and purity and wisdom, and abundance of knowledge and lore—it is into your own throat I would go, so that they would lash you with dog-straps and scourges and horsewhips through all Ireland, and the disease that would kill you would be hunger."

"The sign of the Lord's cross between me and thee," said Mac Conglinne, thrice threatening him with the Gospels.

And the demon said: "Were it not for the little fair woman from the Curragh, by my God's doom before God, O Cathal mac Finguine, I would bear your body into the earth and your soul into hell before long to-night." After that he flew into the air among the people of hell.

"What is to be done now, O Mac Conglinne?" asked Pichan.

"Not hard to tell," answered Mac Conglinne. "Let new milk and fresh butter be boiled along with honey, and drunk for a new drink by the king."

That was done. A cauldron of a hundred measures of fully-boiled milk was given as a special drink to the king. It was the last great bellyful that Cathal took because of the demon. A bed was afterwards prepared for the king on a downy quilt, and musicians and players entertained him from noon until twilight. The king lay in his slumbering rest of sleep. The chieftains lay around Pichan in as pleasant and honorable a manner as ever before. Great respect and honor had they that night for the scholar.

The learned say that the king was three days and three nights in that one sleep. But the books of Cork relate that he only slept the round of the Hours.

The king arose on the morrow, and passed his hand over his face; and no smaller than a full-fragrant apple was each dark-purple drop of dew that was on his face. "Where is Mac Conglinne?" he asked.

"Here he is," answered he.

"Tell us the vision now."

"It shall be done," said Mac Conglinne.

"However long the tale may be to-day," said Cathal, "it will not appear long to me—'tis not the same as yesterday." Cathal left his grace and blessing on everyone who would read it and preserve it.

"Some reward should be given to Mac Conglinne," said the chieftains.

"It shall be done," said Cathal. "He shall have a cow out of every close in Munster, and an ounce for every householder, and a cloak for every church, and a sheep from every house from Carn to Cork. Moreover, he shall be given the treasure that is better than all these, I mean Manchin's little cloak."

It was then that Roennu Ressamnach came into the house, and Cruitfiach his son, and Maelchiar his daughter. And then he made these quatrains:

> Manchin went—a brilliant feat—
> To plead against Mac Conglinne;
> Manchin they defrauded then
> Of the little cloak around him.
> 'Twere not too much for pure Comgan,
> (Said the son of the jester)
> Though we are not his kindred,
> The famous cloaklet which I see,
> Although worth thrice seven bondmaids,
> Though it were of the raven's hue,
> From Cathal, King of Munster.
>
> 'Twere not too much for me to give,
> Though gold were in its border,
> As it was given by his will
> And spoken in pure reason:
> For health of reason Cathal now
> Receives from Manchin's journey.

Then was given to Mac Conglinne a cow out of every close, an ounce for every householder, a cloak for every church, a ring of gold, a Welsh steed, a white sheep out of every house from Carn to Cork. Two-thirds of the right of intercession (one-third being reserved to the men of Ireland) was accorded to him, and that he should sit always at the right hand of Cathal. All these things were granted to him, as we have said.

Let this be heard by every ear, and delivered by every chosen tongue to another, as elders and old men and historians have declared, as it is read and written in the books of Cork, as the angel of God set it forth to Mac Conglinne, as Mac Conglinne himself uttered it to Cathal mac Finguine and to the men of Munster besides. Nothing sorrowful shall be heard by anyone who has heard it; it will be a year's protection to him. There are thirty chief virtues attending this tale, and a few of them are enough for an example. The married couple to whom it is related the first night shall not separate without an heir; they shall not be in dearth of food or raiment. The new house, in which it is the first tale told, no corpse shall be taken out of it; it shall not want food or raiment; fire does not burn it. The king to whom it is recited before battle or conflict shall be victorious. On the occasion of bringing out ale, or of feasting a prince, or of taking an inheritance or patrimony, this tale should be recited.

The reward of the recital of this story is a white-spotted, red-eared cow, a shirt of new linen, a woollen cloak with its brooch, from a king and queen, from married couples, from stewards, from princes, to him who is able to tell and recite it to them.

THE VOYAGE OF BRAN SON OF FEBAL

We have already seen the visit to the Happy Otherworld appearing incidentally in "The Wooing of Etain" (p. 82), "The Sick-Bed of Cu Chulainn" (p. 176), and other romances. Here it constitutes the main purpose of the story. Of the chief traditional characters in Irish literature, the only ones referred to in "The Voyage of Bran" are Manannan mac Lir and Mongan (p. 546). Its literary importance lies in the fact that it is representative of a class of Irish stories called *imrama*, "voyages," that seem to have been rather widely known in other parts of Europe. The voyage literature is also noteworthy in that it frequently appears in ecclesiastical guise; in fact, some authorities are inclined to place the ecclesiastical form earlier than the secular. "The Voyage of Bran" belongs to the early period of Irish literature, being ascribed usually to the eighth century. Though reminding us of the "Odyssey," the Irish narrative is probably based in large part on fantastic stories brought back by sailors who had ventured far out into the Atlantic Ocean long before the discovery of America.

'Twas fifty quatrains the woman from unknown lands sang on the floor of the house to Bran son of Febal, when the royal house was full of kings, who knew not whence the woman had come, since the ramparts were closed.

This is the beginning of the story. One day, in the neighborhood of his stronghold, Bran went about alone, when he heard music behind him. As often as he looked back, 'twas still behind him the music was. At last he fell asleep at the music, such was its sweetness. When he awoke from his sleep, he saw close by him a branch of silver with white blossoms, nor was it easy to distinguish its bloom from the branch. Then Bran took the branch in his hand to his royal house. When the hosts were in the royal house, they saw a woman in strange raiment therein. 'Twas then she sang the fifty quatrains to Bran, while the host heard her, and all beheld the woman.

And she said:

> A branch of the apple-tree from Emne
> I bring, like those one knows;
> Twigs of white silver are on it,
> Crystal brows with blossoms.

There is a distant isle,
Around which sea-horses glisten:
A fair course against the white-swelling surge,—
Four pillars uphold it.

A delight of the eyes, a glorious range,
Is the plain on which the hosts hold games:
Coracle contends against chariot
In the southern Plain of White Silver.

Pillars of white bronze under it
Glittering through beautiful ages.
Lovely land throughout the world's age,
On which the many blossoms drop.

An ancient tree there is with blossoms,
On which birds call the canonical Hours.
'Tis in harmony it is their wont
To call together every Hour.

Splendors of every color glisten
Throughout the gentle-voiced plains.
Joy is known, ranked around music,
In southern White-Silver Plain.

Unknown is wailing or treachery
In the familiar cultivated land,
There is nothing rough or harsh,
But sweet music striking on the ear.

Without grief, without sorrow, without death,
Without any sickness, without debility,
That is the sign of Emne—
Uncommon is an equal marvel.

A beauty of a wondrous land,
Whose aspects are lovely,
Whose view is a fair country,
Incomparable is its haze.

Then if Silvery Land is seen,
On which dragon-stones and crystals drop,
The sea washes the wave against the land,
Hair of crystal drops from its mane.

Wealth, treasures of every hue,
Are in Ciuin, a beauty of freshness,
Listening to sweet music,
Drinking the best of wine.

Golden chariots in Mag Rein,
Rising with the tide to the sun,
Chariots of silver in Mag Mon,
And of bronze without blemish.

Yellow golden steeds are on the sward there,
Other steeds with crimson hue,
Others with wool upon their backs
Of the hue of heaven all-blue.

At sunrise there will come
A fair man illumining level lands;
He rides upon the fair sea-washed plain,
He stirs the ocean till it is blood.

A host will come across the clear sea,
To the land they show their rowing;
Then they row to the conspicuous stone,
From which arise a hundred strains.

It sings a strain unto the host
Through long ages, it is not sad,
Its music swells with choruses of hundreds—
They look for neither decay nor death.

Many-shaped Emne by the sea,
Whether it be near, whether it be far,
In which are many thousands of variegated women,
Which the clear sea encircles.

If he has heard the voice of the music,
The chorus of the little birds from Imchiuin,
A small band of women will come from a height
To the plain of sport in which he is.

There will come happiness with health
To the land against which laughter peals,
Into Imchiuin at every season
Will come everlasting joy.

It is a day of lasting weather
That showers silver on the lands,
A pure-white cliff on the range of the sea,
Which from the sun receives its heat.

The host race along Mag Mon,
A beautiful game, not feeble,
In the variegated land over a mass of beauty.
They look for neither decay nor death.

Listening to music at night,
And going into Ildathach,
A variegated land, splendor on a diadem of beauty,
Whence the white cloud glistens.

There are thrice fifty distant isles
In the ocean to the west of us;
Larger than Erin twice
Is each of them, or thrice.

A great birth will come after ages,
That will not be in a lofty place,
The son of a woman whose mate will not be known,
He will seize the rule of the many thousands.

A rule without beginning, without end,
He has created the world so that it is perfect,
Whose are earth and sea,
Woe to him that shall be under His unwill!

'Tis He that made the heavens,
Happy he that has a white heart,
He will purify hosts under pure water,
'Tis He that will heal your sicknesses.

Not to all of you is my speech,
Though its great marvel has been made known:
Let Bran hear from the crowd of the world
What of wisdom has been told to him.

Do not fall on a bed of sloth,
Let not thy intoxication overcome thee;
Begin a voyage across the clear sea,
If perchance thou mayst reach the land of women.

Thereupon the woman went from them, while they knew not whither she went. And she took her branch with her. The branch sprang from Bran's hand into the hand of the woman, nor was there strength in Bran's hand to hold the branch.

Then on the morrow Bran went upon the sea. The number of his men was three companies of nine. One of his foster-brothers and mates was set over each of the three companies of nine. When he had been at sea two days and two nights, he saw a man in a chariot coming towards him over the sea. That man also sang thirty other quatrains to him, and made himself known to him, and said that he was Manannan son of Lir, and said that it was upon him to go to Ireland after long ages, and that a son would be born to him, Mongan son of Fiachna—that was the name which would be upon him.

So Manannan sang these thirty quatrains to Bran:

> Bran deems it a marvellous beauty
> In his coracle across the clear sea:
> While to me in my chariot from afar
> It is a flowery plain on which he rows about.

> That which is a clear sea
> For the prowed skiff in which Bran is,
> That is a happy plain with profusion of flowers
> To me from the chariot of two wheels.

> Bran sees
> The number of waves beating across the clear sea:
> I myself see in Mag Mon
> Rosy-colored flowers without fault.

> Sea-horses glisten in summer
> As far as Bran has stretched his glance:
> Rivers pour forth a stream of honey
> In the land of Manannan son of Lir.

> The sheen of the main, on which thou art,
> The white hue of the sea, on which thou rowest,
> Yellow and azure are spread out,
> It is land, and is not rough.

> Speckled salmon leap from the womb
> Of the white sea, on which thou lookest:
> They are calves, they are colored lambs
> With friendliness, without mutual slaughter.

> Though but one chariot-rider is seen
> In Mag Mell of many flowers,
> There are many steeds on its surface,
> Though them thou seest not.

> The size of the plain, the number of the host,
> Colors glisten with pure glory,
> A fair stream of silver, cloths of gold,
> Afford a welcome with all abundance.

> A beautiful game, most delightful,
> They play sitting at the luxurious wine,
> Men and gentle women under a bush,
> Without sin, without crime.

> Along the top of a wood has swum
> Thy coracle across ridges,
> There is a wood of beautiful fruit
> Under the prow of thy little boat.

A wood with blossom and fruit,
On which is the vine's veritable fragrance,
A wood without decay, without defect,
On which are leaves of golden hue.

We are from the beginning of creation
Without old age, without consummation of earth,
Hence we expect not that there should be frailty;
Sin has not come to us.

An evil day when the Serpent went
To the father to his city!
She has perverted the times in this world,
So that there came decay which was not original.

By greed and lust he has slain us,
Through which he has ruined his noble race:
The withered body has gone to the fold of torment,
And everlasting abode of torture.

It is a law of pride in this world
To believe in the creatures, to forget God,
Overthrow by diseases, and old age,
Destruction of the soul through deception.

A noble salvation will come
From the King who has created us,
A white law will come over seas;
Besides being God, He will be man.

This shape, he on whom thou lookest,
Will come to thy parts;
'Tis mine to journey to her house,
To the woman in Moylinny.[1]

For it is Manannan son of Lir,
From the chariot in the shape of a man;
Of his progeny will be a very short while
A fair man in a body of white clay.

Manannan the descendant of Lir will be
A vigorous bed-fellow to Caintigern:
He shall be called to his son in the beautiful world,
Fiachna will acknowledge him as his son.

He will delight the company of every fairy-mound,
He will be the darling of every goodly land,
He will make known secrets—a course of wisdom—
In the world, without being feared.

[1] Page 546.

He will be in the shape of every beast,
Both on the azure sea and on land,
He will be a dragon before hosts at the onset,
He will be a wolf in every great forest.

He will be a stag with horns of silver
In the land where chariots are driven,
He will be a speckled salmon in a full pool,
He will be a seal, he will be a fair-white swan.

He will be throughout long ages
A hundred years in fair kingship,
He will cut down battalions,—a lasting grave—
He will redden fields, a wheel around the track.

It will be about kings with a champion
That he will be known as a valiant hero,
Into the strongholds of a land on a height
I shall send an appointed end from Islay.

High shall I place him with princes,
He will be overcome by a son of error;
Manannan the son of Lir
Will be his father, his tutor.

He will be—his time will be short—
Fifty years in this world:
A dragon-stone from the sea will kill him
In the fight at Senlabor.

He will ask a drink from Loch Lo,
While he looks at the stream of blood;
The white host will take him under a wheel of clouds
To the gathering where there is no sorrow.

Steadily then let Bran row,
Not far to the Land of Women,
Emne with many hues of hospitality
Thou wilt reach before the setting of the sun.

Thereupon Bran went from Manannan mac Lir. And he saw an
island. He rowed round about it, and a large host was gaping and
laughing. They were all looking at Bran and his people, but would
not stay to converse with them. They continued to give forth
gusts of laughter at them. Bran sent one of his people on the island. He ranged himself with the others, and was gaping at them
like the other men of the island. Bran kept rowing round about the
island. Whenever his man came past Bran, his comrades would

address him. But he would not converse with them, but would only look at them and gape at them. The name of this island is the Island of Joy. Thereupon they left him there.

It was not long thereafter when they reached the Land of Women. They saw the leader of the women at the port. Said the chief of the women: "Come hither on land, O Bran son of Febal! Welcome is thy coming!" Bran did not venture to go on shore. The woman threw a ball of thread to Bran straight over his face. Bran put his hand on the ball, which adhered to his palm. The thread of the ball was in the woman's hand, and she pulled the coracle towards the port. Thereupon they went into a large house, in which was a bed for every couple, even thrice nine beds. The food that was put on every dish vanished not from them. It seemed a year to them that they were there,—it chanced to be many years. No savor was wanting to them.

Home-sickness seized one of them, even Nechtan son of Collbran. Bran's kindred kept praying him that he should go to Erin with them. The woman said to them their going would make them rue. However, they went, and the woman said that none of them should touch the land, and that they should visit and take with them the man whom they had left in the Island of Joy.

Then they went until they arrived at a gathering at Srub Brain on the coast of Erin. The men asked of them who it was came over the sea. Said Bran: "I am Bran the son of Febal." One of the men said: "We do not know such a one, though the 'Voyage of Bran' is in our ancient stories."

One of Bran's men sprang from them out of the coracle. As soon as he touched the earth of Ireland, forthwith he was a heap of ashes, as though he had been in the earth for many hundred years. 'Twas then that Bran sang this quatrain:

> For Collbran's son great was the folly
> To lift his hand against age,
> Without any one casting a wave of pure water
> Over Nechtan, Collbran's son.

Thereupon, to the people of the gathering Bran told all his wanderings from the beginning until that time. And he wrote these quatrains in ogam, and then bade them farewell. And from that hour his wanderings are not known.

PLACE–NAME STORIES

The strong tendency toward antiquarianism among the early Irish is nowhere better illustrated than in the collection of place-name stories known as "Dinnsenchas." In their present form it is hardly safe to assign the "Dinnsenchas" as a whole to any considerable antiquity. On the other hand, there are certain individual instances in which the stories seem to preserve, embedded in the explanation of place-names, fragments of the most ancient narrative material. The habit of telling stories to explain place-names is by no means limited to the early Irish; it must be granted, however, that Irish antiquarians brought to the task an astounding virtuosity and enthusiasm. Nowhere else in European literature of the Middle Ages are legends of place-names so abundantly recorded.

INBER AILBINE

Ruad son of Rigdonn son of the king of Fir Murig mustered the crews of three ships to go over sea to have speech with his foster-brother the son of the king of Lochlann. When they had got half-way across they were unable to voyage in any direction, just as if an anchor was holding them. So then Ruad went out over the ship's side that he might know what it was that was stopping them, and he swam under the vessel. Then he saw nine women, the loveliest of the world's women, detaining them, three under each ship. So they carried Ruad off with them and he slept for nine nights, one night with each of the women on beds of bronze. And one of them became with child by him, and he promised that he would come again to them if he should perform his journey.

Then Ruad went to his foster-brother's house and stayed with him for seven years, after which he returned and did not keep his tryst truly, but fared on to Mag Murig. So the nine women took the son that had been born among them, and set out singing, in a boat of bronze, to overtake Ruad, but they did not succeed. So the mother then killed her own son and Ruad's only son, and she hurled the child's head after him; and then said every one as if with one mouth, "It is an awful crime (*ailbine*)! It is an awful crime!" Hence "Inber Ailbine."

FAFAINN

Broccaid mac Bricc of the Galeoin of Labraid the Exile had a son, Fafne the poet, and a daughter Aige. His mother was Liber daughter of Lot. Folk were envious of them: so they loosed elves at them who transformed Aige into a fawn and sent her on a circuit all round Ireland, and the warriors of Meilge son of Cobthach king of Ireland, killed her, and of her nought was found save a bag of water, and this he threw into the river, so that from her the "Aige" is named.

Thereafter Fafne her brother, in order to avenge her, went to blemish the king of Ireland, and upon him three blotches were raised by Fafne's satire. Then the poet was arrested by Meilge, for he, Meilge, was guiltless of Aige's death. And Fafne was killed on Fafainn, for satirizing the king of Tara, and therein he was buried; and while they were killing him he entreated that his name might be for ever on that mound, to wit "Duma Faifni."

Liber succumbed to her woe and drowned herself in the river Liber, so that from her it is so called. Broccaid died of disease in Rath maic Bricc.

BOYNE

Boann (Boyne) wife of Nechtan son of Labraid went to the secret well which was in the green of the fairy-mound of Nechtan. No one who went to it could come away from it without his two eyes bursting, except Nechtan himself and his three cup-bearers, whose names were Flesc and Lam and Luam.

Once upon a time Boann went through pride to test the well's power, and declared that it had no secret force which could shatter her form, and thrice she walked from right to left round the well. Whereupon three waves from the well broke over her and deprived her of a thigh and one of her hands and one of her eyes. Then she, fleeing her shame, turned seaward, with the water behind her as far as Boyne-mouth, where she was drowned. Now she was the mother of Angus son of the Dagda.

Or thus: "Bo" the name of the stream [of the fairy-mound of Nechtan] and "Finn" the river of Sliab Guairi, and from their confluence is the name "Boann" (= *Bó* + (*f*)*inn*).

Dabilla was the name of her lapdog, whence "Cnoc Dabilla" ("Dabilla's Hill"), today called "Sliab in Cotaig" ("the Mountain of the Covenant").

DUBLIN

Dub daughter of Rodub son of Cass son of Glas Gamna was wife to Enna son of Nos, an elf out of Forcartan. Enna had another wife, namely Aide daughter of Ochenn son of Cnucha, and when Dub discovered this, for she was a druid and a poetess, she grew jealous of Aide, and she went beside the sea as far as opposite Ochenn's house. There she chanted a sea-spell so that Aide was drowned in that house with all her family.

Mairgine, Ochenn's servant, saw Dub, and turned against her, and made a skillful cast from his sling at her, so that he struck her off her path, and shattered her, and she fell into the pool (*linn*). Whence "Dub-linn" is said.

ATH CLIATH CUALANN (DUBLIN)

Hurdles of wattling the Leinstermen made in the reign of Mesgegra under the feet of the sheep of Athirne the Importunate when delivering them to Dun Etair at the place in which Allainn Etair was taken from Ulster's warriors, where also Mesdedad son of Amergin fell by the hand of Mesgegra king of Leinster. So from those hurdles "Ath Cliath" ("the Ford of Hurdles") was named.

Or thus: "Ath Cliath": When the men of Erin broke the limbs of the Matae, the monster that was slain on the Liacc Benn in the Brug of Mac Oc, they threw it limb by limb into the Boyne, and its shinbone (*colptha*) got to Inber Colptha ("the estuary of the Boyne"), whence "Inber Colptha" is said, and the hurdle (*clíath*) of its frame (*i.e.*, its breast) went along the sea following the coast of Ireland until it reached yon ford (*áth*); whence "Ath Cliath" is said.

TONN CLIDNA

Clidna daughter of Genann son of Tren went out of Tulach Da Roth ("Hill of Two Wheels"), out of the Pleasant Plain of the Land of Promise, with Iuchna Curly-locks to get to the Mac Oc. Iuchna practised guile upon her. He played music to her in the boat of bronze wherein she lay, so that she slept thereat, and then he turned her course back, so that she rounded Ireland southwards till she came to Clidna.

This is the time at which the illimitable seaburst arose and spread throughout the regions of the present world. Because there were at that season Erin's three great floods, namely, Clidna's flood and Ladru's and Baile's; but not in the same hour did they arise: Ladru's flood was the middle one. The flood pressed on aloft and divided throughout the land of Erin till it caught the boat and the damsel asleep in it on the beach. So there she was drowned, Clidna the Shapely, Genann's daughter, from whom "Tonn Clidna" ("Clidna's Wave") is named.

. . . .

LOCH DERGDEIRC

Ferchertne son of Athlo, chief-poet of Ulster, was the cruellest man that ever lived in Erin. 'Twas he that would slay the woman in childbed, and would demand his weapon from one foe and his only eye from another. 'Twas he, moreover, that went to Eochaid son of Luchta son of Lugar son of Lugaid White-hand, King of Munster, to beg his only eye in payment for Boirche's hen which the poets had brought from the west; and Eochaid, to save his honor, gave him his only eye.

Then Eochaid went to wash the blood off his face, and searched the rushry and found no water: so he tore a tuft of rushes from its roots, and water trickled forth. With this he washed his empty eye-socket, and as he dipped his head thrice under the water all the well became red. Then because of the miracle of generosity which Eochaid had performed the King regained both his eyes, and as he looked on the well he said: "A red (*derg*) hollow (*derc*) is this hollow, and this will be every one's name for it." Whence "Loch Dergdeirc" is said.

GLOSSARY

Only the more important personages and places are included in the Glossary. In order to indicate the pronunciation adopted, the following key is used; făt, fāte, ärm, àsk, câre, necklăce, sofạ; mĕt, mēte, ĕnough, hĕr, novĕl; ĭt, īce; nŏt, nōte, ŏbey, hôrse, anchọr; fōod, fŏŏt; ŭs, ūse, fûr, stirrụp; ou as in out; h for the sound of ch in German *ich* and *ach*.

The family relationships of the most prominent personages are given in the Genealogical Table at the end of the book.

The location of the places which have been identified is indicated on the Map at the front of the book.

Aed Slane (ā slôn). King of Tara, ca. A.D. 600.

Aife (ē'fẹ). A female warrior of Alba by whom Cu Chulainn had a son, Connla. According to one story she was sister to Scathach and daughter of Ardgeimm.

Ailbe (ĭl'bẹ). Famous hound of Mac Datho.

Ailill Anglonnach (ĭl'yĭl ān'glŏnạh). Brother to Eochaid Airem; smitten with love for his brother's wife, Etain.

Ailill mac Matach (ĭl'yĭl moc măt'ạh). King of Connacht; husband of Medb. *See* Genealogical Table.

Aingen (ĭn'gẹn). Son of Nera and a fairy woman; owner of the cow bred to the Dun of Cooley.

Ainnle (ĭn'lẹ). Brother of Naisi; son of Usnech.

Almu (ŏl'mōo), Almhain (ŏl-ẹn). [E V] Principal seat of Finn mac Cumaill; now the Hill of Allen 5 miles northeast of Kildare.

Amergin mac Eit (ŏv'âr gĭn moc āt). An Ulster warrior; husband of Findchoem, Conchobar's sister.

Angus. Oengus (1) Son of Boann and the Dagda; a chief of the Tuatha De Danann. Also known as Mac ind Oc, Mac Oc, and Angus of the Brug. (2) Son of Aed Abrat; brother of Fann; a messenger sent to invite Cu Chulainn to the fairy world.

Ath (àh). A ford.

Ath Cliath. *See* Baile Atha Cliath.

Ath Luain (àh lōo'ĭn). [D IV] Now Athlone on the Shannon.

Badb (bôv). A supernatural woman or demon who frequented places of battle; regarded by some as a "battle goddess."

Baile Atha Cliath (bàl'yẹ à'hạ clē'ạh). "Place of the Ford of the Hurdles." [E V] Now Dublin.

Balor (bà'lọr). Son of Net; a king of the Fomorians.

Banba. A poetic name for Ireland.

Ban side (băn shē). Literally, a woman of the fairy-mound. In later tradition the banshee is a sinister personage whose wailing foretells death.

Benen. Bonignus. An early Irish saint; a contemporary of St. Patrick (5th cent.).

Benn Etair (bĕn ād'yẹr). [E V] Now the Hill of Howth near Dublin.

Blai Briuga (blà'ẹ brŏo'hạ). An Ulster warrior famous for his hospitality; one of Cu Chulainn's fosterers.

601

Blathnat (blàh'nĭd). Daughter of Mind and wife of Cu Roi mac Dairi; betrayer of her husband.

Boann (bō'ęn). Mother of Angus of the Brug. The River Boyne is said to have taken its name from her.

Bodb Derg (bôv dârg). A fairy king in Munster; son of the Dagda.

Bregia. A latinized form of Breg. *See* Mag Breg.

brehon. One skilled in the ancient laws and legal institutions of Ireland.

Bres mac Elotha (brĕs' mŏc ĕl'ŏ-hạ). Eochaid Bres. A king of the Tuatha De Danann; son of Eri by a king of the Fomorians.

Bres (brĕs). Son of Balor, king of the Fomorians. Not to be confused with Bres mac Elotha.

Bricriu Nemthenga (brĭc'ryōō nĕv'hyĕngạ). " Bricriu of the Poison Tongue." Son of Carbad; the malicious trouble-maker of Ulster, corresponding to Thersites of the Homeric epic and Sir Kay of the Arthurian legend.

bri (brē). A hill.

Bri Leith (brē' lā'ĭh). [D IV] The location of the fairy-mound of Mider, otherworld lover of Etain; now a hill near Ardagh, co. Longford.

bruiden (brōō'yęn). A banqueting hall, apparently provided with compartments.

Bruiden Da Derga (brōō'yęn dô yâr'gạ). [E V] A famous stronghold on the River Dodder near Dublin.

Brug na Boinne (brōōh' nạ bô'ĭ nę). A famous fairy-mound; a group of prehistoric mounds and the surrounding district, on the River Boyne near Stackallen Bridge, in modern Leinster.

Cailte mac Ronain (cwēl'chę mŏc rōn'ĭn). One of Finn's companions; tells the story of Finn's exploits to St. Patrick.

Cainte (càn'chę), **Sons of.** Cian, Cu, Cethen. Cian was the father of Lugh Long-Arm.

caird. A smith or artificer.

Cairenn (cā'ręn). Mother of Niall of the Nine Hostages.

Cairpre Cuanach (câr'brę cōō'ăn ạh). A warrior drowned during the battle between the Ulstermen and the forces of Cu Roi mac Daire.

Cairpre Liffechair (câr'brę lĭf'ĕ hâr). Son of Cormac, king of Ireland; became king A.D. 277.

Cairpre mac Etain (câr'brę mŏc ā'dĭn). A poet of the Tuatha De Danann, noted as a satirist.

Cairpre Niafer (câr'brę nē'ạ fâr). Son of Ross Ruad; king of Tara; enemy of Cu Chulainn, probably because of rivalry over Fedelm Noichride, daughter of Conchobar. *See* Genealogical Table.

Cathbad (càh'vạh). Chief druid of Ulster; according to one tradition, the father of Conchobar.

Ceithlionn (cĕh'lĭn). Wife of Balor; fought in the Battle of Moytura, in which she mortally wounded the Dagda.

Celtchair mac Uthechair (cĕlt'hâr mŏc ōōh'ĕ hâr). A distinguished Ulster warrior.

Cethern mac Finntain (cĕ'hĕrn mŏc fĭn'tạn). (1) An Ulster warrior, son of Fintan mac Neill; (2) one of Finn's teachers.

Cet mac Matach (cĕt' mŏc má'tạh). A distinguished Connacht warrior; shames the Ulstermen at Mac Datho's feast; wounds Conchobar with the calcified brain of Mesgegra; according to one tradition brother of Ailill, king of Connacht. *See* Genealogical Table.

Ciarraige Luachra (cēr'ĭ yĭ lōō'ăh rạ). [B VII] A hilly district between co. Limerick and co. Kerry.

Clann Conaill (clŏn' cŏn'ạl). The inhabitants of the district later known as Tir Connell in Ulster.

Clann Dedad (clŏn' dā'ghạ). The subjects or followers of Cu Roi mac Dairi.

Clann Eogain (clŏn' yō'wạn). The residents of the district roughly corresponding with modern Tyrone, earlier Tir Eogain.

Clidna (clē'na). *See* Tonn Clidna.

Conaire Mor (cŏn'ắ rẹ mōr'). King of Ireland near the beginning of the Christian era; grandson of Etain and Cormac, king of Ulster, and son of Mess Buachalla by a supernatural father; sometimes referred to as son of Eterscel, king of Ireland, who was the husband of his mother.

Conall Anglonnach (cŏn'ạl ān'glŏn ạh). Son of Iriel Glunma; one of the twelve great chariot fighters of Ulster.

Conall Cernach (cŏn'ạl cârn'ạh). "Conall the Victorious." A distinguished Ulster warrior; fosterer of Cu Chulainn. *See* Genealogical Chart.

Conchenn (cŏn'hĕn). Daughter of Cet mac Matach.

Conchobar (cŏn hō'vạr or cŏn'ŏ hạr). Conor. King of Ulster about the beginning of the Christian era.

Conn Cet-Cathach (cŏn' cāt'cäh'ạh). "Conn the Hundred-Fighter." King of Ireland beginning about A.D. 177; son of Fedlimid Rechtmar.

Conor. *See* Conchobar.

Cormac (côr'mŏc). Son of Lactighe; king of Ulster 48 B.C.; grandfather of Conaire Mor and husband of Etain.

Cormac Connlonges (côr'mŏc cŏn'lŭng yẹs). Son of Conchobar who went into voluntary exile in Connacht after the killing of the sons of Usnech, for whom he was one of the sureties.

Cormac Ulfada (côr'mŏc ŭl'fà dạ). High-King of Ireland; son of Art and grandson of Conn Cet-Cathach.

Craeb Ruad (crāv' rōō'ạ). *See* Red Branch.

crich (crēh). A territory, a boundary.

Crich Cualann (crēh' cōō'ắ lạn). [E V–VI] The District of Cualu, in what is now co. Wicklow, near Dublin.

Crimthann (crĭf'hạn). Griffin, son of Fidach; High-King of Ireland; brother of Mongfind.

Crimthann Nia Nair (crĭf'hạn nē'ạ nà'ĭr). Son of Lugaid of the Red Stripes; King of Ireland; killed in an attempt to slay Cu Chulainn.

Cruachan Ai (crōō'ắ hạn ĭ). Rath Cruachan. [C IV] Royal seat of Ailill and Medb, now Rathcroghan between Belanagare and Elphin in co. Roscommon.

Cualgne (cōō'ắl nyẹ). Cooley. [E III–IV] An ancient district probably corresponding roughly to the modern parish of Cooley in co. Louth; the territory especially assigned to the guardianship of Cu Chulainn.

Cu Chulainn (cōō' hŏŏ'lĭn). "The Hound of Culann." Son of Deichtire, sister of Conchobar, by the Tuatha De Danann prince Lug or by Sualtam (Sualtach), a petty Ulster chieftain; the central hero of the Ulster cycle; the Irish Achilles.

cumal (cōō'vạl). A female slave; also a designation of value equal to three cows.

Cu Roi mac Dairi (cōō' rŏ ē mŏc dā'ĭ rẹ). A powerful chieftain in Munster, usually opposed to Ulster but friendly to Connacht. He possessed supernatural powers.

Cuscraid (cŏŏs'crĭ). "The Stammerer." Son of Conchobar; wounded through the throat by Cet mac Matach.

Dagda (dôh-dạ). A powerful chieftain of the Tuatha De Danann; son of Ethliu; father of Angus Og; noted for his numerous accomplishments. Oafish but benevolent, he resembles in some ways the earlier Greek conception of Hercules.

Daire mac Fiachna (dà'ĭ rẹ mŏc fēē'ặh nạ). An Ulster chieftain; owner of the Dun Bull of Cooley over which the Cattle-Raid of Cooley was fought.

Dechtire (dĕh'tĭ rẹ). Mother of Cu Chulainn; sister of Conchobar.

Deirdre (dâr'drẹ), Derdriu (dâr'dryū). Daughter of Fedlimid mac Daill, Conchobar's chief story-teller; eloped with the sons of Usnech.

Delbchaem (dyăl'ụ hāv). Daughter of Morgan; fairy mistress of Art son of Conn the Hundred Fighter.

Dervorgil (dâr vôr'gĭl). Daughter of Ruad, king of the Isles; rescued from the Fomorians by Cu Chulainn; married Lugaid of the Red Stripes.

Diancecht (dē'ăn hāht). The great physician of the Tuatha De Danann; made an arm of silver for King Nuada; killed his son Miach because of professional jealousy.

Diarmuid (dē'ăr mōō'ĭd). Usually called the grandson of Duibne; one of Finn's warriors; the unwilling abductor of Grainne.

dub (dŏŏv). Black.

Dubtach Doeltenga (dŏŏv'tạh dāl'chĕng ạ). "Duffy Chafer-Tongue." Son of Lugaid; an Ulster warrior noted for his evil disposition; shares with Bricriu the rôle of the Thersites of the Ulster cycle.

dun (dōōn). A stronghold, a royal residence surrounded by an earthen wall.

Dun Delgan (dōōn' dăl'gạn). [E IV] Cu Chulainn's chief stronghold; now an ancient mound near Dundalk, co. Louth.

Emain Macha (ĕv'ĭn mà'hạ). [E III] The capital of ancient Ulster; now the Navan Fort near Armagh.

Emer (ĕv'ẹr). Wife of Cu Chulainn; daughter of Forgall Monach.

Eochaid Airem (yō'hẹ àr'ẹm). Son of Finn, brother of Eochaid Fedlech, with whom he is sometimes confused; husband of Etain.

Eochaid Buide (yō'hẹ bōō'yẹ). Eochaid Salbuide, father of Nessa and grandfather of Conchobar.

Eochaid Fedlech (yō'hẹ fĕd'lẹh). Brother of Eochaid Airem; king of Ireland beginning 3 B.C.; father of Medb and others. *See* Genealogical Table.

Eochaid Mugmedon (yō'hẹ mŭg'mĕ họn). King of Ireland about A.D. 358.

Eogan mac Durthacht (yō'gạn mŏc dōōr'hạht). King of Farney; a dependent of Conchobar, but often at odds with him.

eric. A compensation exacted by the kinsmen of a slain man from his slayers.

Eriu (ā'ryū). "Erin." Ireland. The modern name Erin is derived from the dative case of this word.

Etain (ād'ĭn). (1) A woman of the fairy folk, wife of Eochaid Airem and loved of Midir; heroine of "The Wooing of Etain"; (2) daughter of the above, wife of Cormac, king of Leinster.

Eterscel (ĕd'ẹr scyāl). King of Tara and foster-father of Conaire Mor; husband of Mess Buachalla, daughter of the second Etain.

Ethne Inguba (āh'nẹ ĭn'gōō vạ). Wife of Cu Chulainn.

Ethne Taebfada (āh'nẹ tāv'fădạ). Wife of Conn Cet-Cathach.

Fachtna (fàht'nạ). Chief physician of Eochaid Airem.

Fal (fôl). The Stone of Fal cried out under every legitimate king of Ireland who stepped upon it. *See* Inis Fail.

Fand (fàn). A fairy woman enamored of Cu Chulainn.

Fedelm Noichride (fād'ẹlm nŏy'hrē). " Fresh-Heart." Daughter of Conchobar; wife of Cairpre Niafer.

Fedlimid (fāl'ẹ mĭd). Son of Dall; Conchobar's story-teller.

Felim. See Fedlimid.

fer (fâr), *pl.* fir (fĭr). A man.

Ferchertne (fâr'hârt nẹ). (1) Chief poet and entertainer of Conchobar. (2) Poet of Cu Roi mac Dairi.

Fer Diad (fâr dē'ạ). A friend and sworn brother of Cu Chulainn; killed by Cu Chulainn in the Cattle-Raid of Cualgne.

Fergus mac Leite (fâr'gụs mŏc lā'dẹ). A Red-Branch warrior. Not to be confused with Fergus mac Roich.

Fergus mac Roich (fâr'gụs mŏc rō'ẹh). One of the greatest of the Ulster heroes. According to one account he was king of Ulster until he was tricked into abdicating by Nessa, mother of Conchobar. Later he became a voluntary exile in Connacht in protest against the killing of the sons of Usnech.

Fer Rogain (fâr rō'gĭn). Great-grandson of Donn Desa; foster-brother of Conaire Mor.

Fiacal mac Conchinn (fē'ăc ạl mŏc cŏn'hĭn). Husband of Finn's aunt and one of Finn's fosterers.

Fiacha (fē'ăh ạ). Son of Conchobar.

Fiachra mac Fergusa (fē'ăh rạ mŏc fâr'gụ sạ). Fiachra Caech, son of Fergus mac Roich.

Fiall (fē'ạl). Daughter of Forgall Monach; sister of Emer; rejected by Cu Chulainn on account of her relations with Cairpre Niafer.

fian (fē'ạn), *pl.* Fianna. An organized band of military men who lived partly by pillage on their own account and partly by taking service with various kings; applied especially to the fian of Finn mac Cumaill. The modern English equivalent is Fenians.

fidchell (fĭ'hẹl). A game played with pieces on a board, probably similar to chess.

Findabair (fĭn'ăv ạr). Daughter of Medb and Ailill mac Matach, of Connacht.

finn, find, fionn (fĭn). White, beautiful, a fair-haired person. See also Finn mac Cumaill.

Finn mac Cumaill (fĭn' mŏc cōō'vạl). Leader of the Fian and central figure in the stories of the Finn cycle.

Fintan mac Neill (fĭn'tạn mŏc nā'ĭl). In " The Intoxication of the Ulstermen," the ruler over a third of Ulster along with Cu Chulainn and Conchobar.

Fionn. See finn.

Fir Bolg (fĭr' bŏlg'). One of the ancient peoples of Ireland.

Fir Falgae (fĭr fŏl'gạ). Probably the Manxmen.

Fodla (fōh'lạ). A poetic name for Ireland.

Fomorians. A race of sea-pirates with semi-supernatural characteristics who opposed the earliest settlers in Ireland. They are later identified with the Scandinavians, who invaded the island during the eighth century.

Forgall. (1) Forgall Monach (fôr'gạl mŏn'ạh). A powerful chieftain with semi-supernatural powers; father of Emer. (2) The poet of Mongan.

Furbaide Ferbenn (fōōr'bĭ hẹ fâr'bẹn). A son of Conchobar; slayer of Medb; a protégé of Cu Chulainn.

gae bulga (gā bōōl'gạ). A spear furnished with barbs running in opposite directions and manipulated under water with the toes. Cu Chulainn, who alone knew the use of this weapon, learned it from Scathach.

ges, geis (gĕsh *or* găs). A prohibition or injunction somewhat similar to tabu.

Goibniu (gwĭv'nĭ ū). The smith of the Tuatha De Danann; brewer of the ale that kept the Tuatha De Danann perpetually young.

Goll mac Morna (gŭl' mŏc môr'nȧ). Son of Daire Derc, also called Morna; the great rival of Finn mac Cumaill; slayer of Finn's father in the Battle of Cnucha; previously named Aed, but after losing an eye in battle was named Gol (One-Eyed, lit. blind).

Grainne (grȧn'nyė). Daughter of Cormac mac Airt; wife of Finn; eloped with Diarmuid.

Howth. *See* Benn Etair.

Hui. *See* Ui.

hurley. A game played with sticks and balls, somewhat similar to field hockey.

Id mac Riangabra. *See* Riangabar.

Ildanach (ĭl'dăn ȧh). "The Many-Gifted." A name applied to Lug Lamfada.

Ingcel (ĭng'cĕl). A British pirate associated with Conaire Mor's foster-brothers in the sack of Da Derga's hostel.

inis (ĭn'ĭsh). An island.

Inis Fail (ĭn'ĭsh fô ĭl). An ancient poetic name for Ireland. *See* Fal.

Iubar mac Riangabra. *See* Riangabar.

Labraid Luath-lam-ar-Claidib (lou'rĭ lōō'ȧh läv ȧr clĭv'). "Lowry Swift-Hand-on-Sword." A fairy king; husband of Liban.

Lear. *See* Lir.

Leborcham (lyĕv'ȧr hȧm). A female satirist; the messenger of Conchobar; guardian of Deirdre.

Letha (lyĕ'hȧ). Brittany; sometimes the Continent in general.

Leth Cuinn (lyĕh cōō'ĭn). "Conn's Half." The northern part of Ireland.

Levarcham. *See* Leborcham.

Liath Macha (lē'ȧh mȧ'hȧ). "The Grey of Macha." One of Cu Chulainn's chariot horses.

Liban (lē'vȧn). A fairy woman; messenger of Fann; wife of Labraid.

Lir (lēr). Father of Manannan; apparently the equivalent of the Llyr of Welsh tradition, who figures in the story of Lear and his daughters.

liss. An area surrounded by a wall; usually the enclosure between the wall and the houses of a fortified place; the outer court of a chieftain's dun.

Loeg mac Riangabra (lā mŏc rē'ȧn gȧv'rȧ). Charioteer of Cu Chulainn. *See* Riangabar.

Loegaire Buadach (lā'ȧ rė bōō'yȧh). "Leary the Triumphant." A famous hero of Ulster; son of Connad mac Iliach.

Loegaire mac Neill (lā'ȧ rė mŏc nā'ĭl). Leary mac Neil, king of Ireland in the fifth century; converted by St. Patrick.

lorica (Ir. luirech). A breastplate.

Lug Lamfada (lōōh lô'ŏd ȧ). "Lug Long-Arm." A famous chief of the Tuatha De Danann; son of Cian mac Cainte; supernatural father of Cu Chulainn. *See also* Ildanach *and* Samildanach.

Lugaid (lōō'hė). Son of Cu Roi mac Dairi; one of the warriors who helped to slay Cu Chulainn.

Lugaid Sriab nDerg (lōō'hė srē'ȧv nyȧrg). "Lugaid of the Red Stripes." An Ulster warrior who married Dervorgil, daughter of Ruad; later king of Ireland.

Luin (lōō′ĭn). The name of a famous spear found at the Battle of Moytura and owned, at various times, by Celtchair and other warriors.

Luprecan (lĕp′rä hôn). A pigmy, a leprechaun; the nation of pigmies.

Mac Cecht (môc cĕht′). One of Conaire Mor's chief warriors, otherwise usually connected with Connacht; according to one story he killed Cuscraid Menn, foster-son of Conchobar, with the Luin of Celtchair.

Mac Datho (môc′ dä hō′). A king in Leinster; owner of a famous hound.

Mac ind Oc (môc′ ĭn ōg′). See Angus.

Mac Oc (môc ōg). See Angus.

Mag (môy). A plain.

Mag Breg (môy brāg). [E IV–V] "The Plain of Bray." A district formerly comprising most of eastern Meath; said to have been named after Breaga, son of Breogan and uncle of Mil.

Mag Mell (môy mĕl). "The Pleasant Plain." The fairy Other World; a beautiful land of perpetual spring and sunshine, the Land of Youth (Tir na n-Og). See also Tir Tarngire and Tír na n-Óc.

Mag Muirthemne (môy mōōr′hĕv nĭ). [E III–IV] A plain extending from the River Boyne to the mountains of Cualgne; Cu Chulainn's inheritance.

Maine (mä′nĭ). A name borne by seven sons of Ailill and Medb.

Manannan mac Lir (mŏ′năn ạn môc lēr′). A distinguished prince of the Tuatha De Danann; had a special interest in maritime affairs; associated in tradition with the Isle of Man.

Meath. See Mide.

Medb (māv). Daughter of Eochaid Fedlech, High-King of Ireland; queen of Connacht; wife of Ailill mac Matach.

Mess Buachalla (mĕss′ bōō′ạ hăl ạ). A name given to the daughter of the second Etain; mother of Conaire Mor by a lover who came in the form of a bird.

Miach (mē ạh). Son of Diancecht; a great physician of the Tuatha De Danann and a rival of his father.

Mide (mĭ′hẹ). Meath. The central portion of Ireland.

Mider (mĭ′yâr). A fairy king; lover of Etain.

Morna. See Goll mac Morna.

Morrigan (mōr′rē gạn). A female sprite who haunted battle-fields and incited slaughter; regarded by some as "an ancient Irish battle-goddess"; perhaps the ancestor of the ban side.

Mugan (mŏŏg′ạn). Wife of Conchobar; daughter of Eochaid Fedlech.

Muir n-Icht (mwĭr nĭht). The Sea of Wight; the English Channel.

Muirthemne. See Mag Muirthemne.

Munremar mac Gerrcind (mwĭn′rĕv ạr môc gâr′cĭn). "Fat-Neck son of Short Head." An Ulster warrior.

Naisi (nä′shẹ). Son of Usnech; one of the three brothers who carried off Deirdre from the court of Ulster; a fellow-pupil of Cu Chulainn.

Nuadu (nōō′ä hạ). A famous druid of Cathair Mor.

Nuadu Argat-lam (nōō′ä hạ âr′gạt läv). "Nuada of the Silver Arm." First king of the Tuatha De Danann in Ireland; lost an arm in the First Battle of Moytura; supplied with an arm of silver by Diancecht.

o (ō). A grandson, descendant. Plural ui.

Oengus. See Angus.

ogam. A system of writing composed of a series of notches along the corner of a stone or a piece of wood.

Ogma (ōg′mạ). A distinguished warrior and strong man of the Tuatha De Danann.

ollam (ō'lāv). A learned man of the highest rank.

rath (rà *or* ráth). A fortified place surrounded by a wall or ditch or by both.

Rath Cruachan. *See* Cruachan.

Red Branch. The Craeb Ruad (crāv' rōō'ah), the great assembly hall at Emain Macha; now Creevroe, a townland near the River Callan not far from Navan, the ancient site of Emain Macha.

Riangabar (rē'an gŏv'ar). An Ulsterman whose sons Iubar, Loeg, Sedland, and Id, were the charioteers of Conchobar, Cu Chulainn, Loegaire, and Conall, respectively.

rigdonna (rē'dōōn a). Kingship.

Sadb (sŏv). Daughter of Ailill and Medb.

samain (sŏ'van). An annual pagan festival corresponding roughly to Hallowe'en.

Samildanach (sŏh'vĭl dàn'ah). "Of Many Talents." One of the names applied to Lug Lamfada.

Scathach (scou'ha). A female warrior who lived in Scotland or on the Continent; Cu Chulainn's instructor in the use of arms. According to one account, her sister Aife was mother of Connla by Cu Chulainn.

Sencha mac Aillela (shĕn'ha mŏc ĭl'yĭl la). The wise man of the Ulster cycle, corresponding to Nestor of the Iliad, and somewhat to Merlin of the Arthurian legends.

shanachie. A learned man, a historian, a story-teller.

sid (shē). A fairy-mound.

Sinann (shĭn'an). The River Shannon.

sliab (slēv). A mountain, mountainous district.

Sliab Luachra (slēv lōō'àh ra). [B VIII] A mountainous district on the borders of Kerry and Cork.

Sualtam mac Roig (sōō'àl tah mŏc rō'eh). Mortal father of Cu Chulainn.

Tailltiu (tŏyl'tyū). [E IV] One of the famous royal residences of ancient Ireland; named for Tailltiu, daughter of the king of Spain and mother of Lug; now Telltown, near Navan, co. Meath.

Tain Bo Cualnge (tôn' bō' hōōl'nya). The Cattle-Raid of Cooley, the central epic of the Ulster cycle.

Tara. *See* Temair.

Tech Midchuarta (chăh' mē hōōr'ta). The great assembly hall of the ancient kings of Tara.

Temair (tôw'ĭr). Tara. A name applied to numerous places in Ireland; especially to Temair Mide [E IV], the famous seat of the ancient High-Kings of Ireland.

Temair (Tara) **Luachra** (tôw'ĭr lōō'àh ra). [B VII] A place in Sliab Luachra, the mountains dividing Limerick from Kerry.

Tethra (tĕh'ra). King of the Fomorians; uncle of Forgall Monach.

Tír na n-Óc (tēr' na nōg'). "The Land of Youth." The fairy Other World.

Tir Tairngire (tēr' târn'gĭr e). "The Land of Promise." The fairy Other World.

tonn (tŭn). A wave.

Tonn Clidna (tŭn clē'na). [L VIII] A loud surge in the bay of Glandore, co. Cork.

Tonn Rudraige (tŭn rōō'rĭ). [F III] A loud surge in the bay of Dundrum, co. Down.

traig (trīg). A strand.

Tuatha De Danann (tōō'à ha dā' dàn'an). According to the Book of Invasions, one of the ancient peoples who settled Ireland; often identified with the fairy folk; perhaps originally earth gods.

ui (o͞o′ē). Descendants. The plural of o.

Ui Cellaig (o͞o′ē cĕl′ĭ). [E V] The O'Kelly's, settled in the southern part of what is now co. Dublin.

Urgriu (o͞or′gryū). Son of Lugaid Corr; the opponent of Finn for the chieftaincy of the Fian; his sons appear in the battle in which Finn was slain.

Usnech (o͞osh′nę). [D IV] The father of the youths who eloped with Deirdre; probably a substitute for an older name Uisliu; a hill (now Usney or Ushnagh) in co. Westmeath, the geographical center of Ireland.